NEW RESEARCH ON DNA DAMAGE

NEW RESEARCH ON DNA DAMAGE

HONOKA KIMURA
AND
AOI SUZUKI
EDITORS

Nova Science Publishers, Inc.
New York

NOTICE TO THE READER

The Publisher has taken reasonable care in the preparation of this book, but makes no expressed or implied warranty of any kind and assumes no responsibility for any errors or omissions. No liability is assumed for incidental or consequential damages in connection with or arising out of information contained in this book. The Publisher shall not be liable for any special, consequential, or exemplary damages resulting, in whole or in part, from the readers' use of, or reliance upon, this material. Any parts of this book based on government reports are so indicated and copyright is claimed for those parts to the extent applicable to compilations of such works.

Independent verification should be sought for any data, advice or recommendations contained in this book. In addition, no responsibility is assumed by the publisher for any injury and/or damage to persons or property arising from any methods, products, instructions, ideas or otherwise contained in this publication.

This publication is designed to provide accurate and authoritative information with regard to the subject matter covered herein. It is sold with the clear understanding that the Publisher is not engaged in rendering legal or any other professional services. If legal or any other expert assistance is required, the services of a competent person should be sought. FROM A DECLARATION OF PARTICIPANTS JOINTLY ADOPTED BY A COMMITTEE OF THE AMERICAN BAR ASSOCIATION AND A COMMITTEE OF PUBLISHERS.

Library of Congress Cataloging-in-Publication Data

New research on DNA damage / Honoka Kimura and Aoi Suzuki, editors.
    p. ; cm.
Includes bibliographical references and index.
ISBN 978-1-60456-581-2 (hardcover)
1. DNA damage. I. Kimura, Honoka. II. Suzuki, Aoi.
[DNLM: 1. DNA Damage--genetics. 2. Aging--genetics. 3. Neoplasms--genetics. QU 477 N532 2008]
QH465.A1.N49 2008
616'.042--dc22   2008017044

Published by Nova Science Publishers, Inc. ≃ New York

Contents

Preface

DNA damage, due to environmental factors and normal metabolic processes inside the cell, occurs at a rate of 1,000 to 1,000,000 molecular lesions per cell per day. While this constitutes only 0.000165% of the human genome's approximately 6 billion bases (3 billion base pairs), unrepaired lesions in critical genes (such as tumor suppressor genes) can impede a cell's ability to carry out its function and appreciably increase the likelihood of tumor formation. The vast majority of DNA damage affects the primary structure of the double helix; that is, the bases themselves are chemically modified. These modifications can in turn disrupt the molecules' regular helical structure by introducing non-native chemical bonds or bulky adducts that do not fit in the standard double helix. Unlike proteins and RNA, DNA usually lacks tertiary structure and therefore damage or disturbance does not occur at that level. DNA is, however, supercoiled and wound around "packaging" proteins called histones (in eukaryotes), and both superstructures are vulnerable to the effects of DNA damage. This new book presents the latest research in the field.

Chapter 1 - Cancer and aging appear to be consequences of DNA damage, a pervasive, fundamental problem for living organisms. Un-repaired DNA damages in dividing cells can cause errors during DNA synthesis leading to mutation and ultimately to cancer. Furthermore, un-repaired DNA damages, especially in non- or infrequently dividing cells, can accumulate and cause progressive blockage of transcription, loss of gene expression capability and ultimately aging at the cellular, tissue and organ level. With respect to cancer, the likely sources of DNA damage causing the most frequent deadly cancers are reviewed, and it is concluded that, in general, reactive oxygen species reactions with DNA, and DNA-adduct forming molecule reactions, are the chief sources of damage. Approximately 30 inherited genetic defects in humans have been identified that cause reduced DNA repair. In general, these genetic defects are associated with increased cancer risk, indicating that increased DNA damage is causally related to cancer. Furthermore, evidence indicates that after formation of a mutation that provides a growth or survival advantage to a cell, the succeeding steps of progression to cancer likely involve natural selection and formation of a pre-malignant defective field of cells, a "field defect". With respect to aging, evidence is reviewed that DNA damages, particularly oxidative DNA damages, accumulate with age in the brain (29 studies) and muscle (18 studies), as well as in liver, kidney and hematopoietic stem cells. This accumulation is associated with a decline in expression of genes associated with the aging process. A calorie-restricted diet is known to increase lifespan in mammals and is also associated with decreased oxidative DNA damage. Inherited syndromes such as Werner syndrome, Hutchinson-Guilford progeria, and Cockayne syndrome are due to reduced DNA repair capability and are also associated with early aging, indicating that increased DNA damage is causally related to aging. The principal source of DNA damages leading to normal aging appears to be reactive oxygen species produced as byproducts of cellular respiration.

Chapter 2 - DNA adductomics is the systematic analysis of large numbers of DNA adducts or DNA modifications present in a particular DNA sample obtained at a specific point in time. The resulting DNA adductomes are represented visually by "DNA adduct fingerprint" adductome maps and adductome profiles that are unique to each DNA sample. In combination, the map and profile interfaces serve to provide detailed visualizations of DNA modification occurrence patterns and allow for comparisons between multiple samples. Additionally, the identities of specific DNA modifications revealed by the maps may be determined, e.g. DNA damage in the form of a DNA adduct. The DNA adductome approach utilizes liquid chromatography coupled with electrospray ionization tandem mass spectrometry (LC/ESI-MS/MS) and the methodology is designed to detect the neutral loss of 2'-deoxyribose from positively ionized 2'-deoxynucleoside adducts in multiple reaction monitoring mode (MRM) transmitting the $[M+H]^+ > [M+H-116]^+$ transition over multiple transitions. Data analysis is optimized and coupled with a comprehensive manual screening process designed to minimize the number of artifactual DNA modifications that appear in the final analyses. Identification of DNA adducts is carried out by comparison to authentic standards and by stable isotope dilution methods.

Chapter 3 - The amazing feature of ionizing radiation (IR) as a DNA damaging agent is the range of lesions it induces. Such lesions include base damage, single strand breaks (SSBs), double strand breaks (DSBs) of varying complexity and DNA cross links. A range of DNA damage response mechanisms operate to help maintain genomic stability in the face of such damage. Such mechanisms include pathways of DNA repair and signal transduction mechanisms. Increasing evidence suggests that these pathways operate co-operatively. In addition, the relative impact of one mechanism over another most probably depends upon the cell cycle phase and tissue type. An increased DNA-repair activity in tumor cells has been associated with resistance to treatment to DNA-directed drugs, while defects in DNA repair pathways result in hypersensitivity to these agents. In the past years the unraveling of the molecular basis of these DNA pathways, with a better understanding of the DNA damage caused by different anticancer agents, has provided the rationale for the use of some DNA repair inhibitors to optimize the therapeutic use of DNA-damaging agents currently used in the treatment of tumors. In addition, the possibility to specifically target the differences in DNA repair capacity between normal and tumor cells has recently emerged as an exciting possibility. The authors anticipate that this approach cannot be pursued in all cancer patients and using the same regimes, but it should be tailored according to the specific tumor DNA repair pattern. Therefore, as already clearly demonstrated for other target therapies, it seems essential to develop reliable markers and imaging techniques to be used for an appropriate patient's selection and as predictors of response. This review will focus on the new therapeutic strategies for DNA damage repair inhibition and their application in anticancer therapy.

Chapter 4 - BRIT1 (BRCT-Repeat Inhibitor of hTERT expression) was originally identified from their laboratory as an inhibitor of human telomere reverse transcriptase (hTERT) by a genome-wide genetic screen. The amino acid sequence of BRIT1 was later matched to a putative disease gene called microcephalin (MCPH1). Aberrations of BRIT1 have been identified in breast, ovarian and prostate cancer as well as autosomal recessive primary microcephaly, a neuronal development disorder characterized by reduced brain size of patients. Therefore, the functions of BRIT1 are of critical research interests that can potentially contribute to two fundamental pathological processes, cancer and neuro-developmental disorder. In this chapter, the authors will present the most recent findings on BRIT1's functions in both DNA damage response and cell cycle control. The authors' studies have revealed that BRIT1 functions as a novel regulator in the ATM/ATR pathway and a proximal factor in DNA damage response controlling the recruitment of multiple sensors and early mediators to the DNA damage sites. BRIT1 has also been shown to control G2-M checkpoint and prevents premature entry into mitosis. These results support a role of BRIT1 as a guardian of genomic integrity that prevents the pathogenesis of human cancer and microcephaly. Finally, they will discuss their future research interests in revealing the underlying mechanisms on how BRIT1 defect may contribute to the development of cancer and primary microcephaly.

Chapter 5 - The individual response to genotoxic stress and induction of DNA damage may vary according to various conditions, such as the absorption and metabolism rate of genotoxic agents, the extent and efficacy of DNA-damage induction and repair, the balance between apoptosis and necrosis of exposed cells, the proper functioning of cell-cycle control, and the immune response. All of these processes are governed by certain genes or combinations of genes. Numerous human population studies have evaluated the relationship between genetic polymorphisms and DNA-damage induction and repair in response to genotoxic insult. The most common type of variation in DNA sequence is the single-nucleotide polymorphism, present in about 1 per 1,000 nucleotides in the human genome. However, the role of this type of genetic variant contributing to diseases with a complex etiology such as cancer is poorly understood. Hundreds of polymorphisms in genes that encode enzymes involved in the metabolism of xenobiotics (such as oxidoreductases, P450 cytochromes, glutathione S-transferases, N-acetyl transferases, methyltransferases, hydrolases, dehydrogenases), in DNA repair (participating in direct reversal repair, base-excision repair, nucleotide-excision repair, and double-strand-break repair), and in folate metabolism (methylenetetrahydrofolate reductase, methionine synthase, methionine synthase reductase) have been identified, although for many of these polymorphisms the impact on repair phenotype and cancer susceptibility remains uncertain. The present article reviews which of the many single-nucleotide polymorphisms in genes involved in DNA-damage processing influence cancer risk, and provides insight into the complexity of the genotype-phenotype relationship. Nevertheless, when a specific polymorphism by itself appears to have no or only a weak effect, the identification and characterization of the combined effects of different susceptibility genes for cancer risk require the understanding of gene-gene interactions.

Chapter 6 - An emerging mechanism of cellular transformation by oncogenic viruses is the inhibition or suppression of cellular DNA repair. This review will focus on human T-cell leukemia virus (HTLV-I), which is the causative agent of adult T-cell leukemia (ATL), an aggressive clonal malignancy of CD4+ T lymphocytes. The oncogenic potential of HTLV-I relies on expression of the viral transcriptional modulator, Tax. In addition to activating viral transcription, Tax controls the expression of a large and diverse array of cellular genes. By altering gene expression homeostasis, as well as by direct protein-protein interactions, Tax interferes with normal DNA replication and repair processes, thereby contributing to an increased mutation frequency in HTLV-I infected cells. The authors and others have shown that Tax can suppress DNA base and nucleotide excision repair pathways by altering the expression of important factors involved in these pathways, such as DNA polymerase beta and PCNA. Tax has also been shown to affect protein interactions that regulate DNA repair pathways and to attenuate the ATM mediated damage response, a major pathway for repair of DNA double strand breaks (DSBs). In this chapter they will review the effect of Tax on DNA repair and genome stability and the role of these processes in cellular transformation. They will discuss the inhibitory effect of Tax on ATM kinase activity, which reveals novel insights into the normal function of this signaling and repair pathway. Finally, the authors will discuss recent data suggesting a critical role for the DNA double strand break repair pathway in retroviral replication and tumor suppression.

Chapter 7 - The aim is to raise the importance of the study of genotoxicity, its effects and how to prevent it, as well as the use of a biomonitor to detect these agents. It will point out in a practical and applied manner the use of the micronucleus assay as an indicator of damage and how to detect DNA damage, considering new uses of this technique that are easy to implement and to interpret, as well as being, economical, and also a review of the most current information about this important subject. Addressed specifically in the authors' research is their interest in about the search for new models to be used as biomonitors, taking into account their experience of working with peripheral blood erythrocytes from more than 150 different species, including humans, with an emphasis on the more suitable and feasible models, and to demonstrate their usefulness in different studies, considering the characteristics of the species to be tested, the advantages and disadvantages of each one, the influence of age, the applicability of the model in different areas of biomedical and clinic research, covering also the wide use of this test for detected genotoxic and/or the teratogenic potential, as well as damage marker and a tool to study the effects of diverse pathological conditions, and also to show the technical innovation for genotoxic study using amphibians and rat epithelial cells for genotoxicity studies in the laboratory and in the field by means of noninvasive and easy new proposals. It will also highlight the problem in the design of new methodological approaches and characteristics to be taken into account for a proper development of studies in the genotoxicity area.

Chapter 8 - This chapter presents four ultrasensitive methods (as Hoechst and PicoGreen versions) for the accurate quantification of non-repairable and repairable dsDNA damage, as well as for the concentration of dsDNA. The assays can be applied to genomic, mitochondrial and plasmid dsDNA. The first assay provides an accurate quantification of dsDNA irrespective of size, and the following assays quantify (a) non-repairable and (b) repairable dsDNA damage: for case (a), two assays, one for the direct quantification of small-sized (0–

1000 bp) fragmented necrotic/apoptotic DNA, and the other for the quantification of the 0-23 Kb smearing seen in a typical DNA agarose gel electrophoresis; for case (b), a fourth assay that quantifies the percentage of DNA nicks present in DNA samples.

Chapter 9 - DNA damage via photosensitized reaction such as photo-induced electron transfer and photosensitized reactive oxygen formation contributes to solar carcinogenesis and phototoxic effect. Furthermore, DNA damage by photosensitized reaction is important mechanism of photodynamic therapy, which is a promising treatment of cancer and other non-malignant conditions. The mechanism of photosensitized DNA damage strongly depends on the excitation energy of photosensitizer, i.e. the wavelength is important. In general, ultra-violet photosensitizer induces DNA damage via the electron transfer, whereas photosensitized singlet oxygen generation is important for the mechanism by visible-light photosensitizer. Guanine residue is the important target of the two mechanisms, electron transfer and singlet oxygen generation. The consecutive guanines are selectively oxidized through electron transfer, because these sites act as hole-trap. Singlet oxygen induces base oxidation at every guanine residues. Rarely, superoxide anion radical, which is formed through photo-induced electron transfer from excited photosensitizer to molecular oxygen, contributes to DNA damage. Superoxide itself hardly damages DNA, but hydrogen peroxide and hydroxyl radical formed from superoxide are important reactive species for DNA damage.

Chapter 10 - Upon exposure of our skin to solar UV radiation, the photosensitized DNA damage takes place through two major pathways, i.e., formation of the mutagenic pyrimidine dimmers via excitation of the pyrimidine bases, and one-electron oxidation of nucleobases triggered by electron transfer from the nucleobase to the excited photosensitizer. This chapter shed light on the latter process. In the initial step of the photosensitized DNA damage by one-electron oxidation, a positive charge "a hole" is generated in DNA which can subsequently migrate along DNA. Though a number of kinetic and theoretical studies have been performed, the biological relevance between the charge transfer in DNA and photosensitized DNA damage are still not clear. Herein, the kinetic mechanisms of the photosensitized one-electron oxidation of DNA was assayed both by the direct spectroscopic measurements of the charge transfer in DNA and by quantification of the yield of the guanine oxidative damage. Consecutive adenine sequences were found to be a good launching site for the photosensitizers to inject a hole in DNA, where the following rapid hole transfer through adenines causes a long-lived charge-separated state leading to DNA oxidative damage. It was clearly demonstrated that the consecutive adenine sequences serve as a good target in the photosensitized DNA damage, or G adjacent to such sequences may be a potential hot spot of oxidative DNA damage. The essential requisites for the efficient and/or harmful photosensitizer are given as follows: be able to oxidize adenine, and react rapidly with molecular oxygen following its reduction avoiding the charge recombination and making the reaction irreversible. Elucidation of the kinetic mechanisms of the photosensitized one-electron oxidation of DNA allowed us to know the effective target DNA sequences and the essential requisites for the efficient photosensitizer, which will greatly help the understanding of the harmful compound for health and the improvement of the photosensitizer for therapeutic and biochemical applications.

Chapter 11 – The authors have developed new-conceptual analytical methodology to estimate the DNA damage spectrum on natural DNA without radioisotope and fluorescent labeling.

DNA damage is generally classified into two categories: one is 'strand break', the other is 'nucleobase lesion'. There are two kinds of termini in the strand break pattern: the termini with or without phosphate. The authors have developed the protocols to quantify 3'termini without phosphate (site 1), 3'termini with phosphate (site 2), and nucleobase lesions (site 3). An enzyme, phosphodiestrase I (snake venom phosphodiesterase (SVPD)), can recognize a 3'terminus without phosphate followed by production of DNA monomers (2'-deoxynucleoside-5'-phosphate) sequentially from the 3'terminus ($3' \rightarrow 5'$ exonuclease function). Then, the yield of 'site 1' can be quantified since the amount of the DNA monomers produced during incubation for a given period is proportional to that of 'site 1'. In addition, pre-treatment of irradiated DNA by another enzyme, calf intestine alkaline phosphatase (CIAP) enables 'site 2' to be recognized by SVPD, because CIAP removes phosphate at 'site 2' to convert into 3'OH terminus categorized in 'site 1'. Furthermore, pre-treatment of irradiated DNA by a chemical, piperidine, can covert most electron-withdrawing nucleobase lesions into 'site 2', which can become recognizable by SVPD after CIAP pre-treatment as mentioned above. As a result, in the case of ^{60}Co γ-irradiated dry DNA, the yields of total 3'termini, 3'termini without phosphate, 3'termini with phosphate, and piperidine-labile nucleobase lesions, are estimated to be 0.102, 0.024, 0.078, and 0.084, respectively. The de novo analytical protocol is unique in the idea itself, and future analyses based on the methodology will elucidate unknown DNA damage spectrum using a variety of combinations of enzymes.

Chapter 12 - Chromosomal translocations, a frequent finding in cancer cells, are the result of double-strand breaks that are repaired via non-homologous end-joining in somatic cells. Since many translocations are recurrent and the breakpoints are non-randomly distributed, a widely held view posits that local sequence factors are responsible for the appearance of double-strand breaks at specific genomic sites. However, efforts to identify such factors are complicated by their widespread occurrence throughout the genome. Thus, establishing a convincing direct causal link between specific sequence elements and nearby breakpoints has been difficult.

Other potential factors that could account for the recurrence of chromosomal translocations are frequently overlooked. For instance, the importance of chromosome localization inside the cell nucleus, and the relative positions of chromosomes with respect to each other, could determine which genes participate in specific translocations. Therefore, studies that aim to identify the causes of recurrence of chromosomal translocations should take into account factors responsible for the nuclear co-localization of specific genes.

Likewise, little attention has been given to the power of functional selection in determining the identity of the genes translocated and the localization of breakpoints within those genes. However, careful analysis of reciprocal translocations that create chimeric fusion proteins could show whether recurrence is the result of strong cellular selection pressures for the functions encoded by specific genes. Furthermore, the requirement to keep the reading frame in the fusion product could explain, in these cases, the non-random distribution of translocation breakpoints across those genes.

The author proposes that the generation of DNA double-strand breaks might be widespread throughout the genome, resulting in a relatively high number of potential translocation events. Most of these would never take place because the genes involved are far apart within the nuclear space. Of those rearrangements that would be allowed, only a small subset could generate an in-frame fusion product with oncogenic potential. Thus, the non-random genomic distribution of translocation breakpoints in tumor samples might be due to the fact that these samples contain the limited collection of rearrangements that were able to survive distinct functional requirements imposed by cellular selection pressures.

Chapter 13 - Since most ancient times lead has been widely used due to its physical and chemical unique properties that make it an excellent metal with innumerable uses. Long ago human kind has also found out about its adverse effects to health. Even so its utilisations kept increasing exponentially alongside with industrialization and technology improvements. Not until the two last decades of the 20th century has the earth begun to be protected against its anthropogenic sources of widespread dissemination through environmental systems. Steps taken in this direction are too important of a measure that allows keeping its environmental concentrations essentially under control. Meanwhile this may lead to the misconception that its total world production and use over the last years has been diminishing, although real numbers point out to a constant increase, meaning there is still a huge number of people throughout the world exposed to it and, consequently, to its toxic effects.

Lead is essentially a chronic or cumulative toxin, which can potentially affect every organs and systems. International Agency for Research on Cancer (IARC) has classified lead and inorganic lead compounds, back in 1987, as possibly carcinogenic in humans – IARC group 2B, judging evidences to be inadequate in humans. IARC has however undertaken a recent reevaluation of lead's carcinogenicity and changed that classification to probably carcinogenic to humans – IARC group 2A based in several studies that concluded on a relationship between exposure to lead and cytogenetic markers frequencies, such as micronucleus and chromosomal aberrations and on an increase of incidence of overall cancer, and lung and bladder cancer in individuals exposed.

Genetic effects of lead seem to be mediated by modulation of reactive oxygen species together with interaction with proteins, including those involved in DNA repair in a way that can be considered indirect, by means of decreasing cells capability of protecting and repairing damaged DNA in spite of directly damaging it. Potential genotoxic effects of lead might contribute for development of normal to cancerous cells by inducing or allowing loss of genomic stability and acquisition of genetic alterations.

Within this chapter findings of genotoxicity in human populations and proposed mechanisms for lead effects in genetic systems will be reviewed in order to obtain a state of the art of such effects of lead in humans.

Chapter 14 - Hexavalent chromium (Cr (VI)) is known toxin, mutagen and carcinogen in man. In addition, exposure to Cr (VI) has been associated with skin irritation, deep ulceration and cytotoxicity. Intracellular chemistry of Cr (VI) is complex and involves several enzymatic as well as nonenzymatic reductions resulting in the formation of reactive chromate intermediates and reactive oxygen species. These endproducts react with DNA and cause numerous types of lesions which in turn provoke specific signaling pathways in exposed cells. Although these pathways are generally known, their specific details concerning individual steps and involved molecules with their respective roles in biological response of cell populations to this element remain unspecified. The purpose of this study was to investigate the initial stages of Cr (VI)-induced DNA damaging in normal human skin fibroblasts. Primary human skin fibroblasts were exposed to Cr (VI) at a concentration range of 1-50 μM during 24 h. The authors' results confirm that Cr (VI) dose-dependently stimulates both directly (via its reactive metabolic intermediates) and indirectly (through generated oxidative stress) DNA damaging which results in the activation of DNA damage response pathway during 24 h of treatment. The important members of this pathway include ATM/ATR kinases which stimulate their downstream targets – Chk1, Chk2 and p53 in mediating transient G2/M cell cycle arrest and activating cell death characterized by the specific cleavage of PARP. Inhibition of ATM/ATR pathway and suppresion of oxidative stress in exposed cells significantly suppressed cell damage characterized by specific PARP cleavage.

Chapter 15 - In this study, the authors evaluated the DNA damage and the expression of repair related molecules, including DNA polymerase β, apurinic/apyrimidinic endonuclease /redox factor-1 (APE/ref-1), proliferating cell nuclear antigen (PCNA), and growth arrest and DNA damage (GADD45) in T and B human lymphocytes that were exposed to hydrogen peroxide (H_2O_2) and methyl methane sulfonate (MMS). DNA damage was evaluated by conducting a Comet assay of T and B cells that were exposed to H_2O_2 (25 and 50 μM) and MMS (25 and 50 μM) for 5 min. The mean value of the Olive Tailmoment of the control lymphocytes was 1.34 ± 0.02 and 1.41 ± 0.01 (p=0.084) in the T- and B-lymphocytes, respectively, which indicates that there was no significant difference in the level of DNA damage that occurred. However, after being exposed to 25 μM and 50 μM of H_2O_2, the mean values of the Olive Tailmoments of the T-lymphocytes were 1.92 ± 0.11 (p=0.001) and 2.16 ± 0.32 (p=0.001) whereas those of the B-lymphocytes were 1.98 ± 0.11 (p=0.001) and 2.24 ± 0.30 (p=0.001), which indicates that a significant level of DNA damage occurred. In addition, after cells were exposed to 25 μM and 50 μM of MMS, the mean values of the Olive Tailmoments of the T-lymphocytes were 1.80 ± 0.09 (p=0.001) and 2.02 ± 0.31 (p=0.001) whereas those of the B-lymphocytes were 1.88 ± 0.14 (p=0.001) and 2.12 ± 0.33 (p=0.001), which also indicates that a significant level of DNA damage occurred. Furthermore, the level of DNA damage was found to be significantly greater in B-lymphocytes than in T-lymphocytes. Taken together, these results indicate that human B-lymphocyte may be a more sensitive target than T-lymphocytes for the evaluation of DNA damage when conducting human biomonitoring.

When the expression of DNA polymerase β, APE/ref-1, GADD45 and PCNA was evaluated, their relative intensities were found to increase significantly with increasing concentrations of H_2O_2 and MMS in both T- and B-lymphocytes (p<0.05). In addition, the relative intensity of GADD45 was significantly greater in the B-lymphocytes than in T-lymphocytes.

In summary, a Comet assay showed that DNA damage occurred in response to H_2O_2 and MMS level in human T- and B-lymphocytes, and that this occurred in a dose dependent fashion. In addition, the amount of DNA damage that occurred was greater in B-lymphocytes than in T-lymphocytes, which indicates that human B-lymphocyte are more sensitive target than T-lymphocytes for the evaluation of DNA damage when conducting human biomonitoring. Futhermore, when the DNA repair enzyme and protein expressions were compaired, GADD45 was found to be more sensitive to DNA damage than DNA polymerase β, APE/ref-1, and PCNA in human T- and B-lymphocytes, which could be useful in the evaluation of DNA damage as a result of genetic toxicants.

Chapter 16 - TP53 is the most commonly mutated gene in human cancers, and the p53 protein is a potent inhibitor of cell growth, arresting cell cycle progression at several points and inducing apoptosis of cells undergoing uncontrolled growth. The loss of p53 function by mutation is too common in cancer. However, most natural p53 mutations occur at a late stage in tumor development, and many clinically detectable cancers have reduced p53 expression but no p53 mutations.

Approximately 90% of the TP53 gene mutations are localized between domains encoding exons 5 to 8. Much research suggests that TP53 mutations have prognostic importance and sometimes are a significant factor in clinical Oncology. The presence of specific p53 mutational hotspots in different types of cancer implicates environmental carcinogens and endogenous processes in the etiology of human cancer. Oxidative stress and the generation of reactive species may cause mutations in cancer-related genes, and affect key regulator proteins of DNA repair, cell cycle, and apoptosis.

This review gives a brief perspective of some of the landmark discoveries in mutation research. The molecular and biochemical characteristics of TP53 and p53 are then covered, followed by an overview of how it can be studied in the laboratory. Finally, the implications of mutational hotspots of TP53 gene at the level of DNA damage are discussed.

Chapter 17 - One of the major challenges involved mainly in searching of point mutations for clinical relevance is the technology used; in particular for cancer research the authors will focus on the gains or loss-of-suppression function, v.gr. in cancer genes as RET, TP53, RAS, etc. TP53 has been used as an excellent model for point mutation detection, because of its more than 20,000 different mutations this gene is the most frequently found in many human cancers.

Furthermore, there are uncommon somatic and germline mutations that might be related to specific cancers or predispositions. In particular case, the precise nature of the TP53 mutation presents both challenges and opportunities for alternate treatment strategies in specific cancers. These highlight the clinical need to accurately identify often unknown inherited aberrations or infrequently represented mutations in mixed populations of DNA molecules.

Chapter 18 - DNA-protein crosslinks (DPCs), which are generated by covalent linkage of proteins to the DNA duplex, comprise an under-studied class of DNA lesions. They can be induced by commonly encountered agents including environmental chemicals, cancer-chemotherapeutic drugs and ionizing radiation. DPCs could pose a serious threat to cellular function because they may disrupt the progression of the replication and transcription machineries. A number of problems have plagued researchers examining this type of DNA damage. Many agents can induce DPCs by more than one chemical mechanism. Furthermore, these agents invariably induce other types of DNA damage. Measurements of DPC damage have also been hampered by the lack of stringent and sensitive methodologies for their isolation. However, recent advances in DPC-isolation methodology have allowed for more in-depth analyses of these lesions. Additionally, advances in the study of chromatin structure have provided further understanding of the influence of chromatin dynamics on the induction and repair of DPCs. At the same time, our improving knowledge of many DNA-repair pathways has afforded opportunities for assessing the involvement of these pathways in the removal of DPCs from the genome. This chapter discusses the impact of these advances on our understanding of DPCs and their biological consequences.

In: New Research on DNA Damage
Editors: Honoka Kimura and Aoi Suzuki

ISBN 978-1-60456-581-2
© 2008 Nova Science Publishers, Inc.

Chapter 1

Cancer and Aging as Consequences of Un-repaired DNA Damage

Harris Bernstein[1,3,*], Claire M. Payne[1,3,4], Carol Bernstein[1,4], Harinder Garewal,[2,3,4] and Katerina Dvorak[1,3,4]

1. Departments of Cell Biology and Anatomy,
2. Internal Medicine,
3. Arizona Cancer Center, College of Medicine, University of Arizona, Tucson, Arizona 85724, USA
4. Section of Hematology/Oncology, Southern Arizona Veterans Affairs Health Care System, Tucson, Arizona 85723, USA

Abstract

Cancer and aging appear to be consequences of DNA damage, a pervasive, fundamental problem for living organisms. Un-repaired DNA damages in dividing cells can cause errors during DNA synthesis leading to mutation and ultimately to cancer. Furthermore, un-repaired DNA damages, especially in non- or infrequently dividing cells, can accumulate and cause progressive blockage of transcription, loss of gene expression capability and ultimately aging at the cellular, tissue and organ level. With respect to cancer, the likely sources of DNA damage causing the most frequent deadly cancers are reviewed, and it is concluded that, in general, reactive oxygen species reactions with DNA, and DNA-adduct forming molecule reactions, are the chief sources of damage. Approximately 30 inherited genetic defects in humans have been identified that cause reduced DNA repair. In general, these genetic defects are associated with increased cancer risk, indicating that increased DNA damage is causally related to cancer. Furthermore, evidence indicates that after formation of a mutation that provides a growth or survival advantage to a cell, the succeeding steps of progression to cancer

* Correspondence concerning this article should be addressed to Harris Bernstein, Dept. of Cell Biology and Anatomy, College of Medicine, University of Arizona, Tucson, Arizona 85724 bernstein3@earthlink.net.

likely involve natural selection and formation of a pre-malignant defective field of cells, a "field defect". With respect to aging, evidence is reviewed that DNA damages, particularly oxidative DNA damages, accumulate with age in the brain (29 studies) and muscle (18 studies), as well as in liver, kidney and hematopoietic stem cells. This accumulation is associated with a decline in expression of genes associated with the aging process. A calorie-restricted diet is known to increase lifespan in mammals and is also associated with decreased oxidative DNA damage. Inherited syndromes such as Werner syndrome, Hutchinson-Guilford progeria, and Cockayne syndrome are due to reduced DNA repair capability and are also associated with early aging, indicating that increased DNA damage is causally related to aging. The principal source of DNA damages leading to normal aging appears to be reactive oxygen species produced as byproducts of cellular respiration.

Introduction

DNA damage is a basic problem for life. It is a major source of error in two processes, in the transmission and in the expression of genetic information. DNA damage-caused errors appear to have primary roles in cancer (due to errors of transmission, or mutation) and in aging (largely due to blockage of expression) (Figure 1). In dividing cells, DNA damages that escape accurate repair may be inaccurately repaired or cause inaccurate DNA replication past the site of damage, leading to mutation. In a frequently dividing cell population, mutant cells having a growth advantage will undergo natural selection, clonal expansion and may ultimately give rise to cancer. On the other hand, DNA damages in non-dividing or infrequently dividing cells that escape accurate repair will accumulate over time. Deleterious effects of DNA damage in non- or infrequently dividing cells likely will lead to functional decline due to blocked or faulty gene expression, cell death, loss of tissue and organ function and these defects will lead to aging.

It is evident that cancers ordinarily arise in cells with a proliferative capacity, such as stem cells and differentiated cells that are capable of undergoing mitosis. Aging, to a large extent, is a reflection of loss of function of non-dividing or infrequently dividing cells, such as adult neurons and myocytes. This corresponds to our hypothesis, above, that DNA damage in frequently dividing cells causes cancer, and that DNA damage in non- or infrequently dividing cells is an important cause of aging. Our purpose here is to consider the substantial recent evidence bearing on the hypothesis that cancer and aging are consequences of DNA damage, with frequently-dividing cells being more vulnerable to cancer, and non- or infrequently dividing cells being more vulnerable to aging.

DNA damages and mutations differ in fundamental ways. Damages are physical irregularities in the DNA, such as single- and double-strand breaks, 8-hydroxy-deoxyguanosine (8-OHdG) residues and polycyclic aromatic hydrocarbon adducts. Because damages can be recognized enzymatically, they can be correctly repaired if redundant information is available. If a DNA damage remains in a gene, it can prevent transcription of the gene, and thus production of a protein. On the other hand, a mutation is a change in the base sequence of the genetic material and is not enzymatically recognizable at the DNA level once the base change is present in both strands. Mutations in a cell can cause alterations in protein function or regulation.

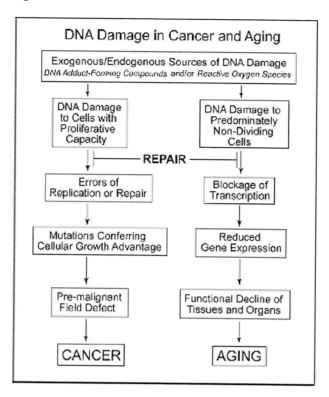

Figure 1. The differing roles of DNA damage in cancer and aging.

Mutations may be replicated and passed on to progeny cells, and will tend to increase or decrease in frequency in a population of cells according to their effects on the ability of the cell to survive and reproduce. An epigenetic change such as a methylation of a CpG island is also inheritable in the somatic line, and can be regarded as a form of mutation, an epimutation. DNA damages and mutations are related, however, because damages can cause errors of DNA synthesis during replication or repair and these errors are a major source of mutations.

Vilenchik and Knudson (2000) estimated the number of DNA damages in human cells to be about 800 damages per hour or 19,200 per day. Further, Vilenchik and Knudson (2003) estimated the number of endogenous double-strand breaks formed per cell cycle in humans to be about 50. Under conditions of oxidative stress, such as produced by inflammation, these rates of DNA damage formation would be increased. Double-strand breaks are important because they are defective in both DNA strands and are thus difficult to repair. Although double-strand damages can be repaired with high fidelity by a process requiring paired homologous chromosomes [i.e. by homologous recombinational repair (HRR)], errors in their repair [e.g. by non-homologous end joining (NHEJ)] probably contribute significantly to the rate of cancer, particularly to the earliest oncogenic events in human carcinomas (Vilenchik and Knudson, 2003).

Ames (1989) and Ames and Gold (1991) were among the first to emphasize that DNA damages are a major cause of the replication errors leading to mutations that give rise to cancer. Jackson and Loeb (2001) and Ames et al. (1993) further emphasized the importance of oxidative DNA damage.

Alexander (1967) was the first to suggest that DNA damage, as distinct from mutation, is a primary cause of aging. By 1981 this idea had gained significant experimental support (Gensler and Bernstein, 1981), and by the early 1990s experimental support was substantial and further indicated that oxidative DNA damage, in particular, was a major source of the DNA damage causing aging (Bernstein and Bernstein, 1991; Ames and Gold, 1991; Holmes et al., 1992; Rao and Loeb, 1992; Ames et al., 1993; Bernstein and Gensler, 1993). Below, we review studies on the types of DNA damage that are the likely major sources of mutations causing cancer. Then we consider studies relevant to whether DNA damage increases in chronologically older people or animals, and whether such increases can plausibly account for major features of aging.

DNA Damage and Cancer

DNA Damage and Mutation in Early Cancer Progression

Vilenchik and Knudson (2003) noted that mutations, including losses of the two alleles of a tumor suppressor gene or translocations that activate, or form, an oncogene, are usually early events in carcinogenesis. Point mutations (i.e. mutations involving one or a few adjacent base pairs) probably arise most often by inaccurate replication past DNA damages in the template strand. Because human cells are diploid, and tumor suppressor mutations are most often recessive, such heterozygous mutations do not ordinarily express when they first arise. However, cells can become homozygous [i.e. undergo loss of heterozygosity (LOH)] in a number of ways. One way is by the action of HRR. Ordinarily, in a somatic cell, HRR occurs between the two identical sister-chromatids formed by replication and involves the use of information from an undamaged chromatid to repair a damaged one. However, occasionally HRR can occur between the non-sister homologs present in the diploid cell. This event can give rise at the next cell division to a cell that is homozygous for a mutant tumor suppressor gene, if the mutated gene is distal to the site of recombination. Homozygosity (i.e. LOH) can also arise by a point mutation or deletion mutation in the remaining wild type allele of a pair of tumor suppressor genes. Translocations most often arise from errors in repair of DNA damage by the inaccurate repair processes of NHEJ or single-strand annealing. Thus DNA damage usually initiates progression to cancer by causing a point mutation, deletion, loss of heterozygosity or translocation.

Major Causes of Cancer Death

The estimated number of cancer deaths in the US for 2007 is 559,650 (Jemal et al., 2007). The cancer with the highest mortality rate among both men and women is cancer of the lung and bronchus (28.7% of all cancer deaths), followed by colon cancer (9.3%) (American Cancer Society, 2007). With regard to hormone-dependent malignancies, breast cancer accounts for 7.3% of all cancer deaths, and prostate cancer accounts for 4.8% of all cancer deaths. Pancreatic cancer accounts for 5.9% of cancer deaths. These major cancers account for 56.0% of all cancer deaths in the US. Estimated mortality rates for other prevalent cancers (American Cancer Society, 2007) are as follows: non-Hodgkin's lymphoma (3.3%); liver (3.0%); esophagus (2.5%); urinary bladder (2.5%); gastric (2.0%); myeloid leukemia (1.7%); malignant melanoma (1.4%); oral cavity and pharynx (1.3%), endometrial cancer (1.3%) and cervical cancer (0.7%).

Since DNA damages cause replication errors leading to mutation and all cancers are associated with mutations, we address, below, the probable causes of DNA damage associated with each of these adult cancers. Carcinogenesis is a multifactorial process with environment (e.g. smoking, toxins, microbes), diet (e.g. high fat, low consumption of fruits and vegetables), genetics (e.g. single-nucleotide polymorphisms in genes encoding DNA repair proteins, antioxidant enzymes, detoxification enzymes) and aging (e.g. loss of immune function) each playing a role. Probable causes of DNA damage include chronic inflammation resulting in oxidative stress, exposure to DNA adduct forming molecules, defects in the maintenance of the genome (e.g. single-nucleotide polymorphisms in DNA repair genes) and epigenetic silencing of DNA repair genes. Although the sex steroids, androgens and estrogens, are often thought to promote cancer through effects on proliferation of target cells, it is becoming clear that compounds derived form the metabolism of hormones can also cause DNA damage. We now discuss in some detail the sources of DNA damage for each type of cancer listed above.

Lung Cancer

Lung cancer is caused primarily by components of tobacco smoke, but it can also be caused by inhalation of radon and asbestos fibers which cause cancer of the pleura. One of the components of tobacco smoke identified as a carcinogen for lung cancer, benzo[a]pyrene-7,8-diol-9,10-epoxide (BPDE), produces a characteristic pattern of adduct formation in the *p53* tumor suppressor gene of lung cells. Selective adduct formation occurs at guanine positions in codons 157, 248 and 273. These same positions are the major mutational hotspots identified in human lung cancers (Denissenko et al., 1996). Smith et al. (2000) mapped the distribution of adducts induced by diol epoxides of additional polycyclic aromatic hydrocarbons found in tobacco smoke and obtained similar results. Feng et al (2006) found that acrolein, a toxic compound occurring in cigarette smoke also produces a spectrum of DNA damages in the *p53* gene of human lung cells similar to the p53 mutational pattern in human lung cancer. Although it is unclear which of these compounds is most important (Feng et al., 2006; Hecht, 2006), these findings indicate a direct link between DNA adduct formation by chemical carcinogens in tobacco smoke and human lung cancer.

Inhaled radon, which is associated with lung cancer, acts, at least in part, through the production of oxidative DNA damage (Narayanan et al., 1997b). Asbestos-associated mesotheliomas (primary tumors of the pleura) and lung cancers are believed to be caused by free radical generation produced by the six fibrous silicates designated by the term asbestos (i.e. chrysotile, amosite, crocidolite, anthophyllite, tremolite and actinollite) (Ghio et al., 2008). Since iron from the host is mobilized and complexed by the surface of these fibrous silicates (Ghio et al., 2004), oxidant production by the fibrous silicate increases with the concentration of the associated iron (Ghio et al., 1992). Inflammatory cells that infiltrate sites of pulmonary damage caused by the fibrous silicates also contribute to oxidative stress and DNA damage. Thus asbestos causes increased production of reactive oxygen species (ROS) and 8-OHdG, a marker of oxidative DNA damage (Marczynski et al., 2000; Upadhyay and Kamp, 2003). Oxidative DNA damage can give rise to mutations (Jackson and Loeb, 2001), though the specific sites of mutations caused by asbestos and radon have not yet been identified.

TNF-α is secreted by inflammatory cells and is a potent pleiotropic, proinflammatory cytokine. In human lung bronchial epithelial cells, TNF-α increases ROS production, with a concomitant increase in the production of 8-OHdG (Babbar and Casero, 2006). The source of the ROS was determined to be spermine oxidase, an enzyme that oxidizes spermine to spermidine, 3-aminopropanol and H_2O_2. Inhibition of spermine oxidase with MDL 72,527 or with a targeted siRNA prevented the ROS production and oxidative DNA damage (Babbar and Casero, 2006).

Since the lung and bronchial epithelial cells are exposed to an oxygen-rich environment and many different environmental toxins, it is not surprising that oxidative DNA damage drives respiratory tract mutations in many people, making lung cancer the major cause of cancer mortality worldwide.

Colon Cancer

A high fat Western style diet is a risk factor for colon cancer. Epidemiological studies indicate a positive association between dietary fat consumption and colon cancer incidence (reviewed in Bernstein et al., 2005 and Sharma and O'Keefe, 2007). A high fat diet is associated with increased bile acid secretion, reflecting the role of bile acids in emulsifying dietary fat for absorption by the small intestine. Numerous epidemiological studies indicate that fecal bile acid concentrations are elevated in populations with a high incidence of colon cancer (see Bernstein et al., 2005). The most important bile acids in relation to colon cancer appear to be the secondary bile acids, deoxycholic acid and lithocholic acid. These bile acids cause both oxidative and nitrosative stresses in human colon epithelial cells (Washo-Stultz et al., 1999; Booth et al., 1997; Venturi et al., 1997; Lechner et al., 2002; Crowley-Weber et al., 2003; Payne et al., 2007) through ROS and reactive nitrogen species (RNS), respectively. ROS cause DNA damage (e.g. Jackson and Loeb, 2001). RNS, such as peroxynitrite, also cause DNA damage (Payne et al., 1999). Numerous studies have directly shown that deoxycholic acid and lithocholic acid induce DNA damage in human colon epithelial cells (Powolny et al., 2001; Glinghammar et al., 2002; Pool-Zobel and Leucht, 1997; Romagnolo et al., 2003; Scott et al., 2005), particularly oxidative DNA damage (Booth and Bilton, 1998; Booth et al., 1997; Venturi et al, 1997). Bile acids also cause mutation (Jenkins et al., 2007; Theisen et al., 2005; Narahara et al., 2000; Watabe and Bernstein, 1985). Intake of dietary heme iron is also associated with increased risk of colon cancer (Lee et al., 2004), suggesting a role of iron-catalyzed formation of ROS in colon cancer. These studies provide mechanisms by which bile acids may be significantly carcinogenic in the colon (Bernstein et al., 2005).

Ulcerative colitis is a chronic inflammatory bowel disease (IBD) associated with increased risk of colon cancer. ROS are produced at abnormally high levels in IBD, and their destructive effects may contribute to the initiation and/or propagation of the disease (Rezaie et al., 2007). The oxidative DNA damage 8-OHdG in the mucosa of ulcerative colitis patients increases with disease duration and dysplasia and these damages are thought to have implications for progression to cancer (D'Inca et al. 2004).

Breast Cancer

Persistently elevated blood levels of estrogen have been found in many studies to be associated with increased risk of breast cancer (reviewed by Yager and Davidson, 2006). Estrogen appears to contribute to carcinogenesis by three processes, the metabolism of estrogen to genotoxic, mutagenic metabolites, the stimulation of tissue growth, and the repression of phase II detoxification enzymes (which metabolize ROS) (Ansell et al., 2004; Belous et al., 2007; Bolton and Thatcher, 2007). Estradiol, the major estrogen in humans, can be metabolized to quinone derivatives that form adducts with DNA (Yue et al., 2003). This can cause depurination, the removal of bases from the phosphodiester backbone of DNA, and then inaccurate repair or replication of the apurinic site leading to mutation and cancer. Recycling of estrogen quinones back to hydroquinones and catechols can also produce ROS leading to additional DNA damage (Seacat et al., 1997). These genotoxic mechanisms may act in synergy with estrogen receptor-mediated, persistent cell proliferation to cause breast cancer (Yue et al., 2003).

Animal studies indicate that inflammation is an important component of mammary carcinogenesis (Calogero et al., 2007). BALB/c mice that are transgenic for the HER-2/neu oncogene show an increase in expression of genes directly linked to inflammation during tumor progression. An in silico meta-analysis in a human breast dataset suggests that proinflammatory activation in mammary glands of these transgenic mice reflects a general pattern of inflammation-linked gene expression in human breast cancer (Calogero et al., 2007).

Dietary, environmental factors and genetic susceptibility also seem to be involved in breast carcinogenesis. A high level of oxidative DNA damage was reported in lymphocyte DNA of premenopausal breast cancer patients from Egypt that paralleled the increase in environmental pollution (Soliman et al., 2004). A high intake of omega-6 polyunsaturated fatty acids (PUFAs) (Bartsch et al., 1999) is associated with increased breast cancer risk. Also, a high intake of beef and pork and a low intake of vegetables are associated with increased breast cancer risk and may account for 85% of the oxidative DNA damage levels among women (Djuric et al., 1998). Excessive ethanol intake also increases breast cancer risk. A possible mechanism for this ethanol effect could be that ethanol inhibits benzo[a]pyrene-DNA adduct removal and increases 8-OHdG formation in human mammary epithelial cells (Singletary et al., 2004). Breast cancer prevention is linked to a high intake of fish oil omega-3 PUFAs and omega-9 monounsaturated fatty acids (e.g. oleic acid), and high tea consumption (Kapiszewska et al., 2006). High tea consumption is associated with a concomitant reduction in salivary 17β-estradiol concentrations (Kapiszewska et al., 2006). A direct test of the hypothesis that green tea catechins and black tea theaflavins reduced DNA damage and breast tumor burden was performed using a transgenic mouse model of mammary carcinogenesis (Kaur et al., 2007). Compared to control mice, mice that received the tea components survived longer, had smaller tumors and had a significantly reduced tumor level of malondialdehyde-DNA adducts. Genetic susceptibility factors play an important role in breast cancer incidence and prognosis. Numerous single-nucleotide polymorphisms and mutations in DNA repair genes are associated with breast cancer risk.

In summary, genetic background, years of estrogen exposure, dietary practices and environmental factors, together, appear to contribute to the incidence of DNA damage, genomic instability, and the ultimate breast cancer risk.

Prostate Cancer

Prostate carcinogenesis appears to be due to multiple processes that lead to prostate tissue injury and chronic inflammation. These processes include environmental influences [e.g. infectious agents such as *E. coli*, HPV, HSV; and heavy metals], dietary factors [e.g. charred meat carcinogens, Western-style diet (high fat, low vegetable intake), low omega-3 fatty acids; low selenium], genetic susceptibility factors and hormonal imbalances (Nelson, 2007; De Marzo et al., 2007a; De Marzo et al., 2007b; Fleshner and Zlotta, 2007).

Bacterial colonization and associated inflammation was demonstrated in human prostate cancer (PC) specimens using PCR-based analysis (Sciarra et al., 2007a; Sciarra et al., 2007b). Evidence for the role of bacteria in prostate carcinogenesis was demonstrated in a mouse model of chronic prostatitis (Elkahwaji et al., 2007). Mice infected with *E. coli* showed foci of uniformly acute inflammation in the glandular lumen and a persistent inflammation at 12 weeks post-inoculation in the stroma. The prostatic glands showing varying degrees of atypical hyperplasia and dysplasia, had stronger staining for oxidative DNA damage and increased epithelial cell proliferation compared to PBS-treated control mice. Cadmium exposure is associated with prostate cancer and may cause DNA damage by interfering with DNA repair and indirectly through the generation of ROS (Bertin and Averbeck, 2006).

Several dietary factors are thought to contribute to prostate carcinogenesis. The consumption of processed meat and dairy foods are associated with increased risk (Rohrmann et al., 2007). Increased dietary fat may underlie this association. Another possibility is that nitrites in smoked or cured meats, added for preservation or improvement of color or taste, are transformed into carcinogenic N-nitroso compounds. The dietary charred meat carcinogen 2-amino-1-methyl-6-phenylimidazo [4,5-b]pyridine (PhIP) acts as a tumor initiator and promoter in the rat prostate and causes both inflammation and DNA damage (Nakai et al., 2007). PhIP treatment of Fisher344 rats (Big Blue rats) resulted in increased mutation in all lobes of the prostate. G:C → T:A transversions were the predominant type of mutation (Nakai et al., 2007). In a dietary intervention study of men with prostate cancer, the consumption of tomato-sauce based entrees, which contain high levels of the antioxidant lycopene, significantly reduced prostate tissue oxidative DNA damage (Chen et al., 2001). In an animal model, lycopene and beta-carotene protected *in vivo* against iron-induced oxidative DNA damage in the rat prostate (Matos et al., 2006). These studies underscore the importance of dietary-related DNA damage-inducing factors, especially oxidative stress, in prostate carcinogenesis.

Our current understanding of the sequence of pathologic lesions in prostate carcinogenesis is that it begins with proliferative inflammatory atrophy (PIA), progresses to prostatic intraepithelial neoplasia (PIN) and dysplastic PIN, high-grade PIN and then to prostate cancer. PIA is believed to arise in a setting of prostatitis and is characterized by proliferating prostatic cells juxtaposed to inflammatory cells. PIA is referred to as a regenerative 'risk factor' lesion that links prostatitis to prostate cancer (De Marza et al., 2007a; De Marzo et al., 2007b). The epithelial cells of the PIA lesion express high levels of the pi-class glutathione S-transferase (GSTP1) (Nelson et al., 2001). GSTP1 may, therefore, serve a "caretaker" function for prostatic cells by reducing oxidative stress that inflicts genome damage (Nelson et al., 2001). In the transition from PIA to PIN, the function of GSTP1 is gradually lost by epigenetic silencing as a result of "CpG island'" DNA methylation changes (Wagenlehner et al., 2007). This somatic epigenetic alteration is present in all prostate cancers, and appears to arise in a setting of inflammation (Nelson, 2001; 2007). An important somatic DNA alteration that affects the epithelial cells of the human high grade PIN lesion is telomere shortening (Meeker et al., 2002; Meeker et al., 2006). Telomere loss is known to occur during cell division and oxidative DNA damage, two byproducts of chronic inflammation, which are common histologic findings in the prostate (Meeker, 2006)

Prostate cancer is strongly associated with sex steroid metabolism (Bosland, 2006). Androgens not only serve as tumor promoters after tumor initiating events, but the metabolism of androgens can produce DNA damaging metabolites. During testosterone metabolism, the action of aromatase results in the production of 17β-estradiol, a carcinogen. The administration of testosterone and 17β-estradiol to Noble rats for 16 weeks induces dysplasia and stromal inflammation of the lateral prostate (Tam et al., 2007). These histopathologic changes were accompanied by an increase in expression of NAD(P)H oxidase, iNOS and COX-2 , and an accumulation of 8-OHdG, 4-hydroxynonenol protein adducts and nitrotyrosine (Tam et al., 2007). In an animal model of prostate cancer (Bosland, 2006), when estradiol is added to testosterone treatment of rats, prostate cancer incidence is markedly increased. Since estrogen receptors are expressed in the prostate, they may mediate the effects of the estrogen treatment. There is also evidence in the human and rodent prostate for the conversion of estrogens to catecholestrogens (Bosland, 2006). Catecholestrogens are converted to reactive intermediates that can form DNA adducts and also cause generation of ROS.

Genetic predisposition to prostate cancer has been well documented in familial studies, and single nucleotide polymorphisms associated with prostate cancer risk have been identified (Naylor et al., 2007). These polymorphisms occur in genes related to steroid metabolism (Nock et al., 2006), oxidative stress (Kang et al., 2007), detoxification (Reszka and Wasowicz, 2002; Nock et al., 2006), inflammatory pathways (Sun et al., 2007; Meyer-Siegler et al., 2007; Hedelin et al., 2007) and DNA repair (van Gils et al., 2002; Rybickie et al., 2004; Chen et al., 2006; Nock et al., 2006; Hirata et al., 2007; Bau et al., 2007). The environmental, dietary and hormonal effects listed above may therefore differ depending on these specific gene polymorphisms.

In summary, chronic inflammation, a reduced antioxidant status, genotoxic and proliferative effects of endocrine, paracrine and autocrine factors, coupled with specific polymorphisms, are now considered to drive prostatic carcinogenesis in the aging male through the progressive increase in DNA damage and mutational events.

Pancreatic Cancer

The risk factors for the development of pancreatic cancer are chronic pancreatitis, a high fat diet and tobacco smoking (American Cancer Society, 2007; Li et al., 2002). As reviewed by Garcea et al. (2005), several studies have reported an increased incidence of pancreatic cancer in individuals with chronic pancreatitis, when compared to the average population. For instance, one study reported an 18.5-fold increased incidence of pancreatic cancer in patients with chronic pancreatitis (Talamini et al., 1999). Pancreatitis is an inflammation of the pancreas, and inflammation generally causes increased ROS (Jackson and Loeb, 2001), and thereby, DNA damage. Diets high in fat stimulate bile secretion, and most pancreatic adenocarcinomas occur in the head of the gland, which is in close proximity to the channel through which bile is excreted from the liver into the small intestine. As discussed above, bile acids can induce oxidative stress and oxidative DNA damage. In addition, a possible link between bile acids and pancreatic cancer has been suggested (Tucker et al., 2004). A significantly higher level of aromatic DNA adducts and oxidative DNA damage (8-OH-dG) was detected in tissues adjacent to pancreatic tumors, and in the tumors themselves compared to pancreatic tissues from individuals without neoplasia (Li et al., 2002). These findings suggest that pancreatic cancer may arise as a consequence of oxidative DNA damages resulting from ROS produced by inflammation and/or exposure to high levels of bile acids. As discussed above for lung cancer, a number of compounds in tobacco smoke cause critical mutations that promote cancer. Such mutations, caused by adduct-forming aromatic carcinogens resulting from smoking, likely contribute to pancreatic cancer as well.

Non-Hodgkin's Lymphoma

Non-Hodgkin's lymphomas comprise a number of distinct subtypes derived from both B-lymphocytes and T-lymphocytes with somewhat different etiologies. The most common subtypes of non-Hodgkin's lymphomas are diffuse large B-cell and follicular lymphomas. Chromosomal instability defined by aberrant interchromosomal translocation and fusion events is characteristic of a number of these lymphomas (Kuppers and Dalla-Favara, 2001; Fernandez et al., 2005; Franco et al., 2006; Ramiro et al., 2006; Lenz et al., 2007). The high incidence of translocations in these cancers most probably arises from the frequent double-strand DNA breaks that are an integral part of the process that generates a diverse immune repertoire in the context of V(D)J and immunoglobulin heavy chain (IgH) class switch recombination (Franco et al., 2006). The double-strand breaks that occur during immunoglobulin remodeling must be appropriately repaired to prevent potentially lethal chromosomal breaks (Franco et al., 2006). During this process of immunoglobulin gene remodeling, errors in the repair of both general and lymphocyte-specific double-strand breaks may occur that result in dysregulated expression of oncogenes brought under the control of Ig enhancers (Kuppers and Dalla-Favera, 2001). For example, the three different antibody diversification reactions, class switch recombination, somatic hypermutation and gene conversion, are initiated by activation-induced deaminase (AID) (Ramiro et al., 2006; 2007). The expression of AID is restricted to germinal-center B cells (de Yebenes and Ramiro, 2006) and is the B-cell-specific factor that deaminates DNA (C to U) in B lymphocyte Ig DNA (Longerich et al., 2007). AID induces DNA break repair events to initiate immunoglobulin gene diversification (Lee et al., 2007; Duquette et al., 2007), but, in addition to this normal antibody diversification, AID can also initiate Burkitt's lymphoma-like c-myc/IgH translocations (Ramiro et al., 2006).

Genetic predispositions (polymorphisms in DNA repair genes) can affect the incidence of non-Hodgkin's lymphomas. Increased risk of non-Hodgkin's lymphoma is associated with particular genetic variants of the DNA repair gene methylguanine methyltransferase (repair of alky adducts) (Shen et al., 2007). Also a gene employed in recombinational repair of double-strand breaks (MRE11) appears to protect against non-Hodgkin's lymphoma (Rollinson et al., 2006). Polymorphisms in DNA repair genes can enhance the error-prone rate of chromosomal translocations and increase the risk of non-Hodgkin's lymphomas. The risk of a certain type of non-Hodgkin's lymphoma, marginal zone lymphoma, has been associated with inflame-mation (Lightfoot et al., 2006), and polymorphisms in oxidative stress genes are associated with increased risk of non-Hodgkin's lymphoma (Lightfoot et al., 2006; Wang et al., 2006; Lan et al., 2007).

Other factors that increase the risk of non-Hodkin's lymphoma include environmental toxins [e.g. pesticides (Dich et al., 1997), benzene from gasoline (Smith et al., 2007), dietary factors (Chang et al., 2006; Kelemen et al., 2006) and viruses [e.g. Epstein-Barr virus (EBV) (Epeldegui et al., 2007; Kamranvar et al., 2007), hepatitis C (HCV) (Machida et al., 2004; Machida et al., 2005; Machida et al., 2006). EBV can induce telomere dysfunction and DNA damage (Kamranvar et al., 2007), important mechanisms in EBV oncogenesis. EBV also induces the expression of somatic hypermutation-inducing molecules (e.g. AID and polymerase eta) and the accrual of oncogene mutations (Epeldegui et al., 2007). HCV induces ROS, nitric oxide, and error-prone DNA polymerase zeta, iota, and AID, which together, contribute to the induction of double-strand breaks and enhancement of mutation frequency (Machida et al., 2004; 2005). HCV therefore induces a mutator phenotype and may transform cells by a "hit-and-run' mechanism (Machida et al., 2005). Among the HCV proteins, core, Ei and NS3 are potent ROS inducers, and their expression leads to DNA damage (Machida et al., 2006). HCV studies have thus identified ROS and RNS as the primary inducers of double-strand breaks in HCV-infected cells.

In summary, viral infections, formation of ROS and RNS, environmental toxins and dietary factors appear to contribute to increased risk of non-Hodgkin's lymphoma in genetically pre-disposed individuals.

Liver Cancer

While hepatocellular carcinoma causes only 3% of cancer mortality in the USA, it causes 12% of cancer mortality in developing countries and 9% world-wide. In areas of China and Africa, foods such as corn, rice and peanuts are often contaminated with aflatoxin B_1 (AFB_1). The mycotoxin AFB_1 forms DNA adducts at the N7 position of guanine in an *E. coli* test system, and this leads to frequent GC to TA transversion mutations (Sambamurti et al., 1988). Likewise AFB_1 forms DNA adducts with guanine in human hepatocytes (Autrub et al., 1984). A point mutation in the *p53* gene at the third position of codon 249[ser] resulting from a G:C to T:A transversion mutation is very common in hepatocellular carcinoma in areas exposed to AFB_1 (Hussain et al., 2007). In areas of the world with frequent aflatoxin contamination, liver cancer is thought to be due to the carcinogenic activity of dietary AFB_1 because of its direct DNA adduct formation and induction of mutation.

Chronic hepatitis B virus (HBV) and hepatitis C virus (HCV) infections are also a major cause of liver cancer worldwide. Infection with HBV or HCV causes inflammation with the release of ROS and RNS that damage DNA (Hussain et al., 2007). In humans, chronic hepatitis is associated with increased formation of 8-OHdG (Shimoda et al., 1994), a major base alteration associated with oxidative DNA damage.

Human cancers often arise in a setting of chronic inflammation (Jackson and Loeb, 2001). Chronic infections that elicit an inflammatory response are an important cause of chronic inflammation [e.g. in liver cancer (HBV, HCV), in gastric cancer (*H. pylori*) and in cervical cancer (human papilloma virus)]. Chronic infections are potent generators of ROS (Jackson and Loeb, 2001). Neutrophils and macrophages/monocytes produce bursts of ROS to destroy the infecting pathogens. These ROS can damage DNA of invaded and nearby host cells ("innocent-bystander injury"), as well as damaging the invading pathogen, and such chronic damage can contribute to tumor development.

Esophageal Cancer

There are two major histologic types of esophageal cancer, adenocarcinoma and squamous cell carcinoma. Barrett's esophagus (BE), is a metaplastic lesion of the distal esophagus characterized by replacement of the normal squamous epithelium by columnar intestinal epithelium containing goblet cells. BE is a major risk factor for esophageal adenocarcinoma development (Falk, 2002). BE is associated with increased duodeno-gastro-esophageal reflux (Nehra et al., 1999; Menges et al., 2001). Increased reflux causes increased exposure of the esophagus to bile acids from the duodenum and low pH produced by stomach acid. Persons with esophageal adenocarcinoma are associated with even greater exposure to bile than persons with uncomplicated BE (Stein et al., 1998). Bile acids and low pH induce oxidative stress and production of ROS in human esophageal tissues and cultured cells (Dvorak et al., 2007; Jenkins et al., 2007), and also induce DNA damage in cultured esophageal cells and biopsies from BE tissue (Dvorak et al., 2007; Jenkins et al., 2007; Jolly et al., 2004). Exposure of cultured esophageal cells to deoxycholic acid increases p53 mutations (Jenkins et al., 2007). Theisen et al. (2005) used an in vivo rat model for measuring mutant cells. Esophagoduodenostomy was carried out on Big Blue F1 lacI transgenic rats to surgically create duodeno-gastric-esophageal reflux. In these surgically altered animals the frequency of mutant lacI cells in the esophageal mucosa was significantly higher than in the nonoperated animals. Forty-six percent of the mutant cells were altered at CpG dinucleotide sites and 61% of these were C to T and G to A transitions. This pattern is similar to the pattern observed in human esophageal adenocarcinoma, suggesting that duodeno-gastric-esophageal reflux is carcinogenic. Taken together, these findings indicate that esophageal adenocarcinoma is due, in large part, to elevated exposure of the esophagus to bile acids and low pH leading to oxidative stress, increased production of ROS, increased DNA damage and mutation. Smoking is also a major risk factor for esophageal cancer, mainly squamous cell carcinoma (Holmes and Vaughan, 2006). Thus, DNA adduct formation by carcinogenic chemicals in tobacco smoke is likely to be important for squamous esophageal cancer. Dietary heme iron, a prooxidant, is also positively associated with upper digestive tract cancer (esophagus or stomach)(Lee et al., 2005).

Urinary Bladder Cancer

Smoking is the major risk factor for bladder cancer (American Cancer Society, 2007). Smokers have about twice the risk of bladder cancer than non-smokers. About 48% of bladder cancer deaths among men and 28% among women are estimated to be due to smoking. Workers in certain industries (e.g. dye, rubber and leather), and persons living in communities with high levels of arsenic in drinking water are also at increased risk. DNA damage is implicated in bladder cancer since genetic variants of the DNA repair gene XPC (nucleotide excision repair) are associated with reduced risk (Zhu et al., 2007). Genetic variants of genes 8-oxoG DNA glycosylase, poly(ADP-ribose)polymerase-1, and polymerase-β (employed in base excision repair, particularly repair of oxidative DNA damage) also significantly affected the risk of bladder cancer (Figueroa et al., 2007a). Polymorphisms of genes related to DNA repair (XRCC3, XRCC1, PCNA and spanning-ERCC1 region) may modulate bladder cancer risk, and some of these effects may preferentially affect smokers (Matullo et al., 2005). In a multigenic study of genetic polymorphisms in relation to bladder cancer, smoking had a significantly increased multiplicative interaction with polymorphisms in DNA repair and cell cycle control genes (Wu et al., 2006). Risk of bladder cancer is also associated with variants in genes encoding proteins of the double-strand break repair pathway (Figueroa et al., 2007b).

Gastric Cancer

H. pylori infection is the major etiologic factor in gastric carcinogenesis. Chronic gastritis (inflammation) caused by H. pylori is often long-standing and can be lifelong if not treated. Infection of gastric epithelial cells with H. pylori results in an increase in ROS generation (Ding et al., 2007). Basal levels of ROS are greater in epithelial cells isolated from gastric mucosal biopsy specimens from H. pylori-infected subjects than in cells from uninfected individuals. ROS generation by H. pylori is also associated with increased apoptosis. The altered base 8-OHdG, resulting from ROS, is increased in chronic gastritis and has mutagenic and carcinogenic potential. H. pylori infection appears to be the major determinant of the formation of this altered base (Farinati et al., 1998; Baik et al., 1996). Thus, oxidatively generated DNA damage appears to be a major cause of gastric cancer.

Summary of Important Known Sources of DNA Damage Leading to Cancer

The discussion, so far, of the sources of DNA damage giving rise to the major cancers, considered above, suggests that, in general, there are two important sources of DNA damage. The first is ROS produced under conditions of chronic oxidative stress (e.g. due to chronic inflammation which may arise from infection, persistent exposure to high levels of bile acids due to a high fat diet, low intake of micronutrients and plant-derived antioxidants, or to elevated metabolic process such as the recycling of estrogen quinones). The second major source is adduct-forming carcinogenic chemicals (e.g. those in tobacco smoke, present as food contaminants, or resulting from estrogen metabolism). The contribution of spontaneous mutation to cancer incidence, in the absence of an extrinsic source of stress, is unknown. However, evidence indicates that even spontaneous mutagenesis in mammalian cells is caused mainly by endogenously produced oxidative damage (Rossman and Goncharova, 1998).

Less Frequent Causes of Cancer Death

Other less frequent cancers may also be due to some of the same, or similar, sources of DNA damage as those discussed above, but for these the situation is more uncertain. Cigarette smoking and exposure to certain chemicals such as benzene, a component of gasoline, are risk factors for myeloid leukemia (1.7% of all cancer deaths) (American Cancer Society, 2007). The key environmental risk factor for malignant melanoma (1.4% of all cancer deaths) is exposure to the ultraviolet (UV) component of sunlight, but it has been speculated that UVA-induced oxidative lesions may also be involved (Povey et al., 2007). UV induces DNA damage in the form of cyclobutane pyrimidine dimers and 6-4 photoproducts. Tobacco and alcohol appear to be the major risk factors for cancer of the oral cavity and pharynx (1.3% of all cancer deaths) (American Cancer Society, 2007). Bile acid and acid reflux also appear to induce DNA damage and genetic alterations in cells of the oral cavity and pharynx. Cancer of the uterine corpus (endometrium) (1.3% of all cancer deaths) is related to increased estrogen exposure, and cancer of the uterine cervix (0.7% of all cancer deaths) is primarily caused by infection with human papillomavirus (American Cancer Society, 2007). The cancers discussed in this subsection account for 6.4% of all cancer deaths in the US. The cancers discussed in the subsections above (69.3% of all cancer deaths) and those in this subsection add up to 75.7% of the estimated cancer deaths in the US. *In general, the evidence indicates that ROS-induced oxidative DNA damages and DNA adducts formed by endogenous and exogenous carcinogenic chemicals are the likely major causes of the most frequent deadly cancers.*

Progressing from DNA Damage to Cancer

As discussed above in the Introduction, DNA damages that are not repaired can give rise to mutations through errors of DNA synthesis during DNA repair or replication. If such a mutation provides a growth or survival advantage, the mutant cell may proliferate at the expense of neighboring cells to give rise to a field of mutant cells (Bernstein et al., 2008). If within this field further DNA damage gives rise to a cell with a second expressing mutation with a growth or survival advantage relative to the first, this new double mutant will expand forming a secondary field within the first field. This process may be repeated several times, often over decades, giving rise to a pre-malignant field, and then ultimately to cancer.

The terms "field defect" or "field cancerization" refer to a region of tissue, a pre-malignant field, that is predisposed to develop cancer. Table 1 lists cancers that are major causes of cancer death, as discussed above, and which likely arise in a field defect. Often field defects are characterized by loss of apoptosis capability (greater survival ability) and increased genomic instability (frequent mutation). The evidence summarized in Table 1 indicates that initiation and progression to cancer likely follows the sequence DNA damage → mutation → selection → field defect → cancer.

Table 1. Pre-malignant field defects

Lung and Bronchus	Large clones of somatically altered cells (e.g., 90,000 cells) are found in grossly normal lung tissue after resection for lung cancer or after biopsy of normal tissue in the airways of smokers. Fields of cells containing loss of heterozygosity for the critical cancer related gene p21 were among the earliest and most frequent events in the normal-appearing lung tissue of smokers and in the lung cancers of smokers.	Review by Wiencke and Kelsey, 2002; Endo et al., 2000
Colon	Epithelial cells of the flat non-neoplastic colonic mucosa of individuals with colon cancer have reduced apoptosis capability compared to cells of individuals without neoplasia. There are numerous field-wide changes in protein expression in the morphologically normal appearing mucosa of patients with colorectal neoplasia. Expression of anti-apoptotic proteins Bcl-X_L and Bcl-2 are increased in non-neoplastic colorectal mucosa of colon cancer patients suggesting the presence of an apoptosis resistant field. Adenocarcinomas often arise in large and/or dysplastic adenomatous polyps within this field.	Payne et al., 1995; Garewal et al., 1996; Bernstein et al., 1999; Bernstein et al., 2002; Polley et al., 2006; Badvie et al., 2006; Bronner et al., 1995
Breast	Loss of heterozygosity in chromosomes 1, 13 and 17 is observed in the normal tissue adjacent to tumors, and apoptosis is decreased in the non-involved tissue from cancer-containing breasts. Non-neoplastic breast tissues from patients with breast carcinoma have increased levels of genomic instability indicating a field defect.	Forsti et al., 2001; Hassan and Walker, 1998; Ellsworth et al., 2004

Table 1. (Continued)

Pancreas	In a transgenic mouse model of pancreatic ductal adenocarcinoma, the development of the carcinoma is preceded by pre-malignant transdifferentiation of acinar cells to ductal-like cells. Bcl-X_L, an anti-apoptotic protein, is highly expressed in pre-malignant tubular complexes formed of ductal-like cells compared to acinar cells in normal appearing areas. Bax, a pro-apoptotic protein, shows the opposite pattern of expression.	Greten et al., 2002
Liver	Chronic infection by hepatitis B and C virus are common causes of cirrhosis of the liver, as well as liver cancer. After resection of a hepatocellular carcinoma, the presence of cirrhosis acts as a field defect contributing to new hepatocellular carcinoma, usually within 5 years.	Bilimoria et al., 2001
Esophagus	BE, the pre-malignant metaplastic lesion predisposing to esophageal adenocarcinoma (see above), is one of the clearest examples of a field defect. BE metaplastic tissue is apoptosis resistant and expresses the anti-apoptotic proteins Bcl-X_L and Mcl-1 at a high level. Esophageal squamous cell carcinoma is also associated with a field characterized by defective p53 protein.	Dvorakova et al., 2005; Tian et al., 1998
Stomach	*H. pylori* infection potently induces methylation of CpG islands in the DNA of the gastric mucosa. These methylations are epigenetic changes (epimutations), and their accumulation constitutes a field defect for gastric cancers.	Ushijima et al., 2006

Inherited Conditions that Indicate a Causal Relationship between DNA Damage and Cancer

We reviewed evidence, above, that cancers of different organs are likely caused by DNA damages arising from assault by specific agents. In this section we review evidence that decreased DNA repair due to germ line mutations, and consequent increased DNA damage, leads to elevated risk of cancer. These findings further support the concept that DNA damage causes cancer. Table 2 lists human genes encoding DNA repair proteins that protect against cancer. These genes are employed in the DNA repair processes of homologous recombinational repair (HRR), non-homologous end joining (NHEJ), base excision repair (BER), global genomic repair [GGR; a form of nucleotide excision repair (NER)], transcription coupled repair (TCR; another form of NER), and mismatch repair (MMR). Inherited defects in these genes give rise to cancer at the various sites listed in Table 2.

Table 2. Inherited human DNA repair gene mutations which increase cancer risk

Gene*	Repair pathway	Cancer Risk
BRCA1, BRCA2	*HRR of DS breaks and daughter strand gaps (Nagaraju and Scully, 2007)*	Breast, ovarian (Lancaster et al., 2007)
Gene*	*Repair pathway*	Cancer Risk
ATM	HRR	Leukemia, lymphoma (Thompson and Schild, 2002)
NBS	HRR	Increased malignancy, AT-like, lymphoma (Thompson and Schild, 2002)
MRE11	HRR	AT-like (Thompson and Schild, 2002)
BLM	HRR	Early development of cancers seen in normal population (Thompson and Schild, 2002)
WRN	HRR, NHEJ, BER	Increase in cancer incidence, mainly sarcomas (Thompson and Schild, 2002)
RTS (RECQ4)	DNA repair but type unknown	Increased cancer incidence, mainly osteogenic sarcomas (Thompson and Schild, 2002)
FANCA, FANCB, FANCC, FANCD1, FANCD2, FANCE, FANCF, FANCG, FANCI, FANCJ, FANCL, FANCM, FANCN	Repair of interstrand DNA crosslinks involving HRR and NER (Levitus et al., 2006)	Acute myeloid leukemia; squamous cell carcinomas of head and neck (Levitus et al., 2006)
XPC, XPE	GGR (Wijnhoven et al., 2007)	Early onset skin cancer (Lichon and Khachemoune, 2007)
XPA, XPB, XPD, XPF, XPG	GGR and TCR (Wijnhoven et al., 2007)	
XPV	Translesion DNA synthesis by polymerase η (Wang et al., 2007)	
hMSH2, hMSH6, hMLH1, hPMS2	MMR, HRR (Jiricny, 2006)	Hereditary non-polyposis colon cancer; endometrial cancer; ovarian cancer (Lynch et al., 1996; Lancaster et al., 2007)

*Gene abbreviations; BRCA1, Breast cancer-associated gene 1; BRCA2, Breast cancer-associated gene 2; AT, ataxia telangiectasia mutated; NBS, Nijmegen breakage syndrome; MRE11, meiotic recombination 11; BLM, Bloom syndrome gene; WRN, Werner syndrome gene; RTS, Rothmund-Thomson syndrome; FANCA, FANCB, FANCC, FANCD1, FANCD2, FANCE, FANCF, FANCG, FANCI, FANCJ, FANCL, FANCM, FANCN, Fanconi anemia complementation groups A, B, C, D1, D2, E, F, G, I, J, L, M, and N; XPC, XPE, XPA, XPB, XPD, XPF, XPG, XPV xeroderma pigmentoum complementation groups C, E, A, B, D, F, G and V respectively; hMSH2 and hMSH6, human MutS homologs 2 and 6, respectively; hMLH1, human MutL homolog 1; hPMS2, human post-meiotic segregation 2; AT-like, ataxia telangiectasia-like; DS breaks, double-strand breaks.

DNA Damage and Aging

Damages may accumulate in DNA of non-dividing or infrequently dividing cells and lead to declining transcription of mRNA and gene expression with age. This decline would result in a general loss of function with age of tissues and organs containing non-dividing or infrequently dividing cells. Brain and muscle are two organs composed largely of terminally differentiated cells, neurons and myocytes respectively, that do not divide. These organs play an important role in aging, and are well studied with respect to DNA damage. In our further discussion we will focus on these organs, but also briefly discuss liver and kidney.

DNA Damages Increase with Age in Mammalian Brain

In most regions of the mammalian brain, the production of neurons is confined to the prenatal period. However, in rodents the hippocampus is one of the few areas of the brain that continues to produce neurons postnatally. In general, adult neurons are post-mitotic cells whose gradual loss of function is a prominent feature of aging. Even in the rodent hippocampus neurogenesis drastically declines with age (Kuhn et al., 1996).

Table 3 lists 29 studies showing accumulation of DNA damage with age in the mammalian brain. The formation of 8-OHdG observed in eleven of the listed studies indicates the presence of oxidative damage presumably caused by ROS. The single-strand breaks (SS breaks) and double-strand breaks (DS breaks) indicated in the Table may also be caused by ROS.

Mandavilli and Rao (1996) estimated the number of DNA SS-strand and DS-strand breaks in neuronal cells of the rat cerebral cortex with age. They estimated that young 4-day-old rats had about 3,000 SS-breaks per neuron and that this increased to 7,000 in neurons of old rats greater than 2 years of age. DS-strand breaks increased from about 156 to 600 in neurons of young versus old rats.

Oxidative DNA damage appears to play an important role in Alzheimer's disease (AD), the most common type of dementia in people over 65 years old. As reviewed by Markesbery and Lovell (2006), several studies have shown an elevation of the oxidized bases 8-OHdG, 8-hydroxyadenine (8-OHA), 5-hydroxycytosine and 5-hydroxyuracil in late stage AD patients. Elevated 8-OHdG and 8-OHA can also be detected in mild cognitive impairment, the earliest detectable form of AD, suggesting that oxidative DNA damage is an early event in AD and not a secondary phenomenon.

Accumulation of DNA Damage in Aging Muscle

Aging in humans and other species is accompanied by an age-dependent reduction of muscle strength and stamina for sustained physical effort, and the underlying cause of this loss may be accumulation of DNA damage. Skeletal muscle is a post-mitotic tissue composed of multinucleated myofibers, elements that arise from the fusion of mononucleated

Table 3. Increase in DNA damage with age in mammalian brain

Species	Damage	Assay*	Age span (months)	Reference
Mouse	SS breaks	DPTA	3 – 33	Price et al., 1971
Mouse	SS breaks	DPTA	3 – 35	Modak and Price, 1971
Mouse	SS breaks	AS, S_1N	6 – 30	Chetsanga et al., 1977
Mouse	SS breaks	IF	1 – 12	Nakanishi et al. 1979
Mouse	SS breaks	S_1N	3 – 27	Mori and Goto, 1982
Mouse	7-methylguanine	HPLC	11 – 28	Tan et al., 1990
Mouse	8-OHdG	HPLC	8 – 27	Sohal et al., 1994
Mouse	8-OHdG	HPLC	3 – 34	Cardozo-Pelaez et al., 1999
Mouse	DNA-protein crosslinks	PD	2 – 25	Zahn et al., 1999
Mouse	8-OHdG and DNA-protein crosslinks	PP	12 – 24	Izzotti et al., 1999
Mouse	SS breaks	AFE	0 – 25	Hosokawa et al., 2000
Mouse/Rat	8-OHdG	HPLC	6 – 24	Hamilton et al., 2001
Mouse	8-OHdG	HPLC	3 to 6 - 26	VanRemmen et al., 2003
Mouse	DS breaks	γ-H2AX foci	2 - 20	Sedelnikova et al., 2004
Mouse	SS breaks	ISNT	12 – 28	Rutten et al., 2007
Rat	SS breaks	S_1N	2 – 24	Murthy et al., 1976
Rat	SS breaks and DS breaks	NT, TT	<1 - >24	Mandavilli and Rao, 1996
Rat	Malondialdehyde adducts	PP	6 – 24	Cai et al., 1996
Rat	8-OHdG	HPLC	2 – 33	Kaneko et al., 1997
Rat	Oxidative DNA damage	Single-cell gel electrophoresis	3 – 24	Giovanelli et al., 2003
Rat	Oxidative DNA damage	Single-cell gel electrophoresis	4 - 24	Juliet et al., 2005
Rat	DNA protein cross-links and 8-OHdG	PD and HPLC	3 or 4 - >22	Haripriya et al., 2005
Rat	8-OHdG	IA	4-24	Wolf et al, 2005
Rat	8-OHdG	HPLC	1 - 17	Gedik et al., 2005
Rat	DNA damages which block PCR of β-actin and p53 genes	PCR	4 to 6 – 20 to 24	Sen et al., 2007
Mongolian gerbil	8-OHdG	HPLC	5 – 25	Sohal et al., 1995
Rabbit	SS breaks	ZC	1 – 93	Bergtold and Lett, 1985
Dog	SS breaks	AS	0 – 120	Wheeler and Lett, 1974
Human	8-OHdG	HPLC	48yrs – 97yrs	Mecocci et al., 1993

*Assay abbreviations: DPTA, DNA polymerase template activity; AS, alkaline sucrose gradient centrifugation; S_1N, S_1 nuclease sensitivity; IF, immunofluorescence with anti-cytidine antibody; HPLC, high pressure liquid chromatography; ZC, zonal centrifugation through alkaline sucrose gradients; NT, nick translation using *E. coli* DNA polymerase I; TT, terminal transferase addition of dNTPs to DNA blunt ends; PP, ^{32}P-postlabeling technique; PD, protein bound DNA; ISNT, in situ nick translation; AFE, alkaline filter elution; IA, immunohistochemical analysis.

myoblasts. Satellite cells, the progenitors of myofibers, are present in low abundance. They are ordinarily mitotically quiescent, but can be activated to form new myofibers in response to injury or disease in the adult muscle (Renault et al., 2002; Jeyapalan et al., 2007). However the number of satellite cells, expressed as a proportion of myonuclei, decreases from 5% in young adults to 1.6% in aged adults (Renault et al., 2002). Heart myocytes that have died byapoptosis or necrosis can also be replaced by new myocytes through activation and differentiation of resident cardiac progenitor cells (Kajstura et al., 2006). With age, cell death presumably occurs slowly and over a long period of time in heart and skeletal muscle, and this may allow progenitor cells to divide and at least partly replace dead myocytes. However this replacement is inadequate to prevent an overall increase in DNA damage with age, as indicated by the 18 studies summarized in Table 4. In 13 of these studies the type of DNA damage measured was 8-OHdG as an indicator of oxidative DNA damage. These DNA damages are likely caused, at least in part, by the ROS formed when single electrons escape the mitochondrial respiratory chain and reduce molecular oxygen to form the superoxide anion. Superoxide dismutase converts superoxide into hydrogen peroxide (H_2O_2) that can then produce the highly reactive hydroxyl radical. Although ROS have been estimated to be 1-2% of the total cellular oxygen consumption (Joenje, 1989) and this estimate is widely used, a more recent estimate is that under physiologic conditions 0.15% of electron flow in skeletal muscle gives rise to ROS (St-Pierre et al., 2002). Nevertheless even the lower estimate may be sufficient to cause accumulation of oxidative damage, ultimately resulting in aging.

Accumulation of DNA Damage in Aging Liver and Kidney

Although liver hepatocytes do not ordinarily divide and appear terminally differentiated they retain the ability to proliferate when the liver is injured. Thus, as discussed above, chronic hepatitis can provoke repeated cell division and ultimately cancer. However, hepatocytes can also accumulate DNA damage and age. Aging of the liver is associated with reduction in its mass, a 30-40% reduction in blood flow, impaired metabolism, and changes in hepatic microcirculation (Ito et al., 2007). Eleven studies performed in the period between 1971 and 1990 showed increases in DNA damage (mainly SS strand breaks) in rodent liver (summarized in Bernstein and Bernstein, 1991). More recently, age related increases in liver have been reported for SS breaks (Hosokawa et al. 2000), DS breaks (Sedelnikova et al., 2004), and 8-OHdG (Fraga et al., 1990; Kaneko et al., 1997; Schmerold and Niedermuller, 2001; Helbock et al., 1998; Hamilton et al., 2001; Van Remmen et al., 2003; Wolf et al., 2005; Gedik et al., 2005). Helbock et al. (1998) estimated that the steady state level of oxidative DNA base alterations in young rat liver to be 24,000 per cell and in old rat liver 66,000 per cell.

Numerous changes occur in the kidney with aging including reduction in both renal blood flow and glomerular filtration rate, and impairment in the ability to concentrate urine and to conserve sodium and water (Muhlberg and Platt, 1999). As the kidney ages there are increases in DNA DS breaks (Sedelnikova et al., 2004; Singh et al., 2001) and 8-OHdG (Fraga et al., 1990; Kaneko et al., 1997; Schmerold and Niedermuller, 2001; Hamilton et al., 2001; Hashimoto et al., 2007).

Table 4. Increase in DNA damage with age in mammalian muscle

Species	Organ	Damage	Assay	Age span (months)	Reference
Mouse	Heart	SS breaks	DPTA	3 – 33	Price et al., 1971
Mouse	Heart	SS breaks	S_1N	6 – 30	Chetsanga et al., 1976
Mouse	Heart	Methylated guanine	C	2 – 39	Gaubatz, 1986
Mouse	Heart, Skeletal Muscle	8-OHdG	HPLC	8 – 27	Sohal et al., 1994
Mouse	Heart	8-OHdG; DNA-protein crosslinks	PP	12 – 24	Izzotti et al., 1999
Mouse	Heart	DNA-protein crosslinks	PD	2 – 25	Zahn et al., 1999
Mouse	Heart, Skeletal Muscle	SS breaks	AFE	0 – 25	Hosokawa et al., 2000
Mouse/Rat	Heart, Skeletal muscle	8-OHdG	HPLC	6 – 24	Hamilton et al., 2001
Mouse	Heart	8-OHdG	HPLC	3 to 6 – 26	Van Remmen et al., 2003
Mouse	Skeletal muscle	8-OHdG	-	9 to 11 – 26-29	Schriner et al., 2005
Rat	Heart	8-OHdG	HPLC	2 – 33	Kaneko et al., 1997
Rat	Heart	8-OHdG	HPLC	2 – 28	Suh et al., 2001
Rat	Heart, Skeletal muscle	8-OHdG	IA	4 – 24	Wolf et al., 2005
Rat	Heart	8-OHdG, DNA-protein crosslinks, DNA fragmentation, SS breaks	HPLC PD AGE Single-cell gel electrophoresis	3-4 to >24	Savitha and Panneerselvam, 2007
Mongolian gerbil	Heart	8-OHdG	HPLC	5 – 25	Sohal et al., 1995
Human	Diaphragm	8-OHdG	HPLC	<55yr – 85yr	Hayakawa et al., 1991
Human	Heart	8-OHdG	HPLC	24yr – 97yr	Hayakawa et al., 1992
Human	Skeletal muscle	8-OHdG	HPLC	25yr – 93yr	Mecocci et al., 1999

See Table 3 footnote for abbreviations except: C, chromatography; AGE, agarose gel electrophoresis.

Dietary Restriction Decreases DNA Damage During Aging

Caloric restriction retards aging and significantly extends life span in rodents (e.g. Barger et al., 2003). Sohal et al. (1994) observed that caloric restriction reduces the concentration of 8-OHdG content in mouse heart, skeletal muscle, brain, liver and kidney. Similarly, Kaneko et al. (1997) found that caloric restriction retards the onset of age-related increases in 8-OHdG in rat heart, brain, kidney and liver. Hamilton et al. (2001) found that caloric restriction significantly reduces the age-related accumulation of 8-OHdG levels of nuclear DNA in rat brain, heart and kidney, and in mouse brain, heart, kidney and liver. Wolf et al. (2005) found that dietary restriction reduced 8-OHdG in rat heart, skeletal muscle, brain and liver. These consistent results indicate that reduction of oxidative DNA damage (as measured by 8-OHdG) in non- or infrequently dividing cells is associated with a slower rate of aging and increased lifespan.

Effects of DNA Damage in the Aging Brain on Gene Expression

Lu et al. (2004) showed that transcription of a set of genes in humans aged 26 to 106 declines in the brain with age. These included (1) genes that underlie learning and synaptic plasticity, (2) genes that are involved in vesicle release and recycling, (3) genes involved in signal transduction systems that mediate memory storage and long-term potentiation, notably the synaptic calcium signaling system, (5) key genes involved in protein turnover, such as ubiquitin-conjugating enzymes and the lysosomal proton pump, and (6) nuclear encoded genes for the mitochondria. Lu et al. (2004) further found that in the aged brain DNA damage is markedly increased in the promoters of genes with reduced expression. In a cultured human neuroblastoma cell line the promoters of some of the genes whose expression was reduced in the aged brain, were selectively damaged by oxidative stress, and also may have been subject to reduced base-excision repair. Thus Lu et al (2004) concluded that DNA damage may reduce the expression of selectively vulnerable genes involved in learning, memory and neuronal survival, initiating a sequence of aging events that starts early in adult life. In addition to the down-regulated genes, the transcription of a subset of genes was upregulated. These included (1) genes involved in stress-response such as hsp-70 and anti-oxidant proteins, (2) genes involved in inflammation, (3) DNA repair enzymes, notably the BER enzymes 8-oxoguanine DNA glycosylase and uracil DNA glycosylase. The pronounced upregulation of the anti-oxidant enzymes, and the DNA repair enzymes that repair oxidized DNA suggests that in old tissues the DNA may be under sustained oxidative attack.

Effects of DNA Damage in Aging Muscle on Gene Expression and Lifespan

Numerous studies have shown that protein synthesis and protein degradation decline with age in skeletal muscle (Carmeli et al., 2002) and in heart muscle (Makrides, 1983), as would be expected if accumulation of DNA damages block gene transcription. When muscle fibers of aged animals are examined by electron microscopy, ultrastructural disorganization is evident as reported in a number of studies summarized by Goldspink and Alnaqeeb (1985). In striated muscle, force is generated by interactions between myosin thick filaments and actin thin filaments. A proteomic analysis of rat skeletal muscle found numerous changes in protein expression during aging (18 to 30 months) (Piec et al., 2005) including lower levels of several proteins related to myosin and actin. In general then, alterations at the molecular and cellular level stemming from accumulated DNA damage may account for the decline in strength and a slowing down of the contractile process in aging muscle.

Overexpression of catalase targeted to mitochondria increases lifespan in mice by about 20%, and decreases oxidative DNA damage (8-OHdG) in skeletal muscle (Schriner et al., 2005; Linford et al., 2006), suggesting that mitochondria are a significant source of the oxidative DNA damages that contribute to aging. This idea is supported by the finding that dietary supplementation with lipoic acid (an anti-oxidant) and L-carnitine, two metabolites that improve mitochondrial function, decrease the accumulation of several types of DNA damage in aged rat heart (Suh et al., 2001; Savitha and Panneerselvam 2007).

Evidence Suggesting a Causal Relationship between DNA Damage and Aging Based on Inherited Alterations in Human and Rodent Genes

The evidence summarized above indicates that DNA damage accumulation is associated with aging in brain, muscle, liver and kidney. This evidence for an association appears robust considering the large number of studies having similar findings, but by itself does not prove that DNA damage causes aging. We reviewed evidence, above, that DNA damage, particularly oxidative damage, may underlie the decline in expression of key genes associated with the aging process. Below we consider further evidence for a causal relationship between DNA damage and aging. Thus, if unrepaired DNA damages are the cause of aging it would be expected that inherited defects in DNA repair pathways might accelerate the aging process. Table 5 summarizes evidence that genetic alterations giving rise to three syndromes that are close partial mimics of normal, but early, aging are defective in DNA repair.

Szekely et al. (2005) presented evidence that the aspects of Werner syndrome (WS) that mimic normal aging may be accounted for by a defect in the repair of specific oxidative DNA damages in slowly dividing or nondividing cells. The defective repair process in WS may be BER, as suggested by Harrigan et al. (2006). In a mouse model of WS, cardiac oxidative DNA damage is increased (Massip et al. 2006).

In a mouse model of Hutchinson-Gilford progeria (HGPS), there is a progressive loss of vascular smooth muscle cells in the medial layer of large arteries, in a pattern very similar to that seen in children with HGPS (Varga et al., 2006). This finding suggests that DNA damage to smooth muscle cells may underlie the cardiovascular disease in these children.

Cockayne syndrome is associated with inefficient repair of oxidatively induced DNA damages, namely 8-OHdG (D'Errico et al., 2007; Licht et al., 2003), suggesting that oxidative DNA damage may give rise to the premature aging features of CS.

In addition to the conditions summarized in Table 5, several additional inherited human syndromes that are defective in DNA repair display some features of premature aging, particularly neurological features. These are reviewed by Rolig and McKannon (2000) and include ataxia telangiectasia and Nijmegan breakage syndrome (defective in recognition of oxidative DNA damages including DS breaks), some subgroups of xeroderma pigmentosum and trichothiodystrophy (defects in NER) and Fanconi anemia, Bloom syndrome and Rothmund-Thomson syndrome (defective in DNA helicases employed in repair).

Several additional genetically altered rodent models, not discussed above, also have some relevance to the causal connection between DNA damage and aging. Van Remmen et al. (2003) found that mice heterozygous for a mutation in the mitochondrial enzyme that processes superoxide, Sod2, have an unexpectedly normal lifespan, despite accumulating higher levels of nuclear and mitochondrial 8-OHdG with age. However, as mentioned above,

Table 5. Inherited genetic defects giving rise to syndromes with features of early aging

Syndrome and affected gene	Function of defective gene product(s)	Basis for DNA damage accumulation	Features of early aging
Werner syndrome (WRN) (Szekely et al., 2005; Otterlei et al., 2006; Harrigan et al., 2006)	RECQ 3' to 5' helicase and 3'to 5' exonuclease	Defect in HRR, BER, and NHEJ	Osteoporosis, arteriosclerosis, thinning of skin, graying of hair, cataracts, diabetes. Mean life span 47 years. Age-associated neuropathology (Leverenz et al., 1998)
Hutchinson-Gilford Progeria (Lamin A) (Kudlow et al., 2007)	Intermediate filament scaffold protein that supports the nucleus and organizes chromatin	Decreased ability to repair DNA damage, including DS-breaks (Liu et al., 2007)	Alopecia, sclerosis, wrinkling soft tissue, cachexia, arteriosclerosis diminished fat; cardiovascular disease that eventually leads to death from myocardial infarction and/or stroke, mean life span 13 years.
Cockayne syndrome CSA and CSB (Puzianowska-Kuznicka and Kuznicki, 2005)	Assists RNA polymerase II in dealing with transcription blocks and the resumption of transcription	Defective in TCR	Senile-like appearance (atrophic skin, sparse hair), progressive neuro-degeneration, retinal and cochlear degeneration, mental retardation, cachexia, cataracts, mean life span 13 years.

Schriner et al. (2005) found, in transgenic mice that over-expression of catalase in mitochondria increased both median and maximum life span, and this increase is accompanied by reduced H_2O_2 production and reduced oxidative DNA damage (8-OHdG).

Ku-80 protein is an activator of the Ku-70 helicase that acts in NHEJ to repair DS-breaks. Ku-80 defective mice show several characteristics of early aging including osteopenia, growth plate closure, atrophic skin, liver pathology and shortened life span (Vogel et al., 1999).

The XPF-ERCC1 endonuclease is required for repair of helix-distorting DNA damages by NER, and DNA interstrand crosslinks. XPF-ERCC1 deficient mice display many features of premature aging and gene expression changes similar to those of aging wild-type mice (Niedernhoffer et al., 2006). Also a patient with a severe XPF mutation leading to profound sensitivity to DNA cross-linking damage displayed dramatic premature aging symptoms (Niedernhoffer et al., 2006).

Mostoslavsky et al. (2006) showed in mice that deficiency of Sirt6, a nuclear chromatin-associated protein, causes both defective BER and premature aging. The findings with Ku-80, XPF-ERCC1 and Sirt6 genetically deficient mice suggest that several repair process, i.e. NHEJ, DNA inter-strand cross-link repair, and BER, have a role in preventing premature aging.

Two inbred genetically related mouse strains, one having accelerated senescence and the other long-lived, were compared with respect to accumulation of single strand breaks in different organs with age (Hosokawa et al., 2000). In all organs tested, including brain, heart and muscle, these damages accumulated more rapidly in the senescence-accelerated strain than in the long-lived strain. In another study of senescence-accelerated mice, 8-OHdG increased in brain as the mice aged from 4 months to 12 months (Morioka et al., 1999). This increase was prevented by oral administration of melatonin, a powerful scavenger of ROS.

Taken together, the evidence summarized in this section indicates a causal relationship between increased DNA damage, particularly oxidative DNA damage, and premature aging.

Stem Cell Aging

As summarized by Sharpless and DePinho (2007), multipotent tissue-specific stem cells produce differentiated effector cells through a series of increasingly more committed progenitor intermediates. This stem-cell derived differentiation process is best understood in the hematopoietic system, although similar sequences of events are thought to occur in other stem-cell containing tissues. In hematopoiesis, long-term hematopoietic stem cells represent the "true" stem cells that self-renew and produce multipotent progenitors, short-term stem cells, and subsequently multipotent progenitors with no self-renewal capacity. These in turn give rise to oligopotent progenitors including the common lymphoid progenitor (which gives rise to T and B cells) and the common myeloid progenitor (which gives rise to erythrocytes, platelets, granulocytes and macrophages).

In mice, deficiencies in repair of DNA damage, i.e. in the NER and NHEJ pathways, limit the functional capacity of hematopoietic stem cells with age (Rossi et al., 2007). This involves loss of reconstitution and proliferative potential, diminished self-renewal, increased apoptosis and ultimately functional exhaustion. Rossi et al. (2007) suggested that endogenous DNA damage also accumulates with age in wild-type, long-lived hematopoietic stem cells. Sharpless and Depinho (2007) summarized several lines of evidence indicating that hematopoietic stem cells, as well as stem cells in other tissues, undergo intrinsic aging in terms of functional decline. They noted that recent evidence supports the model that stem cells in several tissues are largely retained in a quiescent state, but can be coaxed back into the cell cycle in response to extracellular cues, even after prolonged dormancy. As stem cells appear to be less metabolically active in their quiescent state, they may be subjected to lower levels of DNA-damage-inducing metabolic side products such as ROS. However, Sharpless and Depinho (2007) speculated that stem cells eventually grow old as a result of DNA damage, as well as extrinsic forces such as changes in their supporting niches.

Mutation Theories of Aging

Dolle et al. (1997) found that in mouse brain there is no increase in mutation between 6 and 34 months of age. Stuart et al. (2000) also reported no increase in mutation in adult mouse brain between 6 and 25 months. Hill et al. (2005) measured mutation frequency in mouse cerebellum (90% neurons) at ages 10, 14, 17, 23, 25 and 30 months and found the frequency to be maintained at a low constant level with age. These authors considered that their results are inconsistent with the expectation of the somatic mutation theory (Vijg, 2000) and also do not support the "error catastrophe theory of aging" (Orgel, 1963) and disposable soma theory of aging (e.g. Kirkwood and Proctor, 2003).

A critical test of the somatic mutation theory of aging might be provided by a consideration of studies of humans and mice with an inherited defect in a DNA mismatch repair gene, since such defects increase overall mutation frequency. Mice deficient in the mismatch repair genes *Pms2, Mlh1, Msh2 Msh3* and *Msh6* all have increased mutation frequencies compared to wild-type mice (Hegan et al., 2006). Most humans with hereditary non-polyposis colorectal cancer (HNPCC) have mutations in the *Mlh1 or Msh2* genes that, in the mouse, have strong mutator effects (about 5-fold to 50-fold increases, depending on the reporter gene used). On the somatic mutation theory of aging, it would be expected that humans with HNPCC should show conspicuous accelerated aging because of a higher mutation rate in all their somatic cells. We have been unable to find any reports in the literature of accelerated aging in humans with HNPCC, although it is possible that such an effect might have been overlooked. In another study by Narayanan et al. (1997a), mice nullizygous for the mismatch repair gene *Pms2* showed about a 100-fold elevation in mutation frequency compared to wild-type mice in all tissues examined (i.e. skin, liver, spleen, colon, brain and lung). They noted that, on the basis of their results, high rates of mutagenesis in multiple tissues are compatible with normal development and life (except for early onset carcinogenesis and infertility) and are not necessarily associated with accelerated aging.

Xpd$^{m/m}$ mutant mice defective in nucleotide excision repair have prominent premature aging features, and about a 20% reduction in lifespan. However, they do not have elevated cellular mutant frequencies (Dolle et al., 2006). This indicates that increased genomic mutation is not a prerequisite for premature aging in DNA repair deficient mice.

Another mutation-based theory, the error catastrophe theory, assumes that increasing inaccuracy of the protein-synthetic apparatus with age has a snowballing effect leading to "error catastrophe". One of the consequences of inaccurate protein synthesis would be development of an inaccurate DNA synthesis system, which in turn would cause somatic mutations. However, DNA polymerase β, the principal DNA polymerase in neurons, was found by Rao et al. (1985) to not differ significantly in its fidelity in young and very aged mice. These authors considered that this finding was strong evidence against the error catastrophe theory. Filion and Laughrea (1985) found that the translational fidelity of ribosomes did not change with increasing age. Many other experiments have been performed to test the error catastrophe idea, and particularly whether amino acid substitutions increase with age (reviewed by Bernstein and Bernstein, 1991; Rothstein, 1987). The majority of evidence is inconsistent with this theory. Indeed Rothstein (1987) commented that all of the evidence relating to the error catastrophe hypothesis, both direct and indirect, is strongly negative, and some of it is unequivocally so.

Yet another aging theory in which somatic mutation is prominent, the disposable soma theory, assumes that multiple kinds of damage contribute to aging, but also includes a substantial role for somatic mutation (Kirkwood and Proctor, 2003). Based on the evidence of

Dolle et al. (1997), Stuart et al (2000) and Hill et al. (2005) that mutation frequency in post-mitotic neurons does not increase with age, whereas DNA damages do increase (Table 3), it seems more likely that DNA damage, rather than mutation, is the principal cause of aging of the brain.

In general, most non-neutral mutations occurring in diploid cells are deleterious, but recessive, and thus do not ordinarily express. In a frequently dividing cell population, a cell with a deleterious mutation may sometimes be able to express because of some degree of dominance, homozygosity, or loss of heterozygosity of the wild-type allele. Cells with such mutations would usually have a growth disadvantage and thus be lost from the cell population by natural selection. Considering the recessive and deleterious nature of most non-neutral mutations, there is no compelling reason to expect substantial effects of mutations on aging, in frequently dividing cells.

Does Mitochondrial Mutation Contribute Significantly to Aging?

Post-mitotic tissues with high rates of oxygen consumption, such as brain and heart, are highly vulnerable to mitochondrial dysfunction leading to loss of integrity of the electron transport chain and increased formation of ROS. As reviewed by Krishnan et al, (2007), many studies have shown that mutations accumulate in mitochondrial DNA in post-mitotic aging tissues. Since mitochondrial DNA is particularly vulnerable to oxidative DNA damage, it has been speculated that mitochondrial mutations may cause aging. Mutant mice deficient in the proofreading activity of DNA polymerase γ (Polg), the enzyme that replicates mitochondrial DNA, were used to test this idea. In wild-type mice, a ten-fold increase in mitochondrial mutations in brain and heart was measured as mice aged from 1-10 months to 24-33 months. However, heterozygous (Polg$^{+/mut}$) mutator mice were able to sustain a 500-fold higher mutation burden than normal mice without any obvious features of rapidly accelerated aging (Vermulst et al., 2007). Thus it was concluded that mitochondrial mutations do not limit the lifespan of wild-type mice.

Twinkle is a nuclear-encoded mtDNA helicase, and mutant mice defective in this protein have multiple mtDNA deletions. These "deletor" mice do not show premature aging, indicating that accumulation of mtDNA deletions is not sufficient to accelerate aging (Tyynismaa et al., 2005).

Damage to Proteins in Relation to Aging

Proteins are susceptible to damage by free radicals, oxidants and other endogenous reactive agents (reviewed by Pacifici and Davies, 1991). Oxidatively damaged proteins are subject to degradation. Most proteins have a short half-life. For example in mouse liver, protein half-life is about 3 days (Barrows and Kokkonen, 1987). Damages to such short-lived proteins are not likely to be a direct cause of the progressive deterioration of function that characterizes aging. However, some long-lived proteins may contribute to aging. For instance, the crystallins in the eye lenses of mammals that do not turn over may age.

In aged cells, there is often reduced turnover of cellular components and intracellular accumulation of damaged proteins and organelles. The two major proteolytic systems contributing to the continuous removal of intracellular components are the ubiquitin/proteasome and the autophagic/lysosomal systems. Both systems show diminished activity with age, but the decline of the autophagic/lysosomal system seems to be the main cause of reduced removal of damaged macromolecules and organelles (Cuervo et al., 2005). Although the cause of this decline is unknown, DNA damage in the genes controlling these systems may be the underlying cause.

Does the Limited Cellular Proliferative Capacity Seen in Cultured Fibroblasts Contribute to Organismal Aging

The limited replicative capacity of human fibroblasts in culture has been frequently used as a model for aging, even though the number of replications observed in culture is far greater than the number of divisions that would be expected in vivo during a normal postnatal lifespan for non-stem cells (Cristofalo et al., 1998). Although it was formerly thought that proliferative capacity of cell lines was correlated with the age of the human donors from whom the cell lines were established, it is now clear that no such correlation exists (Cristofalo et al., 1998). Furthermore, in comparisons of different species cellular proliferative potential was found to not correlate with species lifespan (Lorenzini et al., 2005). Thus the limited capacity of cells to replicate in culture may not be directly relevant to in vivo cellular aging.

Telomere Shortening and Aging

Telomeres are the physical ends of linear chromosomes. In normal human somatic cells, telomeres shorten at each cell division because of inherent limitations in the mechanics of DNA replication. This progressive shortening has been speculated to play a role in aging. For instance, there is evidence that progressive telomere shortening is related to vascular cell senescence in cardiovascular disease (Minamino and Komuro, 2008). However, telomere shortening does not occur in the rat brain (Cherif et al., 2003). In human skeletal muscle telomere lengths remain stable with age (23 to 74 years) (Renault et al., 2002). In baboon skeletal muscle, consisting of fully differentiated post-mitotic cells, less than 3% of myonuclei contain damaged telomeres and this percentage does not increase with age (Jeyapalan et al., 2007). These findings suggest that telomere shortening does not contribute significantly to aging of the differentiated cells of brain or skeletal muscle. Telomerase is a ribonucleoprotein DNA polymerase that plays a key role in telomere synthesis, and is important for maintaining telomere length. Knockout mice lacking telomerase activity are viable and healthy for at least six animal generations (Blasco et al., 1997), suggesting that telomere shortening does not play a critical role in aging of the mouse. Whether telomere shortening plays a role in human aging is currently an unresolved issue.

Correlation of DNA Repair Capacity with Species Longevity

On the basis of the DNA damage hypothesis of aging, one might expect that among species with differing life spans, the capacity to repair DNA damage might correlate with life span. The first experimental test of this idea was by Hart and Setlow (1974) who determined the ability of skin fibroblasts of seven mammalian species to perform unscheduled DNA synthesis (a measure of repair synthesis) after UV irradiation. The species studied were shrew, mouse, rat, hamster, cow, elephant and human. These animals ranged in life span from 1.5 yr (shrew) to 95 yr (human). They found that both the initial rate and the extent of unscheduled DNA synthesis increased systematically with life span. This correlation was striking and stimulated a series of 16 additional experiments in the period 1977 – 1987 (reviewed in Bernstein and Bernstein, 1991). Overall, the evidence indicated a good correlation between repair of DNA damages and life span in mammals. Since most of these studies were done with UV as the challenging agent, the type of DNA repair capacity usually measured was NER, the repair process that removes bulky damages, including the pyrimidine dimers specifically caused by UV. Since UV-induced pyrimidine dimers are not likely to be generally important in aging, the question is raised whether NER can also remove damages more central to aging. Recently, Brooks (2007) proposed that a type of oxidative damage (8,5'-cyclopurine-2-deoxynucleoside) is both important in neurodegeneration and requires NER for its removal. Thus the correlation found between NER repair capacity and life span of different species suggests that NER promotes longevity, and does this, in part, by removing oxidative damages that would otherwise cause neurodegeneration.

Poly(ADP-ribose)polymerases (PARPs) are activated by DNA strand breaks, and play a role in BER. As reviewed by Burkle et al. (2005), PARPs, and especially PARP-1, appear to be involved in maintaining mammalian longevity. The life span of 13 mammalian species correlated with cellular poly(ADPribosyl)ation capacity of permiabilized mononuclear cells. Also lymphoblastoid cell lines from peripheral blood lymphocytes of human centenarians possessed a significantly higher poly(ADP-ribosyl)ation capacity than control cell lines. Furthermore, PARP-1 physically interacts with WRN, the protein deficient in Werner syndrome, the human early aging disorder (Table 5).

Conclusions

In dividing cells, unrepaired DNA damages can lead to mutation, selection and clonal proliferation of cells with a growth or survival advantage, formation of a field defect and ultimately cancer. In non- or infrequently-dividing cells, unrepaired DNA damages accumulate over time. Such damages can cause gradual loss of function at the cellular, tissue and organ level and are likely a prominent cause of aging.

Although DNA damage appears to be a major underlying cause of both cancer and aging, the source and consequences of DNA damage in these two conditions differ. For cancer, external sources of damage, or external influences on endogenous sources, predominate. In contrast to cancer, aging appears to be much less dependent on exogenous factors, since aging follows a roughly similar pattern with chronological age for all humans. This observation is consistent with the idea that the principal source of DNA damages leading to aging are ROS produced as byproducts of normal respiration that should be roughly similar for all humans.

Acknowledgments

This work was supported in part by grants NIH R21CA111513-01A1, NIH 5 RO1 CA119087, NIH(NCI) SPORE Grant 1 P50 CA95060 and Arizona Biomedical Research Commission Grants (#0012 and #0803), Biomedical Diagnostics and Research, Inc., Tucson, Arizona and a VA Merit Review Grant to H. Garewal.

References

Alexander, P. The role of DNA lesions in processes leading to aging in mice. *Symp. Soc. Exp. Biol.*, 1967, 21, 29-50.

American Cancer Society. Cancer Facts and Figures 2007. Atlanta: American Cancer Society; 2007.

Ames, BN. Endogenous DNA damage as related to cancer and aging. *Mutat. Res*, 1989, 214, 41-46.

Ames BN; Gold LS. Endogenous mutagens and the causes of aging and cancer. *Mutat. Res,* 1991, 250, 3-16.

Ames, BN; Shigenaga, MK; Hagen, TM. Oxidants, antioxidants, and the degenerative diseases of aging. *Proc. Natl. Acad. Sci. USA*, 1993, 90, 7915-7922.

Ansell, PJ; Espinosa-Nicholas, C; Curran, EM; Judy, BM; Philips, BJ; Hannink, M; Lubahn, DB. In vitro and in vivo regulation of antioxidant response element-dependent gene expression by estrogens. *Endocrinology*, 2004,145, 311-317.

Autrup, H; Harris, CC; Wu, SM; Bao, LY; Pei, XF; Lu, S; Sun, TT; Hsia, CC; Activation of chemical carcinogens by cultured human fetal liver, esophagus and stomach. *Chem. Biol. Interact.,* 1984, 50,15-25.

Babbar, N; Casero, RA Jr. Tumor necrosis factor-alpha increases reactive oxygen species by inducing spermine oxidase in human lung epithelial cells: a potential mechanism for inflammation-induced carcinogenesis. *Cancer Res.*, 2006, 66, 11125-11130.

Badvie, S; Hanna-Morris, A; Andreyev, HJN; Cohen, S; Saini, S; Allen-Mersh, TG. A "field change" of inhibited apoptosis occurs in colorectal mucosa adjacent to colorectal adenocarcinoma. *J. Clin. Pathol.*, 2006, 59, 942-946.

Baik, SC; Youn, HS; Chung, MH, Lee, WK; Cho, MJ; Ko, GH; Park, CK; Kasai, H; Rhee, KH. Increased oxidative DNA damage in *Helicobacter pylori*-infected human gastric mucosa. *Cancer Res.*, 1996, 56, 1279-1282.

Barger, JL; Walford, RL; Weindruch, R. The retardation of aging by caloric restriction: its significance in the transgenic era. *Exp. Gerontol.*, 2003, 38, 1343-1351.

Barrows, CH; Kokkonen, G. The effect of age and diet on the cellular protein synthesis of liver and of male mice. *Age*, 1987, 10, 54-57.

Bartsch H; Nair J; Owen RW. Dietary polyunsaturated fatty acids and cancers of the breast and colorectum: emerging evidence for their role as risk modifiers. *Carcinogenesis*, 1999, 20, 2209-2218.

Bau, DT; Wu, HC; Chiu, CF; Lin, CC; Hsu, CM; Wang, CL; Wang, RF; Tsai, FJ. Association of XPD polymorphisms with prostate cancer in Taiwanese patients. *Anticancer Res*, 2007, 27, 2893-2896.

Belous, AR; Hachey, DL; Dawling, S; Roodi, N; Parl, FF. Cytochrome P450 1B1-mediated estrogen metabolism results in estrogen-deoxyribonucleoside adduct formation. *Cancer Res.*, 2007, 67, 812-817.

Bergtold, DS; Lett, JT. Alterations in chromosomal DNA and aging: An overview. In Sohol, RS; Birnbaum, LS; Cutler, RG, editors. *Molecular Biology of Aging: Gene Stability and Gene Expression.* New York, NY: Raven Press; 1985; 23-36.

Bernstein, C; Bernstein, H. *Aging, Sex, and DNA Repair, San Diego*: CA, Academic Press; 1991.

Bernstein, C; Bernstein, H; Garewal, H; Dinning, P; Jabi, R; Sampliner, RE; McCuskey, MK; Panda, M; Roe, DJ; L'Heureux, L; Payne, CM. A bile acid-induced apoptosis assay for colon cancer risk and associated quality control studies. *Cancer Res.*, 1999, 59, 2353-2357.

Bernstein, C; Bernstein, H; Payne, CM, Dvorak, K; Garewal, H. Field defects in progression to gastrointestinal tract cancers. *Cancer Lett.*, 2008, In press.

Bernstein, H; Gensler, HL. DNA damage and aging. In Yu, BP, editor. *Free Radicals and Aging.* Boca Raton, Florida: CRC Press; 1993; 89-122.

Bernstein, H; Holubec, H; Warneke, JA; Garewal, H; Earnest, DL; Payne, CM; Roe, DJ; Cui, H; Jacobson, EL; Bernstein, C. Patchy field defects of apoptosis resistance and dedifferentiation in flat mucosa of colon resections from colon cancer patients. *Ann. Surg. Oncol.*, 2002, 9, 505-517.

Bernstein, H; Bernstein, C; Payne, CM; Dvorakova, K; Garewal, H. Bile acids as carcinogens in human gastrointestinal cancers. *Mutat Res*, 2005, 589, 47-65.

Bertin, G; Averbeck, D. Cadmium: cellular effects, modifications of biomolecules, modulation of DNA repair and genotoxic consequences (a review). *Biochimie*, 2006, 88, 1549-59. *Int. J. Biochem. Cell Biol.*, 2005, 1043-1053.

Bilimoria, MM; Lauwers, GY; Doherty, DA; Nagorney, DM; Belghiti, J; Do, KA; Regimbeau, JM; Ellis, LM; Curley, SA; Ikai, I; Yamaoka, Y; Vauthey, JN. Underlying liver disease, not tumor factors, predicts long-term survival after resection of hepatocellular carcinoma. *Arch. Surg.*, 2001, 136, 528-535.

Blasco, MA; Lee, HW; Hande, MP; Samper, E; Lansdorp, PM; DePinho, RA; Greider, CW. Telomere shortening and tumor formation by mouse cells lacking telomerase RNA. *Cell*, 1997, 91, 25-34.

Bolton, JL; Thatcher, GR. Potential Mechanisms of Estrogen Quinone Carcinogenesis. *Chem. Res. Toxicol.* 2007 Dec 4; [Epub ahead of print]

Booth, LA; Bilton, RF. Genotoxic potential of the secondary bile acids: a role for reactive oxygen species. In: Arouma, OI and Halliwell, B, editors. *DNA and Free Radicals: Techniques, Mechanisms and Applications.* London: OICA International; 1998; 161-177.

Booth, LA; Gilmore, IT; Bilton, RF. Secondary bile acid induced DNA damage in HT29 cells: are free radicals involved? *Free Radic Res.*, 1997, 26, 135-144.

Bosland, MC. Sex steroids and prostate carcinogenesis; Integrated, multifactorial working hypothesis. *Ann. NY ACAD Sci.*, 2006, 1089, 168-176.

Bronner, MP; Culin, C; Reed, JC; Furth, EE. The bcl-2 proto-oncogene and the gastrointestinal epithelial tumor progression model. *Am.. J. Pathol.*, 1995, 146, 20-26.

Brooks, PJ. The case for 8,5'-cyclopurine-2'-deoxynucleosides as endogenous DNA lesions that cause neurodegeneration in xeroderma pigmentosum. *Neuroscience*, 2007, 145, 1407-1417.

Burkle, A; Brabeck, C; Diefenbach, J; Beneke, S. The emerging role of poly(ADP-ribose) polymerase-1 in longevity. *Int. J. Biochem. Cell Biol.*, 2005, 37, 1043-1053.

Cai, Q; Tian, L; Wei, H. Age-dependent increase of indigenous DNA adducts in rat brain is associated with a lipid peroxidation product. *Exp Gerontol*, 1996, 31, 387 – 392.

Calogero, RA; Cordero, F; Forni, G; Cavallo, F. Inflammation and breast cancer. Inflammatory component of mammary carcinogenesis in ErbB2 transgenic mice. Breast *Cancer Res*, 2007, 9, 211 [Epub ahead of print]

Cardozo-Pelaez, F; Song, S; Parthasarathy, A; Hazzi, C; Naidu, K; Sanchez-Ramos, J. Oxidative DNA damage in the aging mouse brain. *Mov. Disord*, 1999, 14, 972-980.

Carmeli, E: Coleman, R; Reznick, AZ. The biochemistry of aging muscle. *Exp. Gerontol*, 2002, 37, 477-489.

Chang, ET; Balter, KM; Torrang, A; Smedby, KE; Melbye, M; Sundstrom, C; Glimelius, B; Adami, HO. Nutrient intake and risk of non-Hodgkin's lymphoma. *Am. J. Epidemiol.*, 2006, 164, 1222-1232.

Chen, L; Ambrosone, CB; Lee, J; Sellers, TA; Pow-Sang, J; Park, JY. Association between polymorphisms in the DNA repair genes XRCC1 and APE1, and the risk of prostate cancer in white and black Americans. *J. Urol.*, 2006, 175, 108-112.

Chen, L; Stacewicz-Sapuntzakis, M; Duncan, C; Sharifi, R; Ghosh, L; van Breemen, R; Ashton, D; Bowen, PE. Oxidative DNA damage in prostate cancer patients consuming tomato sauce-based entrees as a whole-food intervention. *J. Natl. Cancer Inst.*, 2001, 93, 1872-1879.

Cherif, H; Tarry, JL; Ozanne, SE; Hales, CN. Ageing and telomeres: a study into organ- and gender-specific telomere shortening. *Nucleic Acids Res*, 2003, 31, 1576-1583.

Chetsanga, CJ; Tuttle, M; Jacobine, A. Changes in structural integrity of heart DNA from aging mice. *Life Sci*, 1976, 18, 1405-1412.

Chetsanga, CJ; Tuttle, A: Jacobini, A; Johnson, C. Age-associated structural alterations in senescent mouse brain DNA. *Biochim. Biophys. Acta*, 1977, 474, 180-187.

Cristofalo, VJ; Allen, RG; Pignolo, RJ; Martin, BG; Beck, JC. Relationship between donor age and the replicative lifespan of human cells in culture: a reevaluation. *Proc. Natl. Acad. Sci. USA*, 1998, 95, 10614-10619.

Crowley-Weber, CL; Dvorakova, K; Crowley, C; Bernstein, H; Bernstein, C; Garewal, H; Payne, C.M. Nicotine increases oxidative stress, activates NF-kappaB and GRP78, induces apoptosis and sensitizes cells to genotoxic/xenobiotic stresses by a multiple stress inducer, deoxycholate: relevance to colon carcinogenesis. *Chem. Biol. Interact.*, 2003, 145, 53-66.

Cuervo, AM; Bergamini, E; Brunk, UT; Droge, W; French, M; Terman. Autophagy and Aging. *Autophagy*, 2005, 1:3, 131-140.

De Marzo, AM; Nakai, Y; Nelson, WG. Inflammation, atrophy, and prostate carcinogenesis. *Uro. Oncol.*, 2007a, 25, 398-400.

DeMarzo, AM; Platz, EA; Sutcliffe, S; Xu, J; Gronberg, H; Drade, CG; Nakai, Y; Isaacs, WB; Nelson, WG. Inflammation in prostate carcinogenesis. *Nat. Rev. Cancer*, 2007b, 7, 256-269.

Denissenko, MF; Pao, A; Tang, MS, Pfeifer, GP. Preferential formation of benzo(a)pyrene adducts at lung cancer mutational hotspots in *p53*. *Science*, 1996, 274, 430-432.

D'Errico, M; Parlanti, E; Teson, M; Degan, P; Lemma, T; Calcagnile, A; Iavarone, I; Jaruga, P; Ropolo, M; Pedrini, AM; Orioli, D; Frosina, G; Zambruno, G; Dizdaroglu, M, Stefanini, M; Dogliotti, E. The role of CSA in the response to oxidative DNA damage in human cells. *Oncogene*, 2007, 26, 4336-4343.

Dich, J; Zahm, SH; Hanberg, A; Adami, Ho. Pesticides and cancer. *Cancer Causes Control*, 1997, 8, 420-423.

D'Inca, R; Cardin, R; Benazzato, L; Angriman, I; Martines, D; Sturniolo, GC. Oxidative DNA damage in the mucosa of ulcerative colitis increases with disease duration and dysplasia. *Inflamm Bowel Dis*, 2004, 10, 23-27.

De Yebenes, VG; Ramiro, AR. Activation-induced deaminase: light and dark sides. *Trends Mol. Med.*, 2006, 12, 432-439.

Ding, SZ; Minohara, Y; Fan, XJ; Wang, J; Reyes, VE; Patel, J; Dirden-Dramer, B; Boldogh, I; Ernst, PB; Crowe, SE. *Helicobacter pylori* infection induces oxidative stress and programmed cell death in human gastric epithelial cells. *Infect Immun.*, 2007, 75, 4030-4039.

Djuric, Z; Depper, JB; Uhley, V; Smith, D; Lababidi, S; Martino, S; Heilbrun, LK. Oxidative DNA damage levels in blood from women at high risk for breast cancer are associated with dietary intakes of meats, vegetables, and fruits. *J. Am. Diet Assoc.*, 1998, 98, 524-528.

Dolle, MET; Busuttil, RA; Garcia, AM; Wijnhoven, S; van Drunen, E; Niedernhofer, LJ; van der Horst, G; Hoeijmakers, JHJ; van Steeg, H; Vijg, J. Increased genomic instability is not a prerequisite for shortened lifespan in DNA repair deficient mice. *Mutat Res*, 2006, 596, 22-35.

Dolle, MET; Giese, H; Hopkins, CL; Martus, HJ; Hausdorff, JM; Vijg, J. Rapid accumulation of genome rearrangements in liver but not in brain of old mice. *Nature Genetics*, 1997, 17, 431-434.

Duquette, ML; Huber, MD; Maizels, N. G-rich proto-oncogenes are targeted for genomic instability in B-cell lymphomas. *Cancer Res*, 2007, 67, 2586-2594.

Dvorak, K; Payne, CM; Chavarria, M; Ramsey, L; Dvorakova, B; Bernstein, H; Holubec, H; Sampliner, RE; Guy, N; Condon, A; Bernstein, C; Green, SB; Prasad, A; Garewal, HS. Bile acids in combination with low pH induce oxidative stress and oxidative DNA damage: relevance to the pathogenesis of Barrett's oesophagus. *Gut*, 2007, 56, 763-771.

Dvorakova, K; Payne, CM; Ramsey, L; Bernstein, H; Holubec, H; Chavarria, M; Bernstein, C; Sampliner, RE; Riley, C; .Prasad, A; Garewal, H. Apoptosis resistance in Barrett's esophagus: ex vivo bioassay of live stressed tissues. *Am. J. Gastroenterol*, 2005, 100, 424-431.

Elkahwaji, JE; Zhong, W; Hopkins, WJ; Bushman, W. Chronic bacterial infection and inflammation incite reactive hyperperplasia in a mouse model of chronic prostatitis. *Prostate*, 2007, 67, 14-21.

Ellsworth, DL; Ellsworth, RE; Love, B; Deyarmin, B; Lubert, SM; Mittal, V; Hooke, JA; Shriver, CD. Outer breast quadrants demonstrate increased levels of genomic instability. *Ann. Surg. Oncol.*, 2004, 11, 861-868.

Endo, C; Sato, M; Fujimura, S; Sakurada, A; Aikawa, H; Takahashi, S; Usuda, K; Saito, Y; Sagawa, M. Allelic loss on 17p13 (TP53) and allelic loss on 3p21 in early squamous cell carcinoma of the lung. *Surg. Today*, 2000, 30, 695-699.

Epeldegui, M; Hung, YP; McQuay, A; Ambinder, RF; Martinez-Maza, O; Infection of human B cells with Epstein-Barr virus results in the expression of somatic hypermutation-inducing molecules and in the accrual of oncogene mutations. *Mol. Immunol*, 2007, 44, 934-942.

Falk, GW. Barrett's esophagus. *Gastroenterology*, 2002, 122, 1569-1591.

Farinati, F; Cardin, R; Degan, P; Rugge, M; Di Mario, F; Bonvicini, P; Naccarato, R. Oxidative DNA damage accumulation in gastric carcinogenesis. *Gut*, 1998, 42, 351-356.

Feng, Z; Hu, W; Hu, Y; Tang, MS. Acrolein is a major cigarette-related lung cancer agent: preferential binding at *p53* mutational hotspots and inhibition of DNA repair. *Proc. Natl. Acad. Sci.*, 2006, 42, 15404-15409.

Fernandez, V; Hartmann, E; Ott, G; Campo, E; Rosenwald, A. Pathogenesis of mantle-cell lymphoma: all oncogenic roads lead to dysregulation of cell cycle and DNA damage response pathways. *J. Clin. Oncol.*, 2005, 23, 6364-6369.

Figueroa, JD; Malats, N; Real, FX; Silverman, D; Kogevinas, M; Chanock, S; Welch, R; Dosemeci, M; Tardon, A; Serra, C; Carrato, A; Garcia-Closas, R; Castano-Vinyals, G; Rothman, N; Garcia-Closas, M. Genetic variation in the base excision repair pathway and bladder cancer risk. *Hum. Genet.*, 2007a, 121, 233-242.

Figueroa, JD; Malats, N; Rothman, N; Real, FX; Silverman, D; Kogavinas, M; Chanock, S; Yeager, M; Welch, R; Dosemeci, M; Tardon, A; Serra, C; Carrato, A; Garcia-Closas, R; Castano-Vinyals, G; Garcia-Closas, M. Evaluation of genetic variation in the double-strand break repair pathway and bladder cancer risk. *Carcinogenesis*, 2007b, 28, 1788-1793.

Filion, AM; Laughrea, M. Transltional fidelity in the brain, liver, and hippocampus of the aging Fischer 344 rat. In: Sohal, RS; Birnbaum, LS; Cutler, RG, editors. *Molecular Biology of Aging: Gene Stability and Gene Expression.* New York, NY: Raven Press; 1985; 257-261.

Fleshner, N; Zlotta, AR. Prostate cancer prevention: past, present, and future. *Cancer*, 2007, 110, 1889-1899.

Forsti, A; Louhelainen, J; Sodeerberg, M; Wijkstrom, H; Hemminki, K. Loss of heterozygosity in tumour-adjacent normal tissue of breast and bladder cancer. *Eur. J. Cancer*, 2001, 37, 1372-1380.

Fraga, CG; Shigenaga, MK; Park, JW; Degan, P; Ames, BN. Oxidative damage to DNA during aging: 8-hydroxy-2'-deoxyguanosine in rat organ DNA and urine. *Proc. Natl. Acad. Sci. USA*, 1990, 87, 4533-4537.

Franco, S; Alt, FW; Manis, JP. Pathways that suppress programmed DNA breaks from progressing to chromosomal breaks and translocations. *DNA Repair (Amst)*, 2006, 5, 1030-1041.

Garcea, G; Dennison, AR; Steward, WP; Berry, DP. Role of inflammation in pancreatic carcinogenesis and the implications for future therapy. *Pancreatology*, 2005, 5, 514-529.

Garewal, HS; Bernstein, H; Bernstein, C; Sampliner, R; Payne, C. Reduced bile acid-induced apoptosis in "normal" colorectal mucosa: a potential biological marker for cancer risk. *Cancer Res*, 1996, 56, 1480-1483.

Gaubatz, JW. DNA damage during aging of mouse myocardium. *J. Mol. Cell Cardiol*, 1986, 18, 1317-1320.

Gedik, CM; Grant, G; Morrice, PC; Wood, SG; Collins, AR. Effects of age and dietary restriction on oxidative DNA damage, antioxidant protection and DNA repair in rats. *Eur. J. Nutr*, 2005, 44, 263-272.

Gensler, HL; Bernstein, H. DNA damage as the primary cause of aging. *Q Rev. Biol*, 1981, 56, 279-303.

Ghio, AJ; Stonehuerner, J; Richarads, J; Devlin, RB. Forum News and Views. Iron homeostasis in the lung following asbestos exposure. *Antioxidants and Redox Signal*, 2008, 10, 371-377.

Ghio, AJ; Churg, A; Roggli, VL. Ferruginous bodies: Implications in the mechanism of fiber and particle toxicity. *Toxicol Pathol*, 2004, 32, 643-649.

Ghio, AJ; Zhang, J; Piantadosi, CA. Generation of hydroxyl radical by crocidolite increases with surface $[Fe^{3+}]$. *Arch Biochem. Biophys*, 1992, 298, 646-650.

Giovannelli, L; Decorosi, F; Dolara, P; Pulvirenti, L. Vulnerability to DNA damage in the aging rat substantia nigra: a study with the comet assay. *Brain Res*, 2003, 969, 244-247.

Glinghammar, B; Inoue, H; Rafter, JJ. Deoxycholic acid causes DNA damage in colonic cells with subsequent induction of caspases, COX-2 promoter activity and the transcription factors NF-kB and AP-1. *Carcinogenesis*, 2002, 23, 839-845.

Goldspink,G; Alnaqeeb, MA. Aging of skeletal muscle. In: Cristofolo, VJ; Adelman, RC; Roth, GS, editors. *Handbook of Cell Biology and Aging.* Boca Raton, Florida: CRC Press; 1985; 179-194.

Greten, FR; Weber, CK; Greten, TF; Schneider, G; Wagner, M; Adler, G; Schmid, RM. Stat3 and NF-κB activation prevents apoptosis in pancreatic carcinogenesis. *Gastroenterology*, 2002, 123, 2052-2063.

Hamilton, ML; Van Remmen, H; Drake, JA; Yang, H; Guo, ZM; Kewitt, K; Walter, CA; Richardson, A. Does oxidative damage to DNA increase with age? *Proc. Natl. Acad. Sci. USA*, 2001, 98, 10469-10474.

Haripriya, D; Sangeetha, P; Kanchana, A; Balu, M; Panneerselvam, C. Modulation of age-associated oxidative DNA damage in rat brain cerebral cortex, striatum and hippocampus by L-carnitine. *Exp. Gerontology*, 2005, 40, 129-135.

Harrigan, JA; Wilson, DM; Prasad, R; Opresko, PL; Beck, G; May, A; Wilson, SH; Bohr, VA. The Werner syndrome protein operates in base excision repair and cooperates with DNA polymerase β. *Nucleic Acids Res.*, 2006, 745-754.

Hart, RN; Setlow, RB. Correlation between deoxyribonucleic acid excision-repair and lifespan in a number of mammalian species. *Proc. Natl. Acad. Sci. USA*, 1974, 71, 2169-2173.

Hashimoto, K; Takasaki, W; Sato, I; Tsuda, S. DNA damage measured by comet assay and 8-OH-dG formation related to blood chemical analyses in aged rats. *J. Toxicol. Sci.*, 2007, 32, 249-259.

Hassan, HI; Walker, RA. Decreased apoptosis in non-involved tissue from cancer-containing breasts. *J. Pathol,* 1998, 258-264.

Hayakawa, M; Torii, K; Sugiyama, S; Tanaka, M; Ozawa, T. Age-associated accumulation of 8-hydroxydeoxyguanosine in mitochondrial DNA of human diaphragm. *Biochem. Biophys. Res. Commun*, 1991, 179, 1023-1029.

Hayakawa, M; Hattori, K; Sugiyama, S; Ozawa, T. Age-associated oxygen damage and mutations in mitochondrial DNA in human hearts. *Biochem. Biophys. Res. Commun*, 1992,189, 979-985.

Hecht, SS. Smoking and lung cancer—a new role for an old toxicant? *Proc. Natl. Acad. Sci.*, 2006, 103, 15725-15726.

Hedelin, M; Chang, ET; Wiklund, F; Bellocco, R; Klint, A; Adolfsson, J; Shahedi, K; Xu, J; Adami, HO; Gronberg, H; Balter, KA. Association of frequent consumption of fatty fish with prostate cancer risk is modified by COX-2 polymorphism. *Int. J. Cancer*, 2007, 120, 398-405.

Hegan, DC; Narayanan, L; Jirik, FR; Edelmann, W; Liskay, RM; Glazer, PM. Differing patterns of genetic instability in mice deficient in the mismatch repair genes *Pms2, Mlh1, Msh2, Msh3* and *Msh6*. *Carcinogenesis*, 2006, 27, 2402-2408.

Helbock, HJ; Beckman , KB; Shigenaga, MK; Walter, PB; Woodall, AA; Yeo, HC; Ames, BN. DNA oxidation matters: the HPLC-electrochemical detection assay of 8-oxo-deoxyguanosine and 8-oxo-guanine. *Proc. Natl. Acad. Sci. USA*, 1998, 95, 288-293.

Hill, KA; Halangoda, A; Heinmoeller, PW; Gonzalez, K; Chitaphan, C; Longmate, J; Scaringe, WA; Wang, JC; Sommer, SS. Tissue specific time courses of spontaneous mutation frequency and deviations in mutation pattern are observed in middle to late adulthood in big blue mice. *Environ. Mol. Mutagen*, 2005, 45, 442-454.

Hirata, H; Hinoda, Y; Tanaka, Y; Okayama, N; Suehiro, Y; Kawamoto, K; Kikuno, N; Majid, S; Vejdani, K; Dahiya, R. Polymorphisms of DNA repair genes are risk factors for prostate cancer. *Eur. J. Cancer*, 2007, 43, 231-237.

Holmes, GE; Bernstein, C; Bernstein, H. Oxidative and other DNA damages as the basis of aging: a review. *Mutat Res*, 1992, 275, 305-315.

Holmes, RS; Vaughan, TL. Epidemiology and pathogenesis of esophageal cancer. *Semin. Radiat. Oncol*, 2006, 17, 2-9.

Hosokawa, M; Fujisawa, H; Ax, S; Zahn-Daimler, G; Zahn, RK. Age-associated DNA damage is accelerated in the senescence-accelerated mice. *Mech. Age Dev*, 2000, 118, 61-70.

Hussain, SP; Schwank, J; Staib, F; Wang, XW; Harris, CC. TP53 mutations and hepatocellular carcinoma: insights into the etiology and pathogenesis of liver cancer. *Oncogene*, 2007, 26, 2166-2176.

Ito, Y; Sorensen, KK; Bethea, NW; Svistounov, D; McCuskey, MK; Smedsrod, BH; McCuskey, RS. Age-related changes in the hepatic microcirculation in mice. *Exp. Gerontol*, 2007, 42, 789-797.

Izzotti, A; Cartiglia, C; Taningher, M; De Flora, S; Balansky, R. Age-related increases of 8-hydroxy-2'-deoxyguanosine and DNA-protein crosslinks in mouse organs. *Mutat Res*, 1999, 446, 215-223.

Jackson, AL; Loeb, LA. The contribution of endogenous sources of DNA damage to the multiple mutations in cancer. *Mutat Res*, 2001, 7-21.

Jemal, A; Siegel, R; Ward, E; Murray, T; Xu, J; Thun, M.J. Cancer statistics, 2007. *CA Cancer J. Clin*, 2007, 57, 43-46.

Jenkins, GJ; D'Souza, FR; Suzen, SH; Eltahir, ZS; James, SA; Parry, JM; Griffiths, PA; Baxter, JN. Deoxycholic acid at neutral and acid pH, is genotoxic to oesophageal cells through the induction of ROS: the potential role of anti-oxidants in Barrett's oesophagus. *Carcinogenesis*, 2007, 28, 136-142.

Jeyapalan, JC; Ferreira, M; Sedivy JM; Herbig, U. Accumulation of senescent cells in mitotic tissue of aging primates. *Mech. Ageing Dev*, 2007, 128, 36-44.

Jiricny, J. The multifaceted mismatch-repair system. *Nat. Rev. Mol. Cell Biol*, 2006, 7, 335-346.

Joenje, H. Genetic toxicology of oxygen. *Mutat Res*, 1989, 219, 193-208.

Jolly, AJ; Wild, CP; Hardie, LJ. Acid and bile salts induce DNA damage in human oesophageal cell lines. *Mutagenesis*, 2004, 19, 319-324.

Juliet, PAR; Joyee, AG; Jayaraman, G; Mohankumar, MN; Panneerselvam, C. Effect of L-carnitine on nucleic acid status of aged rat brain. *Exp. Neurol*, 2005, 191, 33-40.

Kajstura, J; Rota, M; Urbanek, K; Hosoda, T; Bearzi, C; Anversa, P; Bolli, R; Leri, A. The telomere-teromerase axis and the heart. *Antioxid Redox Signal*, 2006, 8, 2125-2141.

Kamranvar, SA; Gruhne, B; Szeles, A; Masucci, MG. Epstein-Barr virus promotes genomic instability in Burkitt's lymphoma. *Oncogene*, 2007, 5115-5123.

Kaneko, T; Tahara, S; Matsuo, M. Retarding effect of dietary restriction on the accumulation of 8-hydroxy-2'-deoxyguanosine in organs of Fischer 344 rats during aging. *Free Radical Biol. Med.*, 1997, 23, 76-81.

Kang, D; Lee, KM; Park, SK; Berndt, SI; Peters, U; Reding, D; Chatterjee, N; Welch, R; Chanock, S; Huang, WY; Hayes, RB. Functional variant of manganese superoxide dismutase (SOD2 V16A) polymorphism is associated with prostate cancer risk in the prostate, lung, colorectal and ovarian cancer study. *Cancer Epidemiol Biomarkers Prev*, 2007, 16, 1581-1586.

Kapiszewska, M; Miskiewicz, M; Ellison, PT; Thune, I; Jasienska, G. High tea consumption diminishes salivary 17beta-estradiol concentration in Polish women. *Br. J. Nutr*, 2006, 95, 989-995.

Kaur, S; Greaves, P; Cooke, DN; Edwards, R; Steward, WP; Gescher, AJ; Marczylo, TH. Breast cancer prevention by green tea catechins and black tea theaflavins in the C3(1)

SV40 T,t antigen transgenic mouse model is accompanied by increased apoptosis and a decrease in oxidative DNA adducts. *J. Agric. Food Chem*, 2007, 55, 3378-3385.

Kelemen, LE; Cerhan, JR; Lim, U; Davis, S; Cozen, W; Schenk, M; Colt, J; Hartge, P; Ward, MH. Vegetables, fruit, and antioxidant-related nutrients and risk of non-Hodgkin lymphoma; a National Cancer Institute-Surveillance, Epidemiology, and End Results population-based case-control study. *Am. J. Clin. Nutr*, 2006, 83, 1401-1410.

Kirkwood, TB; Proctor, CJ. Somatic mutations and ageing in silico. *Mech. Ageing Dev*, 2003, 124, 85-92.

Krishnan, KJ; Greaves, LC; Reeve, AK; Turnbull, DM. Mitochondrial DNA mutations and aging. *Ann. NY Acad. Sci*, 2007, 1100, 227-240.

Kudlow, BA; Kennedy, BK; Monnat, RJ. Werner and Hutchinson-Gilford progeria syndromes: mechanistic basis of human progeroid diseases. *Nature Reviews, Molecular Cell Biology*, 2007, 8, 394-404.

Kuhn, HG; Dickinson-Anson, H; Gage, FH. Neurogenesis in the dentate gyrus of the adult rat: age-related decrease of neuronal progenitor proliferation. *J. Neurosci*, 1996, 16, 2027-2033.

Kuppers, R; Dalla-Favera, R. Mechanisms of chromosomal translocations in B cell lymphomas. *Oncogene*, 2001, 20, 5580-5594.

Lan, Q; Zheng, T; Shen, M; Zhang, Y; Wang, SS; Zahm, SH; Holford, TR; Leaderer, B; Boyle, P; Chanock, S. Genetic polymorphisms in the oxidative stress pathway and susceptibility to non-Hodgkin lymphoma. *Hum. Genet*, 2007, 121, 161-168.

Lancaster, JM; Powell, CB; Kauff, ND; Cass, I; Chen, LM; Lu, KH; Mutch, DG; Berchuck, A; Karlan, BY; Herzog, TJ. Society of gynecologic oncologists education committee statement on risk assessment for inherited gynecologic cancer predispositions. *Gynecologic Oncology*, 2007, 107, 159-162.

Lechner, S; Muller-Ladner, U; Schlottmann, K; Jung, B; McClelland, M; Ruschoff, J; Welsh, J; Scholmerich, J; Kullmann, F. Bile acids mimic oxidative stress induced upregulation of thioredoxin reductase in colon cancer cell lines. *Carcinogenesis*, 2002, 23, 1281-1288.

Lee, DH; Anderson, KE; Harnack, LJ; Folsom, AR; Jacobs, DR. Heme iron, zinc, alcohol consumption and colon cancer: Iowa women's health study. *J. Natl. Cancer Inst*, 2004, 96, 403-407.

Lee, DH; Anderson, KE; Folsom, AR; Jacobs, DR. Heme iron, zinc and upper digestive tract cancer: Iowa women's health study. *Int. J. Cancer*, 2005, 117, 643-647.

Lee, SA; Parsa, JY; Martin, A; Baker, MD. Activation-induced cytidine deaminase induces DNA break repair events more frequently in the Ig switch region than other sites in the mammalian genome. *Eur. J. Immunol*, 2007, 37, 3529-3539.

Lenz, G; Nagel, I; Siebert, R; Roschke, AV; Sanger, W; Wright, GW; Dave, SS; Tan, B; Zhao, H; Rosenwald, A; Muller-Hermelink, HK, Gascoyne, RD; Cappo, E; Jaffe, ES; Smeland, EB; Fisher, RI; Kuehl, WM; Chan, WC; Stuadt, LM. Aberrant immunoglobulin class switch recombination and switch translocations in activated B cell-like diffuse large B cell lymphoma. *J. Exp. Med*, 2007, 204, 633-643.

Leverenz, JB; Yu, CE; Schellenberg, GD. Aging-associated neuropathology in Werner syndrome. *Acta Neuropathol*, 1998, 96, 421-424.

Levitus, M; Joenje, H; de Winter, JP. The Fanconi anemia pathway of genomic maintenance. *Cellular Oncology*, 2006, 28, 3-29.

Li, D; Firozi, PF; Zhang, W; Shen, J; DiGiovanni, J; Lau, S; Evans, D; Friess, H; Hassan, M; Abbruzzese, J.L. DNA adducts, genetic polymorphisms, and *K-ras* mutation in human pancreatic cancer. *Mutation Res*, 2002, 513, 37-48.

Lichon, V; Khachemoune, A. Xeroderma pigmentosum: beyond skin cancer. *J. Drugs Dermatol*, 2007, 6, 281-288.

Licht, CL; Stevnsner, T; Bohr, VA. Cockayne syndrome group B cellular and biochemical functions. *Am. J. Hum. Genet*, 2003, 73, 1217-1239.

Lightfoot, TJ; Skibola, CF; Smith, AG; Forrest, MS; Adamson, PJ; Morgan, GJ; Bracci, PM; Roman, E; Smith, MT; Holly, EA. Polymorphisms in the oxidative stress genes, superoxide dismutase, glutathione peroxidase and catalase and risk of non-Hodgkin's lymphoma. *Haematologica*, 2006, 91, 1222-1227.

Linford, NJ; Schriner, SE; Rabinovitch, PS. Oxidative damage and aging: Spotlight on mitochondria. *Cancer Res*, 2006, 66, 2497-2499.

Liu, Y; Wang, Y; Rusinol, AE; Sinensky, MS; Liu, J; Shell, SM; Zou, Y. Involvement of xerodema pigmentosum group A (XPA) in progeria arising from defective maturation of Prelamin A. *FASEB J*, 2008, 22, 000-000 (Published on line 9/11/2007)

Longerich, S; Orelli, J; Martin, RW; Bishop, DK; Storb, U. Brca1 in immunoglobulin gene conversion and somatic hypermutation. *DNA Repair (Amst)*, 2007 Nov22 [Epub ahead of print].

Lorenzini, A; Tresini, M; Austad, SN; Cristofalo, VJ. Cellular replicative capacity correlates primarily with species body mass not longevity. *Mech Ageing Dev*, 2005, 126, 1130-1133.

Lu, T; Pan, Y; Kao, SY; Li, C; Kohane, I; Chan, J; Yankner, BA. Gene regulation and DNA damage in the ageing human brain. *Nature*, 2004, 429, 883-891.

Lynch, HT; Smyrk, T; Lynch, JF. Overview of natural history, pathology, molecular genetics and management of HNPCC (Lynch syndrome). *Int. J. Cancer*, 1996, 69, 38-43.

Machida, K; Cheng, KT; Sung, VM; Shimodaira, S; Lindsay, KL; Levine, AM; Lai, MY; Lai, MM. Hepatitis C virus induces a mutator phenotype: enhanced mutations of immunoglobulin and protooncogenes. *Proc. Natl. Acad. Sci. USA*, 2004, 101, 4262-4267.

Machida, K; Cheng, KT; Pavio, N; Sung, VM; Lai, MM. Hepatitis C virus E2-CD81 interaction induces hypermutation of immunoglobulin gene in B cells. *J. Virol*, 2005, 79, 8079-8089.

Machida, K; Cheng, KT; Lai, CK; Jeng, KS; Sung, VM; Lai, MM. Hepatitis C virus triggers mitochondrial permeability transition with production of reactive oxygen species, leading to DNA damage and STAT3 activation. *J. Virol*, 2006, 80, 7199-7207.

Makrides, SC. Protein synthesis and degradation during aging and senescence. *Biol. Rev*, 1983, 58, 343-422.

Mandavilli, BS; Rao, KS. Accumulation of DNA damage in aging neurons occurs through a mechanism other than apoptosis. *J. Neurochem*, 1996, 67, 1559-1565.

Marczynski, B; Rozynek, P; Kraus, T; Schlosser, S; Raithel, HJ, Baur, X. Levels of 8-hydroxy-2'-deoxyguaniosine in DNA of white blood cells from workers highly exposed to asbestos in Germany. *Mutat Res*, 2000, 468, 195-202.

Markesbery, WR; Lovell, MA. DNA oxidation in Alzheimer's disease. *Antioxid Redox Signal*, 2006, 8, 2039-2045.

Massip, L; Garand, C; Turaga, RVN; Deschenes, F; Thorin, E; Lebel, M. Increased insulin, triglycerides, reactive oxygen species, and cardiac fibrosis in mice with a mutation in the helicase domain of the Werner syndrome gene homologue. *Exp. Gerontol*, 2006, 41, 157-168.

Matos, HR; Marques, SA; Gomes, OF; Silva, AA; Heimann, JC; DiMascio, Pmedeiros, MH. Lycopene and beta-carotene protect in vivo iron-induced oxidative stress damage in rat prostate. *Braz. J. Med. Biol. Res*, 2006, 39, 203-210.

Matullo, G; Guarrera, S; Sacerdote, C; Polidoro, S; Davico, L; Gambernini, S; Karagas, M; Casetta, G; Rolle, L; Piazza, A; Vineis, P. Polymorphisms/haplotypes in DNA repair genes and smoking: a bladder cancer case-control study. *Cancer Epidemiol Biomarkers Prev*, 2005, 14, 2569-2578.

Mecocci, P; MacGarvey, U; Kaufman, AE; Koontz, D; Shoffner, JM; Wallace, DC; Beal, MF. Oxidative damage to mitochondrial DNA shows marked age-dependent increases in human brain. *Ann. Neurol*, 1993, 34, 609-616.

Mecocci, P; Fano, G; Fulle, S; MacGarvey, U; Shinobu, L; Polidori, MC; Cherubini, A; Vecchiet, J; Senin, U; Beal, MF. Age-dependent increases in oxidative damage to DNA, lipids, and proteins in human skeletal muscle. *Free Radic. Biol. Med*, 1999, 26, 303-308.

Meeker, AK; Hicks, JL; Platz, EA; March, GE; Bennett, CJ; Delannoy, MJ; DeMarzo, AM. Telomere shortening as an early somatic DNA alteration in human prostate tumorigenesis. *Cancer Res*, 2002, 62, 6405-6409.

Meeker, AK. Telomeres and telomerase in prostatic intraepithelial neoplasia and prostate cancer biology. *Urol Oncol*, 2006, 24, 122-130.

Menges, M; Muller, M; Zeitz, M. Increased acid and bile reflux in Barrett's esophagus compared to reflux esophagitis, and effect of proton pump inhibitor therapy. *Am. J. Gastroenterol*, 2001, 96, 331-337.

Meyer-Siegler, KL; Vera, PL; Iczkowski, KA; Bifulco, C; Lee, A; Gregersen, PK; Leng, L; Bucala, R. Macrophage migration inhibitory factor (MIF) gene polymorphisms are associated with increased prostate cancer incidence. *Genes Immun*, 2007, 646-652.

Minamino, T; Komuro, I. Role of telomeres in vascular senescence. *Front Biosci*, 2008, 13, 2971-2979.

Modak, SP; Price, GB. Exogenous DNA polymerase-catalyzed incorporation of deoxyribonucleotide monophosphates in nuclei of fixed mouse-brain cells. *Exp. Cell Res*, 1971, 65, 289-296.

Mori, N; Goto, S. Estimation of the single-stranded region in the nuclear DNA of mouse tissues during aging with special reference to the brain. *Arch Gerontol Geriatr*, 1982, 1, 143-150.

Morioka, N; Okatani, Y; Wakatsuki, A. Melatonin protects against age-related DNA damage in the brains of female senescence-accelerated mice. *J. Pineal Res*, 1999, 27, 202-209.

Mostoslavsky, R; Chua, KF; Lombard, DB; Pang, WW; Fischer, MR; Gellon, L; Liu, P; Mostoslavsky, G; Franco, S; Murphy, MM; Mills, KD; Patel, P; Hsu, JT; Hong, AL; Ford, E; Cheng, HL; Kennedy, C; Nunez,N; Bronson, R; Frendewey, D; Auerbach, W; Valenzuela, D; Karow, M; Hottiger, MO; Hursting, S; Barrett, JC; Guarente, L;

Mulligan, R; Demple, B; Yancopoulos, GD; Alt, FW. Genomic instability and aging-like phenotype in the absence of mammalian SIRT6. *Cell*, 2006, 124, 315-329.

Muhlberg, W; Platt, D. Age-dependent changes of the kidneys: Pharmacological implications. *Gerontology*, 1999, 45, 243-253.

Murthy, MRV; Bharucha, AD; Roux-Murthy, H; Jocob, J; Ranjekar, PK. Molecular biological models in geriatric neurobiology. In: Deniker, P; Radowco-Thomas, C; Villeneuve, A, editors. *Neuropsychopharmacology*, Oxford: Pergamon Press; 1976; 1615-1622.

Nagaraju, G; Scully, R. Minding the gap: The underground functions of BRCA1 and BRCA2 at stalled replication forks. *DNA Repair*, 2007, 6, 1018-1031.

Nakanishi, K; Shima, A; Fukuda, M; Fujita, S. Age associated increase of single-stranded regions in the DNA of mouse brain and liver cells. *Mech. Ageing Dev*, 1979, 10, 273-281.

Nakai, Y; Nelson, WG; DeMarzo, AM. The dietary charred meat carcinogen 2-amino-1-methyl-6-phenylimidazo[4,5-b]pyridine acts as both a tumor initiator and promoter in the rat ventral prostate. *Cancer Res*, 2007, 67, 1378-1384.

Narahara, H; Tatsuta, M; Iishi, H; Baba, M; Uedo, N; Sakai, N; Yano, H; Ishiguro, S. K-ras point mutation is associated with enhancement by deoxycholic acid of colon carcinogenesis induced by azoxymethane, but not with its attenuation by all-trans-retinoic acid. *Int. J. Cancer*, 2000, 88, 157-161.

Narayanan, L; Fritzell, JA; Baker, SM; Liskay, RM; Glazer, PM. Elevated levels of mutation in multiple tissues of mice deficient in the DNA mismatch repair gene *Pms2*. *Proc. Natl. Acad. Sci. USA*, 1997a, 94, 3122-3127.

Narayanan, PK; Goodwin, EH; Lehnert, BE. Alpha particles initiate biological production of superoxide anions and hydrogen peroxide in human cells. *Cancer Res*, 1997b, 57, 3963-3971.

Naylor, SL. SNPs associated with prostate cancer risk and prognosis. *Front Biosci*, 2007, 12, 4111-4131.

Nehra, D; Howell, P; Williams, CP; Pye, JK; Beynon, J. Toxic bile acids in gastro-oesophageal reflux disease: influence of gastric acidity. *Gut*, 1999, 44, 598-602.

Nelson, WG; DeMarzo, AM; Deweese, TL; Lin, X; Brooks, JD; Putzi, MJ; Nelson, CP; Groopman, JD; Kensler, TW. Preneoplastic prostate lesions: an opportunity for prostate cancer prevention. *Ann. NY Acad. Sci*, 2001, 952, 135-144.

Nelson, WG. Prostate cancer prevention. *Curr. Opin. Urol*, 2007, 17, 157-167.

Niedernhofer, LJ; Garinis, GA; Raams, A; Lalai, AS; Robinson, AR; Appeldoorn, E; Odijk, H; Oostendorp, R; Ahmad, A; van Leeuwen, W; Theil, AF; Vermeulen, W; van der Horst, GTJ; Meinecke, P; Kleijer, WJ; Vijg, J; Jaspers, NGJ; Hoeijmakers, JHJ. A new progeroid syndrome reveals that genotoxic stress suppresses the somatotroph axis. *Nature*, 2006, 444, 1038-1043.

Nock, NL; Cicek, MS; Li, L; Liu, X; Rybicki, BA; Moreira, A; Plummer, SJ; Casey, G; Witte, JS. Polymorphisms in estrogen bioactivation, detoxification and oxidative DNA base excision repair genes and prostate cancer risk. *Carcinogenesis*, 2006, 27, 1842-1848.

Orgel, LE. The maintenance of the accuracy of protein synthesis and its relevance to ageing. *Proc. Natl. Acad. Sci USA*, 1963, 49, 517-521.

Otterlei, M; Bruheim, P; Ahn, B; Bussen, W; Karmakar, P; Baynton, K; Bohr, VA. Werner syndrome protein participates in a complex with RAD51, RAD54, RAD54B and ATR in response to ICL-induced replication arrest. *J. Cell Sci*, 2006, 119, 5137-5148.

Pacifici, RE; Davies, KJA. Protein, lipid and DNA repair systems in oxidative stress: the free radical theory of aging revisited. *Gerontology*, 1991, 37, 166-180.

Payne, CM; Bernstein, H; Bernstein, C; Garewal, H. Role of apoptosis in biology and pathology: resistance to apoptosis in colon carcinogenesis. *Ultrastruct Pathol*, 1995, 19, 221-248.

Payne, CM; Bernstein, C; Bernstein, H; Gerner, EW; Garewal, H. Reactive nitrogen species in colon carcinogenesis. *Antioxidants and Redox Signaling*, 1999, 1, 449-467.

Payne, CM; Weber, C; Crowley-Skillicorn, C; Dvorak,K; Bernstein, H; Bernstein, C; Holubec, H; Dvorakova, B; Garewal, H. Deoxycholate induces mitochondrial oxidative stress and activates NF-κB through multiple mechanisms in HCT-116 colon epithelial cells. *Carcinogenesis*, 2007, 28, 215-222.

Piec, I; Listrat, A; Alliot, J; Chambon, C; Taylor , RG; Bechet, D. Differential proteome analysis of aging in rat skeletal muscle. *FASEB J*, 2005, 19, 1143-1145.

Polley, ACJ; Mulholland, F; Pin, C; Williams, EA; Bradburn, MD; Mills, SJ; Mathers, JC; Johnson, IT. Proteomic analysis reveals field-wide changes in protein expression in the morphologically normal mucosa of patients with colorectal neoplasia. *Cancer Res*, 2006, 66, 6553-6562.

Pool-Zobel, BL; Leucht, U. Induction of DNA damage by risk factors of colon cancer in human colon cells derived from biopsies. *Mutat Res*, 1997, 375, 105-115.

Povey, JE; Darakshan, F; Robertson, K; Bisset, Y; Mekky, M; Rees, J; Doherty, V; Kavanagh, G; Anderson, N; Campbell, H; MacKie, RM; Melton, DW. DNA repair gene polymorphisms and genetic predisposition to cutaneous melanoma. *Carcinogenesis*, 2007, 28, 1087-1093.

Powolny, A; Xu, J; Loo, G. Deoxycholate induces DNA damage and apoptosis in human colon epithelial cells expressing either mutant or wild-type p53. *Int. J. Biochem Cell Biol*, 2001, 33, 193-203.

Price, GB; Modak, SP; Makinodan, T. Age-associated changes in the DNA of mouse tissue. *Science*, 1971, 171, 917-920.

Puzianowska-Kuznicka, M; Kuznicki, J. Genetic alterations in accelerated ageing syndromes. Do they play a role in natural aging? *Int. J. Biochem. Cell Biol*, 2005, 37, 947-960.

Ramiro, AR; Nussenzweig, MC; Nussenzweig, A. Switching on chromosomal translocations. *Cancer Res*, 2006, 15, 66, 7837-7839.

Ramiro, A; San-Martin, BR; McBride, K; Jankovic, M; Barreto, V; Nussenzweig, A; Nussenzweig, MC. The role of activation-induced deaminase in antibody diversification and chromosome translocations. *Adv Immunol*, 2007, 94, 75-107.

Rao, KS; Loeb, LA. DNA damage and repair in brain: relationship to aging. *Mutat. Res*, 1992, 275, 317-329.

Rao, KS; Martin, GM; Loeb, LA. Fidelity of DNA polymerase-β in neurons form young and very aged mice. *J. Neurochem*, 1985, 45, 1273-1278.

Renault, V; Thorn, LE; Eriksson, PO; Butler-Browne, G; Mouly, V. Regenerative potential of human skeletal muscle during aging. *Aging Cell*, 2002, 1, 132-139.

Rezaie, A; Parker, RD; Abdollahi, M. Oxidative stress and pathogenesis of inflammatory bowel disease: an epiphenomenona or the cause? *Dig. Dis. Sci*, 2007, 52, 2015-2021.

Reszka, E; Wasowicz, W. Genetic polymorphism of N-acetyltransferase and glutathione S-transferase related to neoplasm of genitourinary system. Minireview. *Neoplasma*, 2002, 49, 209-216.

Rohrmann, S; Platz, EA; Kavanaugh, CJ; Thuita, L; Hoffman, SC; Helzlsouer, KJ. Meat and dairy consumption and subsequent risk of prostate cancer in a US cohort study. *Cancer Causes Control*, 2007, 18, 41-50.

Rolig, RL; McKinnon, PJ. Linking DNA damage and neurodegeneration. *TINS*, 2000, 23, 417-424.

Rollinson, S; Kesby, H; Morgan, GJ. Haplotypic variation in MRE11, RAD50 and NBS1 and risk of non-Hodgkin's lymphoma. *Leuk Lymphoma*, 2006, 47, 2567-2583.

Romagnolo, DF; Chirnomas, RB; Ku, J; Jeffy, BD; Payne, CM; Holubec, H; Ramsey, L; Bernstein, H; Bernstein, C; Kunke, K; Bhattacharyya, A; Warneke, J; Garewal, H. Deoxycholate, an endogenous tumor promoter and DNA damaging agent modulates BRCA-1 expression in apoptosis-sensitive epithelial cells: loss of BRCA-1 expression in colonic adenocarcinomas. *Nutr. Cancer*, 2003, 46, 82-89.

Rossi, DJ; Bryder, D: Seita, J; Nussenzweig, A; Hoeijmakers, Weissman, IL. Deficiencies in DNA damage repair limit the function of haematopoietic stem cells with age. *Nature*, 2007, 447, 725-730.

Rossman, TG; Goncharova, EI. Spontaneous mutagenesis in mammalian cells is caused mainly by oxidative events and can be blocked by antioxidants and metallothionein. *Mutat Res*, 1998, 402, 103-110.

Rothstein, M. Evidence for and against the error catastrophe hypothesis. In: Modern Biological Theories of Aging. In: Warner, HR; Butler, RN; Sprott, R; Schneier, EL, editors. New York: Raven Press; 1987; 139-154.

Rutten, BPF; Schmitz, C; Gerlach, OHH; Oyen, HM; de Mesquita, EB; Steinbusch, HWM; Korr, H. The aging brain: accumulation of DNA damage or neuron loss? *Neurobiology of Aging*, 2007, 28, 91-98.

Rybicki, BA; Conti, DV; Moreira, A; Cicek, M; Casey, G; Witte, JS. DNA repair gene XRCC1 and XPD polymorphisms and risk of prostate cancer. *Cancer Epidemiol Biomarkers Prev*, 2004, 13, 23-29.

Sambamurti, K; Callahan, J; Luo,X; Perkins, CP; Jacobsen, JS; Humayun, MZ. Mechanisms of mutagenesis by a bulky DNA lesion at the guanine N7 position. *Genetics*, 1988, 120,863-873.

Savitha, S; Panneerselvam, C. Mitigation of age-dependent oxidative damage to DNA in rat heart by carnitine and lipoic acid. *Mech Ageing Dev*, 2007, 128, 206-212.

Schmerold, I; Niedermuller, H. Levels of 8-hydroxy-2'-deoxyguanosine in cellular DNA from 12 tissues of young and old Sprague-Dawley rats. *Exp. Gerontol*, 2001, 36, 1375-1386.

Schriner, SE; Linford, NJ; Martin, GM; Treuting, P; Ogburn, CE; Emond, M; Coskun, PE; Ladiges, W; Wolf, N; van Remmen, H; Wallace, DC; Rabinovitch, PS. Extension of murine life span by overexpression of catalase targeted to mitochondria. *Science*, 2005, 308, 1909-1911.

Sciarra, A; DiSilverio, F; Salciccia, S; Autran Gomez, AM; Gentilucci, A; Gentile, V. Inflammation and chronic prostatic diseases: evidence for a link? *Eur. Urol*, 2007a, 52, 964-972.

Sciarra, A; Mariotti, G; Salciccia, S; Gomez, AA; Monti S; Toscano, V; DiSilverio, F. Prostate growth and inflammation. *J. Steroid Biochem Mol. Biol*, 2007b Sep 7 [Epub ahead of print].

Scott, DW; Mutamba, S; Hopkins, RG; Loo, G. Increased GADD gene expression in human colon epithelial cells exposed to deoxycholate. *J. Cell Physiol*, 2005, 202, 295-303.

Seacat, AM; Kuppusamy, P; Zweier, JL; Yager, JD. ESR identification of free radicals formed from the oxidation of catechol estrogens by Cu^{2+}. *Arch Biochem Biophys*, 1997, 347, 45-52.

Sedelnikova, OA; Horikawa, I; Zimonjic, DB; Popescu, NC; Bonner, WM; Barrett, JC. Senescing human cells and ageing mice accumulate DNA lesions with unrepairable double-strand breaks. *Nature Cell Biol*, 2004, 6, 168-170.

Sen, T; Jana, S; Sreetama, S; Chatterjee, U; Chakrabarti, S. Gene specific oxidative lesions in aged rat brain detected by polymerase chain reaction inhibition assay. *Free Radical Res*, 2007, 41, 288-294.

Sharma, S; O'Keefe, SJD. Environmental influences on the high mortality from colorectal cancer in African Americans. *Postgrad Med. J.*, 2007, 83, 583-589.

Sharpless, NE; DePinho, RA. How stem cells age and why this makes us grow old. *Nat. Rev. Mol. Cell Biol*, 2007, 8, 703-713.

Shen, M; Purdue, MP; Kricker, A; Lan, Q; Grulich, AE; Vajdic, CM; Turner, J; Whitby, D; Chanock,S; Rothman, N; Armstrong, BK. Polymorphisms in DNA repair genes and risk of non-Hodgkin's lymphoma in New South Wales, Australia. *Haematologica*, 2007, 92, 1180-1185.

Shimoda, R; Nagashima, M; Sakamoto, M; Yamaguchi, N; Hirobashi, S; Yokota, J; Kasai, H. Increased formation of oxidative DNA damage 8-hydroxydeoxyguanosine, in human livers with chronic hepatitis. *Cancer Res*, 1994, 54, 3171-3172.

Singh, PN; Ogburn, CE; Wolf, NS; van Belle, G; Martin, GE. DNA double-strand breaks in mouse kidney cells with age. *Biogerontology*, 2001, 2, 261-270.

Singletary, KW; Barnes, SL; van Breemen, RB. Ethanol inhibits benzo[a]pyrene-DNA adduct removal and increases 8-oxo-deoxyguanosine formation in human mammary epithelial cells. *Cancer Lett*, 2004, 203, 139-144.

Smith, LE; Denissenko, MF; Bennett, WP; Li H; Amin S; Tang, MS; Pfeifer, GP. Targeting of lung cancer mutational hotspots by polycyclic aromatic hydrocarbons. *J. Natl. Cancer Instit*, 2000, 92, 803-811.

Smith, MT; Jones, RM; Smith, AH. Benzene exposure and risk of non-Hodgkin lymphoma. *Cancer Epidemiol Biomarkers Prev*, 2007, 16, 385-391.

Sohal, RS; Agarwal, S; Candas, M; Forster, MJ; Lal, H. Effect of age and caloric restriction on DNA oxidative damage in different tissues of C57BL/6 mice. *Mech Ageing Dev*, 1994, 76, 215-224.

Sohal, RS; Agarwal, S; Sohal, BH. Oxidative stress and aging in the Mongolian gerbil (*Meriones unguiculatus*). *Mech Ageing Dev*, 1995, 81, 15-25.

Soliman, AS; Vulimiri, SV; Kleiner, HE; Shen, J; Eissa, S; Morad, M; Taha, H; Lukmanji, F; Li, D; Johnston, DA; Lo, HH; Lau, S; Digiovanni, J; Bondy, ML. High levels of oxidative DNA damage in lymphocyte DNA of premenopausal breast cancer patients form Egypt. *Int. J. Environ Health Res*, 2004, 14, 121-134.

Stein, HJ; Kauer, WK; Feussner, H; Siewert, JR. Bile reflux in benign and malignant Barrett's esophagus: effect of medical acid suppression and nissen fundoplication. *J. Gastrointest Surg*, 1998, 2, 331-337.

St-Pierre, J; Buckingham, JA; Roebuck, SJ; Brand, MD. Topology of superoxide production from different sites in the mitochondrial electron transport chain. *J. Biol. Chem*, 2002, 277, 44784-44790.

Stuart, GR; Oda, Y; deBoer, JG; Glickman, BW. Mutation frequency and specificity with age in liver, bladder and brain of *lacI* transgenic mice. *Genetics*, 2000, 154, 1291-1300.

Suh, JH; Shigeno, ET; Morrow, JD; Cox, B; Rocha, AE; Frei, B; Hagen, TM. Oxidative stress in the aging rat heart is reversed by dietary supplementation with (R)-α-lipoic acid. *FASEB J*, 2001, 15, 700-706.

Sun, J; Turner, A; Xu, J; Gronberg, H; Isaacs, W. Genetic variability in inflammation pathways and prostate cancer risk. *Urol Oncol*, 2007, 25, 250-259.

Szekely, AM; Bleicheert, F; Numann, A; Van Komen, S; Manasanch, E; Ben Nasr, A; Canaan, A; Weissman, SM. Werner protein protects nonproliferating cells from oxidative DNA damage. *Mol Cell Biol*, 2005, 25, 10492-10509.

Talamini, G; Falconi, M; Bassi, C; Sartori, N; Salvia, R; Caldiron, E; Frulloni, L; Di Francesco, V; Vaona, B; Bovo, P; Vantini, I; Pederzoli, P; Cavallini, G. Incidence of cancer in the course of chronic pancreatitis. *Am. J. Gastroenterol*, 1999, 94, 1253-1260.

Tam, NN; Leav, I; Ho, SM. Sex hormones induce direct epithelial and inflammation-mediated oxidative/nitrosative stress that favors prostatic carcinogenesis in the noble rat. *Am. J. Pathol*, 2007, 171, 1334-1341.

Tan, BH; Bencsath, A; Gaubatz, JW. Steady-state levels of 7-methylguanine increase in nuclear DNA of postmitotic mouse tissues during aging, *Mutat Res*, 1990, 237, 229-238.

Theisen, J; Peters, JH; Fein, M; Hughes, M; Hagen, JA; Demeester, SR; Demeester, TR; Laird, PW. The mutagenic potential of duodenoesophageal reflux. *Ann. Surg*, 2005, 241, 63-68.

Thompson, LH; Schild, D. Recombinational DNA repair and human disease. *Mutat Res*, 2002, 509, 49-78.

Tian, D; Feng, Z; Hanley, NM; Setzeer, RW; Mumford, JL, DeMarini, DM. Multifocal accumulation of p53 protein in esophageal carcinoma: evidence for field cancerization. *Int. J. Cancer*, 1998, 78, 568-575.

Tucker, ON; Dannenberg, AJ; Yang, EK; Fahey, TJ. Bile acids induce cyclooxygenase-2 expression in human pancreatic cancer cell lines. *Carcinogenesis*, 2004, 25, 419-423.

Tyynismaa, H; Mjosund, KP; Wanrooij, S; Lappalainen, I; Ylikallio, E; Jalanko, A; Spelbrink, JN; Paetau, A; Suomalainen, A. Mutant mitochondrial helicase Twinkle causes multiple mtDNA deletions an a late-onset mitochondrial disease in mice. *Proc. Natl. Acad. Sci*, 2005, 102, 17687-17692.

Upadhyay, D; Kamp, DW. Asbestos-induced pulmonary toxicity: role of DNA damage and apoptosis. *Exp. Biol. Med*, 2003, 228, 650-659.

Ushijima, T; Nakajima, T; Maekita, T. DNA methylation as a marker for the past and future. *J. Gastroenterol*, 2006, 41, 401-407.

Van Gils, CH; Bostick, RM; Stern, MC; Taylor, JA. Differences in base excision repair capacity may modulate the effect of dietary antioxidant intake on prostate cancer risk: an example of polymorphisms in the XRCC1 gene. *Cancer Epidemiol Biomarkers Prev*, 2002, 11, 1279-1284.

Van Remmen, H; Ikeno, Y; Hamilton, M; Pahlavani, M; Wolf, N; Thorpe, SR; Alderson, NL; Baynes, JW; Epstein, CJ; Huang, TT; Nelson, J; Strong, R; Richardson, A. Life-long reduction in MnSOD activity results in increased DNA damage and higher incidence of cancer but does not accelerate aging. *Physiol Genomics*, 2003, 16, 29-37.

Varga, R; Eriksson, M; Erdos, MR; Olive, M; Harten, I; Kolodgie, F; Capell, BC; Cheng, J; Faddah, D; Perkins, S; Avallone, H; San, H; Qu, X; Ganesh, S; Gordon, LB; Virmani, R; Wight, TN; Nabel, EG; Collins, FS. Progressive vascular smooth muscle cell defects in a mouse model of Hutchinson-Gilford progeria syndrome. *Proc. Natl. Acad. Sci. USA*, 2006, 103, 3250-3255.

Venturi, M; Hambly, RJ; Glinghammar, B; Rafter, JJ; Rowland, IR. Genotoxic activity in human faecal water and the role of bile acids: a study using the alkaline comet assay. *Carcinogenesis*, 1997, 18, 2353-2359.

Vermulst, M; Bielas, JH; Kujoth, GC; Ladiges, WC; Rabinovitch, PS; Prolla, TA; Loeb, LA. Mitochondrial point mutations do not limit the natural lifespan of mice. *Nature Genetics*, 2007, 39, 540-543.

Vijg, J. Somatic mutations and aging: a re-evaluation. *Mutat Res*, 2000, 447, 117-135.

Vilenchik, MM; Knudson AG Jr. Inverse radiation dose-rate effects on somatic and germ-line mutations and DNA damage rates. *Proc. Natl. Acad. Sci. USA*, 2000, 97, 5381-5386.

Vilenchik, MM; Knudson, AG. Endogenous DNA double-strand breaks: Production, fidelity of repair, and induction of cancer. *Proc. Natl. Acad. Sci. USA*, 2003, 100, 12871-12876.

Vogel, H; Lim, DS; Karsenty, G; Finegold, M; Hasty, P. Deletion of Ku80 causes early onset of senescence in mice. *Proc. Natl. Acad. Sci. USA*, 1999, 96, 10770-10775.

Wagenlehner, FM; Elkahwaji, JE; Algaba, F; Bjerklund-Hohansen, T; Naber, KG; Hartung, R; Weidner, W. The role of inflammation and infection in the pathogenesis of prostate carcinoma. *BJU Int*, 2007, 100, 733-737.

Wang, SS; Davis, S; Cerhan, JR; Hartge, P; Severson, RK; Cozen, W; Lan, Q; Welch, R; Chanock, SJ; Rothman, N. Polymorphisms in oxidative stress genes and risk for non-Hodgkin lymphoma. *Carcinogenesis*, 2006, 27, 1828-1834.

Wang, Y; Woodgate, R; McManus, TP; Mead, S; McCormick, JJ; Maher, VM. Evidence that in xeroderma pigmentosum variant cells, which lack DNA polymerase eta, DNA polymerase iota causes the very high frequency and unique spectrum of UV-induced mutations. *Cancer Res*, 2007, 67, 3018-3026.

Washo-Stultz, D; Hoglen, N; Bernstein, H; Bernstein, C; Payne, C.M. Role of nitric oxide and peroxynitrite in bile salt-induced apoptosis: relevance to colon carcinogenesis. *Nutr Cancer*, 1999, 35, 180-188.

Watabe, J; Bernstein, H. The mutagenicity of bile acids using a fluctuation test. *Mutat Res*, 1985, 158, 45-51.

Wheeler, KT; Lett, JT. On the possibility that DNA repair is related to age in non-dividing cells. *Proc. Natl. Acad. Sci. USA*, 1974, 71, 1862-1865.

Wiencke, JK; Kelsey, KT. Teen smoking, field cancerization, and a "critical period" hypothesis for lung cancer susceptibility. *Environ Health Perspect*, 2002, 110, 555-558.

Wijnhoven, SWP; Hoogervorst, EM; de Waard, H; van der Horst, GTJ; van Steeg, H. Tissue specific mutagenic and carcinogenic responses in NER defective mouse models. *Mutat Res*, 2007, 614, 77-94.

Wolf, FI; Fasanella, S; Tedesco, B; Cavallini, G; Donati, A; Bergamini, E; Cittadini, A. Peripheral lymphocyte 8-OHdG levels correlate with age-associated increase of tissue oxidative DNA damage in Sprague-Dawley rats. Protective effects of caloric restriction. *Exp. Gerontol*, 2005, 40, 181-188.

Wu, X; Gu, J; Grossman, HB; Amos, CI; Etzel, C; Huang, M; Zhang, Q; Millikan, RE; Lerner, S; Dinney, CP; Spitz, MR. Bladder cancer predisposition: a multigenic approach to DNA-repair and cell-cycle-control genes. *Am. J. Hum. Genet*, 2006, 78, 464-479.

Yager, JD; Davidson, NE. Estrogen carcinogenesis in breast cancer. *N. Engl. J. Med*, 2006, 354, 270-282.

Yue, W; Santen, RJ; Wang, JP; Li, Y; Verderame, MF; Bocchinfuso, WP; Korach, KS; Devanesan, P; Todorovic, R; Rogan, EG; Cavalieri, EL. Genotoxic metabolites of estradiol in breast: potential mechanism of estradiol induced carcinogenesis. *J. Steroid. Biochem. Mol. Biol*, 2003, 86, 477-486.

Zahn, RK; Zahn-Daimler, G; Ax, S; Hosokawa, M; Takeda, T. Assessment of DNA-protein crosslinks in the course of aging in two mouse strains by use of a modified alkaline filter elution applied to whole tissue samples. *Mech Age Devel*, 1999, 108, 99-112.

Zhu, Y; Lai, M; Yang, H; Lin, J; Huang, M; Grossman, HB; Dinney, CP; Wu, X. Genotypes, haplotypes and diplotypes of XPC and risk of bladder cancer. *Carcinogenesis*, 2007, 28, 698-703.

In: New Research on DNA Damage
Editors: Honoka Kimura and Aoi Suzuki

ISBN 978-1-60456-581-2
© 2008 Nova Science Publishers, Inc.

Chapter 2

DNA Adductomics: Global Assessment of DNA Damage

Robert A. Kanaly[1] and Tomonari Matsuda[2]

[1]Laboratories of Environmental Microbiology and Molecular Toxicology, Department of Environmental Biosciences, Yokohama City University, Yokohama, Japan 236-0027, and
[2]Department of Technology and Ecology, Graduate School of Global Environmental Studies, Kyoto University, Kyoto, Japan 606-8501

Abstract

DNA adductomics is the systematic analysis of large numbers of DNA adducts or DNA modifications present in a particular DNA sample obtained at a specific point in time. The resulting DNA adductomes are represented visually by "DNA adduct fingerprint" adductome maps and adductome profiles that are unique to each DNA sample. In combination, the map and profile interfaces serve to provide detailed visualizations of DNA modification occurrence patterns and allow for comparisons between multiple samples. Additionally, the identities of specific DNA modifications revealed by the maps may be determined, e.g. DNA damage in the form of a DNA adduct. The DNA adductome approach utilizes liquid chromatography coupled with electrospray ionization tandem mass spectrometry (LC/ESI-MS/MS) and the methodology is designed to detect the neutral loss of 2'-deoxyribose from positively ionized 2'-deoxynucleoside adducts in multiple reaction monitoring mode (MRM) transmitting the $[M+H]^+ > [M+H-116]^+$ transition over multiple transitions. Data analysis is optimized and coupled with a comprehensive manual screening process designed to minimize the number of artifactual DNA modifications that appear in the final analyses. Identification of DNA adducts is carried out by comparison to authentic standards and by stable isotope dilution methods.

Introduction

The development of comprehensive DNA damage detection methods that are coupled to specific DNA damage identification processes will greatly expand our capabilities to assess DNA damage in organisms across a wide spectrum of potential experimental designs and real-life scenarios in the future. The emerging field of DNA adductomics attempts to bring these elements together through a combination of techniques that currently rely upon the use of liquid chromatography electrospray ionization tandem mass spectrometry (LC/ESI-MS/MS) as the main analytical tool necessary for performing such DNA damage assessments.

From the time of its inception, ^{32}P-postlabeling (Randerath et al., 1981) has been the most widely applied DNA adduct detection method and until recently, mass spectrometry in the field of DNA adduct study was mostly used in the process of DNA adduct identification or for characterization of synthesized DNA adduct standards. However, the development of ESI as an interface between the LC and MS now allows users to successfully apply LC/ESI-MS/MS to carry out both sensitive and selective detection of DNA adducts. Although slightly less sensitive than ^{32}P-postlabeling which has a detection limit of approximately one DNA adduct per 10^{10} nucleotides, LC/ESI-MS/MS still allows for DNA adduct detection in the picogram range as low as one per 10^8 or 10^9 nucleotides and in addition provides powerful selectivity options through the use of the tandem MS. It is this balance of selectivity and sensitivity that makes LC/ESI-MS/MS quite powerful for certain applications including the detection of multiple DNA adduct types from the same sample. To date, a variety of different DNA adduct types have been detected from biological samples by LC/ESI-MS/MS by different methods from different matrices, and from different organisms (Doerge et al., 2000; Thomson et al., 2004; Beland et al., 2005; Ricicki et al., 2005; Liu et al., 2006; Chen et al., 2007; Matter et al., 2007 for example), and although less frequent, the detection of multiple DNA adducts from the same biological samples has also been carried out by various groups using LC/ESI-MS/MS (Churchwell et al., 2002; Matsuda et al., 2006; Matsuda et al., 2007; Williams et al., 2007; Zhang et al., 2007).

DNA Adductomics Methodology

It is understood that cellular DNA is continuously vulnerable to modification by both exogenous and endogenous sources and that living cells have developed complex strategies to manage this vulnerability. For example, when reactive environmental chemical or physical agents or endogenously-produced reactive oxygen or nitrogen species make contact with cellular DNA, modifications may result in the form of DNA adducts. Generally, DNA adducts are repaired with high efficiency in cells, however, when such adducts are misrepaired or unrepaired they may lead to the development of different types of pathologies including cancer. Although associations have been observed between DNA adduct formation and the processes of mutagenesis and tumorigenesis for example, the molecular mechanisms by which these and other biological effects occur through carcinogen exposure are still not well understood (Poierer et al., 2000; Rundle 2006). It is agreed however, that whether or not a particular exposure will result in downstream damaging effects depends on a vartiey of extrinsic and intrinsic factors and there is much interest to elucidate which intrinisic factors are most influential regarding individual variations in response to DNA-damaging chemicals (Au et al., 2002). Access to tools such as the DNA adductome approach shall facilitate more rapid and detailed screening of DNA adducts and may therefore expedite the process of hypothesis testing in this regard.

Some of the challenges that DNA adductomics aims to overcome include the development of sensitive and reliable methods by which to simultaneously detect multiple types of DNA damage from the same sample DNA, identify each DNA damage type, and organize the information into an efficient interface for the maximum benefit of the analyst. In its current form of development, the DNA adductomics methodology is predicated on the observation that the neutral loss of 2'-deoxyribose occurs when positively ionized 2'-deoxynucleoside adducts pass through the collision cell of the tandem MS. This may be partly explained by the fact that the glycosidic bond between the modified base and 2'-deoxyribose readily undergoes cleavage at relatively low collision energies when compared to the base group which is generally more stable and requires higher energy to bring about dissociation in the collision cell.

Part of this process is summarized in Figure 1. Following purification of DNA from target tissue, DNA is enzymatically and thermally digested to produce 2'-deoxynucleosides with target adducted bases attached. In the collision cell of the tandem MS, the bond between 2'-deoxribose and the target adducted base is broken and a proton is transferred from the 2'-deoxyribose to the base when operating in positive ion mode. This results in the production of a protonated adducted base ion. The signal is transmitted to the detection system and recorded during sample monitoring in MRM mode transmitting the $[M + H]^+ > [M + H - 116]^+$ transition. This process is followed by comprehensive data analysis and final data presentation. In Figure 1, $1,N^6$-etheno-2'-deoxyadenosine is given as a representative DNA adduct and is monitored at MRM transition m/z 276 > 160.

In the human studies conducted thus far, target tissue, or more precisely, specific regions of target tissue were chosen for DNA adductome analysis. The process begins with target tissue DNA extraction with attention to minimize the production of artifactual DNA oxidation products during the extraction process by the inclusion of 0.1 mM desferroxamine. Extracted and purified DNA is suspended in distilled water and quantified by UV-visible spectrophotometry and based upon the concentration of DNA successfully extracted, aliquots containing 100 µg of DNA each are transferred into 1.5-ml Eppendorf tubes and subjected to vacuum concentration. Following, the DNA is enzymatically hydrolyzed to its corresponding 2'-deoxyribonucleoside-3'-monophosphates and this is carried out by adding 100 µl of a reaction buffer that consists of 200 mM citrate, 100 mM $CaCl_2$ at pH 6.0, plus 10 µl of 15 U/µl concentration micrococcal nuclease and 10 µl of 0.05 U/µl concentration bovine spleen phosphodiesterase. The solutions are gently mixed and incubated for 2 hours at 37°C. After incubation, 30 units of bacterial alkaline phosphatase type II (E. coli), 100 µl of 0.5 M Tris HCl at pH 8.5, 50 µl of 20 mM $ZnSO_4$ and 700 µl of distilled water are added. The solution is gently mixed again and incubated for 3 more hours at 37°C. After these treatments the sample

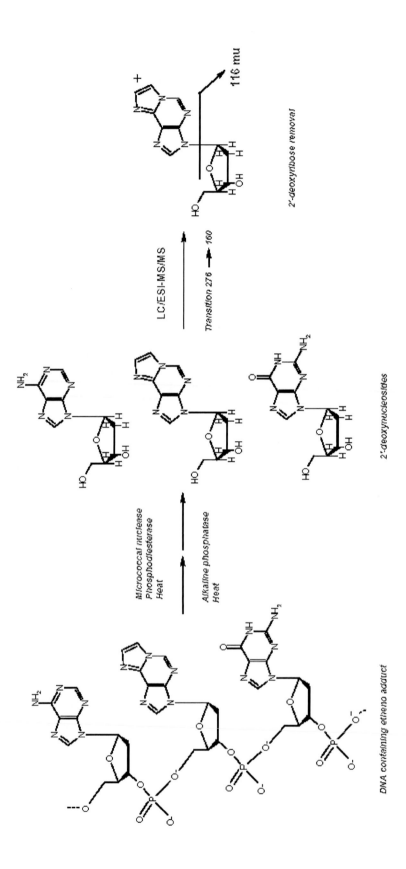

Figure 1. Schematic indicating the process for detection of DNA adducts. In this example, 1,N^6-etheno-2'-deoxyadenosine is shown as a representative DNA adduct and is monitored at MRM transition m/z 276 > 160.

volume is reduced to approximately 40 μl by vacuum centrifugal concentration and the tube contents are extracted twice with chilled methanol. Lastly, the methanol is removed by vacuum centrifugal concentration and the remaining 2'-deoxynucleoside product is resuspended in a solution of internal standard in distilled water. In the case of a negative control such as unreacted calf thymus DNA, 100 μg of such DNA is treated in an identical manner.

LC/ESI-MS/MS analyses are performed using a Shimadzu HPLC system that consists of dual LC-10ADVP pumps equipped with an SPD-10ADVP UV-visible detector interfaced with a Quattro Ultima triple stage quadrupole mass spectrometer (Micromass, Manchester, UK). The LC column is eluted over a gradient that begins at a ratio of 15% methanol to 85% water and is changed to 80% methanol to 20% water over a period of 10 minutes. The 80:20 conditions are held for 10 minutes and then returned to the original starting conditions, 15:85, which is held for the remaining 8 minutes. The total run time is 28 minutes during which the sample components were delivered to the MS by ESI.

Sample injection volumes are 50 μl each and are injected via a Shimadzu SIL-10ADVP autoinjector, separated on a Shim-pack FC-ODS, 150 x 4.6 mm column (Shimadzu) and eluted at a flow rate of 0.5 ml/min. Mass spectral analyses are carried out in positive ion mode with nitrogen as the nebulizing gas. The ion source temperature is 130°C, the desolvation temperature is 380°C, and the cone voltage is operated at a constant 35 V. Nitrogen gas is also used as the desolvation gas (700 L/h) and cone gas (35 L/h) and argon is used as the collision gas at a collision cell pressure of 1.5×10^{-3} mBar. Positive ions are acquired in MRM mode and the strategy is designed to detect the neutral loss of 2'-deoxyribose from positively ionized 2'-deoxynucleoside adducts by monitoring the samples transmitting their $[M + H]^+ > [M + H – 116]^+$ transitions. For each target tissue DNA sample, for example, 300 to 400 or more MRM transitions may be monitored. Originally 374 MRM transitions were monitored over an m/z range from transition m/z 229 > 113 to transition m/z 603 > 487 (Kanaly et al, 2006). For each 50-μl sample injection, a total of 32 transitions are monitored simultaneously by our Micromass system with one or two transitions for each injection reserved to monitor internal standard(s). By using this strategy for example, for each DNA target tissue sample, 50-μl of DNA sample was injected into the LC/ESI-MS/MS 12 times each to complete the monitoring of 374 transitions from m/z 229 to 603. On column, approximately 5 μg of DNA was analyzed in each injection totaling approximately 60 μg of DNA to complete this type of analysis.

After LC/ESI-MS/MS analyses, data processing is carried out in stages whereby all putative DNA adduct peaks are integrated manually in sets of five transitions each by using the MassLynx 4.0 Global Mass-Informatics software, the peak integration data are transferred to spreadsheets and normalized based upon the quantity of internal standard(s) detected for each injection series, and lastly manually screened for unmodified 2'-deoxynucleoside artifacts, their salts, and dimers. In the final stage of analysis, chromatograms for each $[M + H]^+ > [M + H – 116]^+$ transition are examined to identify and eliminate DNA adduct "ghost" isotope peaks and all data are finally organized to produce adductome maps.

DNA Adductome Mapping and Unambiguous Adduct Identification

DNA adductome maps are created from bubble-type charts and a representative DNA adductome map is shown in Figure 2. Each bubble on the map represents a putative DNA adduct. The LC column retention time of each putative DNA adduct is indicated on the x-axis, the mass to charge ratio of each putative DNA adduct is indicated on the y-axis, and the size of each bubble represents the putative DNA adduct peak area normalized by the internal standard peak area, and is referred to as the area response. Relative DNA adduct abundances may be determined by comparing the relative sizes of the bubbles. In Figure 2, each bubble represents a putative DNA adduct detected in human lung tissue. This is a map adapted from a study comparing intertissue and intratissue variation between lung and esophagus tissue from the same person (Kanaly et al., 2007).

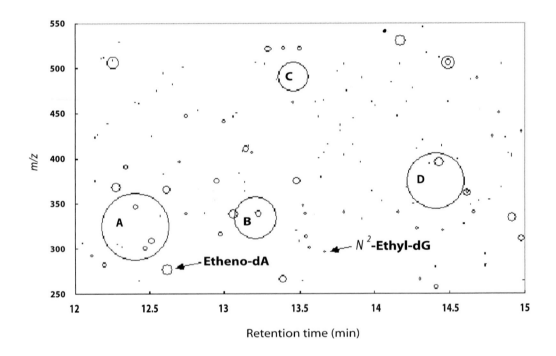

Figure 2. An example of a DNA adductome map that shows various putative DNA adducts detected in human lung tissue DNA. Letters A through D designate the most abundantly occurring putative adducts in the *m/z* range from 250 to 550 and LC range from 12 to 15 minutes. Two DNA adducts were unambiguously identified as etheno-dA and N2-ethyl-dG and are indicated on the adductome map.

As shown in the example given in Figure 2, for the mass range of *m/z* 250 to *m/z* 550 and LC column retention time from 12 to 15 minutes, the adductome mapping technique revealed the presence of many putative DNA adducts. Four of the most abundantly occurring putative adducts are indicated on the map as putative adducts A through D. Although the identities of putative adducts A through D are unknown it may be possible to determine their identities in the future because the molecular weight of each putative adduct may be inferred from the map. For example, after referring to the literature, it is possible to determine if such an adduct of a certain molecular weight has been previously reported, and if so, it may be possible to synthesize an authentic standard or stable isotope standard of the target adduct and test one's hypothesis. Indeed, this process allowed for the discovery of three acrolein-type DNA adducts in human lung and esophagus tissue (Kanaly et al., 2007). In that study, one of the most abundant putative adducts detected in the lung and esophagus tissue DNA samples as revealed by the adductome mapping process possessed an m/z value of 324, $[M + H]^+$, and due to its large abundance there was interest to know its identity. After consulting the literature, we attempted to identity the putative adduct by synthesizing and purifying three DNA adduct standards derived from reactions with the compound acrolein, 3-(2'-deoxyribosyl)-5,6,7,8-tetrahydro-8-hydroxy-pyrimido[1,2-a]purine-(3H)-one (8-OH-PdG) plus two stereoisomers 3-(2'-deoxyribosyl)-5,6,7,8-tetrahydro-6-hydroxypyrimido[1,2-a]purine-(3H)-one (6-OH-PdG) that all possess molecular weights of approximately 323. To do this, 6 µl of acrolein was reacted with 10 mg of both 2'-deoxyguanosine and the ^{15}N-stable isotope analogue of deoxyguanosine in phosphate buffer, purified and analyzed by HPLC. The HPLC profiles matched those indicated in previous studies by Cheng et al. 2003 and Liu et al. 2005 and the reaction products were purified as 8-OH-PdG and the two stereosiomers of 6-OH-PdG. Subsequent utilization of the 8-OH-PdG and 6-OH-PdG acrolein-derived DNA adduct standards in LC/ESI-MS/MS analyses then allowed for the identification of these adducts in the lung and esophagus tissue samples and finally their locations were identified on the adductome maps. Interestingly, the 8-OH-PdG and 6-OH-PdG adducts identified in the samples were less abundantly occurring adducts and the identity of the original abundant target putative adduct was not identified. Nevertheless, the DNA adductome mapping technique allowed for the discovery of these three DNA adducts in human tissues and confirmed the first published report of the detection of acrolein-type adducts in human lung tissue published three months earlier by Zhang et al. 2007 who were specifically targeting these adducts.

Indeed, a major point for expanding the power of DNA adductomics and for validation of the adductome mapping technique is the unambiguous assignment of identities to the putative adducts that appear in the DNA adductome maps. This process is paramount to the usefulness of the methodology in the future. The exact positions and identities of two DNA adducts, 1,N^6-etheno-2'-deoxyadenosine and N^2-ethyl-2'-deoxyguanosine are indicated in the DNA adductome map in Figure 2. Their identities were determined by similar processes utilized to identify the acrolein adducts just discussed. DNA adductomics maps have revealed the presence of numerous abundant and not very abundant unidentified putative adducts and it shall be a challenge to either attach identities to all of these putative adducts or re-adjust the final analyses based upon the results of future research.

DNA Adductome Profiling

The adductome mapping technique was originally devised to enable an analyst to make comparisons of multiple DNA adducts from multiple samples simultaneously. In an original assessment, two samples of lung tissue DNA, one from a smoker and one from a non-smoker were overlayed for the purpose of comparison (Kanaly et al., 2006). Indeed, adductome maps were shown to be valuable interfaces that revealed DNA adduct occurrence patterns in different tissues that were previously unknown to the analyst (Kanaly et al., 2007), however, after the creation of multiple DNA adductome maps it was realized that a second generation interface would also be helpful and therefore DNA adductome profiling was created (Kanaly et al., 2007a). DNA adductome profiling allows for the comparison of multiple samples more quickly than the adductome maps but does not replace the maps because some of the data presentation advantages of adductome mapping are lost during profiling.

Figure 3 shows an example of DNA adductome profiling whereby the profiles were created from three different DNA samples from two different regions of lung and from one region of esophagus from the same person (Kanaly et al., 2007). Similarly to the adductome mapping technique, profiling utilizes the LC retention time on the x-axis, however the y-axis reflects the DNA sample type coupled to the mass to charge to ratio, and the color scale indicates putative adduct abundance. The profiles may therefore be rapidly scanned for the most abundant putative DNA adducts (for example) and comparisons across multiple samples may be made. In this case, red color represents those putative adducts that occurred in highest abundance (the most abundant 25 putative adducts), green color represents the most abundantly occurring putative adducts ranked 26th to 50th in abundance, yellow color, 51st to 100th, blue color, 101st to 200th, and grey color represents all remaining putative adducts with abundance rankings greater than 200. As shown in Figure 4, the adductome profiles are expanded after deciding to examine a specific region of the total map. In the example given, a region representing m/z 380 to m/z 389 is used and illustrates how DNA adduct profiling clearly reveals similarities and differences in the occurrence of putative DNA adducts in the three samples. In this adductome profile, for each m/z transition that was analyzed, three samples are indicated on the y-axis whereby the topmost sample represents DNA from esophagus tissue, the middle sample represents DNA from peripheral lung tissue and the bottommost sample for each transition represents DNA from centrally-located lung tissue. In this example, adductome profiling reveals a putative adduct at transition m/z 382 that occurs with high abundance in both lung tissue samples but less so in the esophagus sample, and the opposite is shown to occur at m/z 384 and m/z 396. Also revealed for example, are that there are putative DNA adducts that are not only conserved in all tissue samples but that they also occurred at the same relative abundances, e.g., transition m/z 396 (for 3 putative DNA adducts), m/z 387, m/z 386, and m/z 381. Finally, the utility of the DNA adductome profiling technique may be best illustrated by showing how it reveals the presence of a putative DNA adduct at m/z 396 (indicated by the arrow) that occurred at relatively high abundances in both regions of lung tissue but that was not detected at all in esophagus tissue. This result may be indicative of DNA adduct intertissue variation between lung and esophagus tissue while also showing intratissue conservation in different regions of lung. Indeed, in the future, adductome profiling may be able to serve as a tool for screening large numbers of samples to detect intertissue variation among different tissue DNA samples but may also expanded to investigate interindividual differences, interspecies differences, differences in exposure history, etc.

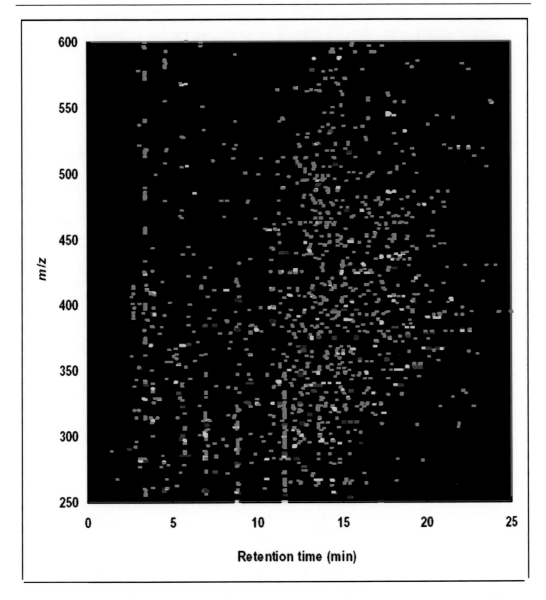

Figure 3. An example of DNA adductome profiling that allows for comparison of multiple samples. The profiles were created from three DNA samples from two different regions of lung and from one region of esophagus from the same person. The color designations are relative: red, most abundant 25 putative adducts; green, most abundant 26 to 50 putative adducts; blue, most abundant 51 to 100 putative adducts; yellow, most abundant 101 to 200 putative adducts; grey, remaining least abundant putative adducts.

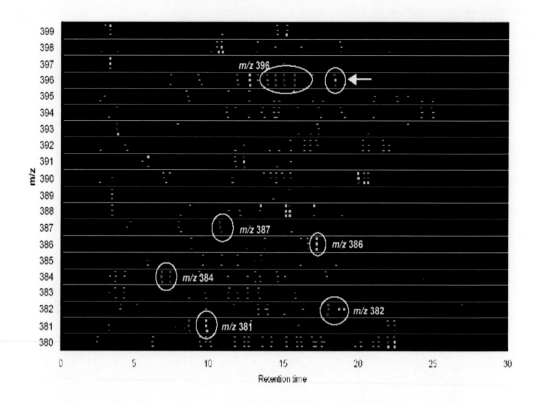

Figure 4. An expansion of the adductome profiles given in Figure 3 over the region representing transitions *m/z* 380 to *m/z* 389. At each transition on the y-axis, each triplicate series of putative adducts represents esophagus tissue DNA, peripheral lung tissue DNA and centrally-located lung tissue DNA from top to bottom. Details of the adductome profile in Figure 4 are discussed in the text.

Conclusion

DNA adductomics is an emerging field that aims to improve our chances of performing global assessments of certain types of DNA damage. Through the creation of DNA adductome mapping and DNA adductome profiling techniques, a more comprehensive understanding of the known and unknown DNA modifications that occur in the human genome may be revealed. However, unlike the human genome which is the same in most cells, the human DNA adductome is dynamic and distinct types of DNA damage and DNA modifications will occur in different tissue types, within different regions of tissues and at different developmental stages. Additionally, the human DNA adductome will be heavily influenced by both acute and chronic environmental exposures and endogenous cellular processes, sex, age, lifestyle, health status and a host of other intrinsic and extrinsic factors.

The creation of DNA adductome maps and profiles from different tissue DNA samples facilitates the visualization of putative DNA adducts and allows for comprehensive comparisons between samples that would otherwise prove to be difficult. As we continue to assign identities to the putative adducts that are revealed by these methodologies and as the

DNA adductomics methodology matures, tissue-specific and/or exposure-specific patterns may continue to emerge and provide further insight into DNA modification in living organisms.

Acknowledgements

This work was supported in part by grants-in-aid for cancer research from the Japanese Ministry of Health, Labor and Welfare, for scientific research (15681002) from MEXT, Japan, from NEDO, Japan and by funding through Yokohama City University.

References

Au, W.W., Oberheitmann, B. and C. Harms. (2002). Assessing DNA damage and health risk using biomarkers. *Mutat Res* 509:153-163.

Beland, F.A., Churchwell, M.I., Von Tungeln, L.S., Chen, S., Fu, P.P., Culp, S.J., Schoket, B., Gyorffy, E., Minárovits, J., Poirier, M.C., Bowman, E.D., Weston, A., and D.R. Doerge. (2005). High-performance liquid chromatography electrospray ionization tandem mass spectrometry for the detection and quantitation of benzo[*a*]pyrene-DNA adducts. *Chem. Res. Toxicol.* 18:1306-1315.

Chen, L., Wang, M., Villalta, P.W., and S. Hecht. (2007). Liquid chromatography electrospray ionization tandem mass spectrometry analysis of 7-ethylguanine in human liver DNA. *Chem Res Toxicol* 20:1498-1502.

Cheng, G., Shi, Y., Sturla, S.J., Jalas, J.R., McIntee, E.J., Villalta, P.W., Wang, M., and S.S. Hecht. (2003). Reactions of formaldehyde plus acetaldehyde with deoxyguanosine and DNA: formation of cyclic deoxyguanosine adducts and formaldehyde cross-links. *Chem. Res. Toxicol.* 16:145-152.

Churchwell, M.I., Beland, F.A. and D.A.. Doerge. (2002). Quantification of multiple DNA adducts formed through oxidative stress using liquid chromatography and electrospray tandem mass spectrometry. *Chem. Res. Toxicol.* 15: 1295-1301.

Doerge, D.R., Churchwell, M.I., Fang, J.L., and F.A. Beland. (2000). Quantification of etheno-DNA adducts using liquid chromatography, on-line sample processing, and electrospray tandem mass spectrometry. *Chem. Res. Toxicol.* 13:1259-1264.

Kanaly, R.A., Hanaoka, T., Sugimura, H., Toda, H., Matsui, S., and T. Matsuda. (2006). Development of the adductome approach to detect DNA damage in humans. *Antoxid. Redox. Signal.* 8:993-1001.

Kanaly, R.A., Hanaoka, T. and T. Matsuda. (2007a). Mapping and identification of DNA damage in human organs by the adductome approach. *J. Craig Venter Institute: Genomes, Medicine and the Environment 2007 (GME2007)*, October 8-10, San Diego, CA, USA. Abstr. 21.

Kanaly, R.A., Matsui, S., Hanaoka, T., and T. Matsuda. (2007). Application of the adductome approach to assess intertissue DNA damage variations in human lung and esophagus. *Mutat. Res.* 8:993-1001.

Liu, X., Lovell, M.A. and B.C. Lynn. (2005). Development of a method for quantification of acrolein-deoxyguanosine adducts in DNA using isotope dilution-capillary LC/MS/MS and its application to human brain tissue. *Anal. Chem.* 77:5982-5989.

Liu, X., Lovell, M.A. and B.C. Lynn. (2006). Detection and quantification of endogenous cyclic DNA adducts derived from trans-4-hydroxy-2-nonenal in human brain tissue by isotope dilution capillary liquid chromatography nanoelectrospray tandem mass spectrometry. *Chem. Res. Toxicol.* 625:83-93.

Liu, X., M. A. Lovell and B.C. Lynn. 2005. Development of a method for quntification of acrolein-deoxyguanosine adducts in DNA using isotope dilution-capillary LC/MS/MS and its application to human brain tissue. *Anal. Chem.* 77:5982-5989.

Matsuda, T., Matsumoto, A., Uchida, M., Kanaly, R.A., Misaki, K., Shibutani, S., Kawamoto, T., Kitagawa, K., Nakayama K.I., Tomokuni, K., and M. Ichiba. (2007). Increased formation of hepatic N^2-ethylidene-2'-deoxyguanosine DNA adducts in *aldehyde dehydrogenase* 2-knockout mice treated with ethanol. *Carcinogenesis* 11:2363-2366.

Matsuda, T., Yabushita, H., Kanaly, R. A., Shibutani, S., and A. Yokoyama. (2006). Increased DNA damage in ALDH2-deficient alcoholics. *Chem. Res. Toxicol.* 19:1374-1378.

Matter, B., Guza, R., Zhao, J., Zhong-ze, L., Jones, R., and N. Tretyakova. (2007). Sequence distribution of acetaldehyde-derived N^2-ethyl-dG adducts along duplex DNA. *Chem. Re.s Toxicol* 20:1379-1387.Randerath, K., Reddy, M. V., and R. C. Gupta. (1981). ^{32}P-labeling test for DNA damage. *Proc. Natl. Acad. Sci.* USA, 78:6126-6129.

Poirier, M.C., Santella, R.M. and A. Weston. (2000). Carcinogen molecular adducts and their measurement. *Carcinogenesis* 21:353-359.

Ricicki, E.M., Soglia, J.R., Teitel, C., Kane, R., Kadlubar, F., and P. Vouros. (2005). Detection and quantification of *N*-(deoxyguanosin-8-yl)-4-aminobiphenyl adducts in human pancreas tissue using capillary liquid chromatography-microelectrospray mass spectrometry. *Chem. Res. Toxicol.* 18:692-699.

Rundle, A. (2006). Carcinogen-DNA adducts as a biomarker for cancer risk. *Mutat. Res.* 600:23-36.

Thomson, N.M., Mijal, R.S., Ziegel, R., Fleischer, N.L., Pegg, A.E., Tretyakova, N.Y., and L.A. Peterson. (2004). Development of a quantitative liquid chromatrography/electrospray mass spectrometric assay for a mutagenic tobacco specific nitrosamine-derived DNA adduct, O^6-[4-oxo-4-(3-pyridyl)butyl]-2'-deoxyguanosine. *Chem. Res. Toxicol.* 17:1600-1606.

Williams, M.V., Lee, S.H., Pollack, M., and I.A. Blair. (2007). Endogenous lipid hydroperoxide-meidated DNA-adduct formation in Min mice. *J. Biol. Chem.* 281:10127-10133.

Zhang, S., Villalta, P.W., Wang, M., and S. Hecht. (2007). Detection and quantitation of acrolein-derived 1,N2-propanodeoxyguanosine adducts in human lung by liquid chromatography-electrospray ionization-tandem mass spectrometry. *Chem. Res. Toxicol.* 20:565-571.

In: New Research on DNA Damage
Editors: Honoka Kimura and Aoi Suzuki

ISBN 978-1-60456-581-2
© 2008 Nova Science Publishers, Inc.

Chapter 3

Radiation-Induced DNA Damage Responses as Novel Targets in Cancer Treatments

Wei-Dong Wang[1], Rong Li[2] and Zheng-tang Chen[1]

1. Department of Radiation Oncology, Cancer Institute of PLA, Xinqiao Hospital, Chongqing 400037, China
2. Institute of Combined Injuries, College of Preventive Medicine, Third Military Medical University, Chongqing 400038, China

Abstract

The amazing feature of ionizing radiation (IR) as a DNA damaging agent is the range of lesions it induces. Such lesions include base damage, single strand breaks (SSBs), double strand breaks (DSBs) of varying complexity and DNA cross links. A range of DNA damage response mechanisms operate to help maintain genomic stability in the face of such damage. Such mechanisms include pathways of DNA repair and signal transduction mechanisms. Increasing evidence suggests that these pathways operate co-operatively. In addition, the relative impact of one mechanism over another most probably depends upon the cell cycle phase and tissue type. An increased DNA-repair activity in tumor cells has been associated with resistance to treatment to DNA-directed drugs, while defects in DNA repair pathways result in hypersensitivity to these agents. In the past years the unraveling of the molecular basis of these DNA pathways, with a better understanding of the DNA damage caused by different anticancer agents, has provided the rationale for the use of some DNA repair inhibitors to optimize the therapeutic use of DNA-damaging agents currently used in the treatment of tumors. In addition, the possibility to specifically target the differences in DNA repair capacity between normal and tumor cells has recently emerged as an exciting possibility. We anticipate that this approach cannot be pursued in all cancer patients and using the same regimes, but it should be tailored according to the specific tumor DNA repair pattern. Therefore, as already clearly demonstrated for other target therapies, it seems essential to develop reliable markers and imaging techniques to be used for an appropriate patient's selection and as predictors of response. This review will focus on the new therapeutic strategies for DNA damage repair inhibition and their application in anticancer therapy.

Introduction

Ionising radiation (IR) and most chemotherapeutic agents currently used in the treatment of cancer, directly or indirectly damage DNA, causing the formation of DNA-breaks (single strand breaks (SSB) or double strand breaks (DBS), DNA-DNA or DNA-protein cross-links) and interfering with important DNA-interacting proteins, e.g. DNA-topoisomerases. The cellular response to these DNA lesions is orchestrated in such a way that the detection of the damage activates a number of signal transduction pathways leading to cell cycle arrest and thus allowing repair, or if the damage is too heavy, induction of apoptosis [1, 2]. In the former case the cell fate will be survival, whilst in the latter case, the cell fate will be death. In this scenario the repair activity of the cell is profoundly interplayed with all the other cellular responses to the damage and is an important determinant of cell sensitivity to anticancer agents. Indeed, it has been reported that resistance to DNA-damaging agents can be associated with increased cellular repair activities while defects in DNA repair pathways result in hypersensitivity to these agents [3,4].

The importance of DNA damage responses in cancer treatment is based on the following considerations: 1. increased levels of DNA repair proteins have been correlated with resistance to anticancer agents acting as DNA-damaging agents; 2. somatic or inherited mutations in DNA repair genes have been described in tumours determining a selective loss of function that can be exploited to obtain anti-tumour selectivity. 3. most chemotherapeutic agents, including ionising radiations, act causing DNA damage and their effects are influenced by the efficiency of DNA repair pathways; 4. the unravelling of the DNA repair pathways and the definition of their molecular partners have made available potentially 'druggable' targets suitable for the identification of new anticancer therapies or for the enhanced anti-tumour activity of DNA-damaging agents.

Pathways Responding to Radiation-Induced DNA Damages and Signal Transduction

1. DNA Double-Strand Breaks

Faithful propagation of genetic material and transmission into daughter cells is critical to life, yet our genomes are incessantly exposed to environmental and endogenous agents that create thousands of DNA lesions per cell each day[5]. While some DNA lesions are considered to be relatively benign, other lesions can be quite toxic. The DNA double-strand break (DSB) is one of the most toxic and mutagenic DNA lesions experienced in human cells: a single DSB can potentially lead to loss of more than 100 million base pairs of genetic information (e.g., loss of an entire chromosome arm). Interestingly, despite the potential danger of DSBs, mammals have evolved clever ways of exploiting the intentional generation of DSBs to control biological processes. For example, programmed DSBs occur to initiate rearrangements during maturation of immunoglobulin genes[6], and DSBs are critical for genetic recombination between homologous chromosomes during meiosis[7]. Furthermore, DSBs also occur as transient intermediates when the topoisomerase II–DNA complex decatenates two DNA strands[8]. To combat the risk of large scale sequence rearrangements that could potentially result from both intentional and unintentional DSBs, mammals have evolved intricate DNA damage response and repair mechanisms. Here, we describe the major DSB sensor and repair processes, with a particular focus on the importance of accurate coordination among repair pathways in combating cancer and disease.

Historically, attention to DSBs has been focused primarily on two-ended DSBs that can be formed when a duplex molecule is fractured into two parts. Such two-ended breaks can be formed at any time during the cell cycle, and they can be accurately repaired by the non-homologous end joining in a process that rejoins the broken ends. While such two-ended DSBs are important DNA lesions, it is becoming increasingly clear that a significant portion of DSBs do not arise from direct fracture of a DNA duplex, but rather as a consequence of DNA replication. For example, one-ended DSBs can arise when the replication fork collides into an unrepaired DNA single-strand break (SSB) [9]. Replication forks may also stall or breakdown when they run into certain base lesions. Homology directed repair provides a mechanism for accurate repair of such a broken replication fork[10,11]. Importantly, non-homologous end joining of a one-ended DSB could be disadvantageous, since joining ends from independent loci will inevitably result in large scale sequence rearrangements. Thus, DNA replication is associated with the risk of converting base damage and SSBs into highly toxic DSBs, and these one-ended breaks require complex signaling and processing in order to be accurately repaired.

In addition to the complexities of repair pathway choice, the cell also has to cope with a variety of DNA end structures. DNA ligase can readily rejoin juxtaposed broken ends with ligatable 3′ hydroxyl groups and 5′ phosphates. However, many conditions simultaneously introduce both strand breaks and covalent modifications to nearby nucleotides. For example, DSBs caused by ionizing radiation result in a large fraction of DNA ends that contain additional DNA lesions at or close to the end, so-called 'difficult' DSBs[12]. Here, we describe the non-homologous end joining and homology directed repair pathways required to repair different types of DSBs.

1.1. Non-Homologous End Joining and Homologous Recombination—Partners in Repair

The simplest repair mechanism for a DSB is non-homologous end joining. In essence, this DSB repair pathway directly rejoins the two severed DNA ends in a sequence independent fashion [13]. This DSB repair pathway is mostly precise for simple breaks, such as blunt ends [14], but can lead to sequence alterations at the breakpoint when the ends are not compatible. Although the term "non-homologous" is used to describe this repair pathway, a tiny 1–6 bp region of sequence homology (microhomology) near the DNA end often facilitates rejoining. In contrast to non-homologous end joining, homology directed repair is guided by much longer stretches of homology, generally encompassing 100 bp or more.

Thus, a major difference between non-homologous end joining and homology directed repair is the span of homologous sequences associated with repair processing.

Many proteins are required to efficiently perform non-homologous end joining. The core machinery consists of DNA-dependent protein kinase (DNA-PK) and the ligase IV/XRCC4/XLF complex. The Ku70/80 heterodimer is the DNA binding component of DNA-PK, which forms a ring that can specifically bind to DNA ends[15]. This DNA–Ku complex then attracts and activates the catalytic subunit (DNA-PK$_{CS}$), a serine/threonine protein kinase. After juxtaposition of the two DNA ends, DNA-PK$_{CS}$ is autophosphorylated[16-18] and the ends become available for ligation by the ligase IV complex, which also contains the XRCC4 and XLF cofactors that are probably required for proper targeting of the ligase to DNA ends[19-22]. The Mre11, Rad50 and Nbs1 protein complex may facilitate tethering of the two DNA ends, and may be less critical under conditions where ends can be directly ligated than under conditions when ends require processing[23-25].

1.2. Non-Homologous End Joining of 'Difficult' DSBs

As a result of associated lesions, not all DNA ends are readily ligatable. DNA ends can contain aberrant 3' phosphate groups, 5' hydroxyl groups, damaged backbone sugar residues and damaged DNA bases. Such DNA ends require processing before proper joining can proceed. DNA ends carrying 3' phosphates or 5' hydroxyl groups can be polished by polynucleotide kinase, which interacts with XRCC4[26, 27]. Another subclass of incompatible DNA end structures can be polished by the structure-specific Artemis nuclease, which can cleave both DNA hairpins (which are intermediates in V(D)J recombination) and 3' overhanging single-stranded regions[28,29]. Furthermore, the WRN protein, which is mutated in Werner syndrome patients, may polish another subset of DNA ends with its exonuclease activity[30]. Finally, several DNA polymerases, including polymerases μ and λ, can fill in 5' single-stranded extensions[31]. It is to be expected that additional processing factors will surface in the future.

Indeed, in addition to these relatively well-defined activities, several other genes have been found to be required for efficient repair of a subset of ill-defined 'difficult' breaks (also referred to as 'dirty' or 'complex' breaks). Although the mechanistic details of such non-homologous end joining subpathways are not yet fully elucidated, they probably involve the ATM, 53BP1 and Mre11/Rad50/Nbs1 proteins and require phosphorylation of histone H2AX[32].

1.3. Homology Directed Repair

While non-homologous end joining operates in a template-independent fashion by rejoining two broken ends (and this process is often error-prone), homology directed repair has the capacity to accurately resynthesize damaged or missing sequence information at the break site by using a template located elsewhere in the genome. This error-free process can be accomplished by finding homologous sequences, preferably in the sister chromatid, and inserting a 3' end so that repair synthesis occurs across the breakpoint. All homology directed repair pathways are initiated by 5'–3' resection at the DSB end, which is facilitated by the Mre11/Rad50/Nbs1 complex[33]. From here on, several possible homology directed repair subpathways have been identified. Here, we discuss the synthesis-dependent strand annealing pathway, the classical double-Holliday Junction model for DSB repair, and single-strand annealing, all of which contribute to the repair of two-ended DSBs. In addition, we will also describe how homology directed repair can mend a one-ended DSB in replication fork repair. Finally, in addition to these traditional models of homology directed repair subpathways, we also briefly discuss template switching events, which are potentially initiated by single-stranded gaps.

Synthesis-dependent strand annealing is thought to be the predominant mechanism by which homology directed repair handles two-ended DSBs[34]. To demonstrate the inherent simplicity of synthesis-dependent strand annealing, an animation accompanies the text below. In addition, we have separated the text description of this process into two parts: the first section focuses on the movement of DNA strands, whereas the latter describes some key features of the proteins that catalyze each of the major steps in this process.

In common with all homology directed repair subpathways, the synthesis-dependent strand annealing pathway is initiated by resection of a broken end to create single-stranded DNA. After resection and protein binding, the resulting nucleoprotein filament invades the sister chromatid, forming heteroduplex DNA wherever it base pairs. This process of strand invasion and formation of heteroduplex DNA displaces a DNA strand, forming a so-called D-loop. Strand invasion is then followed by DNA synthesis beyond the original break site to restore the missing sequence information at the break point. The sister chromatid provides an ideal template for such error-free repair synthesis, and indeed it is the preferred template for homology directed repair[35]. On the other side of the D-loop, an "X" shaped structure called a Holliday Junction is formed at the border between hetero- and homoduplex[36]. Several proteins can bind Holliday Junctions and modulate the ability of these junctions to slide in either direction (this process is often called 'branch migration'). If the Holliday Junction is transported in the same direction as replication, it will release the newly synthesized strand. It is noteworthy that only one DNA end needs to invade the template DNA, as long as replication extends beyond the gap and into the region that is homologous to the opposite DNA end. Thus, by sliding the Holliday Junction, the invading strand can be released, and the newly synthesized 3' single-stranded end can then anneal to the other side of the DSB. Final processing to remove flaps, fill in gaps, and ligate remaining nicks then completes this pathway. It is important to point out that repair synthesis requires that sequence information be copied into the breakpoint in the synthesis-dependent strand annealing model for two-ended homology directed repair. This associated transfer of sequence information, termed gene conversion, has indeed been demonstrated experimentally in mammalian cells[37-41].

The central player in almost all homology directed repair events is Rad51. With the help of a series of associated proteins (i.e., BRCA2, RAD52, RAD54, RAD54B, and likely also the RAD51 paralogues RAD51B, RAD51C, RAD51D, XRCC2 and XRCC3), Rad51 forms the nucleoprotein filament that facilitates homology searching and strand invasion[42-48]. Interestingly, vertebrate cells rapidly accumulate chromosome aberrations and cease to divide when Rad51 expression is suppressed[49] and mice lacking Rad51 are inviable[50,51]. These studies clearly demonstrate that Rad51 is an essential protein and call attention to the critical role that homology directed repair plays in maintaining genomic integrity.

After D-loop formation, the annealed 3′ end is then extended by repair synthesis. Recent studies show that DNA polymerase η (eta) can perform 3′ end extension at a D-loop[52], which is consistent with the observation that cells lacking polymerase η showed a defect in homologous recombination[53]. Although Pol η, clearly affects homology directed repair, it remains likely that other DNA polymerases can compensate in absence of Pol η, since humans with mutant Pol η, are alive and mostly healthy, which likely would not be the case if they were completely defective in homology directed repair.

Once repair synthesis is complete, the next step in this pathway is to release the newly synthesized end, which can be accomplished simply by sliding the Holliday Junction toward the 3′ end. Many proteins have been shown to bind and/or modulate Holliday Junctions in vitro (e.g., WRN, BLM, p53, RAD54, BLAP75 and hMSH2-hMSH6)[54-58], but exactly how these proteins are coordinated during synthesis-dependent strand annealing is not yet fully elucidated. For example, while it is clear that RAD54, WRN and BLM facilitate Holliday Junction migration[57-60], it is not clear how the direction of migration is controlled, nor is it clear whether these proteins are involved in all homologous recombination events or only in certain subpathways. Following branch migration, the freed 3′ end likely becomes rapidly bound by RPA. If the opposite end of the DSB was similarly recessed, then simple annealing is all that is required to reconnect the two broken ends, and this annealing step can be facilitated by Rad52 or possibly p53[61-63]. Depending on the degree to which the 3′ end was extended during repair synthesis, there may or may not be a flap following the annealing step. If such a flap is formed, it can potentially be removed by structure specific endonucleases, such as XPF/ERCC1[64, 65]. Finally, remaining gaps are filled and ligase seals the nicks. It is to be expected that the normal cadre of proteins involved in repair synthesis would be recruited for these final steps (e.g., polymerase δ/ε, PCNA, and DNA ligase I)[66].

The double-Holliday Junction model for DSB repair was initially designed to explain gene conversion and crossover events occurring simultaneously following a DSB during meiosis[34]. In this model, both DNA ends invade the homologous DNA template and form a double Holliday Junction that may be resolved to create a crossover or a non-crossover product. The model is very elegant and gained popularity to also explain repair of DSBs during mitosis. However, there are several complications that arise when applying this model to explain how mammalian mitotic DSB repair occurs. Importantly, when resolution products are analyzed following introduction of a site-specific double-strand break, crossover products are rarely observed[37]. Furthermore, there is little direct evidence to support the possibility that this model accurately reflects strand processing in vivo. Nevertheless, it is important to point out that the human BLM and topoisomerase III proteins may resolve double Holliday Junctions to avoid cross-over products[58, 67], which is consistent with the possibility that such double crossover intermediates indeed can form in mitotic cells. Furthermore, extensive studies of polymorphism patterns associated with sites of loss of heterozygosity in human and rodent cells have shown that large stretches of chromosomes can be exchanged in mitotic cells[68-71]. Although the underlying mechanism of such large scale exchanges is not yet known, it remains possible that cleavage of double Holliday Junctions could drive these events.

If two adjacent repeat sequences are present, single-strand annealing may be utilised to repair a two-ended DSB. In this case the two 3′ overhangs are simply aligned and annealed. This process is facilitated by RPA and RAD52 in a RAD51-independent manner [72]. It is noteworthy that single-strand annealing is associated with inevitable loss of the sequences between the repeats, as well as one of the repeats. As such, single-strand annealing is always error-associated, since it leads to permanent large deletions. Haber has made a strong case that single-strand annealing is actually a 'spandrel'[73] (a term applied by S.J. Gould to describe an unintentional consequence[74]) in this case referring to the possibility that single-strand annealing is an unintentional consequence of the need to create single-stranded DNA in order to initiate synthesis-dependent strand annealing. Despite the inevitable loss of sequence information, single-strand annealing may play a role in DSB repair. The human genome is repleat with repetitive elements, e.g., there are $>10^6$ Alu repeats in the human genome[75], and more than 10% of the human genome is comprised of repeat sequences [76]. However, it is noteworthy that these repeats exhibit high sequence diversity[77], and mismatches between the repeat elements can dramatically suppress single-strand annealing in mammalian cells [78]. Thus, although single-strand annealing between Alu elements can occur at repeat sequences in the human genome, this pathway is likely to play a fairly limited role in the repair of DSBs in human mitotic cells.

One-ended DSBs arise when replication forks break down, for example upon encounter with a SSB. Resection at this DNA end provides a 3′ overhang which is a substrate for RAD51-mediated strand invasion. Strand invasion is then followed by Holliday Junction cleavage, which allows resumption of DNA replication. This recombination pathway has been called break-induced replication, as suggested by Haber[79, 80], or replication fork repair. If the replication fork breaks down when the leading strand encounters a single-strand break, then the leading strand template can potentially become covalently joined to the newly forming lagging strand (this depends on the direction by which the single Holliday Junction behind the replication fork is resolved)[81]. In this fashion, cleavage of the Holliday Junction can result in a sister chromatid exchange (SCE) that can be detected by BrdU labeling. Indeed, consistent with this model, mammalian cells with a defect in SSB repair show increased susceptibility to SCEs. For example, high levels of SCEs have been observed in cells harboring mutations in XRCC1 or Poly(ADP-ribose) polymerase 1 (PARP-1), presumably as a result of deficiencies in key proteins necessary to assemble repair factors at SSBs or to prevent replication fork encounter with SSBs[82-85]. Furthermore, one-ended DSBs at replication forks trigger a RAD51-dependent homologous recombination event that can result in a SCE [38]. It is interesting to consider the possibility that the need to repair broken replication forks may be the driving force behind the evolution of homology directed repair, which is supported by the observation that a complete lack of homology directed repair is lethal at the single cell level[49].

Emerging evidence suggests that homologous recombination is also part of a bypass mechanism for handling replication-blocking lesions. If replication on the lagging strand is obstructed by lesions, persistent gaps between Okazaki fragments could potentially stimulate template switching. Indeed, the RAD51 paralog proteins have been shown to assist formation of a RAD51 filament on gapped DNA[46], suggesting that homologous recombination can be initiated in the absence of a DNA end. Lesions obstructing leading strand synthesis may similarly induce template switching in the absence of a DSB. It is important to note that template-switching is transient, and it only facilitates bypass of DNA lesions; other repair pathways are needed to actually remove the offending lesion.

While it is clear that two-ended DSBs are preferentially repaired by non-homologous end joining[86], it remains unclear to what extent two-ended breaks drive spontaneous recombination, which is a question that is important to address if we are to understand the role of homologous recombination in disease. There is now substantial data supporting the notion that homology directed repair is critical for repair at the replication fork[87]. Several potentially recombinogenic lesions have been discussed that can be formed during replication (e.g., one- or two-ended DSBs, as well as single-stranded gaps)[88]. Here, we argue that one-ended DSBs are likely to be the underlying cause of a significant portion of spontaneous homology directed repair events. First, it has been shown that inability to efficiently repair SSBs increases the frequency of one-ended DSBs [89] and also increases the spontaneous levels of both SCEs and RAD51 foci in mammalian cells, in some cases by more than an order of magnitude [90-92]. Second, analysis of recombination products shows that approximately a third of spontaneous recombination events in mouse embryonic stem cells are consistent with repair of broken replications forks. Finally, most spontaneous recombination events in human cells showed similar resolution products as those created when cells were subjected to increased levels of single-strand breaks. Thus, it is clear that single-strand breaks induce replication fork breakdown, and it has been shown that a significant portion of recombination products show resolution patterns that are consistent with the repair of broken replication forks.

1.4. How does the cell choose between homology directed repair and non-homologous end joining?

Choosing between homology directed repair and non-homologous end joining depends on several factors. One quite obvious factor is the cell cycle stage at which the DSB is generated. Most homologous recombination events occur between sister chromatids and should therefore be largely confined to the S and G2 phases of the cell cycle [93,94]. A question thus arises: how does the cell know whether a certain part of the genome has already been replicated? Although the complete answer to this question is not yet known, several findings suggest that the initiation of homologous recombination is tightly cell-cycle regulated. One way to restrict homologous recombination activity to the S/G2 phases is to link initiation of this pathway to cyclin-dependent kinases that are specifically active during these stages of the cell cycle. Indeed, it has been demonstrated that generation of the 3′ ssDNA overhang is regulated by CDK activity, which prevents resection of DNA ends outside the S and G2 phases of the cell cycle in eukaryotic cells [95,96]. By preventing homologous recombination outside of S and G2, exchanges between homologous chromosomes can be reduced, thus suppressing loss of heterozygosity events that potentially could result from such exchanges [93].

In addition to confining homology directed repair to S/G2, the cell needs to ensure that non-homologous end joining does not act on one-ended DSBs, since this activity could promote misjoining between different loci. Interestingly, the Ku70/80 heterodimer appears at DNA ends much more quickly than homologous recombination factors [97]. This observation is consistent with the possibility that non-homologous end joining is the preferred DSB repair pathway for two-ended DSBs, even in S phase, and also implies that mechanisms must exist to prevent non-homologous end joining from acting at broken replication forks. Possibilities for ensuring that one-ended breaks are acted upon by homologous recombination include the fact that a one-ended break in the lagging strand could have a relatively long 3′ single-stranded extension that could prevent Ku70/80 binding[98]. In addition, the leading strand may exploit a hand-off mechanism from the replication machinery to the homologous recombination pathway.

The DSB repair pathway choice may also be influenced by the structure of the DNA end. A simple, directly ligatable DSB makes a good substrate for non-homologous end joining, whereas more difficult breaks may be more prone to attract the homologous recombination machinery. A more detailed investigation of the influence of DNA end structure on DSB repair has been hampered by the absence of agents that can specifically produce one type of DNA end. However, it is clear that difficult DSBs require more time for repair, which is consistent with the possibility that they are somehow shunted toward homologous recombination.

An additional layer of control over DSB repair pathway choice is provided by DNA damage signaling pathways. It has been clear for many years that ionizing radiation directly impairs replication origin firing through ATM signaling [99,100], in a process that is facilitated by the MRN complex[101]. This intra-S phase checkpoint suppresses creation of new replication forks, and thus diminishes the odds that replication forks will run into lesions that might otherwise stimulate fork breakdowns. Furthermore, an intra-S checkpoint may also help to provide the time required to perform homologous recombination.

Nevertheless, even under optimal conditions for DNA replication, replication forks are likely to encounter DNA lesions, and these encounters require signaling and appropriate pathway choice to prevent catastrophe in S phase. Mammalian cells sustain more than 10,000 abasic sites per day and it is estimated that hundreds of thousands of damaged bases are formed each day[102]. Therefore, one would expect the replication fork to run into DNA lesions multiple times per round of replication, which is consistent with the observations that normal human cells undergo about 10 sister chromatid exchanges per round of replication [103], and that recombination events accumulate throughout the lifespan of mammals [104].

Conceptually, one could envision two ways to counteract the problem of encounters with DNA lesions and single-strand breaks during replication: repairing the broken replication fork and preventing the replication fork from advancing through DNA lesions. Among researchers interested in homologous recombination, most research has focussed on the first scenario, repairing one-ended DSBs to restore replication fork integrity. Clearly, this process requires homology directed repair, as elaborated above. Equally important is the question of how cells prevent replication forks from encountering DNA lesions in the first place. Many signaling proteins, such as ATR and Chk1 [105-107] are required for maintenance of replication fork integrity under conditions that cause replication stress (e.g., hydroxyurea treatment, which depletes the nucleotide pool). Furthermore, depletion of the MRN complex or ATM and ATR from Xenopus egg extracts causes accumulation of DSBs during normal replication [108,109], suggesting that replication is not properly regulated under these conditions. Interestingly, exposure to an alkylating agent has been shown to inhibit origin firing and also to slow down replication fork progression[110], which may result from direct inhibition of replication fork progression by 3-methyladenine [111,112]. It is tempting to speculate that DNA damage ahead of the replication fork might lead to signals not only to suppress origin firing (as described above), but also possibly to slow down or halt replication fork progression in order to repair the damage before a DSB might be formed. It will be interesting to learn the extent to which DNA lesions that slow replication fork progression do so via active signaling versus passive inhibition of DNA polymerases.

1.5. Defective DSB Repair in Association with Cancer and Aging

Chromosomal instability is a hallmark of many tumors. Interestingly, careful analysis of translocation breakpoints in lymphoid malignancies has revealed that most junctions have characteristics of normal non-homologous end joining [113]. Therefore, one might expect that non-homologous end joining deficient mice would have a reduced incidence of transformed cells containing chromosomal translocations. However, the opposite effect has been observed in several non-homologous end joining mouse models [114,115]. Deficiencies in non-homologous end joining most often lead to an increased risk of cancer, with enhanced chromosomal instability, including translocations. This phenomenon was particularly obvious in combination with a mutation in the tumor suppressor gene p53 [115], probably because of a decreased apoptosis rate. Strikingly, a relatively subtle decrease in non-homologous end joining capacity (caused by heterozygosity at the ligase IV locus) resulted in a cancer-prone phenotype in an Ink4a deficient background, suggesting that subtle variations in non-homologous end joining capacity in the population might contribute to carcinogenesis [116]. Indeed, patients with hypomorphic mutations in the Artemis gene have been found to develop thymic lymphomas, showing that a decrease in non-homologous end joining capacity can increase the risk of cancer in humans as well as mice [117].

Given the high stakes involved in assuring accurate rejoining of two-ended breaks, and accurate reinsertion of one-ended breaks during replication fork repair, it is not surprising that defects in key proteins involved in homologous recombination are also associated with an increased risk of cancer [118]. While many proteins that modulate homologous recombination are known to be cancer genes (e.g., BRCA1 and FANC genes, MMR genes, p53, and ATM [119-122]), these genes have pleiotropic effects, so it is difficult to dissect out the importance of homologous recombination in these cases. On the other hand, there are also cancer genes where a direct link to homologous recombination is more apparent. For example, BRCA2 plays a central role in displacing RPA and facilitating loading of Rad51 onto single-stranded DNA [123]. The resulting homology directed repair deficiency in BRCA2 null cells results in the accumulation of chromosome aberrations [124], which is quite similar to what has been observed in vertebrate cells depleted of Rad51. Thus, a defect in the ability to initiate homologous recombination is associated with an increased cancer risk. Another interesting example is the BLM helicase. Unlike BRCA2, BLM mutant cells are proficient in initiating homologous recombination, but the outcome of these repair events is apparently shifted toward exchange-associated events [125]. The resulting increase in exchanges between homologous chromosomes leads to increased rates of loss of heterozygosity, which has been proposed to be the driving force behind the increased risk of cancer in Bloom's syndrome patients [126]. Finally, as another example, defects in the WRN helicase are associated with accelerated aging and increased cancer risk. In this case, the rate of initiation of homologous recombination appears to be increased, but there are problems in resolution of homologous recombination events, which apparently increases the risk of cell death [127,128]. These three examples demonstrate that deficiencies in both homologous recombination initiation and resolution lead to disease and call attention to the fundamental role of homologous recombination in genome maintenance. Undoubtedly research in the next decade will reveal additional connections between homologous recombination, genomic stability, and disease.

It is important to emphasize that loss of homologous recombination in a normal cell is generally more toxic than it is mutagenic. For example, conditional knock out of Rad51 in vertebrate cells leads to increased levels of chromosome aberrations, but within a short time, no cells survive. In other words, severe deficiencies in homologous recombination are as toxic as they are genome destabilizing. One might then ask how loss of function of BRCA2 promotes cancer. At least two possible explanations exist. First, cells might tolerate a partial deficiency in homologous recombination more readily than complete loss of function. Indeed, cells lacking BRCA2 retain some homologous recombination capacity [129,130]. Another possibility is that suppression of homologous recombination capacity is a late event in tumorigenesis (as has been observed in the case of pancreatic cancer [131]), preceded by mutations that confer resistance to apoptosis, thus allowing highly unstable cells to survive.

The enzyme O^6-alkylguanine-DNA-alkyltransferase (AGT/MGMT) transfers the methyl/alkyl adducts from the O^6 position of guanine to the cysteine residue within its active site, by a direct repair process. This protein is unique in its ability to remove the methyl/alkyl group from the O^6 position of guanine independently from any other proteins and without causing DNA strand break. In addition, it repairs with a stechiometric and auto-inactivating reaction rendering this repair system saturable. Many alkylating agents, including temozolomide, streptozotocin, procarbazine, dacarbazine and nitrosoureas, cause O^6 adducts that are repaired by MGMT[132,133].

2. Base Excision Repair (BER)

The base excision repair (BER) pathway recognises and removes damaged bases such as oxidised-reduced, alkylated and deaminated bases, caused by environmental mutagens and by anticancer agents, such as alkylating agents and ionising radiation[134]. In this process the damaged base is removed by a DNA glycosylase with the formation of a potentially cytotoxic apurinic or apirimidinic (AP) site, that is processed by an AP endonuclease (APE1), with the generation of a strand break. Replacement of the damaged base and re-ligation of the DNA involve binding of poly(ADP-ribose)polymerase (PARP) and recruitment of DNA polymerase β and ligase III. The broad substrate specificity of BER relies on the existence of diverse damage-specific glycosylases that remove the damaged bases.

3. Nucleotide Excision Repair (NER)

The nucleotide excision repair (NER) is certainly the most versatile DNA repair mechanism recognising and dealing with bulky, helix-distorting lesions, such as the ones induced by UV (cyclobutane dimers and 6–4 photoproducts)[135]. This is a multi-step process with many (more than twenty) different proteins involved in sequential steps that deal with lesion recognition, damage removal and DNA synthesis. Two major pathways can be recognised in NER: the transcription coupled repair (TCR) and the global genome repair (GGR); the former is a highly specific and efficient system that detects and removes the DNA damage that blocks the progression of RNA polymerase II, while the latter is a slow process that inspects the entire genome. Cell derived from Xeroderma Pigmentosum or Cockaine Syndrome patients are deficient in NER and are exquisitively sensitive to cisplatin and alkylating agents, whereas they are resistant to Trabectedin[136-138], a marine natural product that binds in the minor groove of DNA. In fact for Trabectedin evidence exists that the activation of NER following exposure with the drug causes cytotoxicity through a mechanism still to be elucidated[139].

4. Mismatch Repair (MR)

The mismatch repair removes biosynthetic errors from newly synthesised DNA and in particular it efficiently recognises base-base mismatches and insertion/deletion loops improving the fidelity of DNA replication by several orders of magnitude. Lack of MR is responsible for a mutator phenotype and predisposes to cancer. In addition it has been clearly demonstrated how the cellular MR status influences the cytotoxic activities of different anticancer agents such as (mainly) cisplatin, methylating agents and some antimetabolites[140].

5. The Fanconi Anaemia/BRCA (FA/BRCA) Pathway

The Fanconi anaemia/BRCA (FA/BRCA) pathway is involved in the repair of interstrand DNA cross-links possibly through the coordination of NHEJ, HR and postreplication/translesion DNA synthesis pathways [141]. Clinically this pathway is important as many anticancer agents cause DNA crosslinks, e.g. cisplatin, mytomicin, cyclophosphamide, melphalan, nitrosoureas.

Targeting DNA Damage Responses as a Strategy for Cancer Treatment

Since the function of DNA repair systems is to protect living organisms from the mutagenic and toxic lesions caused by DNA-damaging agents, it is understandable that any strategy aimed at inhibiting DNA repair enzymes is inherently associated with a high degree of risk to produce damage to normal tissues. For this reason DNA-repair inhibitor strategies have been directed to enzymes/pathways for which there are reasons to believe that some degree of selectivity for some human neoplasms can be achieved. In addition it should be considered that many of the proteins involved in some complex DNA repair pathways, e.g. NER or MR, do have a role in other important cellular pathways and/or important physiological backup functions and inhibition of their activities might have deleterious side effects for normal cells. This explains why the available inhibitors of DNA repair that are under clinical investigation are so far directed to pathways such as MGMT, BER and PARP, involving few steps with key proteins and for which some degree of selectivity seems to exist[142,143].

1. Targeting MGMT

The repair protein O^6-alkylguanine-DNA alkyltransferase, also known as O^6-methylguanine-DNA methyltransferase (MGMT), acts by transferring the alkyl groups present on the O^6 position of guanine to a cysteine residue in the active site of the protein[144]. Therefore, the repair process of O^6-alkylguanine occurs without generating DNA breakage.

This repair mechanism is evolutionarily well conserved from bacteria to mammalian cells, as repair methylation of O^6-guanine can occur as an endogenous metabolic reaction and is highly mutagenic. MGMT is not a typical enzyme as the transfer of the alkyl group to a cysteine residue inactivates the protein (i.e. suicide enzyme), that is then ubiquinated and digested by the proteosome.

It has been known for more than 20 years that MGMT is involved in the mechanism of resistance to several anticancer drugs that act as methylating agents, like temozolomide, dacarbazine and procarbazine, or as chloroethylating agents such as chloroethylnitrosoureas like BCNU, CCNU or fotemustine[145-147].

Plenty of preclinical data support the notion that there is an inverse correlation between the amount of MGMT and the sensitivity to methylating and chloroethylating agents of cancer cell lines and xenografts. It has been suggested that the reason why most murine tumours are extremely sensitive to nitrosoureas is that these tumours have a very low expression of MGMT. These considerations have provided the rationale for studies conducted on clinical samples aimed at establishing a link between the tumour sensitivity to alkylating agents and MGMT expression. The most convincing data have certainly been obtained in primary CNS tumours. Higher overall survival was reported in patients with osteocytoma and glioblastoma treated with CCNU combined with radiotherapy when the tumour concentration of MGMT was low [148]. Other studies indicate that when the levels of MGMT in osteocytomas and glioblastomas were low, the response rate to temozolomide was 60% compared to 9% in the cases in which tumour concentrations of MGMT were high [149].

More recently the efficacy of both CCNU and temozolomide in glioblastoma patients was found to be correlated to the methylation status of the promoter of the MGMT gene. The most extensive studies were performed by Hegi et al.[150] who found that MGMT promoter was methylated in 45% of 206 glioblastoma cases investigated. The survival benefit observed in patients treated with temozolomide and radiotherapy was significantly greater for patients whose tumours contained a methylated MGMT promoter. Esteller et al.[151]found that methylation of MGMT is a useful indicator of responsiveness of gliomas to alkylating agents such as nitrosoureas. Levin et al.[152]found that in oligodendrogliomas the response to temozolomide treatment was associated with 1p deletion and low protein expression. The importance of MGMT for the response to alkylating agents has been highlighted not only in studies performed in adult glioblastomas but also in paediatric CNS tumours treated with methylating agents[153, 154]. Interesting to note that MGMT promoter methylation was found to be a useful marker for predicting survival of patients with diffuse large B cell lymphomas too[155], independent from other relevant molecular alterations such as 10q loss or p53 expression[156].

MGMT also appears to play a role in the modulation of response to poisons of DNA-topoisomerase I[157], an effect presumably related to the fact that O^6methylguanine containing DNA appears to favour the enzyme entrapment compared to the same sequence containing not alkylated guanines.

2. Depletion of MGMT

The well documented evidence that a major mechanism of resistance to methylating or chloroethylating agents is related to an increased expression of MGMT, led to the development of methods to deplete MGMT as a strategy to overcome drug resistance. Two different approaches have been pursued: an indirect inhibition of MGMT by the use of methylating agents and a direct inhibition by using analogues of guanine.

The first approach involves the methylation of O^6 guanine by methylating agents, then subsequent removal of the methyl group by MGMT that is inactivated by the repair reaction itself, as previously explained[146]. The extent of the depletion of MGMT is related to the number of methylguanine present in DNA and thus ultimately to the methylating agent dose, whereas the duration of the depletion will depend on the cellular rate of biosynthesis of new MGMT molecules. In several cell lines the turn-over time of MGMT has been estimated to be around 4 h, thus suggesting that giving a first dose of a methylating agent, e.g. temozolomide, followed after 4 h by a second dose of the same methylating agent or of a chloroethylating agent, e.g. BCNU or fotemustine could result in a potentiation of the effect. This approach with multiple doses of drugs given with selected intervals on the MGMT depletion concept have been shown to be feasible[158-160], but large studies to assess the antitumour efficacy compared to standard protocols are still to be reported. The most likely reason for the lack of these studies is related to the fact that in small pilot studies the bone marrow toxicity appeared to be higher than expected with sequential combinations[161]. A further reported drawback was related to lung toxicity (manifested as interstitial pneumonitis) that was shown in patients receiving sequential treatment with dacarbazine and nitrosoureas[162,163].

A weak aspect of most published studies is that most information was obtained by determining the enzyme level in lymphocytes, that does not necessarily reflect what happens in the tumour. A further limitation is the finding that MGMT levels assessed by immunohistochemistry appear to be variable in different areas of the same tumour, e.g. melanomas. Thus, if a significant MGMT depletion is achieved, this does not mean that all tumour cells have a similar depletion of the enzyme. A variety of different proportions of cells with low or high levels of MGMT may co-exist; the cells that express high concentrations of MGMT presumably being resistant.

The second approach involves the use of direct MGMT inhibitors. Most available data on the two inhibitors that have been developed in the clinic, O^6-benzylguanine (O^6-BG) and O^6-(4-bromothenyl) guanine (lomeguatrib) are herein shortly reviewed. O^6-BG is a non-toxic inhibitor of MGMT that works by transferring the benzoyl group to the cysteine residue in the active site of the protein. The preclinical activity of O^6-BG was demonstrated both in cultured cells and in xenografts, where it was shown to restore the sensitivity to nitrosoureas[164]. Phase I clinical trials indicated that O^6-BG can effectively suppress MGMT activity, but the doses required were different for different tumours[165-169]. For example, 100–120 mg/m^2 O^6-BG were effective in causing a complete depletion of MGMT in gliomas. The combination of O^6-BG at the dose of 120 mg/m^2 with BCNU at the reduced dose of 40 mg/m^2 showed no activity in resistant glioblastomas or melanomas[169]. These studies are difficult to interpret because the tumour levels of MGMT were not assessed. It may be that the dose reduction of BCNU, required to limit bone marrow toxicity, was the reason for the failure. In recurrent progressive gliomas, a loading dose of 120 mg/m^2 of O^6-BG over 1 h followed by a continuous infusion of 30 mg/m^2 for 48 h – effective in depleting tumour levels of MGMT – was combined with temozolomide at doses up to 472 mg/m^2, higher doses being too bone-marrow toxic. Although the results of the studies are not available yet, it appears that the bone-marrow toxicity represents the main drawback of the combination, not allowing the use of temozolomide at full doses.

O^6 (4-bromothenyl)guanine (lomeguatrib) appears more promising than O^6-BG. It has shown good bioavailability when given by an oral route. It works by transferring the bromothenyl group to the cystein residue in the active site of MGMT, thus inactivating it. The co-administration of lomeguatrib at the dose of 10 mg/m^2, which is effective in causing depletion of MGMT in tumour tissues, with temozolomide appears to be feasible with a dose reduction of temozolomide less than that required for O^6-BG. Lomeguatrib also increases the bone-marrow toxicity of temozolomide but, for unclear reasons, in a less severe way compared to other inhibitors and this justifies a significant clinical interest and phase II trials are ongoing.

Since methylating agents produce DNA breaks it has been suggested to combine them with inhibitors of PARP. Studies have been initiated to assess whether temozolomide activity can be enhanced by the concomitant use of PARP inhibitors. If this approach proves successful, as preliminary data seem to indicate, one can envisage the possibility of combining temozolomide with a MGMT depleting agent, e.g. lomeguatrib, and with a PARP inhibitor. These combinations should overcome the resistance mechanisms related to DNA repair, but presumably might increase the toxicity on normal tissues too, as discussed in previous sections there may be some selectivity in tumours exhibiting specific DNA repair defects.

3. Targeting BER Pathway

As mentioned above, BER is able to recognise and repair the DNA damage caused by alkylating agents. Preclinical studies suggest that it can represent an attractive target for anticancer therapy as its inhibition has been shown to sensitise cells to the cytotoxic effects of different alkylating agents [170]. BER can be inhibited by small molecules that bind to the AP site preventing its processing by the AP endonuclease/redox effector factor-1 (APE1) enzyme, by molecules that directly target the function of APE1 enzyme and by interfering with Polβ.

Methoxyamine (MX) is a small molecule that binds avidly to the AP sites on the DNA reducing the APE cleavage of the backbone by more than 300-fold compared with the cleavage of normal AP sites. It was first introduced as a tool to study the BER pathway and then investigated therapeutically in the attempt to potentiate the antitumour effect of alkylating agents as well as other compounds causing AP sites both *in vitro* and *in vivo* systems[171-173]. These data not only proved that this type of inhibitor could be of potential therapeutic value, but also put forward the evidence that molecules binding to the AP sites could be developed to synergistically improve the therapeutic efficacy of DNA damaging agents. A phase I clinical trial with this compound is currently being undertaken in patients with solid tumours, but no data are available yet.

Another way to inhibit the BER pathway is through the targeting of APE1. APE1 is a multifunctional enzyme playing a role in BER and DNA strand break repair unrelated to the processing of the AP site[174]. In fact, it has been described to have a role in the protection of the toxic effects caused by bleomycin and IR treatments through its 3′phosphoglycolate diesterase activity. The protein is also endowed with a so-called redox activity regulating the binding activity of different DNA transcriptional factors. In addition, APE1 protein has been shown to be over-expressed in some human tumours and this expression pattern seems to be correlated with poor response to therapy. CRT0044876 was isolated by screening a chemical library as a specific and potent APE1 inhibitor, lacking inherent toxicity to human cell lines but able to potentiate the cytotoxic effects of different DNA damaging drugs, including alkylating agents[175]. These preliminary data provided the proof of principle that APE1 can be targeted, even if further development is required to identify a clinical lead compound. Recently, E3330, able to inhibit the redox activity of APE1, has been isolated and shown to dramatically increase the cytotoxic activity of alkylating agents in ovarian cancer cell lines[176].

Polβ has a crucial role in creating an intact DNA strand after the removal of the damaged base[177]. Many natural products are non-specific inhibitors of Polβ including glycoglycerolipids and triterpenoids. It has been shown that the synthetic compound palmoic acid inhibits the DNA polimerase and lyase activities of the enzyme *in vitro* sensitising wild-type but not Polβ-null fibroblast to the cytotoxic activity of alkylating agents[178]. It is, however, still to be defined the degree to which inhibition of Polβ would interfere with normal DNA synthesis and therefore further studies are indeed needed.

4. Targeting PARP

PARP1 is the best characterised, most abundant and active member of the PARP family, comprising of as many as 18 related proteins. It has an important role in regulating cell death and cellular response to DNA damage[179]. When activated this multifunctional enzyme transfers ADP-ribose unit from NAD+ to nuclear target proteins and itself, forming long and branched polymers of poly (ADP-ribose) (PAR) at the expense of cellular NAD pools. The controversial reported results on the role of the enzyme in the DNA signalling and DNA-damage induced cell death have been unified by Virag et al[180].who suggested that when DNA is moderately damaged, PARP1 participates in the DNA repair and the cell survives; in the presence of severe DNA damage, apoptosis is activated and caspases inactivate PARP1 by cleavage and finally, in the case of extreme damage, PARP1 is overactivated and induces a decrease in NAD+ and ATP levels leading to cell dysfunction or even to necrosis. The pleiotropic involvement of the enzyme in such different cellular responses to damage makes it amenable for therapeutical intervention in different pathophysiological conditions such as cancer, inflammation, stroke, and hypertension. We will here consider the inhibition of its DNA repair functions as a tool to potentiate the activity of chemo-radiotherapy.

PARP1 has been shown to have a key role in BER pathway, stimulating and facilitating the process[181]. It does in fact interact with DNA ligase III, the adaptor factor XRCC1, DNA polymerase and other components of the single–strand break repair. In addition, PARP1 cooperates with Cockayne syndrome B protein, Werner syndrome nuclear protein and DNA topoisomearse I, proteins involved in other DNA repair processes, favouring their activities. It has been proposed that the negatively charged polymers of poly (ADP-ribose) catalysed by activated PARP1 help the opening of the damaged DNA to allow the access of other components of the repair process. In addition, it is likely that the polyADP ribosylation serves as a scaffold for the recruitment of different repair proteins at the sites of damage with a local amplification of the response. The data from the literature suggest that PARP1 has a more important role in the repair of DNA under stress conditions (such as after IR and certain anticancer agent exposure) than in normal (non-stressed) conditions. PARP knock out mice are more susceptible to the cytotoxic activity of different anticancer agents and IR. These data, together with the cumulating evidence that PARP1 inhibitors were able to potentiate *in vitro* the cytotoxic activity of the same agents, made PARP1 a target for the clinical development of specific PARP1 inhibitors as potential chemo- and radio-sensitisers.

Inhibitors were largely designed on the structure of nicotidamine, and were competitive of the catalytic domain of the enzyme. The first nicotidamine analogues were the benzamides (3-amino-benzamide) developed in the 1980s and mainly used for *in vitro* studies[182].These molecules had, however, a weak inhibitory activity and possessed many other side effects unrelated to PARP inhibition. During the last decade, structure-based drug design studies and a better understanding of the molecular details of the active site of PARP have facilitated the discovery of inhibitors with increased potency, increased specificity and better pharmacokinetic and toxicological properties[183]. All these compounds have been shown to potentiate the *in vitro* and *in vivo* anti-tumour activity of anticancer agents, in particular temozolomide, topoisomerase I poisons, platinum compounds and IR. In most cases the observed potentiation has been correlated with the ability of PARP inhibitors to inhibit the repair of the DNA lesions caused by the treatment of the anticancer agents.

Most of the PARP1 inhibitors are in early stage clinical development and the data from these clinical studies are awaited [184,185]. As much of the pre-clinical work has been focused on the potentiation of temozolomide, this was the first combination with PARP inhibitors introduced in the clinic for cancer patients in 2003. The phase I of AG014699 + temozolomide (TMZ) showed that a full dose of TMZ could be given in the presence of a profound inhibition of PARP[186]. No toxicity specific to the PARP inhibitor was observed, even if an enhancement of TMZ mielo-toxicity was observed with the higher doses of AG014699. Recently, the final report of a phase II study of AG014699 in combination with TMZ in patients with malignant melanoma was presented at the 2006 ASCO meeting showing an encouraging activity of the combination. Still awaited are the data on the correlation between clinical outcome and PARP expression and activity in blood cells and tumour[187].

Even if pre-clinical data showed that PARP inhibitor treatment strengthen the effect of radiotherapy both in cell lines and in tumour xenografts and, as mentioned before, PARP1 knocked out mice are hypersensitive to IR, the combination trials of PARP1 inhibitors and radiotherapy are still challenging as regards to the definition of end-points to define a benefit. Radiotherapy is generally given in an adjuvant setting to improve local tumour control. This implies not only the need to investigate dose reduction of established regimens, but also long follow-up times. For these reasons, these combination trials, even if potentially interesting, are still at a design stage.

While these PARP inhibitors have been thought to be used in combination with IR and with other different anticancer agents, two exciting papers have been published on the possible application of PARP inhibitors as single agents in tumour cells harbouring defects in recombination repair, due to mutations of the genes BRCA1 and BRCA2[188,189]. It was reported that both BRCA-1 and -2 homozygous mutant cells lines and tumour xenografts were hypersensitive to PARP inhibitor treatment, while wild type and heterozygous cell lines showed a normal sensitivity. As PARP is a non-redundant component of BER that repairs SSBs normally formed during cell cycle, the treatment with PARP inhibitors in normal cells will lead to persistent SSBs that are converted to double strand breaks (DSB) when they meet the replication fork. In the presence of a functional recombination repair, these DSBs are efficiently repaired by Rad51-mediated homologous recombination. BRCA1/2 proteins have been shown to physically interact with Rad51 and play a pivotal role in recombination repair. In a BRCA-1 and –2 homozygous setting background, the DSBs originated by the treatment with a PARP inhibitor cannot be properly processed and repaired due to the lack of the functional recombination repair with the collapse of the replicative fork and illegitimated DNA ends joining leading to cell growth arrest and apoptosis. As germ line mutations of BRCA1 and BRCA2 have been found to contribute to most of the familial breast cancer cases, the above mentioned exciting preclinical results open new chemo-preventive and therapeutic strategies for BRCA1/2-associated breast cancers. These data have indeed prompted the evaluation of PARP1 as mono-therapy for BRCA-deficient tumours[190,191].

5. Targeting Double Strand Break Repair

A DSB is a lethal lesion that needs to be repaired to avoid chromosomal rearrangement and aneuplody. This requires a coordinated cellular response that not only involves the recruitment of proteins that physically repair the damage (effector proteins), but also the activation of signal transduction pathways leading to cell cycle arrest necessary to perform the repair (sensing and transducer molecules). Even if this division is likely to be too simplistic as many proteins have redundant and overlapping functions, it helps to understand the different classes of molecules developed to inhibit this repair process. In particular, two kinases of the phosphatidylinositol 3-kinase (PI3K) super-family, ataxia-teleangectasia mutated (ATM) and ATM-RAD3-related (ATR), play a crucial role in sensing DSBs and in activating transduction pathways with phosphorylating events on target proteins leading to cell cycle arrest and facilitation of the repair process[192-195]. ATM-mutated cells show hypersensitivity to DBS inducers suggesting that ATM inhibition could sensitise to IR and other chemotherapeutic agents. The first selected inhibitors, as caffeine, wortmannin and LY294002, were rather unspecific being able to target multiple members of the PI3 kinase super-family and too toxic for clinical exploitation. Recently, an ATP-competitive inhibitor KU-55933 has been screened for its greater specificity toward ATM than the other components of the PI3K super-family and it has been shown to chemo-sensitise and radio-sensitise wild type ATM cells to IR, etoposide, doxorubicin and camptothecin. However, more data are necessary to fully develop this class of compound in a clinical setting.

The other approach undertaken to inhibit DSB repair has been focus on inhibiting NHEJ. Cells deficient in components of the NHEJ pathway are highly sensitive to IR and topoisomerase II poisons, such as etoposide, doxorubicin and mAMSA. Over-expression of DNA-PKcs correlated with increased repair of IR-, etoposide- and doxorubicin-induced DNA DSBs and with resistance to these agents[196]. DNA-PK, as ATR and ATM, is a member of the PI3K-related protein kinase. A number of compounds have been developed as potent and specific inhibitors of DNA-PK with 100-fold selectivity for the enzyme as compared with other PI3K family members. One of the first novel LY294002-based compounds with an increased activity toward DNA-PK was NU7026[197]. This compound enhanced the cytotoxicity of both IR and topoisomerase II poisons and retarded DSB repair. Further compound elaboration lead to the identification of NU7441 as a yet more potent and specific inhibitor for the DNA-PK and able to enhance the antitumour activity of etoposide in the human colon cancer xenograft model[198]. However, even these data provided excellent proof of principle of the *in vitro* and *in vivo* chemo-sensitisation and radio-sensitisation potential of this class of compounds; the limited aqueous solubility and oral bioavailability restrict NU7441's further development. Other compounds have been shown to inhibit NHEJ pathway such as vanillin, a plant-derived natural compound that sensitises cells to cisplatin[199]or a chemically synthesised inhibitor of DNA-PKcs, SU11752, that competitively inhibits DNA-PK binding to the ATP pocket[200].

6. Targeting Fanconi Anaemia/BRCA Pathway

Data from the literature suggest that cells deficient in this pathway are hypersensitive to cross-linking agents. Attempts to identify small molecule inhibitors of the FA/BRCA pathway that could sensitise cancer cells to DNA damaging cross-linking agents have recently been published using a cell-based strategy [201]. Four inhibitors (three protein kinase inhibitors and one natural compound) have been identified. This targeting approach is still very much in its infancy though and further biochemical and preclinical work needs to be done.

7. Exploiting DNA Repair Defects for Cancer Therapy

With the implementation of microarray and proteomic technologies, the molecular characterisation of human tumours has been cumulating in the past years. This information, together with the unravelling of both the mechanisms of action of the anticancer agents and the pathways involved in the repair of the lesions they cause, have opened up the possibility to tailor the treatment of cancer, with a potential increase of the therapeutic index. In particular, the definition of a sub-set of tumours with specific defect in DNA repair pathways has envisaged the possibility to differentially treat the patients whose tumours harbour such defects.

Individuals with heterozygous, germ line mutations in either *BRAC1* and *BRCA2* have an increased life time risk of developing breast and others tumours[202]. These tumours have generally lost the wild type allele resulting in a non expressing *BRAC1* or *BRCA2* protein. Normal tissues of the patients harbouring *BRAC1* and *BRCA2* defective tumours do not seem to show haplo-insufficiency, suggesting a difference in the capacity of DNA DSBs repair between normal and tumour cells[203]. The *in vitro* data clearly show that cell lines lacking these genes are selective and exquisitely sensitive to agents causing DNA interstrand cross-links, such as cisplatin, carboplatin, mitomycin C, and recently to PARP inhibitors. Even if these agents are not generally used in metastatic sporadic breast cancer, the great difference in the HR repair between the normal cells and tumour cells of *BRCA1* and *BRCA2* mutation carrier patients suggests the possibility of a potent and selective tumour cell killing by these agents in familiar breast cancer. To corroborate this hypothesis, a clinical study has been implemented randomising BRCA1 or BRCA2 mutation carriers with metastatic breast cancer to either the DNA cross-linking agent carboplatin or docetaxel, the current gold standard treatment[204].

Recent data emerging from the literature suggest that BRCA-associated pathways seem to be inactivated in a substantial fraction of sporadic cancers. These tumours display a phenotype similar to the BRCA germ line mutation in the absence of a mutation in BRCA genes, a phenomenon named 'BRCA-ness'[205-207]. For example, epigenetic silencing of the critical gene involved in HR through methylation of promoter region has been described for BRCA1 and components of the FA pathways (FANCF, FANCC, FANCG) and by amplification of a novel gene, called EMSY, that negatively regulates the transcription of

BRCA2. These BRCA mutant tumours should also be very sensitive to the treatment with PARP inhibitors, used as mono-therapy, as already discussed in the PARP inhibition section.

Beside the BRACness phenotype mentioned above, disruption or altered expression of other DNA repair pathways have been reported in sporadic human tumours, accounting, at least in part, for the specific drug and radiation sensitivity of these tumours. NER is compromised in testicular cancer which is fairly sensitive to cisplatin[208,209]. Recently, it has been published that patients with completely resected non-small cell lung ERCC1-negative tumours appear to benefit from adjuvant cisplatin-based chemotherapy expressed as longer survival, whereas patients with ERCC1-positive tumour do not. ERCC1 is one of the limiting factors in NER, involved in the removal of platinum-DNA adducts[210]. Finally, MR genes involved in MR (*MLH1, MSH2, MLH3, MSH6, PMS1, PMS2*) are either mutated in the germ-line or inactivated by hyper-methylation of the promoter as a somatic epigenetic phenomenon. The products of these genes are indeed important for the cellular response to different anticancer agents. It has in fact been shown that MR deficiency is associated with resistance to antimetabolites, methylating agents, platinum compounds and some DNA minor groove binders. Considering the high incidence of defects in this pathway in colorectal cancer, the different sensitivity to chemotherapeutic agents may be relevant to the treatment of this neoplasia. Prospective clinical trails will have to assess whether patients with MR deficient tumours would benefit from adjuvant chemotherapy as compared with MR proficient tumours[211].

There is emerging literature focused on the polymorphisms of DNA repair genes that, even if they have a less dramatic functional impact, might also influence the patient's cancer risk and tumour response to therapy[212,213]. Polymorphisms in DNA repair genes have been described to confer suboptimal DNA repair capacity leading to an increase in the cancer predisposition, to influence the natural biology and progression of the tumour and to affect both the toxicity and response to the therapy.

Conclusions

In the last decade much research has been focused on the discovery and development of novel drugs that interact with signal transduction pathways found to be overexpressed or aberrantly regulated in cancer cells. It was anticipated by many authoritative scientists that the new therapeutic approaches would lead to the development of non-toxic drugs that would rapidly make obsolete the standard anticancer treatments based mostly on DNA–directed drugs[214-216]. This prediction was essentially incorrect. There is no question that DNA-damaging agents such as platinum coordination complexes, alkylating agents, topoisomerase I and II and antimetabolites that inhibit DNA synthesis still represent the most effective drugs for a large fraction of human malignancies. This consideration suggests that to use the current available knowledge to increase the selectivity and efficacy of conventional treatments is a potentially useful approach that can realistically lead to significant therapeutic improvements. In this respect, much work is currently in progress to exploit the very recent knowledge on cell cycle checkpoints and on the cell death pathways to potentiate the activity of conventional chemotherapeutics[217-219]. At least in preclinical systems, evidence exists that combining DNA damaging agents with inhibitors of cell cycle checkpoints, or with proapototic compounds, results in a selective antitumour advantage, and clinical studies pursuing this approach are currently in progress. Another approach, overviewed in the present paper, is related to inhibitors of DNA repair to be used in combination anticancer agents or radiotherapy.

As explained in detail within this article, definition of the molecular pathways involved in the repair of the lesions, induced by the anticancer agents commonly used in the clinic, has envisaged the possibility to inhibit such pathways. This approach should certainly improve the efficacy of radiotherapy with relatively low risk of increased toxicity. In addition, in metastatic melanoma, a phase II study combining temozolomide and a PARP inhibitor showed a 18% confirmed CR/PR rate with 40% of patients remaining on treatment for 6 months or more.What appears extremely attractive is the ability to potentiate systemic anticancer treatment of human tumours exhibiting DNA repair defects that can be intelligently exploited, as highlighted in the ongoing clinical studies testing the PARP inhibitors as single agents in BRCA1/2 deficient tumours.

In exploiting this opportunity however, it is worth bearing in mind that this approach, as it was discussed, is still too far away to be specific for the tumour and has two major potential drawbacks: an increased toxicity and an increased tumourigenic risk of the concomitant antitumour treatment. DNA repair inhibitors are unlikely to be toxic by their own, but as they are expected to potentiate cytotoxicity of IR or chemotherapeutic agents, a greater effect on normal proliferating tissues (bone marrow and gastrointestinal tract) is to be seen, as the clinical studies with MGMT inhibitors suggest. This means that greater caution has to be put in the design of clinical investigations that should be driven by appropriate laboratory studies aimed at establishing the most rational dosage-schedules of the combination, the optimisation of the antitumour activity and reduction of the treatment toxicity.

A further anticipated drawback is related to the expected increased tumourigenic risk as the repair process is needed for normal cells to counteract mutagenic lesions of anticancer agents. It has been proved that IR, alkylating agents and topoisomerase II inhibitor treatments induce secondary tumours several years after the initial exposure and this is related to the potentially mutagenic lesions they induced in normal tissues. The addition of an inhibitor of DNA repair is likely to potentiate the mutagenic risk and hence the risk of secondary cancers of such treatments. Until long-term safety follow-ups to prove the safety of such an approach are available, these combinations should be limited to refractory cancers for which no standard therapy exists and not applied for the therapy of potentially curable tumours occurring in children or young adults.

One relevant aspect of medical oncology that cannot be ignored is that most human tumours, at the diagnosis, have multiple genetic aberrations involving the abnormal regulation of many pathways, and the use of relatively unspecific DNA damaging agents seems to be one of the few realistic ways to achieve tumour regressions in an effective way. Nevertheless, the growing knowledge on cell response to DNA damage and DNA repair is providing the rationale for new therapies based on the combination of DNA damaging agents with modulators of cell response including DNA repair inhibitors. We anticipate that this approach cannot be pursued in all cancer patients and using the same regimes, but it should be tailored according to the specific tumour DNA repair pattern. Therefore, as already clearly demonstrated for other target therapies, it seems essential to develop reliable markers and imaging techniques to be used for an appropriate patient's selection and as predictors of response.

References

[1]   K. Ishikawa, H. Ishii and T. Saito, DNA damage-dependent cell cycle checkpoints and genomic stability, *DNA Cell Biol.* 25 (2006), pp. 406–411.

[2]   S. Gasser and D. Raulet, The DNA damage response, immunity and cancer, *Semin. Cancer Biol.* 16 (2006), pp. 344–347.

[3]   L. Tentori and G. Graziani, Chemopotentiation by PARP inhibitors in cancer therapy, *Pharmacol. Res.* 52 (2005), pp. 25–33.

[4]   C.A. Rabik and M.E. Dolan, Molecular mechanisms of resistance and toxicity associated with platinating agents, *Cancer Treat. Rev.* 33 (2007), pp. 9–23.

[5]   T. Lindahl, Instability and decay of the primary structure of DNA, *Nature* 362 (1993), pp. 709–715.

[6]   M. Gellert, J.E. Hesse, K. Hiom, M. Melek, M. Modesti, T.T. Paull, D.A. Ramsden and D.C. van Gent, V(D)J recombination: links to transposition and double-strand break repair, *Cold Spring Harb. Symp. Quant. Biol.* 64 (1999), pp. 161–167.

[7]   M.J. Neale and S. Keeney, Clarifying the mechanics of DNA strand exchange in meiotic recombination, *Nature* 442 (2006), pp. 153–158.

[8]   A.J. Schoeffler and J.M. Berger, Recent advances in understanding structure-function relationships in the type II topoisomerase mechanism, *Biochem. Soc. Trans.* 33 (2005), pp. 1465–1470.

[9]   D. Strumberg, A.A. Pilon, M. Smith, R. Hickey, L. Malkas and Y. Pommier, Conversion of topoisomerase I cleavage complexes on the leading strand of ribosomal DNA into 5'-phosphorylated DNA double-strand breaks by replication runoff, *Mol. Cell. Biol.* 20 (2000), pp. 3977–3987.

[10] C. Arnaudeau, C. Lundin and T. Helleday, DNA double-strand breaks associated with replication forks are predominantly repaired by homologous recombination involving an exchange mechanism in mammalian cells, *J. Mol. Biol.* 307 (2001), pp. 1235–1245.

[11] B. Michel, M.J. Flores, E. Viguera, G. Grompone, M. Seigneur and V. Bidnenko, Rescue of arrested replication forks by homologous recombination, *Proc. Natl. Acad. Sci. U.S.A.* 98 (2001), pp. 8181–8188.

[12] M. O'Driscoll and P.A. Jeggo, The role of double-strand break repair—insights from human genetics, *Nat. Rev. Genet.* 7 (2006), pp. 45–54.

[13] E. Weterings and D.C. van Gent, The mechanism of non-homologous end joining: a synopsis of synapsis, *DNA Repair (Amst.)* 3 (2004), pp. 1425–1435.

[14] D. van Heemst, L. Brugmans, N.S. Verkaik and D.C. van Gent, End joining of blunt DNA double-strand breaks in mammalian fibroblasts is precise and requires DNA-PK and XRCC4, *DNA Repair (Amst.)* 3 (2004), pp. 43–50.

[15] J.R. Walker, R.A. Corpina and J. Goldberg, Structure of the Ku heterodimer bound to DNA and its implications for double-strand break repair, *Nature* 412 (2001), pp. 607–614.

[16] Q. Ding, Y.V. Reddy, W. Wang, T. Woods, P. Douglas, D.A. Ramsden, S.P. Lees-Miller and K. Meek, Autophosphorylation of the catalytic subunit of the DNA-dependent protein kinase is required for efficient end processing during DNA double-strand break repair, *Mol. Cell. Biol.* 23 (2003), pp. 5836–5848.

[17] Y.V. Reddy, Q. Ding, S.P. Lees-Miller, K. Meek and D.A. Ramsden, Non-homologous end joining requires that the DNA-PK complex undergo an autophosphorylation-dependent rearrangement at DNA ends, *J. Biol. Chem.* 279 (2004), pp. 39408–39413.

[18] E. Weterings, N.S. Verkaik, H.T. Bruggenwirth, J.H. Hoeijmakers and D.C. van Gent, The role of DNA dependent protein kinase in synapsis of DNA ends, *Nucleic Acids Res.* 31 (2003), pp. 7238–7246.

[19] S.A. Nick McElhinny, C.M. Snowden, J. McCarville and D.A. Ramsden, Ku recruits the XRCC4-ligase IV complex to DNA ends, *Mol. Cell. Biol.* 20 (2000), pp. 2996–3003.

[20] P. Ahnesorg, P. Smith and S.P. Jackson, XLF interacts with the XRCC4-DNA ligase IV complex to promote DNA non-homologous end joining, *Cell* 124 (2006), pp. 301–313.

[21] D. Buck, L. Malivert, R. de Chasseval, A. Barraud, M.C. Fondaneche, O. Sanal, A. Plebani, J.L. Stephan, M. Hufnagel, F. le Deist, A. Fischer, A. Durandy, J.P. de Villartay and P. Revy, Cernunnos, a novel non-homologous end joining factor, is mutated in human immunodeficiency with microcephaly, *Cell* 124 (2006), pp. 287–299.

[22] P.O. Mari, B.I. Florea, S.P. Persengiev, N.S. Verkaik, H.T. Brüggenwirth, M. Modesti, G. Giglia-Mari, K. Bezstarosti, J.A.A. Demmers, T.M. Luider, A.B. Houtsmuller and D.C. van Gent, Dynamic assembly of end joining complexes requires interaction between Ku70/80 and XRCC4, *Proc. Natl. Acad. Sci. U.S.A.* 103 (2006), pp. 18597–18602.

[23] F. Moreno-Herrero, M. de Jager, N.H. Dekker, R. Kanaar, C. Wyman and C. Dekker, Mesoscale conformational changes in the DNA-repair complex Rad50/Mre11/Nbs1 upon binding DNA, *Nature* 437 (2005), pp. 440–443.

[24] K.P. Hopfner, L. Craig, G. Moncalian, R.A. Zinkel, T. Usui, B.A. Owen, A. Karcher, B. Henderson, J.L. Bodmer, C.T. McMurray, J.P. Carney, J.H. Petrini and J.A. Tainer, The Rad50 zinc-hook is a structure joining Mre11 complexes in DNA recombination and repair, *Nature* 418 (2002), pp. 562–566.

[25] M. de Jager, J. van Noort, D.C. van Gent, C. Dekker, R. Kanaar and C. Wyman, Human Rad50/Mre11 is a flexible complex that can tether DNA ends, *Mol. Cell* 8 (2001), pp. 1129–1135.

[26] C. Chappell, L.A. Hanakahi, F. Karimi-Busheri, M. Weinfeld and S.C. West, Involvement of human polynucleotide kinase in double-strand break repair by non-homologous end joining, *EMBO J.* 21 (2002), pp. 2827–2832.

[27] C.A. Koch, R. Agyei, S. Galicia, P. Metalnikov, P. O'Donnell, A. Starostine, M. Weinfeld and D. Durocher, Xrcc4 physically links DNA end processing by

polynucleotide kinase to DNA ligation by DNA ligase IV, *EMBO J.* 23 (2004), pp. 3874–3885.

[28] Y. Ma, U. Pannicke, K. Schwarz and M.R. Lieber, Hairpin opening and overhang processing by an Artemis/DNA-dependent protein kinase complex in non-homologous end joining and V(D)J recombination, *Cell* 108 (2002), pp. 781–794.

[29] D. Moshous, I. Callebaut, R. de Chasseval, B. Corneo, M. Cavazzana-Calvo, F. Le Deist, I. Tezcan, O. Sanal, Y. Bertrand, N. Philippe, A. Fischer, J.P. de and Villartay, Artemis, a novel DNA double-strand break repair/V(D)J recombination protein, is mutated in human severe combined immune deficiency, *Cell* 105 (2001), pp. 177–186.

[30] J.J. Perry, S.M. Yannone, L.G. Holden, C. Hitomi, A. Asaithamby, S. Han, P.K. Cooper, D.J. Chen and J.A. Tainer, WRN exonuclease structure and molecular mechanism imply an editing role in DNA end processing, *Nat. Struct. Mol. Biol.* 13 (2006), pp. 414–422.

[31] S.A. Nick McElhinny, J.M. Havener, M. Garcia-Diaz, R. Juarez, K. Bebenek, B.L. Kee, L. Blanco, T.A. Kunkel and D.A. Ramsden, A gradient of template dependence defines distinct biological roles for family × polymerases in non-homologous end joining, *Mol. Cell* 19 (2005), pp. 357–366.

[32] E. Riballo, M. Kuhne, N. Rief, A. Doherty, G.C. Smith, M.J. Recio, C. Reis, K. Dahm, A. Fricke, A. Krempler, A.R. Parker, S.P. Jackson, A. Gennery, P.A. Jeggo and M. Lobrich, A pathway of double-strand break rejoining dependent upon ATM, Artemis, and proteins locating to gamma-H2AX foci, *Mol. Cell* 16 (2004), pp. 715–724.

[33] T.T. Paull and M. Gellert, The 3′ to 5′ exonuclease activity of Mre 11 facilitates repair of DNA double-strand breaks, *Mol. Cell* 1 (1998), pp. 969–979.

[34] J.W. Szostak, T.L. Orr-Weaver, R.J. Rothstein and F.W. Stahl, The double-strand-break repair model for recombination, *Cell* 33 (1983), pp. 25–35.

[35] C. Richardson, M.E. Moynahan and M. Jasin, Double-strand break repair by interchromosomal recombination: suppression of chromosomal translocations, *Genes Dev.* 12 (1998), pp. 3831–3842.

[36] R. Holliday, A mechanism for gene conversion in fungi, *Genet. Res.* 5 (1964), pp. 282–304.

[37] R.D. Johnson and M. Jasin, Sister chromatid gene conversion is a prominent double-strand break repair pathway in mammalian cells, *EMBO J.* 19 (2000), pp. 3398–3407.

[38] N. Saleh-Gohari, H.E. Bryant, N. Schultz, K.M. Parker, T.N. Cassel and T. Helleday, Spontaneous homologous recombination is induced by collapsed replication forks that are caused by endogenous DNA single-strand breaks, *Mol. Cell. Biol.* 25 (2005), pp. 7158–7169.

[39] V.S. Jonnalagadda, T. Matsuguchi and B.P. Engelward, Interstrand crosslink-induced homologous recombination carries an increased risk of deletions and insertions, *DNA Repair (Amst.)* 4 (2005), pp. 594–605.

[40] B. Elliott, C. Richardson, J. Winderbaum, J.A. Nickoloff and M. Jasin, Gene conversion tracts from double-strand break repair in mammalian cells, *Mol. Cell. Biol.* 18 (1998), pp. 93–101.

[41] R.M. Liskay and J.L. Stachelek, Evidence for intrachromosomal gene conversion in cultured mouse cells, *Cell* 35 (1983), pp. 157–165.

[42] Z. Shen, K.G. Cloud, D.J. Chen and M.S. Park, Specific interactions between the human RAD51 and RAD52 proteins, *J. Biol. Chem.* 271 (1996), pp. 148–152.

[43] P. Baumann, F.E. Benson and S.C. West, Human Rad51 protein promotes ATP-dependent homologous pairing and strand transfer reactions in vitro, *Cell* 87 (1996), pp. 757–766.

[44] G. Petukhova, S. Stratton and P. Sung, Catalysis of homologous DNA pairing by yeast Rad51 and Rad54 proteins, *Nature* 393 (1998), pp. 91–94.

[45] S. Sigurdsson, S. Van Komen, W. Bussen, D. Schild, J.S. Albala and P. Sung, Mediator function of the human Rad51B-Rad51C complex in Rad51/RPA-catalyzed DNA strand exchange, *Genes Dev.* 15 (2001), pp. 3308–3318.

[46] J.Y. Masson, M.C. Tarsounas, A.Z. Stasiak, A. Stasiak, R. Shah, M.J. McIlwraith, F.E. Benson and S.C. West, Identification and purification of two distinct complexes containing the five RAD51 paralogs, *Genes Dev.* 15 (2001), pp. 3296–3307.

[47] T. Sugiyama and S.C. Kowalczykowski, Rad52 protein associates with replication protein A (RPA)-single-stranded DNA to accelerate Rad51-mediated displacement of RPA and presynaptic complex formation, *J. Biol. Chem.* 277 (2002), pp. 31663–31672.

[48] J. Essers, R.W. Hendriks, J. Wesoly, C.E. Beerens, B. Smit, J.H. Hoeijmakers, C. Wyman, M.L. Dronkert and R. Kanaar, Analysis of mouse Rad54 expression and its implications for homologous recombination, *DNA Repair (Amst.)* 1 (2002), pp. 779–793.

[49] E. Sonoda, M.S. Sasaki, J.M. Buerstedde, O. Bezzubova, A. Shinohara, H. Ogawa, M. Takata, Y. Yamaguchi-Iwai and S. Takeda, Rad51-deficient vertebrate cells accumulate chromosomal breaks prior to cell death, *EMBO J.* 17 (1998), pp. 598–608.

[50] D.S. Lim and P. Hasty, A mutation in mouse rad51 results in an early embryonic lethal that is suppressed by a mutation in p53, *Mol. Cell. Biol.* 16 (1996), pp. 7133–7143.

[51] T. Tsuzuki, Y. Fujii, K. Sakumi, Y. Tominaga, K. Nakao, M. Sekiguchi, A. Matsushiro, Y. Yoshimura and T. Morita, Targeted disruption of the Rad51 gene leads to lethality in embryonic mice, *Proc. Natl. Acad. Sci. U.S.A.* 93 (1996), pp. 6236–6240.

[52] M.J. McIlwraith, A. Vaisman, Y. Liu, E. Fanning, R. Woodgate and S.C.. West, Human DNA polymerase eta promotes DNA synthesis from strand invasion intermediates of homologous recombination, *Mol. Cell* 20 (2005), pp. 783–792.

[53] T. Kawamoto, K. Araki, E. Sonoda, Y.M. Yamashita, K. Harada, K. Kikuchi, C. Masutani, F. Hanaoka, K. Nozaki, N. Hashimoto and S. Takeda, Dual roles for DNA polymerase eta in homologous DNA recombination and translesion DNA synthesis, *Mol. Cell* 20 (2005), pp. 793–799.

[54] S. Lee, L. Cavallo and J. Griffith, Human p53 binds Holliday junctions strongly and facilitates their cleavage, *J. Biol. Chem.* 272 (1997), pp. 7532–7539.

[55] P. Mohaghegh, J.K. Karow, R.M. Brosh Jr., V.A. Bohr and I.D. Hickson, The Bloom's and Werner's syndrome proteins are DNA structure-specific helicases, *Nucleic Acids Res.* 29 (2001), pp. 2843–2849.

[56] D. Subramanian and J.D. Griffith, Interactions between p53, hMSH2-hMSH6 and HMG I(Y) on Holliday Junctions and bulged bases, *Nucleic Acids Res.* 30 (2002), pp. 2427–2434.

[57] D.V. Bugreev, O.M. Mazina and A.V. Mazin, Rad54 protein promotes branch migration of Holliday Junctions, *Nature* 442 (2006), pp. 590–593.

[58] S. Raynard, W. Bussen and P. Sung, A double Holliday Junction dissolvasome comprising BLM, topoisomerase IIIalpha, and BLAP75, *J. Biol. Chem.* 281 (2006), pp. 13861–13864.

[59] A. Constantinou, M. Tarsounas, J.K. Karow, R.M. Brosh, V.A. Bohr, I.D. Hickson and S.C. West, Werner's syndrome protein (WRN) migrates Holliday Junctions and co-localizes with RPA upon replication arrest, *EMBO Rep.* 1 (2000), pp. 80–84.

[60] J.K. Karow, A. Constantinou, J.L. Li, S.C. West and I.D. Hickson, The Bloom's syndrome gene product promotes branch migration of Holliday Junctions, *Proc. Natl. Acad. Sci. U.S.A.* 97 (2000), pp. 6504–6508.

[61] E. Van Dyck, A.Z. Stasiak, A. Stasiak and S.C. West, Visualization of recombination intermediates produced by RAD52-mediated single-strand annealing, *EMBO Rep.* 2 (2001), pp. 905–909.

[62] J.H. New, T. Sugiyama, E. Zaitseva and S.C. Kowalczykowski, Rad52 protein stimulates DNA strand exchange by Rad51 and replication protein A, *Nature* 391 (1998), pp. 407–410.

[63] P. Oberosler, P. Hloch, U. Ramsperger and H. Stahl, p53-catalyzed annealing of complementary single-stranded nucleic acids, *EMBO J.* 12 (1993), pp. 2389–2396.

[64] G.M. Adair, R.L. Rolig, D. Moore-Faver, M. Zabelshansky, J.H. Wilson and R.S. Nairn, Role of ERCC1 in removal of long non-homologous tails during targeted homologous recombination, *EMBO J.* 19 (2000), pp. 5552–5561.

[65] L.J. Niedernhofer, H. Odijk, M. Budzowska, E. van Drunen, A. Maas, A.F. Theil, J. de Wit, N.G. Jaspers, H.B. Beverloo, J.H. Hoeijmakers and R. Kanaar, The structure-specific endonuclease Ercc1-Xpf is required to resolve DNA interstrand cross-link-induced double-strand breaks, *Mol. Cell. Biol.* 24 (2004), pp. 5776–5787.

[66] D.P. Batty and R.D. Wood, Damage recognition in nucleotide excision repair of DNA, *Gene* 241 (2000), pp. 193–204.

[67] L. Wu and I.D. Hickson, The Bloom's syndrome helicase suppresses crossing over during homologous recombination, *Nature* 426 (2003), pp. 870–874.

[68] R.G. Shao, C.X. Cao, H. Zhang, K.W. Kohn, M.S. Wold and Y. Pommier, Replication-mediated DNA damage by camptothecin induces phosphorylation of RPA by DNA-dependent protein kinase and dissociates RPA:DNA-PK complexes, *EMBO J.* 18 (1999), pp. 1397–1406.

[69] A.A. Morley, S.A. Grist, D.R. Turner, A. Kutlaca and G. Bennett, Molecular nature of in vivo mutations in human cells at the autosomal HLA-A locus, *Cancer Res.* 50 (1990), pp. 4584–4587.

[70] X. Zhu, J.M. Dunn, A.D. Goddard, J.A. Squire, A. Becker, R.A. Phillips and B.L. Gallie, Mechanisms of loss of heterozygosity in retinoblastoma, *Cytogenet. Cell. Genet.* 59 (1992), pp. 248–252.

[71] P.K. Gupta, A. Sahota, S.A. Boyadjiev, S. Bye, C. Shao, J.P. O'Neill, T.C. Hunter, R.J. Albertini, P.J. Stambrook and J.A. Tischfield, High frequency in vivo loss of heterozygosity is primarily a consequence of mitotic recombination, *Cancer Res.* 57 (1997), pp. 1188–1193.

[72] F. Prado and A. Aguilera, Role of reciprocal exchange, one-ended invasion crossover and single-strand annealing on inverted and direct repeat recombination in yeast: different requirements for the RAD1, RAD10, and RAD52 genes, *Genetics* 139 (1995), pp. 109–123.

[73] J.E. Haber, Transpositions and translocations induced by site-specific double-strand breaks in budding yeast, *DNA Repair (Amst.)* 5 (2006), pp. 998–1009.

[74] S.J. Gould, The exaptive excellence of spandrels as a term and prototype, *Proc. Natl. Acad. Sci. U.S.A.* 94 (1997), pp. 10750–10755.

[75] M.A. Batzer and P.L. Deininger, Alu repeats and human genomic diversity, *Nat. Rev. Genet.* 3 (2002), pp. 370–379.

[76] C.W. Schmid, Alu: structure, origin, evolution, significance and function of one-tenth of human DNA, *Prog. Nucleic Acid Res. Mol. Biol.* 53 (1996), pp. 283–319.

[77] A.F. Smit, The origin of interspersed repeats in the human genome, *Curr. Opin. Genet. Dev.* 6 (1996), pp. 743–748.

[78] B. Elliott, C. Richardson and M. Jasin, Chromosomal translocation mechanisms at intronic alu elements in mammalian cells, *Mol. Cell* 17 (2005), pp. 885–894.

[79] J.E. Haber, Lucky breaks: analysis of recombination in *Saccharomyces*, *Mutat. Res.* 451 (2000), pp. 53–69.

[80] E. Kraus, W.Y. Leung and J.E. Haber, Break-induced replication: a review and an example in budding yeast, *Proc. Natl. Acad. Sci. U.S.A.* 98 (2001), pp. 8255–8262.

[81] C. Richardson and M. Jasin, Frequent chromosomal translocations induced by DNA double-strand breaks, *Nature* 405 (2000), pp. 697–700.

[82] K.W. Caldecott, J.D. Tucker and L.H. Thompson, Construction of human XRCC1 minigenes that fully correct the CHO DNA repair mutant EM9, *Nucleic Acids Res.* 20 (1992), pp. 4575–4579.

[83] Z.Q. Wang, L. Stingl, C. Morrison, M. Jantsch, M. Los, K. Schulze-Osthoff and E.F. Wagner, PARP is important for genomic stability but dispensable in apoptosis, *Genes Dev.* 11 (1997), pp. 2347–2358.

[84] C.M. Simbulan-Rosenthal, B.R. Haddad, D.S. Rosenthal, Z. Weaver, A. Coleman, R. Luo, H.M. Young, Z.Q. Wang, T. Ried and M.E. Smulson, Chromosomal aberrations in PARP(−/−) mice: genome stabilization in immortalized cells by reintroduction of poly(ADP-ribose) polymerase cDNA, *Proc. Natl. Acad. Sci. U.S.A.* 96 (1999), pp. 13191–13196.

[85] J.M. de Murcia, C. Niedergang, C. Trucco, M. Ricoul, B. Dutrillaux, M. Mark, F.J. Oliver, M. Masson, A. Dierich, M. LeMeur, C. Walztinger, P. Chambon and G. de Murcia, Requirement of poly(ADP-ribose) polymerase in recovery from DNA damage in mice and in cells, *Proc. Natl. Acad. Sci. U.S.A.* 94 (1997), pp. 7303–7307.

[86] R.G. Sargent, M.A. Brenneman and J.H. Wilson, Repair of site-specific double-strand breaks in a mammalian chromosome by homologous and illegitimate recombination, *Mol. Cell. Biol.* 17 (1997), pp. 267–277.

[87] M.M. Cox, M.F. Goodman, K.N. Kreuzer, D.J. Sherratt, S.J. Sandler and K.J. Marians, The importance of repairing stalled replication forks, *Nature* 404 (2000), pp. 37–41.

[88] C. Lundin, N. Schultz, C. Arnaudeau, A. Mohindra, L.T. Hansen and T. Helleday, RAD51 is involved in repair of damage associated with DNA replication in mammalian cells, *J. Mol. Biol.* 328 (2003), pp. 521–535.

[89] H.E. Bryant, N. Schultz, H.D. Thomas, K.M. Parker, D. Flower, E. Lopez, S. Kyle, M. Meuth, N.J. Curtin and T. Helleday, Specific killing of BRCA2-deficient tumours with inhibitors of poly(ADP-ribose)polymerase, *Nature* 434 (2005), pp. 913–917.

[90] L.H. Thompson, K.W. Brookman, L.E. Dillehay, A.V. Carrano, J.A. Mazrimas, C.L. Mooney and J.L. Minkler, A CHO-cell strain having hypersensitivity to mutagens, a defect in DNA strand-break repair, and an extraordinary baseline frequency of sister-chromatid exchange, *Mutat. Res.* 95 (1982), pp. 427–440.

[91] V. Schreiber, D. Hunting, C. Trucco, B. Gowans, D. Grunwald, G. De Murcia and J.M. De Murcia, A dominant-negative mutant of human poly(ADP-ribose) polymerase affects cell recovery, apoptosis, and sister chromatid exchange following DNA damage, *Proc. Natl. Acad. Sci. U.S.A.* 92 (1995), pp. 4753–4757.

[92] N. Schultz, E. Lopez, N. Saleh-Gohari and T. Helleday, Poly(ADP-ribose) polymerase (PARP-1) has a controlling role in homologous recombination, *Nucleic Acids Res.* 31 (2003), pp. 4959–4964.

[93] J.M. Stark and M. Jasin, Extensive loss of heterozygosity is suppressed during homologous repair of chromosomal breaks, *Mol. Cell. Biol.* 23 (2003), pp. 733–743.

[94] K. Rothkamm, I. Kruger, L.H. Thompson and M. Lobrich, Pathways of DNA double-strand break repair during the mammalian cell cycle, *Mol. Cell. Biol.* 23 (2003), pp. 5706–5715.

[95] G. Ira, A. Pellicioli, A. Balijja, X. Wang, S. Fiorani, W. Carotenuto, G. Liberi, D. Bressan, L. Wan, N.M. Hollingsworth, J.E. Haber and M. Foiani, DNA end resection, homologous recombination and DNA damage checkpoint activation require CDK1, *Nature* 431 (2004), pp. 1011–1017.

[96] Y. Aylon, B. Liefshitz and M. Kupiec, The CDK regulates repair of double-strand breaks by homologous recombination during the cell cycle, *EMBO J.* 23 (2004), pp. 4868–4875.

[97] J.S. Kim, T.B. Krasieva, H. Kurumizaka, D.J. Chen, A.M. Taylor and K. Yokomori, Independent and sequential recruitment of NHEJ and HR factors to DNA damage sites in mammalian cells, *J. Cell. Biol.* 170 (2005), pp. 341–347.

[98] D. Ristic, M. Modesti, R. Kanaar and C. Wyman, Rad52 and Ku bind to different DNA structures produced early in double-strand break repair, *Nucleic Acids Res.* 31 (2003), pp. 5229–5237.

[99] J.M. Larner, H. Lee and J.L. Hamlin, Radiation effects on DNA synthesis in a defined chromosomal replicon, *Mol. Cell. Biol.* 14 (1994), pp. 1901–1908.

[100] J. Falck, N. Mailand, R.G. Syljuasen, J. Bartek and J. Lukas, The ATM-Chk2-Cdc25A checkpoint pathway guards against radioresistant DNA synthesis, *Nature* 410 (2001), pp. 842–847.

[101] T. Uziel, Y. Lerenthal, L. Moyal, Y. Andegeko, L. Mittelman and Y. Shiloh, Requirement of the MRN complex for ATM activation by DNA damage, *EMBO J.* 22 (2003), pp. 5612–5621.

[102] G.P. Holmquist, Endogenous lesions, S-phase-independent spontaneous mutations, and evolutionary strategies for base excision repair, *Mutat. Res.* 400 (1998), pp. 59–68.

[103] W.F. Morgan and P.E. Crossen, The incidence of sister chromatid exchanges in cultured human lymphocytes, *Mutat. Res.* 42 (1977), pp. 305–311.

[104] D.M. Wiktor-Brown, C.A. Hendricks, W. Olipitz and B.P. Engelward, Age-dependent accumulation of recombinant cells in the mouse pancreas revealed by in situ fluorescence imaging, *Proc. Natl. Acad. Sci. U.S.A.* 103 (2006), pp. 11862–11867.

[105] E. Petermann and K.W. Caldecott, Evidence that the ATR/Chk1 pathway maintains normal replication fork progression during unperturbed S phase, *Cell Cycle* 5 (2006), pp. 2203–2209.

[106] E. Petermann, A. Maya-Mendoza, G. Zachos, D.A. Gillespie, D.A. Jackson and K.W. Caldecott, Chk1 requirement for high global rates of replication fork progression during normal vertebrate S phase, *Mol. Cell. Biol.* 26 (2006), pp. 3319–3326.

[107] R.G. Syljuåsen, C.S. Sørensen, L.T. Hansen, K. Fugger, C. Lundin, F. Johansson, T. Helleday, M. Sehested, J. Lukas and J. Bartek, Inhibition of human Chk1 causes increased initiation of DNA replication, phosphorylation of ATR targets, and DNA breakage, *Mol. Cell. Biol.* 25 (2005), pp. 3553–3562.

[108] V. Costanzo, K. Robertson, M. Bibikova, E. Kim, D. Grieco, M. Gottesman, D. Carroll and J. Gautier, Mre11 protein complex prevents double-strand break accumulation during chromosomal DNA replication, *Mol. Cell* 8 (2001), pp. 137–147.

[109] D. Shechter, V. Costanzo and J. Gautier, ATR and ATM regulate the timing of DNA replication origin firing, *Nat. Cell. Biol.* 6 (2004), pp. 648–655.

[110] C.J. Merrick, D. Jackson and J.F. Diffley, Visualization of altered replication dynamics after DNA damage in human cells, *J. Biol. Chem.* 279 (2004), pp. 20067–20075.

[111] B.P. Engelward, J.M. Allan, A.J. Dreslin, J.D. Kelly, M.M. Wu, B. Gold and L.D. Samson, A chemical and genetic approach together define the biological consequences of 3-methyladenine lesions in the mammalian genome, *J. Biol. Chem.* 273 (1998), pp. 5412–5418.

[112] K. Larson, J. Sahm, R. Shenkar and B. Strauss, Methylation-induced blocks to in vitro DNA replication, *Mutat. Res.* 150 (1985), pp. 77–84.

[113] Y. Zhang and J.D. Rowley, Chromatin structural elements and chromosomal translocations in leukemia, *DNA Repair (Amst.)* 5 (2006), pp. 1282–1297.

[114] G.C. Li, H. Ouyang, X. Li, H. Nagasawa, J.B. Little, D.J. Chen, C.C. Ling, Z. Fuks and C. Cordon-Cardo, Ku70: a candidate tumor suppressor gene for murine T cell lymphoma, *Mol. Cell* 2 (1998), pp. 1–8.

[115] D.C. van Gent, J.H. Hoeijmakers and R. Kanaar, Chromosomal stability and the DNA double-stranded break connection, *Nat. Rev. Genet.* 2 (2001), pp. 196–206.

[116] N.E. Sharpless, D.O. Ferguson, R.C. O'Hagan, D.H. Castrillon, C. Lee, P.A. Farazi, S. Alson, J. Fleming, C.C. Morton, K. Frank, L. Chin, F.W. Alt and R.A. DePinho, Impaired non-homologous end joining provokes soft tissue sarcomas harboring chromosomal translocations, amplifications, and deletions, *Mol. Cell* 8 (2001), pp. 1187–1196.

[117] D. Moshous, C. Pannetier, R. Chasseval Rd, F. Deist Fl, M. Cavazzana-Calvo, S. Romana, E. Macintyre, D. Canioni, N. Brousse, A. Fischer, J.L. Casanova and J.P.

Villartay, Partial T and B lymphocyte immunodeficiency and predisposition to lymphoma in patients with hypomorphic mutations in Artemis, *J. Clin. Invest.* 111 (2003), pp. 381–387.

[118] L.H. Thompson and D. Schild, Recombinational DNA repair and human disease, *Mutat. Res.* 509 (2002), pp. 49–78.

[119] D. Gebow, N. Miselis and H.L. Liber, Homologous and non-homologous recombination resulting in deletion: effects of p53 status, microhomology, and repetitive DNA length and orientation, *Mol. Cell. Biol.* 20 (2000), pp. 4028–4035.

[120] M.E. Moynahan, J.W. Chiu, B.H. Koller and M. Jasin, Brca1 controls homology-directed DNA repair, *Mol. Cell* 4 (1999), pp. 511–518.

[121] E. Bolderson, J. Scorah, T. Helleday, C. Smythe and M. Meuth, ATM is required for the cellular response to thymidine induced replication fork stress, *Hum. Mol. Genet.* 31 (2004), pp. 2937–2945.

[122] A.D. D'Andrea and M. Grompe, The Fanconi anaemia/BRCA pathway, *Nat. Rev. Cancer* 3 (2003), pp. 23–34.

[123] A.A. Davies, J.Y. Masson, M.J. McIlwraith, A.Z. Stasiak, A. Stasiak, A.R. Venkitaraman and S.C. West, Role of BRCA2 in control of the RAD51 recombination and DNA repair protein, *Mol. Cell* 7 (2001), pp. 273–282.

[124] K.J. Patel, V.P. Yu, H. Lee, A. Corcoran, F.C. Thistlethwaite, M.J. Evans, W.H. Colledge, L.S. Friedman, B.A. Ponder and A.R. Venkitaraman, Involvement of Brca2 in DNA repair, *Mol. Cell* 1 (1998), pp. 347–357.

[125] R.S. Chaganti, S. Schonberg and J. German, A manyfold increase in sister chromatid exchanges in Bloom's syndrome lymphocytes, *Proc. Natl. Acad. Sci. U.S.A.* 71 (1974), pp. 4508–4512.

[126] G. Luo, I.M. Santoro, L.D. McDaniel, I. Nishijima, M. Mills, H. Youssoufian, H. Vogel, R.A. Schultz and A. Bradley, Cancer predisposition caused by elevated mitotic recombination in Bloom mice, *Nat. Genet.* 26 (2000), pp. 424–429.

[127] Y. Saintigny, K. Makienko, C. Swanson, M.J. Emond and R.J. Monnat Jr., Homologous recombination resolution defect in werner syndrome, *Mol. Cell. Biol.* 22 (2002), pp. 6971–6978.

[128] M. Lebel, Increased frequency of DNA deletions in pink-eyed unstable mice carrying a mutation in the Werner syndrome gene homologue, *Carcinogenesis* 23 (2002), pp. 213–216.

[129] N. Saleh-Gohari and T. Helleday, Strand invasion involving short tract gene conversion is specifically suppressed in BRCA2-deficient hamster cells, *Oncogene* 23 (2004), pp. 9136–9141.

[130] M. Tarsounas, D. Davies and S.C. West, BRCA2-dependent and independent formation of RAD51 nuclear foci, *Oncogene* 22 (2003), pp. 1115–1123.

[131] N. Bardeesy, N.E. Sharpless, R.A. DePinho and G. Merlino, The genetics of pancreatic adenocarcinoma: a roadmap for a mouse model, *Semin. Cancer Biol.* 11 (2001), pp. 201–218.

[132] S.L. Gerson, MGMT: its role in cancer aetiology and cancer therapeutics, *Nat. Rev. Cancer* 4 (2004), pp. 296–307.

[133] A. Sabharwal and M.R. Middleton, Exploiting the role of O6-methylguanine-DNA-methyltransferase (MGMT) in cancer therapy, *Curr. Opin. Pharmacol.* 6 (2006), pp. 355–363.

[134] K.K. Chan, Q.M. Zhang and G.L. Dianov, Base excision repair fidelity in normal and cancer cells, *Mutagenesis* 21 (2006), pp. 173–178.

[135] P.C. Hanawalt, Subpathways of nucleotide excision repair and their regulation, *Oncogene* 21 (2002), pp. 8949–8956.

[136] G. Damia, S. Silvestri and L. Carrassa *et al.*, Unique pattern of ET-743 activity in different celluar systems with defined deficiencies in DNA-repair pathways, *Int. J. Cancer* 92 (2001), pp. 583–588.

[137] E. Erba, E. Cavallaro and G. Damia *et al.*, The unique biological features of the marine product Yondelis (ET-743, trabectedin) are shared by its analog ET-637, which lacks the C ring, *Oncol. Res.* 14 (2004), pp. 579–587.

[138] Y. Takebayashi, P. Pourquier and D.B. Zimonjic *et al.*, Antiproliferative activity of eceteinascidin 743 is dependent upon transcription-coupled nucleotide excision repair, *Nat. Med.* 7 (2001), pp. 961–966.

[139] Tavcchio M, Natoli C, Ubezio P, Erba E, D'Incalci M. Dynamics of cell cycle phase perturbations by Trabectedin (ET-743) in NER deficient and proficient cells, untravelled by a novel mathematical simulation approach. *Cell Prolif* 2007, in press.

[140] J. Jiricny, The multifaceted mismatch-repair system, *Nat. Rev. Mol. Cell Biol.* 7 (2006), pp. 335–346.

[141] T. Taniguchi and A.D. D'Andrea, Molecular pathogenesis of Fanconi anemia: recent progress, *Blood* 107 (2006), pp. 4223–4233.

[142] J. Ding, Z.H. Miao, L.H. Meng and M.Y. Geng, Emerging cancer therapeutic opportunities target DNA-repair systems, *Trends Pharmacol Sci.* 27 (2006), pp. 338–344.

[143] S. Madhusudan and I.D. Hickson, DNA repair inhibition: a selective tumour targeting strategy, *Trends Mol. Med.* 11 (2005), pp. 503–511.

[144] A.E. Pegg, Mammalian O6-alkylguanine-DNA alkyltransferase: regulation and importance in response to alkylating carcinogenic and therapeutic agents, *Cancer Res* 50 (1990), pp. 6119–6129.

[145] D.A. Scudiero, S.A. Meyer, B.E. Clatterbuck, M.R. Mattern, C.H. Ziolkowski and R.S. Day 3rd., Sensitivity of human cell strains having different abilities to repair O6-methylguanine in DNA to inactivation by alkylating agents including chloroethylnitrosoureas, *Cancer Res.* 44 (1984), pp. 2467–2474.

[146] M. D'Incalci, P. Taverna and E. Erba *et al.*, O6-methylguanine and temozolomide can reverse the resistance to chloroethylnitrosoureas of a mouse L1210 leukemia, *Anticancer Res.* 11 (1991), pp. 115–121.

[147] C.V. Catapano, M. Broggini and E. Erba *et al.*, In vitro and in vivo methazolastone-induced DNA damage and repair in L-1210 leukemia sensitive and resistant to chloroethylnitrosoureas, *Cancer Res.* 47 (1987), pp. 4884–4889.

[148] K.A. Jaeckle, H.J. Eyre and J.J. Townsend *et al.*, Correlation of tumor O6 methylguanine-DNA methyltransferase levels with survival of malignant astrocytoma

patients treated with bis-chloroethylnitrosourea: a Southwest Oncology Group study, *J. Clin. Oncol.* 16 (1998), pp. 3310–3315.

[149] H.S. Friedman, R.E. McLendon and T. Kerby *et al.*, DNA mismatch repair and O6-alkylguanine-DNA alkyltransferase analysis and response to Temodal in newly diagnosed malignant glioma, *J. Clin. Oncol.* 16 (1998), pp. 3851–3857.

[150] M.E. Hegi, A.C. Diserens and T. Gorlia *et al.*, MGMT gene silencing and benefit from temozolomide in glioblastoma, *N Engl. J. Med.* 352 (2005), pp. 997–1003.

[151] M. Esteller, J. Garcia-Foncillas and E. Andion *et al.*, Inactivation of the DNA-repair gene MGMT and the clinical response of gliomas to alkylating agents, *N. Engl. J. Med* 343 (2000), pp. 1350–1354.

[152] N. Levin, I. Lavon and B. Zelikovitsh *et al.*, Progressive low-grade oligodendrogliomas: response to temozolomide and correlation between genetic profile and O6-methylguanine DNA methyltransferase protein expression, *Cancer* 106 (2006), pp. 1759–1765.

[153] A.M. Donson, S.O. Addo-Yobo, M.H. Handler, L. Gore and N.K. Foreman, MGMT promoter methylation correlates with survival benefit and sensitivity to temozolomide in pediatric glioblastoma, *Pediatr Blood Cancer* 48 (2007), pp. 403–407.

[154] I.F. Pollack, R.L. Hamilton and R.W. Sobol *et al.*, O6-methylguanine-DNA methyltransferase expression strongly correlates with outcome in childhood malignant gliomas: results from the CCG-945 Cohort, *J. Clin. Oncol.* 24 (2006), pp. 3431–3437.

[155] M. Esteller, G. Gaidano and S.N. Goodman *et al.*, Hypermethylation of the DNA repair gene O(6)-methylguanine DNA methyltransferase and survival of patients with diffuse large B-cell lymphoma, *J. Natl. Cancer Inst.* 94 (2002), pp. 26–32.

[156] M. Esteller and J.G. Herman, Generating mutations but providing chemosensitivity: the role of O6-methylguanine DNA methyltransferase in human cancer, *Oncogene* 23 (2004), pp. 1–8.

[157] C.C. Kuo, J.F. Liu and J.Y. Chang, DNA repair enzyme, O6-methylguanine DNA methyltransferase, modulates cytotoxicity of camptothecin-derived topoisomerase I inhibitors, *J. Pharmacol Exp. Ther.* 316 (2006), pp. 946–954.

[158] M. Gander, S. Leyvraz and L. Decosterd *et al.*, Sequential administration of temozolomide and fotemustine: depletion of O6-alkyl guanine-DNA transferase in blood lymphocytes and in tumours, *Ann. Oncol* 10 (1999), pp. 831–838.

[159] M. Clemons, M. Ranson and J.M. Margison *et al.*, Pharmacokinetic, biochemical and clinical effects of dimethyltriazenoimidazole-4-carboxamide-bischloroethylnitrosourea combination therapy in patients with advanced breast cancer, *Int. J. Cancer* 103 (2003), pp. 686–692.

[160] U. Herrlinger, J. Rieger and D. Koch *et al.*, Phase II trial of lomustine plus temozolomide chemotherapy in addition to radiotherapy in newly diagnosed glioblastoma: UKT-03, *J. Clin. Oncol.* 24 (2006), pp. 4412–4417.

[161] M. Barrie, C. Couprie and H. Dufour *et al.*, Temozolomide in combination with BCNU before and after radiotherapy in patients with inoperable newly diagnosed glioblastoma multiforme, *Ann. Oncol.* 16 (2005), pp. 1177–1184.

[162] S. Aamdal, B. Gerard, T. Bohman and M. D'Incalci, Sequential administration of dacarbazine and fotemustine in patients with disseminated malignant melanoma–an

effective combination with unexpected toxicity, *Eur. J. Cancer* 28 (1992), pp. 447–450.

[163] B. Gerard, S. Aamdal and S.M. Lee *et al.*, Activity and unexpected lung toxicity of the sequential administration of two alkylating agents–dacarbazine and fotemustine–in patients with melanoma, *Eur. J. Cancer* 29A (1993), pp. 711–719.

[164] E.L. Kreklau, N. Liu, Z. Li, K. Cornetta and L.C. Erickson, Comparison of single- versus double-bolus treatments of O(6)-benzylguanine for depletion of O(6)- methylguanine DNA methyltransferase (MGMT) activity in vivo: development of a novel fluorometric oligonucleotide assay for measurement of MGMT activity, *J. Pharmacol. Exp. Ther.* 297 (2001), pp. 524–530.

[165] H.S. Friedman, D.M. Kokkinakis and J. Pluda *et al.*, Phase I trial of O6-benzylguanine for patients undergoing surgery for malignant glioma, *J. Clin. Oncol.* 16 (1998), pp. 3570–3575.

[166] R.L. Schilsky, M.E. Dolan and D. Bertucci *et al.*, Phase I clinical and pharmacological study of O6-benzylguanine followed by carmustine in patients with advanced cancer, *Clin. Cancer Res.* 6 (2000), pp. 3025–3031.

[167] M.E. Dolan, M. Posner and T. Karrison *et al.*, Determination of the optimal modulatory dose of O6-benzylguanine in patients with surgically resectable tumors, *Clin. Cancer Res.* 8 (2002), pp. 2519–2523.

[168] S.C. Schold Jr., D.M. Kokkinakis and S.M. Chang *et al.*, O6-benzylguanine suppression of O6-alkylguanine-DNA alkyltransferase in anaplastic gliomas, *Neuro-oncol* 6 (2004), pp. 28–32.

[169] T.F. Gajewski, J. Sosman and S.L. Gerson *et al.*, Phase II trial of the O6-alkylguanine DNA alkyltransferase inhibitor O6-benzylguanine and 1,3-bis(2-chloroethyl)-1-nitrosourea in advanced melanoma, *Clin. Cancer Res.* 11 (2005), pp. 7861–7865.

[170] L. Liu, Y. Nakatsuru and S.L. Gerson, Base excision repair as a therapeutic target in colon cancer, *Clin. Cancer Res.* 8 (2002), pp. 2985–2991.

[171] L. Liu and S.L. Gerson, Therapeutic impact of methoxyamine: blocking repair of abasic sites in the base excision repair pathway, *Curr. Opin. Investig. Drugs* 5 (2004), pp. 623–627.

[172] P. Taverna, L. Liu, H.S. Hwang, A.J. Hanson, T.J. Kinsella and S.L. Gerson, Methoxyamine potentiates DNA single strand breaks and double strand breaks induced by temozolomide in colon cancer cells, *Mutat Res* 485 (2001), pp. 269–281.

[173] M.L. Fishel, Y. He, M.L. Smith and M.R. Kelley, Manipulation of base excision repair to sensitize ovarian cancer cells to alkylating agent temozolomide, *Clin. Cancer Res.* 13 (2007), pp. 260–267.

[174] B. Demple and J.S. Sung, Molecular and biological roles of Ape1 protein in mammalian base excision repair, *DNA Repair (Amst)* 4 (2005), pp. 1442–1449.

[175] S. Madhusudan, F. Smart and P. Shrimpton *et al.*, Isolation of a small molecule inhibitor of DNA base excision repair, *Nucleic Acids Res* 33 (2005), pp. 4711–4724.

[176] M. Luo, D. Caldwell and Y. Xu *et al.*, Inhibition of the human apurinic/apyrimidinic endonuclease DNA base excision repair enzyme/redox factor (APE1/Ref-1) using small molecule redox and repair inhibitors: Therapeutics implications [abstract], *Proc. Amer. Assoc. Cancer Res.* 45 (2004), p. 3042.

[177] J.K. Horton and S.H. Wilson, Hypersensitivity phenotypes associated with genetic and synthetic inhibitor-induced base excision repair deficiency, *DNA Repair (Amst)* 6 (2007), pp. 530–543.

[178] H.Y. Hu, J.K. Horton and M.R. Gryk *et al.*, Identification of small molecule synthetic inhibitors of DNA polymerase beta by NMR chemical shift mapping, *J. Biol. Chem.* 279 (2004), pp. 39736–39744.

[179] V. Schreiber, F. Dantzer, J.C. Ame and G. de Murcia, Poly(ADP-ribose): novel functions for an old molecule, *Nat. Rev. Mol. Cell Biol.* 7 (2006), pp. 517–528.

[180] L. Virag and C. Szabo, The therapeutic potential of poly(ADP-ribose) polymerase inhibitors, *Pharmacol Rev.* 54 (2002), pp. 375–429.

[181] P. Jagtap and C. Szabo, Poly(ADP-ribose) polymerase and the therapeutic effects of its inhibitors, *Nat. Rev. Drug Discov.* 4 (2005), pp. 421–440.

[182] M.R. Purnell and W.J. Whish, Novel inhibitors of poly(ADP-ribose) synthetase, *Biochem. J.* 185 (1980), pp. 775–777.

[183] E.R. Plummer, Inhibition of poly(ADP-ribose) polymerase in cancer, *Curr. Opin. Pharmacol* 6 (2006), pp. 364–368.

[184] G. Graziani and C. Szabo, Clinical perspectives of PARP inhibitors, *Pharmacol. Res.* 52 (2005), pp. 109–118.

[185] K. Ratnam and J.A. Low, Current development of clinical inhibitors of poly(ADP-ribose) polymerase in oncology, *Clin. Cancer Res.* 13 (2007), pp. 1383–1388.

[186] Plummer R, Middleton M, Wilson R, et al. First in human phase I trial of the PARP inhbitor AG-014699 with temozolomide (TMZ) in patients (pts) with advanced solid tumors [abstract]. *J. Clin. Oncol.* 2005 ASCO Annual Meeting Proceedings.Part I 2005;23:3065.

[187] Plummer R, Lorigan P, Evans J, et al. First and final report of a phase II study of the poly(ADP-ribose) polymerase (PARP) inhibitor, AG014699, in combination with temozolomide (TMZ) in patients with metastatic malignant melanoma (MM) [abstract]. *J. Clin. Oncol.* 2006 ASCO Annual Meeting Proceedings.Part I 2006;24:8013.

[188] H. Farmer, N. McCabe and C.J. Lord *et al.*, Targeting the DNA repair defect in BRCA mutant cells as a therapeutic strategy, *Nature* 434 (2005), pp. 917–921.

[189] H.E. Bryant, N. Schultz and H.D. Thomas *et al.*, Specific killing of BRCA2-deficient tumours with inhibitors of poly(ADP-ribose) polymerase, *Nature* 434 (2005), pp. 913–917.

[190] J.S. de Bono, P.C. Fong and D. Boss *et al.*, Phase I pharmacokinetic (PK) and pharmacodynamic (PD) evaluation of an oral small molecule inhibitor of Poly ADP-Ribose Polymerase (PARP), u in patients (p) with advanced tumors [abstract], *Eur. J. Cancer Suppls.* 4 (2006), p. 153.

[191] R. Plummer, Poly(ADPribose)polymerase inhibitors-the current clinical status [abstract], *Eur. J. Cancer Suppls.* 4 (2006), p. 141.

[192] Y. Shiloh, The ATM-mediated DNA-damage response: taking shape, *Trends Biochem. Sci.* 31 (2006), pp. 402–410.

[193] P.J. Hurley and F. Bunz, ATM and ATR: components of an integrated circuit, *Cell Cycle* 6 (2007), pp. 414–417.

[194] J.C. Harrison and J.E. Haber, Surviving the breakup: the DNA damage checkpoint, *Annu. Rev. Genet.* 40 (2006), pp. 209–235.

[195] I. Hickson, Y. Zhao and C.J. Richardson *et al.*, Identification and characterization of a novel and specific inhibitor of the ataxia-telangiectasia mutated kinase ATM, *Cancer Res.* 64 (2004), pp. 9152–9159.

[196] S.J. Collis, T.L. DeWeese, P.A. Jeggo and A.R. Parker, The life and death of DNA-PK, *Oncogene* 24 (2005), pp. 949–961.

[197] E. Willmore, S. de Caux and N.J. Sunter *et al.*, A novel DNA-dependent protein kinase inhibitor, NU7026, potentiates the cytotoxicity of topoisomerase II poisons used in the treatment of leukemia, *Blood* 103 (2004), pp. 4659–4665.

[198] Y. Zhao, H.D. Thomas and M.A. Batey *et al.*, Preclinical evaluation of a potent novel DNA-dependent protein kinase inhibitor NU7441, *Cancer Res* 66 (2006), pp. 5354–5362.

[199] S. Durant and P. Karran, Vanillins—a novel family of DNA-PK inhibitors, *Nucleic Acids Res* 31 (2003), pp. 5501–5512.

[200] I.H. Ismail, S. Martensson and D. Moshinsky *et al.*, SU11752 inhibits the DNA-dependent protein kinase and DNA double-strand break repair resulting in ionizing radiation sensitization, *Oncogene* 23 (2004), pp. 873–882.

[201] D. Chirnomas, T. Taniguchi and M. de la Vega *et al.*, Chemosensitization to cisplatin by inhibitors of the Fanconi anemia/BRCA pathway, *Mol. Cancer Ther.* 5 (2006), pp. 952–961.

[202] E. Levy-Lahad and E. Friedman, Cancer risks among BRCA1 and BRCA2 mutation carriers, *Br J Cancer* 96 (2007), pp. 11–15.

[203] M. Santarosa and A. Ashworth, Haploinsufficiency for tumour suppressor genes: when you don't need to go all the way, *Biochim. Biophys. Acta* 1654 (2004), pp. 105–122.

[204] http://www.sciencedirect.com/science?_ob=RedirectURL&_method=externObjLink&_locator=url&_plusSign=%2B&_targetURL=http%253A%252F%252Fwww.brcatrial.org.

[205] N. Turner, A. Tutt and A. Ashworth, Hallmarks of 'BRCAness' in sporadic cancers, *Nat. Rev. Cancer* 4 (2004), pp. 814–819.

[206] R.D. Kennedy and A.D. D'Andrea, DNA repair pathways in clinical practice: lessons from pediatric cancer susceptibility syndromes, *J. Clin. Oncol.* 24 (2006), pp. 3799–3808.

[207] 207. C.J. Lord, M.D. Garrett and A. Ashworth, Targeting the double-strand DNA break repair pathway as a therapeutic strategy, *Clin. Cancer Res.* 12 (2006), pp. 4463–4468.

[208] B. Koberle, J.R. Masters, J.A. Hartley and R.D. Wood, Defective repair of cisplatin-induced DNA damage caused by reduced XPA protein in testicular germ cell tumours, *Curr. Biol.* 9 (1999), pp. 273–276.

[209] C. Welsh, R. Day, C. McGurk, J.R. Masters, R.D. Wood and B. Koberle, Reduced levels of XPA, ERCC1 and XPF DNA repair proteins in testis tumor cell lines, *Int. J. Cancer.* 110 (2004), pp. 352–361.

[210] K.A. Olaussen, A. Dunant and P. Fouret *et al.*, DNA repair by ERCC1 in non-small-cell lung cancer and cisplatin-based adjuvant chemotherapy, *N Engl. J. Med.* 355 (2006), pp. 983–991.

[211] A.M. Valentini, R. Armentano, M. Pirrelli and M.L. Caruso, Chemotherapeutic agents for colorectal cancer with a defective mismatch repair system: the state of the art, *Cancer Treat Rev.* 32 (2006), pp. 607–618.

[212] S. Madhusudan and M.R. Middleton, The emerging role of DNA repair proteins as predictive, prognostic and therapeutic targets in cancer, *Cancer Treat Rev.* 31 (2005), pp. 603–617.

[213] J. Abraham, H.M. Earl, P.D. Pharoah and C. Caldas, Pharmacogenetics of cancer chemotherapy, *Biochim. Biophys. Acta* 1766 (2006), pp. 168–183.

[214] D.C. Altieri, Targeted therapy by disabling crossroad signaling networks: the survivin paradigm, *Mol. Cancer Ther.* 5 (2006), pp. 478–482.

[215] J.E. Dancey and H.X. Chen, Strategies for optimizing combinations of molecularly targeted anticancer agents, *Nat. Rev. Drug Discov.* 5 (2006), pp. 649–659.

[216] S. Kummar, M. Gutierrez, J.H. Doroshow and A.J. Murgo, Drug development in oncology: classical cytotoxics and molecularly targeted agents, *Br. J. Clin. Pharmacol.* 62 (2006), pp. 15–26.

[217] I. Collins and M.D. Garrett, Targeting the cell division cycle in cancer: CDK and cell cycle checkpoint kinase inhibitors, *Curr. Opin. Pharmacol.* 5 (2005), pp. 366–373.

[218] Y. Luo and J.D. Leverson, New opportunities in chemosensitization and radiosensitization: modulating the DNA-damage response, *Expert. Rev. Anticancer Ther.* 5 (2005), pp. 333–342.

[219] C.F. Wong, A. Guminski, N.A. Saunders and A.J. Burgess, Exploiting novel cell cycle targets in the development of anticancer agents, *Curr. Cancer Drug Targets* 5 (2005), pp. 85–102.

In: New Research on DNA Damage
Editors: Honoka Kimura and Aoi Suzuki

ISBN 978-1-60456-581-2
© 2008 Nova Science Publishers, Inc.

Chapter 4

BRIT1, a Novel DNA Damage Responsive Protein Dysfunctioned in Primary Microcephaly and Cancer

Guang Peng and Shiaw-Yih Lin[*]

Department of Systems Biology, The University of Texas M. D. Anderson Cancer
Center, Houston, Texas 77030, USA

Abstract

BRIT1 (BRCT-Repeat Inhibitor of hTERT expression) was originally identified from our laboratory as an inhibitor of human telomere reverse transcriptase (hTERT) by a genome-wide genetic screen. The amino acid sequence of BRIT1 was later matched to a putative disease gene called microcephalin (MCPH1). Aberrations of BRIT1 have been identified in breast, ovarian and prostate cancer as well as autosomal recessive primary microcephaly, a neuronal development disorder characterized by reduced brain size of patients. Therefore, the functions of BRIT1 are of critical research interests that can potentially contribute to two fundamental pathological processes, cancer and neuro-developmental disorder. In this chapter, we will present the most recent findings on BRIT1's functions in both DNA damage response and cell cycle control. Our studies have revealed that BRIT1 functions as a novel regulator in the ATM/ATR pathway and a proximal factor in DNA damage response controlling the recruitment of multiple sensors and early mediators to the DNA damage sites. BRIT1 has also been shown to control G2-M checkpoint and prevents premature entry into mitosis. These results support a role of BRIT1 as a guardian of genomic integrity that prevents the pathogenesis of human cancer and microcephaly. Finally, we will discuss our future research interests in revealing the underlying mechanisms on how BRIT1 defect may contribute to the development of cancer and primary microcephaly.

[*] Corresponding author: Dr. Shiaw-Yih Lin, Department of Systems Biology, Unit 950, The University of Texas M. D. Anderson Cancer Center, South Campus Research Building II, 7435 Fannin, Houston, TX 77054, USA. Phone: (713) 563-4217, Fax: (713) 563-4235, email: sylin@mdanderson.org.

BRIT1/MCPH1, a Gene Implicated in Cancer and Primary Microcephaly

BRIT1 (BRCT-repeat inhibitor of hTERT expression) is a gene previously identified from our laboratory as a novel repressor of hTERT (human telomere reverse transcriptase) by using a functional genomic screen. As a transcriptional repressor, loss of BRIT1 reactivates hTERT expression in hTERT-negative cells [1].

BRIT1, a Tumor Suppressor Gene in the Development of Human Cancer

BRIT1 is located on chromosomal 8p23.1. Alterations in this chromosomal region have frequently been evidenced in the development of multiple malignancies, including breast cancer, ovarian cancer and prostate cancer. The link between defects in BRIT1 and human cancer development has been clearly demonstrated in our findings by analyzing human tumor samples and a variety of cancer cell lines. Using high-density array comparative genomic hybridization (hCGH), we found substantial decreases in *BRIT1* DNA copy number in 40% of advanced epithelial ovarian cancer. More interestingly, the loss of gene copy number of BRIT1 significantly correlated with overall genomic instability in these specimens. This result strongly supports the potential dual role of BRIT1 in maintaining genomic stability and in repressing hTERT. In consistent with the aberrations of BRIT1 DNA, BRIT1 mRNA levels were also found to be markedly decreased in 63% of ovarian cancer specimens relative to BRIT1 mRNA levels in benign ovarian tissue specimens. As 8p23.1 is one of two most common sites of allelic loss or chromosomal deletions in prostate cancer, we further examined the expression of BRIT1 in prostate cancer specimens. Immunohistochemical analysis indicated that decreases of BRIT1 protein expression in benign prostate hypertrophy with further decreases in cancer cells, as compared with surrounding normal prostate tissue. This observation reveals the loss of BRIT1 expression contributes to the transition of cells from normal to malignant in a single prostate specimen.

BRIT1 also plays very significant role in suppressing breast cancer development. By analyzing a large variety of breast cancer cell lines, we found that 72% of the 54 breast cell lines tested showed decreases in *BRIT1* DNA copy number. Significantly decreases of BRIT1 mRNA and protein levels have also been shown in established breast cancer cell lines compared to nontransformed breast epithelial cells. In consistent with our findings, BRIT1 expression has been shown to inversely correlated with the likelihood of breast cancer metastasis and with the duration of relapse-free survival. Notably, in addition to the reduced expression of BRIT1, we identified a genetic aberration occurred within the BRIT1 coding region in breast cancer specimens. We found a 38 base pair *BRIT1* deletion in exon 10 that resulted in a premature stop codon in exon 11, which led to a C-terminal truncated, nonfunctional BRIT1 protein. Collectively, these findings clearly indicate that BRIT1 functions as a tumor suppressor gene in which aberrations of BRIT1 contribute to both cancer initiation and progression through its critical roles in both suppression of hTERT expression and maintenance of genomic stability [2].

BRIT1, a Disease Gene Underlying Primary Microcephaly

The amino acid sequence of BRIT1 was matched to a putative disease gene called microcephalin (MCPH1), which is implicated in a human genetic disease primary microcephaly (MCPH) (OMIM 251200). MCPH is a neuro-developmental disorder characterized by a marked reduction in brain size in the absence of other malformations or significant neurological deficits [3]. Despite this significant reduction in size, the gyral pattern is relatively well preserved without major abnormality in cortical architecture [4]. The only remarkable neurological deficit is a reduction in cognitive abilities [5]. MCPH is inherited as an autosomal recessive trait and exhibits genetic heterogeneity. To date six loci *(MCPH1-6)* have been mapped that, when mutated, confer MCPH. BRIT1/MCPH1 was the first of four causative gene identified in MCPH. Several mutations in BRIT1 have been identified in MCPH patients, including an early truncating mutation S25X [3], a missense mutation Thr27Arg, and deletion of the promoter and first nine exons [5]. All cases share common phenotypic feature of MCPH: a small size brain with normal cortical architecture. This observation suggests that dysfunction of BRIT1 might lead to reduction in production of central nervous system neurons either as a results of reduced neuroprogenitor division or increased apoptosis during neurogenesis rather than defective neuron migration [5].

BRIT1, a DNA Damage Response Protein

BRIT1 encodes an 835 amino acid protein. Analysis by the Simple Modular Architecture Research Tool (SMART) program revealed that BRIT1 contains three BRCT (breast cancer carboxyl-terminal) domains, one in its N-terminus and two in its C-terminus. BRCT domains are peptide- and phosphopeptide-binding modules present in a range of proteins involved in DNA damage response, including checkpoint control and DNA repair, such as 53BP1, MDC1, TopBP1 and BRCA1. In fact, defective DNA damage response signaling has been causatively linked to genetic disorders displaying microcephaly. A striking example is Seckel Syndrome (SS) (OMIM 210600), characterized by microcephaly and growth delay. A hypomorphic mutation in Ataxia telangiectasia and Rad3-related (ATR) was identified as a causative genetic defect in SS. ATR functions as a central regulator in DNA damage response signaling. NBS1, a defective protein identified in Nijmegen Breakage Syndrome (NBS) (OMIM 251260) with microcephaly phenotype, also plays a critical role in response to DNA damage [6]. These evidences strongly supported our hypothesis that BRIT1 might function as novel DNA damage response protein in surveillance of genomic stability, which are the underlying mechanism for the development of cancer and microcephaly.

Overview of DNA Damage Response Signaling

The human genome is constantly challenged by extracellular and intracellular insults such as reactive oxygen species, ionizing radiation and radiomimetic drugs, which can alter its chemical structure and corrupt its encoded message. In order to overcome these attacks and maintain the integrity of the genome, a complex network has been evolved to detect, signal the presence of and repair DNA damage, which is referred as DNA damage response pathway (DDR). DDR involves the sensing of DNA damage followed by transduction of the damage signal to cellular response pathways, including cell cycle checkpoints, DNA repair, transcription and the apoptotic pathway. As shown in Figure 1, this signaling transduction pathway is composed of five basic core components: the signal, sensors of the signal, transducers, mediators and effectors. The current model of the DNA damage response describes a linear progression beginning with sensors that recognize DNA damage sites and convey the initial damage signal to the mediators and transducers. Mediators are a group of proteins, which lack catalytic activity but facilitate signaling by promoting physical interaction between proteins. Mediators and transducers together relay and amplify the signal to downstream effectors, which execute cellular responses to DNA damage such as cell cycle arrest, DNA repair and apoptosis.

There are two phosphatidylinositol-3-related kinases, ATM (ataxia telangiectasia mutated) and ATR (ATM-Rad3 related) located at the top of this signaling transduction cascade. Generally, ATM is activated by double-strand breaks induced by ionizing radiation (IR), whereas ATR also responses to UV or stalled replication forks. Once activated in response to DNA damage, ATM and ATR phosphorylate a large array of proteins in DNA damage response pathway. One of their substrates is H2AX, a histone variant. Phosphorylation of H2AX on a conserved Serine, (Ser139) is referred to as γ-H2AX, which is rapidly induced upon DNA damage and marks sites of damaged DNA. Sensors and early mediators are promptly recruited to the damaged DNA sites such as the Mre11/Rad50/NBS1 complex, MDC1, 53BP1, RPA and Rad17, which result in the formation of immunostainable nuclear foci, called IRIF (irradiation-induced foci). IRIF are thought to serve as the platform where checkpoint and DNA repair proteins accumulate to facilitate propagation of the damage signals and DNA repair.

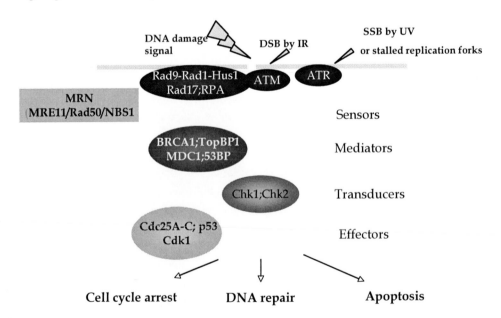

Figure 1. The general outline of DNA damage response signaling pathway.

The two effector kinases Chk1 and Chk2 are phosphorylated and activated by ATM and ATR, which are primarily responsible for the cell cycle regulation in response to DNA damage [7, 8].

Mammalian cell cycles contain G1, S, G2, and M phases. DNA damage response can induce cell cycle arrest at multiple transitions at each point. In general, arrest before or during S phase (G1/S and intra-S checkpoints) is controlled by inhibition of Cdk2 activity either by decrease of Cdc25 phosphatase activity or by binding of a Cdk inhibitor. Chk1 and/or Chk2 mediate phosphorylation and subsequent degradation of Cdc25A, an activator of Cdk2 and result in activation of both G1/S and intra S checkpoints. IR also induces p53-mediated transcriptional activation of p21 that binds and inhibits Cdk2/Cyclin E complexes. Arrest of G2/M transition is triggered by targeting Cdk1, the mitotic cdk, directly or via Cdc25C. Chk1 and Chk2 phosphorylate Cdc25C on a conserved Serine in response to IR-induced DNA damage. This modification leads to its cytoplasmic sequestration by the binding to the 14-3-3 proteins and inhibition of its phosphatase activity. In addition, p53 mediates the transcriptional activation of 14-3-3δ that binds to and excludes Cdk1/Cyclin B complexes from the nucleus. It is vital that cell cycle progression is arrested after DNA damage, which allows time to accurately and timely repair damaged DNA before the cell enters critical periods of the cell cycle, such as DNA synthesis. Therefore, activation of checkpoints in response to DNA damage is essential to maintain the integrity of cellular DNA [9].

BRIT1, in the Control of Cell Cycle Checkpoints

To test our hypothesis that BRIT1 may play an additional role in DNA damage response besides as a transcriptional suppressor of hTERT, we utilized two sets of siRNAs to deplete BRIT1 in U2OS cells. After exposure to γ-irradiation (IR), control cells transfected with siRNAs against luciferase were arrested with a G2 DNA content, suggesting the presence of an intact DNA damage checkpoint in these cells. In contrast, BRIT1 knockdown cells failed to arrest with a G2 DNA content. Nocodazole, an agent targeting spindle assembly, can induce BRIT1 depleted cells to arrest with G2 DNA content. Thus, the lack of cell cycle arrest with a G2 DNA content in BRIT1 knockdown cells were resulted from a defect in the DNA damage checkpoint. To determine the checkpoint defects, we labeled the cells with anti-phospho-histone H3 antibody, a marker for cells in M phase. After IR exposure, BRIT1 knockdown cells had a significantly higher proportion of cells in mitosis phase compared to control cells arrested in G2. This finding demonstrated that BRIT1 is required for G2/M cell cycle arrest in response to DNA damage.

We further determined the function of BRIT1 in intra-S checkpoint by using radioresistant DNA synthesis assay to measure DNA synthesis in response to IR in BRIT1 knockdown cells. In the control cells, IR triggered a reduction in DNA synthesis through activation of the intra-S checkpoint. However, BRIT1 deficiency conferred cells a significant resistant to the reduction in DNA synthesis, indicating that BRIT1 also functions in the intra-S checkpoint. In consistent with the lack of checkpoint activation, BRIT1 knockdown cells showed remarkably increased sensitivity to IR than control cells, which was caused by the continuous progression of cell cycle with damaged DNA [6].

Next we sought to investigate the molecular mechanism responsible for the lack of the intra-S and G2-M checkpoints in BRIT1 deficient cells. We tested the effect of BRIT1 knockdown on the phosphorylation and expression of key checkpoint-regulated molecules involved in cell cycle arrest. Among them, BRCA1 and Chk1 are two key regulators of both intra-S and G2/M checkpoints. As a substrate for both ATM and ATR, Chk1 is activated by DNA damage signaling and phosphorylates downstream Cdc25 phosphatase, which targets the cyclin dependent kinases Cdk1 and Cdk2. BRCA1 (breast cancer associated gene 1) as a tumor suppressor has multiple functions in cell cycle checkpoints, genome integrity and DNA damage response. BRCA1 deficiency consequently causes abnormalities in the S-phase and the G2/M checkpoints. Our studies revealed that BRIT1 knockdown significantly reduced the expression level of BRCA1 and Chk1. The specificity of regulation of these two molecules was demonstrated by rescuing their expression with transfection of siRNA resistant mutant BRIT1. These findings were also confirmed by another study [10]. In addition, these authors also examined the effect of BRIT1 deficiency on the expression of exogenous BRCA1 or Chk1 under the control a heterogeneous promoter. Their results showed that BRIT1 might regulate BRCA1 and Chk1 by different mechanisms. BRIT1 regulates both protein and mRNA stability of Chk1, possibly not the promoter activity since both protein and transcript levels of endogenous and exogenous Chk1 were decreased in BRIT1 knockdown cells. In contrast, BRIT1 deficiency only caused a decrease of endogenous BRCA1, but not exogenous BRCA1 at both protein and transcript levels, suggesting that BRIT1 might be involved in the regulation of BRCA1 promoter activity and/or maturation of BRCA1 mRNA.

In addition to BRCA1 and Chk1, NBS1 is another checkpoint regulator required for the intra-S checkpoint. Upon DNA damage, NBS1 is phosphorylated by ATM and this phosphorylation is required for its checkpoint function. We found that BRIT1 knockdown significantly inhibited NBS1 phosphorylation without affecting its protein expression level, suggesting a defective ATM signaling upon DNA damage [6].

These findings indicate that BRIT1 functions in the control of the intra-S and G2-M checkpoints not only through regulating the expression levels of key checkpoint regulators, but also through affecting DNA damage response signaling cascades and regulating the activity of the components inside this signaling network. With respect to its role in the DNA damage response, BRIT1 appears to function both in the ATR branch of the pathway through Chk1 and BRCA1 regulation and in the ATM branch by the regulation of NBS1 phosphorylation. Therefore, in the following studies we sought to dissect the role of BRIT1 in checkpoint signaling and its position within the signaling pathway.

BRIT1, an Early DNA Damage Responsive Protein

When DNA is damaged in cells, many proteins that play key roles in the DNA damage response are physically recruited to the DNA damage sites and form discrete nuclear foci (IRIF). The order and timing of these events are thought to be critical for checkpoint response and DNA repair. A hierarchy of proteins is involved in the assembly of IRIF and the resultant hierarchy of foci formation provides a means of ordering the molecular events ensuing from DNA damage detection and signal transduction. First, we examined how quickly BRIT1 formed IRIF following DNA damage and the hierarchy between recruitment of BRIT1 and other key checkpoint regulators. BRIT1 promptly formed IRIF, which could be detected as early as 2 min after IR. The result placed BRIT1 very upstream of the DNA damage signaling. We also demonstrated that BRIT1 colocalized with γ-H2AX, one of the earliest molecules to response DNA damage as a marker of DNA damage sites. However, BRIT1 deficiency did not affect γ-H2AX foci formation, indicating that BRIT1 is not required for γ-H2AX foci formation. Thus, BRIT1 may function in parallel with or downstream of γ-H2AX.

In the early DNA damage response, γ-H2AX marks the chromatin region at or near the DNA damage site and serves as a platform for the recruitment of DNA checkpoint signaling and repair factors including 53BP1, MDC1, MRN and BRCA1. Formation of 53BP1, MDC1 and NBS1 seems to be coincident with formation of the γ-H2AX foci. Next, we examined whether BRIT1 colocalized with these proteins after IR and whether BRIT1 expression was required for the formation of IRIF of these early DNA damage response proteins. We found that IR induced sharp increase of BRIT1 foci, which colocalized with 53BP1, MDC1, p-ATM and NBS1 foci. Moreover, depletion of BRIT1 abolished the formation of the IRIF of these molecules. These results suggest that BRIT1 is likely to function upstream of 53BP1, MDC1 and the MRN complex and is required for the recruitment of active p-ATM to the damaged loci, through direct binding or indirectly bridging via 53BP1, MDC1 or NBS1.

To determine whether BRIT1 plays a parallel role in the regulation of the ATR pathway, we examined the foci formation of BRIT1 and three known sensors or early mediators in the ATR pathway-ATR, RPA and Rad17. We observed that BRIT1 formed discrete foci after UV irradiation, which colocalized with ATR and RPA.

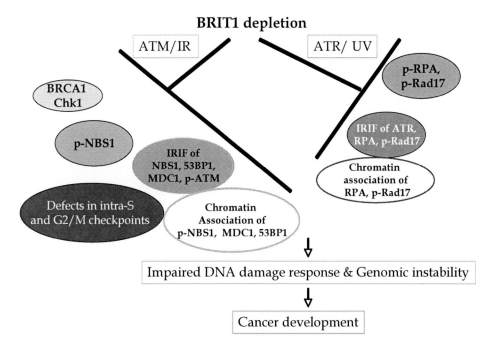

Figure 2. BRIT1 functions as a key regulator in the proximal DNA damage response. Its dysfunction contributes to the genomic instability and cancer development.

Depletion of BRIT1 showed that BRIT1 was required for the formation of ATR and RPA foci, indicating BRIT1 is essential for the proper recruitment of ATR and RPA to the DNA damage foci. Both RPA and Rad17, another checkpoint protein that serves as a sensor after UV exposure and binds to the damaged DNA, are phosphorylated by ATR. Depletion of BRIT1 also abolished the phosphorylation of both RPA and Rad17 detected by both immunostaing of foci and western blot analysis, which was consistent with a lack of recruitment of RPA and Rad17 to the damaged DNA loci or of the failure of recruitment of ATR to the complex [2]. Collectively, these results indicate that BRIT1 functions in signaling upstream of both ATM and ATR pathways.

It has been known that DNA damage results in enhanced binding of checkpoint regulators including MDC1, 53BP1, NBS1, RPA, and Rad17 to chromatin. The association of these factors with chromatin is thought to take place in parallel with their recruitment into IRIF on damaged DNA. Our studies demonstrated that BRIT1 is a chromatin binding protein and is required for the recruitment of sensors and early mediators to damaged DNA foci. In consistent with these observations, we found that BRIT1 depletion also significantly reduced both basal and ionizing irradiation-induced association of MDC1, 53BP1, and p-NBS1 with chromatin by utilizing chromatin fractionation assay. The total levels of these molecules were not affected by BRIT1 knockdown. Thus, the reduction of their recruitment to the chromatin by depletion of BRIT1 is resulted from changes in the access or affinity of these molecules to the chromatin structure. In parallel, BRIT1 deficiency also markedly decreased UV-induced binding of two subunits of the RPA molecule (RPA70 and RPA34) and of p-Rad17 to chromatin. These findings implicate that BRIT is required for the recruitment of sensors and early mediators in both IR-induced ATM pathway and UV-triggered ATR pathway to the chromatin [2].

In consistent with our findings, a recent study utilized an exhaustive panel of human cells and MEFs (Mouse embryonic fibroblasts) that are defective in various DNA damage checkpoint components to further delineate how BRIT1 is regulated in the DNA damage response. BRIT1 formed foci independent of the MRN complex, Fanconi anemia complex, MDC1, 53BP1, BRCA1. However, in H2AX-/- cells, BRIT1 foci formation was abolished. This places BRIT1 at the early steps in the DNA damage induced signal transduction pathways. In addition, this study also showed that BRIT1 interacted with a phospho-H2AX peptide in vitro and over-expression BRIT1 can interfere with the foci formation of MDC1 and 53BP1, which are known to be recruited to DNA damage sites by interaction with γ-H2AX. C-terminal BRCT domains are required for BRIT1 foci formation and interaction with γ-H2AX. This result indicated that BRIT1 is potentially recruited to DNA damage site via its interaction with γ-H2AX [11].

As summarized in Figure 2, our studies reveal that BRIT1 functions as a novel regulator in the ATM/ATR pathway and a proximal factor in DNA damage response controlling the recruitment of multiple sensors and early mediators to the DNA damage sites. Its critical role in the DNA damage response strongly supported the role of BRIT1 as a novel tumor suppressor through its function in surveillance of genomic stability.

BRIT1 and the Development of Cancer

One of the fundamental mechanisms driving the development of cancer is the loss of genomic integrity. To express the full complement of malignant transformation, a single cell must acquire multiple gene alterations and transmit them to daughter cells. However, cells have a complex network of DNA monitoring and repair molecules designed to ensure that DNA information remains immaculate, and so passing gene mutations on to daughter cells is a rare event.Therefore, the genomes of tumor cells must acquire increased mutability so that the process of cancer development can be completed during the lifetime of the host. It is now believed that defects in these genome maintenance protein complexes contribute to mutability of the cancer cell genome. One of the most crucial mechanisms to maintain genomic integrity is through the intact DNA damage response. Disruption of this mechanism leads to chromosomal aberrations and genomic instability, both of which contribute to neoplastic transformation. As evidenced from previous publications, deficiency of a variety of DNA damage genes including ATM, ATR, γ-H2AX, Chk1, NBS1, RPA, Rad17, BRCA1, and BRCA2, is associated with genomic instability. As our studies clearly indicated that BRIT1 functions in the early DNA damage response, we sought to assess whether depletion of BRIT1 in cells would lead to an increase in chromosome aberrations and genomic instability, which might directly contribute to the cancer development. We used siRNA to knockdown BRIT1 in normal human mammary epithelial cells (HMECs) and analyzed their chromosomes by metaphase spreads. BRIT1-depleted HMECs showed a variety of chromosome aberrations, including chromosomal breaks, dicentric chromosomes, and chromosomal telomeric association. More severe chromosomal abnormalities were detected in BRIT1 knockdown cells after IR exposure. We also observed similar results in a variety of cell lines evaluated including normal human fibroblast BJ cells, MCF-7 cells and Hela cells [2]. These results support the importance of BRIT1 in maintaining chromosomal integrity with or without exogenous genotoxic stress; the essential function of BRIT1 in early DNA damage response may therefore contribute to its role as a novel tumor suppressor.

Impact of BRIT1 on the Development of Microcephaly

Regulation of Chk1 Function

In addition to its physiological role as a tumor suppressor, BRIT1 is the first causative gene identified in MCPH. Microcephaly phenotype has also been observed in Seckel syndrome and Nijimegen Breakage syndrome. Like BRIT1 deficient cells, both Seckel and Nijmegen breakage syndrome cells are defective in checkpoint signaling. Interestingly, all these three microcephaly disorders have defects in Chk1 regulation. As shown in previous studies, ATR mutations, as well as the defects in its downstream signaling pathway, have been reported in cells derived from patients with Seckel syndrome with Chk1 being the key downstream target of ATR. NBS1, a gene defective in Nijmegen breakage syndrome, is also required for Chk1 activation in response to IR and the regulation of ATR pathway in response to UV. ATR-Chk1 pathway is essential for cellular viability. Given this fact, we have proposed that dysfunction of BRIT1 in DNA damage response, particularly Chk1 function might contribute to the development of microcephaly via increased cellular lethality in neural lineages and severely decreased brain and head size [6].

Regulation of Mitotic Entry

A recent study utilizing cell lines derived from MCPH1 patients indicated that BRIT1 has a function downstream of Chk1 in the ATR-dependent signaling and an ATR-independent role in maintaining inhibitory Cdk1 phosphorylation, which prevents premature entry into mitosis [4, 12].

In this study, two lymphoblastoid cell lines (LBLs) with different truncating mutations in *MCPH1* (*MCPH1^{C74G}* and *MCPH^{427insA}*) were analyzed in parallel with cells derived from ATR-SS (ATR-Seckel syndrome) patients due to the overlapping of clinical features of BRIT1 deficiency and ATR-SS. Like ATR-SS cells, MCPH1 patient cells showed defective G2-M checkpoint arrest and nuclear fragmentation after DNA damage, and contained supernumerary mitotic centrosomes. However, MCPH1 patient cells expressed normal protein levels of Chk1 and BRCA1, and Chk1 was phosphorylated normally after DNA damage. These results revealed that BRIT1 functions downstream of Chk1 in ATR-dependent signaling response, suggesting that BRIT1 deficiency in MCPH1 patient cells has a second impact distinct to its impact on the DNA damage response observed in BRIT1 knockdown by siRNA. As discussed by the authors, the different impacts may be due to residual function conferred by null mutation or a strong selection for hypomorphic mutations that permit patient viability. It is possible that hypomorphic MCPH1 mutations in the patients confer separation of function phenotypes that impact upon some but not all MCPH1 functions. The different impact could also be due to cell or tissue specificity.

The Cdc25A phosphatase is a downstream effector of Chk1-ATR pathway and a major regulator for mitotic entry. Upon phosphorylation by Chk1, Cdc25A is targeted for ubiquitin-dependent degradation. Despite of intact normal Chk1 function, MCPH1 mutant cells exhibited impaired degradation of Cdc25A both in unperturbed cell growth as well as following UV irradiation. Cdc25 phosphatases are known to regulate Cdk1-cyclin B1 activity, and hence mitotic entry, by reversing inhibitory Tyr-15-Cdk1 phosphorylation. MCPH1 mutant cells also showed a low level of Tyr-15 phosphorylated Cdk1 and consequently high Cdk1-cyclin B1 activity. The level of Tyr-15 phosphorylated Cdk1 decreased with progression through S phase and preceded but correlated temporally with appearing premature chromosome condensation (PCC) cells, which is a unique phenotype displaying in MCPH1 mutant cells. In the developmental perspective, BRIT1 has been found to coordinates the S-M transition in fly embryos. Deficiency of the drosophila homolog of BRIT1 results in premature chromosome condensation and mitotic entry with unreplicated DNA and genomic instability [13]. Thus this evidence suggests that MCPH1 has an important role in regulating mitotic entry that is distinct to its role in the DNA damage response [12].

Perspective of BRIT1 Functions

BRIT1 and Centrosomes

The centrosome is the main microtubule organizing center (MTOC) of the cell as well as a regulator of cell-cycle progression. It is composed of the paired centrioles and the surrounding protein aggregates known as pericentriolar material (PCM). Its primary function is to nucleate and anchor microtubules. Centrosome has a key role in the establishment of the interphase cytoplasmic microtubule network and bipolar mitotic spindles. The centrosome, like DNA, must duplicate once before the next mitosis; during cytokinesis, each daughter cell receives one and only one centrosome. Therefore, in animal cells, initiation of DNA and centrosome duplication must be coupled. The presence of two centrosomes at mitosis is crucial for the formation of bipolar mitotic spindles. Thus, numeral integrity of centrosomes needs to be also tightly controlled. Any failures in these regulatory steps that result in numeral as well as functional abnormalities of centrosomes lead to chromosome segregation errors, defects in mitosis and genomic instability [14].

Evidence suggesting a role of BRIT1 in the regulation of centrosome function includes: 1) the majority of MCPH proteins (MCPH3, MCPH5, MCPH6) have a centrosomal localization. 2) A distinguishing feature observed in MCPH1 cell line is the presence of mitotic cells with supernumerary centrosomes, which occur in up to 30% of the cells within a population. 3) Primary microcephaly has been hypothesized to be a primary disorder of neurogenic mitosis [4, 5]. Thus it is intriguing to determine the function of BRIT1 as a centrosomal protein, which might be an undefined mechanism that directly contributes to microcephaly by controlling the number of neuron generated by neural precursor cells. This mechanism potentially provides a common developmental and cellular pathway underlying other primary microcephaly proteins. It will also provide a new insight into the function of BRIT1 in the control of genomic instability and malignant transformation in addition to its role in early DNA damage response.

The role of BRIT1 in the developmental process as a mitotic regulator has been examined in a Drosophila model. BRIT1 is a mitotically regulated protein, which co-localizes with decondensed chromosomes. A short isoform BRIT1 containing only one N-terminal BRCT domain, localizing to the centrosome and spindle during mitosis. This short form BRIT1 is essential for the early rapid syncytial nuclear divisions, where it is required to co-ordinate centrosome and nuclear division cycles, prior to the physiological requirement for DNA damage signaling in the blastoderm embryo [15].

Analysis of chicken BRIT1 (cMCPH1) function indicates that full length BRIT1 localized to centrosomes throughout the cell cycle. The C-terminal BRCT domains are necessary for IRIF formation while the N-terminal BRCT domain is required for centrosomal localization in irradiated cells. Centrosomal targeting of cMCPH1 is independent of ATM, BRCA1 and Chk1 [16].

In the mammalian cells, BRIT1 has been reported to localize at the centrosomes and colocalized with γ-tubulin [17]. Our unpublished data also supported this notion. The mechanisms explaining how BRIT1 maintains integrity and normal function of centrosome and how dysregulation of centrosome due to BRIT1 deficiency contributes to the cancer development are under our current investigation.

BRIT1 and Double Strand Break (DSB) Repair

In order to maintain genomic stability, one of most critical cellular functions in response to DNA damage is to repair damaged DNA. Cells have evolved elaborate pathways that repair a large variety of DNA lesions. One of the most harmful lesions is the DNA double-strand breaks, which arise during DNA replication or after DNA damage. There are two distinct biochemical pathways to repair DNA double-strand breaks, homologous recombination (HR) or non-homologous end joining (NHEJ). The fundamental difference between these two pathways is the requirement of HR for homologous sequence to repair damaged sites. Therefore, HR is generally error-free repair that uses a homologous information from a sister chromatid as template DNA to repair damaged lesions in the S/G2 phase. In contrast, NHEJ is involved in the direct linkage of broken ends, which is usually error-prone process and present throughout cell cycle.

HR mediated repair initially involves an MRE11-RAD50-NBS1 mediated 5'-3' resection followed by RAD51, RAD52 and RAD54 proteins to promote strand invasion and subsequent recombination. Then DNA polymerase completes the DNA repair. NHEJ repair involves the DNA dependent protein kinase (DNA-PK) and the DNA ligase IV complex, which together facilitate re-joining of broken non-compatible DNA ends [18].

Multiple observations support a role of BRIT1 in DNA repair. 1) Our kinetic study of radiation-induced γ-H2AX foci in BRIT1 depleted cells indicated an enhanced and prolonged γ-H2AX response. This phenomenon might be due to the impaired DNA repair, which leads to sustained γ-H2AX activation [2]. 2) Deficiency of BRIT1 has an impact on many upstream DNA damage response proteins including MDC1, NBS1, BRCA1 and RPA, which are known to play a critical role in DNA repair [2]. 3) Defects in DNA repair have been linked to a variety of neurodegenerative disease and defective neurological disorders, suggesting brain cells may be particularly prone to the progressive accumulation of unrepaired DNA lesions. For example, *NBS1* is a disease gene underlying Nijmegen breakage syndrome with microcephaly phenotype. The product of NBS1 gene associates with MRE11 and RAD50 and form a complex, which is important for sensing DSBs and for DNA repair [19]. We have substantial evidences to believe that BRIT1 also plays a significant role in DNA repair process. The critical step to repair damaged DNA is to gain the access to the damaged lesion. However, DNA present in the nucleus in the form of chromatin, which consists of DNA wrapped around of an octamer of histone proteins. Highly condensed chromatin structure creates a significant barrier to the detection and timely repair of DNA [18]. As we observed that BRIT1 has a wide range effects on the recruitment of early DNA damage response proteins to the chromatin and DNA damage sites, it is attempting to hypothesize that BRIT1 might cooperate with chromatin remodeling molecules to modulate chromatin structure at DNA damage lesions. Our ongoing research is centered to understand whether BRIT1 participates in the DNA repair process and whether multiple impact of BRIT1 on DNA damage response is resulted from chromatin remodeling.

Summary

BRIT1 is originally identified in our laboratory as a transcriptional suppressor of hTERT. Our current studies identified that BRIT1, as a novel tumor suppressor and a causative gene underlying human genetic disease primary microcephaly, plays a critical role in the early DNA damage response. BRIT1 is a key regulator in the ATM/ATR pathways. Normal function of BRIT1 is required for the recruitment of proximal DNA damage response factors such as 53BP1, MDC1, NBS1, ATM, RPA, and ATR to the DNA damage foci. It also functions as a crutial regulator in the checkpoint activation in response to DNA damage signaling and prevent premature mitosis entry. In addition to directly participating in DNA damage signaling as a sensor/early mediator, BRIT1 regulates DNA damage response via controlling Chk1 and BRCA1 expression. Interestingly, BRIT1 may also exert novel functions in centrosome integrity and DNA repair. We hypothesized that BRIT1 might have an influence on chromatin structure remodeling to facilitate the detection of DNA damage lesion, the transduction of DNA damage signaling, the transcription of checkpoint genes and the repair of damaged DNA.

Reference

[1]   Lin, S.Y. and S.J. Elledge, Multiple tumor suppressor pathways negatively regulate telomerase. *Cell*, 2003. 113(7): p. 881-9.

[2]   Rai, R., et al., BRIT1 regulates early DNA damage response, chromosomal integrity, and cancer. *Cancer Cell*, 2006. 10(2): p. 145-57.

[3]   Jackson, A.P., et al., Identification of microcephalin, a protein implicated in determining the size of the human brain. *Am. J. Hum. Genet*, 2002. 71(1): p. 136-42.

[4]   O'Driscoll, M., A.P. Jackson, and P.A. Jeggo, Microcephalin: a causal link between impaired damage response signalling and microcephaly. *Cell Cycle*, 2006. 5(20): p. 2339-44.

[5]   Cox, J., et al., What primary microcephaly can tell us about brain growth. *Trends Mol. Med*, 2006. 12(8): p. 358-66.

[6]   Lin, S.Y., et al., BRIT1/MCPH1 is a DNA damage responsive protein that regulates the Brca1-Chk1 pathway, implicating checkpoint dysfunction in microcephaly. *Proc. Natl. Acad. Sci.* U S A, 2005. 102(42): p. 15105-9.

[7]   Kao, J., et al., Cellular response to DNA damage. *Ann. N. Y. Acad. Sci.*, 2005. 1066: p. 243-58.

[8]   Zhou, B.B., M.R. Mattern, and K.K. Khanna, Role of tumor suppressors in DNA damage response. *Methods Mol. Biol.*, 2003. 223: p. 39-50.

[9]   Zhou, B.B. and S.J. Elledge, The DNA damage response: putting checkpoints in perspective. *Nature*, 2000. 408(6811): p. 433-9.

[10]   Xu, X., J. Lee, and D.F. Stern, Microcephalin is a DNA damage response protein involved in regulation of CHK1 and BRCA1. *J. Biol. Chem.*, 2004. 279(33): p. 34091-4.

[11] Wood, J.L., et al., MCPH1 functions in an H2AX-dependent but MDC1-independent pathway in response to DNA damage. *J. Biol. Chem*, 2007. 282(48): p. 35416-23.

[12] Alderton, G.K., et al., Regulation of mitotic entry by microcephalin and its overlap with ATR signalling. *Nat. Cell Biol*, 2006. 8(7): p. 725-33.

[13] Rickmyre, J.L., et al., The Drosophila homolog of MCPH1, a human microcephaly gene, is required for genomic stability in the early embryo. *J. Cell Sci*, 2007. 120(Pt 20): p. 3565-77.

[14] Bettencourt-Dias, M. and D.M. Glover, Centrosome biogenesis and function: centrosomics brings new understanding. *Nat. Rev. Mol. Cell Biol*, 2007. 8(6): p. 451-63.

[15] Brunk, K., et al., Microcephalin coordinates mitosis in the syncytial Drosophila embryo. *J. Cell Sci*, 2007. 120(Pt 20): p. 3578-88.

[16] Jeffers, L.J., et al., Distinct BRCT domains in Mcph1/Brit1 mediate ionizing radiation-induced focus formation and centrosomal localization. *Oncogene,* 2007.

[17] Zhong, X., G.P. Pfeifer, and X. Xu, Microcephalin encodes a centrosomal protein. *Cell Cycle*, 2006. 5(4): p. 457-8.

[18] Ataian, Y. and J.E. Krebs, Five repair pathways in one context: chromatin modification during DNA repair. *Biochem Cell Biol*, 2006. 84(4): p. 490-504.

[19] Rass, U., I. Ahel, and S.C. West, Defective DNA repair and neurodegenerative disease. *Cell*, 2007. 130(6): p. 991-1004.

In: New Research on DNA Damage
Editors: Honoka Kimura and Aoi Suzuki

ISBN 978-1-60456-581-2
© 2008 Nova Science Publishers, Inc.

Chapter 5

Polymorphisms in Genes Involved in DNA-Damage Processing and their Effect on Cancer Risk

G. Iarmarcovai[1]*, S. Bonassi[2], A. Botta[1], R.A. Baan[3], and T. Orsière[1]

1. Laboratory of Biogenotoxicology and Environmental Mutagenesis, Université de la Méditerranée, France
2. Unit of Molecular Epidemiology, National Cancer Research Institute, Genoa, Italy
3. Carcinogen Identification and Evaluation Group, WHO - International Agency for Research on Cancer, Lyon, France

Abstract

The individual response to genotoxic stress and induction of DNA damage may vary according to various conditions, such as the absorption and metabolism rate of genotoxic agents, the extent and efficacy of DNA-damage induction and repair, the balance between apoptosis and necrosis of exposed cells, the proper functioning of cell-cycle control, and the immune response. All of these processes are governed by certain genes or combinations of genes. Numerous human population studies have evaluated the relationship between genetic polymorphisms and DNA-damage induction and repair in response to genotoxic insult. The most common type of variation in DNA sequence is the single-nucleotide polymorphism, present in about 1 per 1,000 nucleotides in the human genome. However, the role of this type of genetic variant contributing to diseases with a complex etiology such as cancer is poorly understood. Hundreds of polymorphisms in genes that encode enzymes involved in the metabolism of xenobiotics (such as oxidoreductases, P450 cytochromes, glutathione *S*-transferases, *N*-acetyl transferases, methyltransferases, hydrolases, dehydrogenases), in DNA repair (participating in direct reversal repair, base-excision repair, nucleotide-excision repair, and double-strand-break

---

* Corresponding author: G. Iarmarcovai, Laboratory of Biogenotoxicology and Environmental Mutagenesis (EA 1784; IFR PMSE 112), Faculty of Medecine, Université de la Méditerranée, 27 Bd Jean Moulin, 13385 Marseille Cedex 5, France, Phone: 33 (0)4 91 32 45 48, Fax: 33 (0)4 91 32 45 72. E-mail address: Gwenaelle.Iarmarcovai@medecine.univ-mrs.fr.

repair), and in folate metabolism (methylenetetrahydrofolate reductase, methionine synthase, methionine synthase reductase) have been identified, although for many of these polymorphisms the impact on repair phenotype and cancer susceptibility remains uncertain. The present article reviews which of the many single-nucleotide polymorphisms in genes involved in DNA-damage processing influence cancer risk, and provides insight into the complexity of the genotype-phenotype relationship. Nevertheless, when a specific polymorphism by itself appears to have no or only a weak effect, the identification and characterization of the combined effects of different susceptibility genes for cancer risk require the understanding of gene-gene interactions.

Keywords: *Single-nucleotide polymorphism; DNA-damage processing; Molecular epidemiology; Cancer*

Abbreviations

SNP, single nucleotide polymorphism; NQO1, NAD(P)H quinone oxidoreductase; CYP, P450 cytochromes; GST, Glutathione *S*-transferases; NAT, *N*-acetyl transferases; *EPHX* gene/mEH enzyme, microsomal epoxide hydrolase; ADH, alcohol dehydrogenases; ALDH, aldehyde dehydrogenases; MGMT, methylguanine DNA methyltransferase; DRR, direct reversal repair; BER, base-excision repair; APEX1 or APE1, apurinic/apyrimidinic endonuclease; hOGG1, human 8-oxoguanine glycosylase; XRCC1, X-ray repair cross-complementing protein (group 1); NER, nucleotide-excision repair; XPD/ERCC2, *xeroderma pigmentosum* group D/excision repair cross-complementing rodent repair deficiency; DSBR, double-strand-break repair; BRCA1/BRCA2, breast cancer genes; XRCC3, X-ray repair cross-complementing protein (group 3); MTHFR, methylenetetrahydrofolate reductase, MTR, methionine synthase; MTRR, methionine synthase reductase; PAH, polycyclic aromatic hydrocarbons; IR, ionizing radiation.

1. Introduction

Cells in the body are constantly exposed to DNA-reactive chemical species, both from intracellular and environmental sources [1]. The individual response to genotoxic stress and induction of DNA damage may vary according to various conditions, such as the absorption and metabolism rate of genotoxic agents, the extent and efficacy of DNA-damage induction and repair, the balance between apoptosis and necrosis of exposed cells, the proper functioning of cell-cycle control, and the immune response. All of these processes are controlled by certain genes or combinations of genes. Numerous human population studies and some reviews have evaluated the relationship between genetic polymorphisms and DNA-damage induction and repair in response to genotoxic insult [2, 3]. Most studies of genotoxic endpoints involve the assessment of DNA damage either directly, e.g., with biochemical techniques, or indirectly, e.g., through analysis of sister chromatid exchange, chromosomal aberrations, or micronuclei [4]. The potential importance of a specific genetic polymorphism for a particular endpoint largely depends on the exposing agent, the biological material examined, and the ethnicity of the population under study. As there is inter-individual variation also in the extent and nature of the exposure, correct identification of individual exposure levels is essential [5].

The successful sequencing of the human genome has allowed the identification of a large number of low-penetrance alleles, while molecular epidemiology has acquired the technology to develop large-scale case-control association studies [6]. The most common type of variation in DNA sequence is the single-nucleotide polymorphism (SNP), present in about 1 per 1,000 nucleotides in the human genome.

Table 1. Widely studied polymorphisms in genes involved in DNA-damage processing

	Gene studied	Function	Polymorphism
Metabolism of genotoxicants	*NQO1*	Oxidative scavenger	Pro187Ser
	CYP1A1	Phase 1	m1(Msp1 site), m2 (Ile462Val), and m4 (Thr461Asn) alleles
	CYP2D6	Phase 1	
	CYP2E1	Phase 1	RsaI, PstI or DraI sites
	GSTM1	Phase 2	Gene deletion
	GSTT1	Phase 2	Gene deletion
	GSTP1	Phase 2	Ile105Val
	GSTP1	Phase 2	Ala114Val
	NAT2	Phase 2	Slow/rapid acetylator
	EPHX1/mEH (exon 3)	Phase 2	Tyr113His
	EPHX1/mEH (exon 4)	Phase 2	His139Arg
	ADH1B	Phase 2	Arg47His
	ALDH2	Phase 2	Glu487Lys
DNA repair	*MGMT*	DRR	Leu84Phe
	APE1	BER	Asp148Glu
	hOGG1	BER	Ser326Cys
	XRCC1	BER	Arg194Trp
	XRCC1	BER	Arg280His
	XRCC1	BER	Arg399Gln
	ERCC2/XPD	NER	Asp312Asn
	ERCC2/XPD	NER	Lys751Gln
	XRCC3	DSBR	Thr241Met
	BRCA1/BRCA2	DSBR	
	TP53	Cell cycle	Arg72Pro
Folate metabolism	*MTHFR*	Folates	677 C>T
	MTHFR	Folates	1298 A>C
	MTR	Folates	2756 A>G
	MTRR	Folates	66 A>G

As many as 7 million common SNPs with an allelic frequency of more than 5% may exist across the entire population [7].Inherited and acquired deficiencies in host defense mechanisms against DNA damage, e.g., metabolic and DNA repair enzymes, can modify cancer susceptibility [1]. However, the role of genetic variants contributing to diseases with a complex etiology such as cancer is poorly understood [8]. Hundreds of polymorphisms in genes that encode enzymes involved in the metabolism of xenobiotics (such as oxidoreductases, P450 cytochromes, glutathione S-transferases, N-acetyl transferases, methyltransferases, hydrolases, dehydrogenases), in DNA repair (participating in direct reversal repair, base-excision repair, nucleotide-excision repair, and double-strand-break repair), and in folate metabolism (methylenetetrahydrofolate reductase, methionine synthase, methionine synthase reductase) have been identified, although for many of these polymorphisms the impact on repair phenotype and cancer susceptibility remains uncertain.

Today, it is difficult to present a systematic overview of papers reporting on the association between genotype and cancer risk. The size of most study populations is usually too small to properly evaluate rare polymorphisms, and different genotypes are selected in different studies, which precludes a meaningful compilation/comparison of the results. Furthermore, in different ethnic populations, the allele frequencies for each genotype vary widely. Finally, statistical methods are often inappropriate for evaluating possible confounding factors, and negative findings are not very meaningful and are probably not fully reported, with the possibility of preferential publication of positive results (publication bias) [6]. An essential step in understanding the complexity of the genotype-phenotype relationship is to determine which of the many SNPs in genes involved in DNA-damage induction and repair may influence cancer risk [8] (Table 1).

2. Polymorphisms in Genes Involved in Metabolism of Xenobiotics

Among the known environmental risk factors are many genotoxic chemicals that are metabolized in the organism to products that are either more DNA-reactive or are detoxified. Genetic polymorphisms have been identified in many of these enzymes, and the biological consequence of some of these changes is an altered enzyme activity, which may influence the ratio between activation and deactivation, and thus affect cancer risk. Enzymes involved in biotransformation can be divided into phase-1 enzymes involved in oxidative processes and phase-2 enzymes involved in the detoxification of the primary compounds or their metabolites. Genetic polymorphisms in phase-1 and phase-2 metabolic enzymes have been shown to influence both DNA damage and cancer risk [9].

2.1. Polymorphisms in Genes Encoding Phase-1 Enzymes

NQO1 (NAD(P)H quinone oxidoreductase) is a two-electron reductase involved in the activation/detoxification of quinones and benzene metabolites [10, 11]. Two competing quinone metabolism pathways exist in human cells [11]. In one pathway, quinones undergo one-electron reduction catalyzed by phase-1 enzymes, such as cytochrome b5 reductase and P450 reductase. This process leads to the formation of alkylating species and free radicals, due to auto-oxidation of the metabolite semiquinone under aerobic conditions. Alternatively, NQO1 protects cells from oxidative damage by preventing quinones from entering the one-electron reduction pathway and by catalyzing a two-electron reduction, which leads to the less toxic hydroquinones [11]. A single-nucleotide replacement at codon 187 leads to a Pro → Ser amino acid change, which results in an enzyme with reduced quinone reductase activity (frequency of the homozygous variant genotype: 2% in Caucasians, 20% in Asians) [11]. The variant *NQO1* Pro187Ser genotype is reported to affect increase individual susceptibility to lung, bladder, and colorectal cancers [11, 12].

Enzymes associated with P450 cytochromes (CYP) catalyze the insertion of oxygen into a substrate. This is a typical activation reaction (phase 1) that converts indirect carcinogens into active electrophiles capable of interacting with the biological macromolecules DNA, RNA, and proteins. CYP1A1 catalyzes the first step of the metabolism of polycyclic aromatic hydrocarbons (PAHs) to electrophilic compounds and is involved in the metabolic activation of complex mixtures of aromatic compounds [10, 13]. CYP2E1 metabolizes many indirect carcinogens, such as nitrosamines and chlorinated and non-chlorinated organic solvents. This enzyme is induced by ethanol, and alcohol consumption may thus influence carcinogenesis induced by CYP2E1-activated carcinogens [10]. The major variant alleles of *CYP1A1* and *CYP2E1* genes are known (for more details, see [2]), but the phenotypic consequences of the polymorphisms are still under investigation. However, the association between *CYP1A1* polymorphisms and lung cancer risk seems clear [13].

2.2. Polymorphisms in Genes Encoding Phase-2 Enzymes

Glutathione *S*-transferases (GST) are a major group of detoxifying enzymes. Lack of the isoenzyme mu (GSTM1) is associated with reduced efficiency in binding and detoxifying genotoxic substrates, including aflatoxin and epoxides derived from PAHs [10]. About 50% of Caucasians and Asians (Caucasians: 0.42-0.60; Asians: 0.42-0.54), and about 20% of Africans (0.16-0.36) lack GSTM1 activity [14]. The theta form of GST (GSTT1) detoxifies monohalomethanes (e.g., methyl bromide) and the epoxides of the alkenes ethylene and butadiene, but GSTT1 activates methylene chloride and certain bifunctional alkylating agents [10]. As this enzyme has both detoxifying and activating properties with respect to many environmental pollutants, it is difficult to predict the biological consequences of the *GSTT1*-null genotype. The frequency of homozygous carriers of *GSTT1*-null varies in different populations, being about 20% in Caucasians (0.13-0.26) and about 40% in Asians (0.35-0.52) [10, 14]. The pi form of GST (GSTP1) is involved in the inactivation of important carcinogens such as PAH diol-epoxides and has two polymorphisms: Ile105Val (occurrence among Caucasians, 26%) and Ala114Val (occurrence among Caucasians, 9%) [14, 15]. Genetic polymorphisms in GST have been shown to affect cancer risk [16]. The *GSTM1*-null genotype is associated with an increased risk for head and neck, colorectal, lung, larynx and bladder cancer, and acute leukemia; the *GSTT1*-null genotype with increased risks for astrocytoma and meningioma, breast cancer, lung cancer, and acute leukemia, and mutant *GSTP1* with increased prostate and lung cancer risk [17, 18]. It should be noted that a higher relative risk for breast cancer was observed for Caucasian women with GSTM1-positive genotype than for women with the null genotype [19]. To explain this result, the author suggested that the combined conjugating activities of all GSTs may lead to depletion of glutathione and thereby become counterproductive.

N-acetyl transferases (NAT) catalyze reactions that lead to detoxification, such as *N*-acetylation, or activation, such as *O*-acetylation of *N*-hydroxyaryl amines, giving rise to the formation of DNA-reactive metabolites [10]. Various variant alleles leading to amino acid changes in the NAT1 and NAT2 enzymes are known (for more details, see [2]). The different genotypes are classified as either 'rapid' or 'slow' according to their acetylation capacity (slow *NAT2* acetylator genotype in Caucasians: 0.50-0.63, rapid-acetylator genotypes in Asians: 0.80-0.92) [14]. For chemically induced cancers, in which *N*-acetylation plays a role as a detoxification step (e.g., aromatic amine-related urinary bladder cancer), the NAT2 slow-acetylator phenotype is at higher risk [20]. The rapid-acetylator phenotype is at higher risk for colon cancer.

Microsomal epoxide hydrolase (the mEH enzyme encoded by the *EPHX* gene) catalyzes the hydrolysis of an epoxide to a dihydrodiol. Although mEH is considered a detoxifying enzyme, the dihydrodiols derived from PAHs may be further transformed by specific CYP enzymes into still more reactive species, such as dihydrodiol epoxides, the ultimate mutagenic and carcinogenic metabolites of many PAH. A single-nucleotide change at codon 113 of exon 3 (leading to a Tyr →His amino acid change), which is found in 32% of Caucasians, reduces the mEH enzyme activity and is associated with a decreased lung cancer risk [10, 14]. A codon 139 substitution (His → Arg) in exon 4, found in 22% of Caucasians, is associated with increased enzyme activity and lung cancer risk [10, 14]. On the basis of these exon-3 and exon-4 genotypes, the expected individual mEH activity can be classified as low, intermediate, or high.

The major alcohol-metabolizing enzymes in humans are the alcohol dehydrogenases (ADH) that oxidize alcohol (ethanol) to acetaldehyde, and the aldehyde dehydrogenases (ALDH) that detoxify acetaldehyde to acetate. ALDH2 is also involved in the metabolism of toluene – in particular, in the step from benzyl alcohol to benzoic acid – and appears to be implicated in the metabolism of vinyl chloride monomer [10]. The *ADH1B* gene has a polymorphism at codon 47 (leading to an Arg → His amino acid change in the enzyme). The *ADH1B*2* allele carrying this mutation is much more common in East Asians (> 90% of the population) than in Caucasians and Africans (< 20%) [21]. The individuals with *ADH1B*2* allele show a higher elimination rate for blood ethanol compared with those that have the *ADH1B*1/*1* genotype. The variant allele *ALDH2*2*, which encodes an inactive sub-unit of the enzyme ALDH2, is dominant and highly prevalent among certain populations of Asian ethnicity (0.28-0.45), but rare in other ethnic groups [22]. Most homozygous carriers of this allele (*ALDH2*2/*2,* which encodes the enzyme ALDH2 with an amino acid change in position 487 (Glu → Lys) are abstainers or infrequent drinkers, because the enzyme deficiency would cause a strong facial flushing response, physical discomfort and severe toxic reactions upon alcohol consumption. In heterozygous carriers (*ALDH2*1/*2,* with about 10% residual ALDH2 activity) these acute adverse effects are less severe, but when they consume alcohol these carriers are at high risk for several alcohol-related aerodigestive cancers [23-25].

3. Polymorphisms in Genes Encoding DNA-Repair Proteins

Hundreds of polymorphisms in DNA-repair genes have been identified in humans, although for many of them the impact on repair phenotype and cancer susceptibility remains uncertain [26]. The hypothesis is that SNPs in the DNA-repair genes may cause modifications in the structure and function of the encoded DNA repair proteins, leading to altered repair capacity. This, in turn, may give rise to accumulation of genetic damage in humans exposed to genotoxic agents in the environment or in occupational settings [27]. Different pathways of DNA repair operate on specific types of DNA damage, as discussed below (for more details, see [28]).

The base-excision repair (BER) pathway operates on small lesions such as oxidized or reduced bases, non-bulky adducts, or those produced by most alkylating agents. Enzymes involved in the restoration phase of BER include apurinic/apyrimidinic endonuclease (APEX1 or APE1), human 8-oxoguanine glycosylase (hOGG1), and the X-ray repair cross-complementing protein (group 1; XRCC1). The variant *APE1* Asp148Glu (rare allele frequency, 22%) may be associated with hypersensitivity to ionizing radiation (IR), but no association between this variant and cancer risk has been found [29]. Risks for esophageal, lung, nasopharyngeal, orolaryngeal, and prostate cancers are related to the *hOGG1* Ser326Cys polymorphism (rare allele frequency: 0.22-0.45) [28, 30]. Three non-synonymous coding SNPs in *XRCC1* are common and lead to amino acid substitutions in the XRCC1 protein at codon 194 (Arg → Trp, rare allele frequency: 0.06-0.35), codon 280 (Arg → His, rare allele frequency: 0.00-0.10), and codon 399 (Arg → Gln, rare allele frequency: 0.14-0.39) [28, 31]. Although association trends with specific cancer types have occasionally been found, the functional significance of these SNPs remains to be established [32].

The nucleotide-excision repair (NER) pathway removes bulky lesions such as pyrimidine dimers and other photo-products, larger chemical adducts, and intra-strand cross-links. The NER pathway involves *xeroderma pigmentosum* group D (*XPD*) and excision repair cross-complementing rodent repair-deficiency (*ERCC2*) genes. A number of SNPs in the *XPD* gene have been reported, consisting mainly of polymorphisms at codons 156 (Arg156Arg, rare allele frequency: 0.40-0.45, linked with skin cancer), 312 (Asp312Asn, rare allele frequency: 0.33-0.44), and 751 (Lys751Gln, rare allele frequency: 0.06-0.42) [28]. The variants XPD Asp312Asn and XPD Lys751Gln are deficient in the repair of chromosome aberrations induced by ultraviolet light, but not of those induced by X-rays, and they could play a role in individual susceptibility to lung and breast cancers [26].

Double-strand breaks can be produced by replication errors, during the processing of inter-strand cross-links, or directly, by clastogens. The two pathways of double-strand-break repair (DSBR) are (i) the homologous recombination pathway, in which the breast cancer proteins BRCA1 and BRCA2 and the X-ray repair cross-complementing protein (group 3; XRCC3) are involved, and (ii) the non-homologous end-joining repair pathway, which involves direct ligation of the two double-strand-breaks. Increased risks for breast, bladder, head and neck cancers and decreased risk for non-melanoma skin cancer were associated with the XRCC3 Thr241Met protein variant (rare allele frequency in controls: 0.23-0.38) in some studies [28, 33], but not in others [26]. The inability of the XRCC3 Thr241Met variant to complement the centrosome amplification defect may result in aberrant cells that are unable to enter apoptosis, and in genetic instability [34].

BRCA1 and *BRCA2* encode proteins required for maintaining genome stability, with important functions in cell-cycle checkpoint control, ubiquitylation, mitotic spindle formation, transcriptional regulation and DNA repair. The BRCA1 protein is also involved in non-homologous end joining and NER (especially transcription-coupled repair of oxidative damage) [35]. Hereditary breast and ovarian cancers have been linked to *BRCA1* and *BRCA2* germ-line mutations [35, 36]. Chromosomal mutagen sensitivity, e.g., to IR or various chemicals, may also be explained by mutations in *BRCA1/2* genes [37].

4. Polymorphisms in Genes Involved in Folate-Metabolism

Evidence is accumulating that the relative risks for colorectal carcinoma and acute leukemia are reduced by a diet that is high in folate [38, 39]. Many of the genes involved in folate metabolism are polymorphic. Examples are methylenetetrahydrofolate reductase (*MTHFR* 677 C>T, rare allele frequency: 0.01-0.20, and 1298 A>C, rare allele frequency: 0.02-0.12), methionine synthase (*MTR* 2756 A>G, rare allele frequency: 0.01-0.12), and methionine synthase reductase (*MTRR* 66 A>G, rare allele frequency: 0.19-0.29). Polymorphisms affecting genes involved in folate metabolism may be expected to modulate genome stability through an effect on nucleotide pools and DNA methylation (for more details, see [2]).

Low folate status may increase the risk for malignancy through two principal mechanisms. Through reduction of intracellular S-adenosylmethionine, folate deficiency can alter cytosine methylation in DNA, which may lead to inappropriate activation of proto-oncogenes and induction of malignant transformation. Alternatively, because of the crucial role of folic acid in normal DNA synthesis and repair, folate deficiency may cause an imbalance in DNA precursors, uracil misincorporation into DNA, and – ultimately – chromosome breakage [40]. Under conditions of folic-acid deficiency the *MTHFR* variant genotype (677 C>T change) is associated with an increased risk for developmental defects *in utero* and cancer at various sites (colon, breast, stomach, cervix, lung, and prostate) [6, 41, 42].

5. Conclusion

A large number of variant alleles (occurring in the genome with significant frequency) are known to be present in the various genes involved in DNA-damage processing, with the consequence that each individual is expected to carry about one dozen variants in each pathway [43]. Nevertheless, when a specific polymorphism by itself appears to have no or only a weak effect, the identification and characterization of the combined effects of different susceptibility genes for cancer risk require the understanding of gene-gene interactions [9].

Predisposition to hereditary cancer syndromes is dominated by the strong effects of some high-penetrance tumor susceptibility genes, while growing evidence suggests that genetic predisposition to sporadic cancer acts *via* a combination of multiple low- and medium-penetrance genes, rather than via a few high-penetrance genes [1, 6, 44]. This may lead to the identification of a genetic profile that is responsible for the susceptibility to DNA-damage induction. From a public health perspective, the identification of such a genetic profile will have a far-reaching long-term impact on primary prevention and early detection of disease-associated genes, by identifying high-risk individuals [27].

References

[1] Bartsch, H; Dally, H; Popanda, O; Risch, A; Schmezer, P. Genetic risk profiles for cancer susceptibility and therapy response. *Recent Results Cancer Res*,2007,174,19-36.

[2] Norppa, H. Cytogenetic biomarkers and genetic polymorphisms. *Toxicol. Lett*, 2004,149,309-334.

[3] Iarmarcovai, G; Bonassi, S; Botta, A; Baan, RA; Orsière, T. Genetic polymorphisms and micronucleus formation: a review of the literature. *Mutat. Res*, 2007, doi: 10.1016/j.mrrev.2007.10.001,

[4] Albertini, RJ; Anderson, D; Douglas, GR; Hagmar, L; Hemminki, K; Merlo, F; Natarajan, AT; Norppa, H; Shuker, DE; Tice, R; Waters, MD; Aitio, A. IPCS guidelines for the monitoring of genotoxic effects of carcinogens in humans. International Programme on Chemical Safety. *Mutat. Res,*2000,463,111-172.

[5] Norppa, H. Genetic polymorphisms and chromosome damage. *Int. J. Hyg. Environ. Health*,2001,204,31-38.

[6] Naccarati, A; Pardini, B; Hemminki, K; Vodicka, P. Sporadic colorectal cancer and individual susceptibility: a review of the association studies investigating the role of DNA repair genetic polymorphisms. *Mutat. Res*, 2007,635,118-145.

[7] Au, WW. Heritable susceptibility factors for the development of cancer. *J. Radiat. Res. (Tokyo)*,2006,47 Suppl B,B13-17.

[8] Bonassi, S; Ugolini, D; Kirsch-Volders, M; Stromberg, U; Vermeulen, R; Tucker, JD. Human population studies with cytogenetic biomarkers: review of the literature and future prospectives. *Environ. Mol. Mutagen*,2005,45,258-270.

[9] Manuguerra, M; Matullo, G; Veglia, F; Autrup, H; Dunning, AM; Garte, S; Gormally, E; Malaveille, C; Guarrera, S; Polidoro, S; Saletta, F; Peluso, M; Airoldi, L; Overvad, K; Raaschou-Nielsen, O; Clavel-Chapelon, F; Linseisen, J; Boeing, H; Trichopoulos, D; Kalandidi, A; Palli, D; Krogh, V; Tumino, R; Panico, S; Bueno-De-Mesquita, HB; Peeters, PH; Lund, E; Pera, G; Martinez, C; Amiano, P; Barricarte, A; Tormo, MJ; Quiros, JR; Berglund, G; Janzon, L; Jarvholm, B; Day, NE; Allen, NE; Saracci, R; Kaaks, R; Ferrari, P; Riboli, E; Vineis, P. Multi-factor dimensionality reduction applied to a large prospective investigation on gene-gene and gene-environment interactions. *Carcinogenesis*,2007,28,414-422.

[10] Pavanello, S; Clonfero, E. Biological indicators of genotoxic risk and metabolic polymorphisms. *Mutat. Res.*,2000,463,285-308.

[11] Chao, C; Zhang, ZF; Berthiller, J; Boffetta, P; Hashibe, M. NAD(P)H:quinone oxidoreductase 1 (NQO1) Pro187Ser polymorphism and the risk of lung, bladder, and colorectal cancers: a meta-analysis. *Cancer Epidemiol Biomarkers Prev*,2006,15,979-987.

[12] Kiyohara, C; Yoshimasu, K; Takayama, K; Nakanishi, Y. NQO1, MPO, and the risk of lung cancer: a HuGE review. *Genet. Med*,2005,7,463-478.

[13] Agundez, JA. Cytochrome P450 gene polymorphism and cancer. *Curr. Drug. Metab*,2004,5,211-224.

[14] Garte, S; Gaspari, L; Alexandrie, AK; Ambrosone, C; Autrup, H; Autrup, JL; Baranova, H; Bathum, L; Benhamou, S; Boffetta, P; Bouchardy, C; Breskvar, K; Brockmoller, J; Cascorbi, I; Clapper, ML; Coutelle, C; Daly, A; Dell'Omo, M; Dolzan, V; Dresler, CM; Fryer, A; Haugen, A; Hein, DW; Hildesheim, A; Hirvonen, A; Hsieh, LL; Ingelman-Sundberg, M; Kalina, I; Kang, D; Kihara, M; Kiyohara, C; Kremers, P; Lazarus, P; Le Marchand, L; Lechner, MC; van Lieshout, EM; London, S; Manni, JJ; Maugard, CM; Morita, S; Nazar-Stewart, V; Noda, K; Oda, Y; Parl, FF; Pastorelli, R; Persson, I; Peters, WH; Rannug, A; Rebbeck, T; Risch, A; Roelandt, L; Romkes, M; Ryberg, D; Salagovic, J; Schoket, B; Seidegard, J; Shields, PG; Sim, E; Sinnet, D; Strange, RC; Stucker, I; Sugimura, H; To-Figueras, J; Vineis, P; Yu, MC; Taioli, E. Metabolic gene polymorphism frequencies in control populations. *Cancer Epidemiol. Biomarkers Prev*,2001,10,1239-1248.

[15] Watson, MA; Stewart, RK; Smith, GB; Massey, TE; Bell, DA. Human glutathione S-transferase P1 polymorphisms: relationship to lung tissue enzyme activity and population frequency distribution. *Carcinogenesis*,1998,19,275-280.

[16] Landi, S. Mammalian class theta GST and differential susceptibility to carcinogens: a review. *Mutat. Res*,2000,463,247-283.

[17] Habdous, M; Siest, G; Herbeth, B; Vincent-Viry, M; Visvikis, S. [Glutathione S-transferases genetic polymorphisms and human diseases: overview of epidemiological studies]. *Ann. Biol. Clin. (Paris)*,2004,62,15-24.

[18] Dalhoff, K; Buus Jensen, K; Enghusen Poulsen, H. Cancer and molecular biomarkers of phase 2. *Methods Enzymol*,2005,400,618-627.

[19] Parl, FF. Glutathione S-transferase genotypes and cancer risk. *Cancer Lett*,2005,221,123-129.

[20] Hein, DW. Molecular genetics and function of NAT1 and NAT2: role in aromatic amine metabolism and carcinogenesis. *Mutat. Res*,2002,506-507,65-77.

[21] Ishikawa, H; Ishikawa, T; Yamamoto, H; Fukao, A; Yokoyama, K. Genotoxic effects of alcohol in human peripheral lymphocytes modulated by ADH1B and ALDH2 gene polymorphisms. *Mutat. Res*,2007,615,134-142.

[22] Goedde, HW; Agarwal, DP; Fritze, G; Meier-Tackmann, D; Singh, S; Beckmann, G; Bhatia, K; Chen, LZ; Fang, B; Lisker, R; et al. Distribution of ADH2 and ALDH2 genotypes in different populations. *Hum. Genet*,1992,88,344-346.

[23] Lewis, SJ; Smith, GD. Alcohol, ALDH2, and esophageal cancer: a meta-analysis which illustrates the potentials and limitations of a Mendelian randomization approach. *Cancer Epidemiol Biomarkers Prev*,2005,14,1967-1971.

[24] Yokoyama, A; Omori, T. Genetic polymorphisms of alcohol and aldehyde dehydrogenases and risk for esophageal and head and neck cancers. *Alcohol*,2005,35,175-185.

[25] Hashibe, M; Boffetta, P; Zaridze, D; Shangina, O; Szeszenia-Dabrowska, N; Mates, D; Janout, V; Fabianova, E; Bencko, V; Moullan, N; Chabrier, A; Hung, R; Hall, J; Canzian, F; Brennan, P. Evidence for an important role of alcohol- and aldehyde-metabolizing genes in cancers of the upper aerodigestive tract. Cancer Epidemiol Biomarkers Prev,2006,15,696-703.

[26] Manuguerra, M; Saletta, F; Karagas, MR; Berwick, M; Veglia, F; Vineis, P; Matullo, G. XRCC3 and XPD/ERCC2 single nucleotide polymorphisms and the risk of cancer: a HuGE review. *Am. J. Epidemiol*,2006,164,297-302.

[27] Angelini, S; Kumar, R; Carbone, F; Bermejo, JL; Maffei, F; Cantelli-Forti, G; Hemminki, K; Hrelia, P. Inherited susceptibility to bleomycin-induced micronuclei: Correlating polymorphisms in GSTT1, GSTM1 and DNA repair genes with mutagen sensitivity. *Mutat. Res*,2007,

[28] Goode, EL; Ulrich, CM; Potter, JD. Polymorphisms in DNA repair genes and associations with cancer risk. *Cancer Epidemiol Biomarkers Prev*,2002,11,1513-1530.

[29] Hung, RJ; Hall, J; Brennan, P; Boffetta, P. Genetic polymorphisms in the base excision repair pathway and cancer risk: a HuGE review. *Am. J. Epidemiol*,2005,162,925-942.

[30] Weiss, JM; Goode, EL; Ladiges, WC; Ulrich, CM. Polymorphic variation in hOGG1 and risk of cancer: a review of the functional and epidemiologic literature. *Mol. Carcinog*,2005,42,127-141.

[31] Hu, Z; Ma, H; Chen, F; Wei, Q; Shen, H. XRCC1 polymorphisms and cancer risk: a meta-analysis of 38 case-control studies. *Cancer Epidemiol Biomarkers Prev*,2005,14,1810-1818.

[32] Ladiges, WC. Mouse models of XRCC1 DNA repair polymorphisms and cancer. *Oncogene*,2006,25,1612-1619.

[33] Han, S; Zhang, HT; Wang, Z; Xie, Y; Tang, R; Mao, Y; Li, Y. DNA repair gene XRCC3 polymorphisms and cancer risk: a meta-analysis of 48 case-control studies. *Eur. J. Hum. Genet*,2006,14,1136-1144.

[34] Lindh, AR; Rafii, S; Schultz, N; Cox, A; Helleday, T. Mitotic defects in XRCC3 variants T241M and D213N and their relation to cancer susceptibility. *Hum. Mol. Genet*,2006,15,1217-1224.

[35] Beetstra, S; Salisbury, C; Turner, J; Altree, M; McKinnon, R; Suthers, G; Fenech, M. Lymphocytes of BRCA1 and BRCA2 germ-line mutation carriers, with or without breast cancer, are not abnormally sensitive to the chromosome damaging effect of moderate folate deficiency. *Carcinogenesis*,2006,27,517-524.

[36] Levy-Lahad, E; Friedman, E. Cancer risks among BRCA1 and BRCA2 mutation carriers. *Br. J. Cancer*,2007,96,11-15.

[37] Speit, G; Trenz, K. Chromosomal mutagen sensitivity associated with mutations in BRCA genes. *Cytogenet. Genome Res*,2004,104,325-332.

[38] Sharp, L; Little, J. Polymorphisms in genes involved in folate metabolism and colorectal neoplasia: a HuGE review. *Am. J. Epidemiol*,2004,159,423-443.

[39] Hubner, RA; Houlston, RS. MTHFR C677T and colorectal cancer risk: A meta-analysis of 25 populations. *Int. J. Cancer*,2007,120,1027-1035.

[40] Duthie, SJ. Folic acid deficiency and cancer: mechanisms of DNA instability. *Br. Med. Bull*,1999,55,578-592.

[41] Leopardi, P; Marcon, F; Caiola, S; Cafolla, A; Siniscalchi, E; Zijno, A; Crebelli, R. Effects of folic acid deficiency and MTHFR C677T polymorphism on spontaneous and radiation-induced micronuclei in human lymphocytes. *Mutagenesis*,2006,21,327-333.

[42] Hung, RJ; Hashibe, M; McKay, J; Gaborieau, V; Szeszenia-Dabrowska, N; Zaridze, D; Lissowska, J; Rudnai, P; Fabianova, E; Mates, I; Foretova, L; Janout, V; Bencko, V; Chabrier, A; Moullan, N; Canzian, F; Hall, J; Boffetta, P; Brennan, P. Folate related genes and the risk of tobacco-related cancers in Central Europe. *Carcinogenesis*,2007,

[43] Kyrtopoulos, SA. Biomarkers in environmental carcinogenesis research: striving for a new momentum. *Toxicol Lett*,2006,162,3-15.

[44] Pharoah, PD; Dunning, AM; Ponder, BA; Easton, DF. Association studies for finding cancer-susceptibility genetic variants. *Nat. Rev. Cancer*,2004,4,850-860.

In: New Research on DNA Damage
Editors: Honoka Kimura and Aoi Suzuki

ISBN 978-1-60456-581-2
© 2008 Nova Science Publishers, Inc.

Chapter 6

HTLV-I Tax Promotes Genomic Instability by Interfering with Repair of DNA Breaks

Razvan I. Ducu and Susan J. Marriott[*]

Department of Molecular Virology and Microbiology, Baylor College of Medicine, USA

Abstract

An emerging mechanism of cellular transformation by oncogenic viruses is the inhibition or suppression of cellular DNA repair. This review will focus on human T-cell leukemia virus (HTLV-I), which is the causative agent of adult T-cell leukemia (ATL), an aggressive clonal malignancy of CD4+ T lymphocytes. The oncogenic potential of HTLV-I relies on expression of the viral transcriptional modulator, Tax. In addition to activating viral transcription, Tax controls the expression of a large and diverse array of cellular genes. By altering gene expression homeostasis, as well as by direct protein-protein interactions, Tax interferes with normal DNA replication and repair processes, thereby contributing to an increased mutation frequency in HTLV-I infected cells. We and others have shown that Tax can suppress DNA base and nucleotide excision repair pathways by altering the expression of important factors involved in these pathways, such as DNA polymerase beta and PCNA. Tax has also been shown to affect protein interactions that regulate DNA repair pathways and to attenuate the ATM mediated damage response, a major pathway for repair of DNA double strand breaks (DSBs). In this chapter we will review the effect of Tax on DNA repair and genome stability and the role of these processes in cellular transformation. We will discuss the inhibitory effect of Tax on ATM kinase activity, which reveals novel insights into the normal function of this signaling and repair pathway. Finally, we will discuss recent data suggesting a critical role for the DNA double strand break repair pathway in retroviral replication and tumor suppression.

[*] Corresponding author: Susan J. Marriott, Baylor College of Medicine, One Baylor Plaza, Houston, TX 77030, phone: (713) 798-4440, fax: (713) 798-3491, e-mail: susanm@bcm.tmc.edu.

Keywords: viral transformation; genomic instability; viral-associated cancer; HTLV-I; DNA repair

1. Introduction

Several viruses have been etiologically linked to specific forms of cancer, [1] and many other human viruses not formally implicated in human tumorigenesis encode proteins capable of immortalizing cells in culture and causing tumors in transgenic animals [2]. It is generally accepted that for a virus to cause cancer, it has to establish persistent or latent infections. To do so, viruses capable of persistently infecting cells have to establish symbiotic relationships with the host by efficiently using the cell's resources to maintain and transmit the viral genome and to inhibit the host's natural defense mechanisms that eliminate the infection. On the other hand, cells possess highly versatile mechanisms for sensing cellular stress, such as the DNA damage response (DDR) and the p53 tumor suppressor pathway, which can become activated by alterations in cellular homeostasis induced by viral infection [3]. Emerging evidence suggests that these mechanisms play critical roles *in vivo* not only in the initial steps of tumorigenesis, but also during tumor evolution from pre-malignant or low-grade malignant lesions to invasive cancer. Therefore, inhibition of these stress-sensing mechanisms by human tumor viruses might play decisive roles in the initiation and progression of virally induced cancers [4]. Deciphering the intimate details of these processes could lead to further insight into tumor biology as well as provide new targets for rationally designed therapy. This review focuses on mechanisms of genomic instability and cellular transformation mediated by the HTLV-I oncoprotein Tax, and describes some recent evidence for the opposing effect of Tax on the DNA damage signaling and repair pathways.

2. HTLV-I Epidemiology and Pathogenesis

2.A. HTLV-I Induced Cellular Transformation

Human T-cell leukemia virus type I (HTLV-I) is associated with the development of adult T-cell leukemia (ATL), an aggressive malignancy of mature CD4+ T lymphocytes [5]. HTLV-I, the first identified human retroviral pathogen, was first isolated in 1980 from leukemic cells of a patient with ATL [6] and is now recognized as the etiological agent of this fatal disease as well as a progressive neurological syndrome called tropical spastic paraparesis or HTLV-I-associated myelopathy (TSP/HAM) (reviewed in [7]). It is estimated that 10 to 20 million people are currently infected with HTLV-I worldwide, with higher rates concentrated in endemic areas such as Japan, Africa, South America, the Caribbean, Eastern Europe and southeastern United States [8]. While most HTLV-I infected individuals remain asymptomatic throughout their lives, 1-5% will develop ATL after a long latency period, typically of 2 to 5 decades [5]. HTLV-I transmission occurs horizontally through body fluids (i.e. blood transfusion, intravenous drug use and sexual contact) and vertically through breastfeeding. Regardless of the route of inoculation HTLV-I requires intimate cell-cell contact for efficient transmission. To transmit the virus, infected cells become attached to uninfected target lymphocytes through engagement of cell surface adhesion molecules, such as ICAM-1 and, after the polarization of the microtubule organizing center to the junction, a viral bolus is delivered to the uninfected cell. This mode of viral spread, also referred to as "virological synapse" [9] is very advantageous by protecting the virus from the host humoral immune response .

ATL can present in four clinical subtypes: acute, lymphoma type, chronic and smoldering. The first two types show aggressive progression, whereas the last two have a more indolent clinical progression. Importantly, in spite of the more insidious course these two subtypes tend to lead to the more aggressive forms, suggesting that genetic variation and clonal selection lead to the emergence of rapidly proliferating highly resistant malignant cells [10]. After the onset of the acute disease, the progression is rapid, with a median survival of 12 months, only marginally affected by combined chemotherapy. Acute disease is typically characterized by fever, cough, lymphadenopathy, skin infiltrates, hepatosplenomegaly and lymphocytosis. Hypercalcemia and immunodeficiency are also common features of the acute disease and are thought to arise due to aberrant secretion of cytokines and growth factors by the leukemic cells. The diagnostic criteria for ATL include seropositivity for HTLV-I, high serum levels of lactate dehydrogenase and the presence of atypical lymphocytes (CD4+, CD8- and CD25+) with convoluted or lobulated nuclei, characteristically referred as "flower cells" [5]. Demonstration of monoclonal integration of HTLV-I in the leukemic cells is used to confirm the diagnosis.

2.B. ATL is Initiated and Sustained by Increased Proliferation and Genomic Instability

The low incidence and late onset of ATL as well as the progression from a lower grade disease to more aggressive, acute ATL suggest that, in addition to the viral infection, genomic mutations are required for the initiation and progression of the oncogenic process *in vivo*. HTLV-I induced malignancy presumably follows a multistep oncogenic process in which the virus induces cell proliferation as well as increases the mutation rate of replicating infected cells, resulting in an accumulation of genetic defects and deregulated growth.

In culture, HTLV-I has been shown to transform human T-cells as well as cells from other species [11,12,13]. HTLV-I-infected cells phenotypes and surface markers associated with activated T-cells, such as interleukin-2 (IL-2) receptor alpha subunit and exhibit increased expression of genes critical for T-cell growth and proliferation, including granulocyte-macrophage colony stimulating factor (GM-CSF), tumor necrosis factor-alpha (TNF-α), IL-2, and IL-15 [14,15,16]. It is believed that the increased proliferation of infected cells is a way to maintain persistent infection *in vivo* [17,5]. Since cell-free virus is poorly infectious, viral persistence and amplification of infection is mainly achieved by clonal expansion of infected cells [18,17,5]. Evidence in support of this mechanism resulted from studies using administration of reverse transcriptase inhibitors to patients with TSP/HAM. These studies have shown that proviral loads do not change with administration of RTI in chronically infected people or in animals acutely infected with HTLV-I [19,20]. These results suggest that de novo infection of T cells *in vivo* has a minor contribution to viral burden [17]. Additionally, studies have shown that infected T cells undergo persistent clonal proliferation and that some clones persist for more than 7 years in the same HTLV-I carriers [21].

HTLV-I transformed lymphocytes isolated from patients, and those immortalized in culture, demonstrate a wide range of chromosomal abnormalities, including deletions, translocations, rearrangements, duplications, and aneuploidy [22,23,24,25,26,27], however no specific type of chromosomal change has been associated with the development of HTLV-I associated malignancy. Based on the complexity and variability of karyotypic abnormalities found in ATL cells, it has been proposed that a multistep oncogenic process, including a minimum of five genetic hits, leads to the development of ATL [28]. It has been hypothesized that five serial genetic events must occur in the immortalization and transformation process of an HTLV-I infected cell [28]. Supporting this model, several studies have demonstrated that various tumor suppressor genes were disrupted in ATL cells. Alteration of the p53 gene was found in 40% of ATL cases [29,30,31], while the p15INK4B, p16INK4A, and retinoblastoma (Rb) genes are altered in about 30, 35, and 5% of ATL cases, respectively [32,33,34]. Interestingly, mutations in either p53 or p16 were found in more than half of pediatric HTLV-I associated leukemia/lymphoma, suggesting that alteration of tumor suppressor genes that regulate the G1/S transition may promote an early onset of leukemia [35].

Based on these data and other results that will be discussed in this chapter, it has been proposed that HTLV infection decreases the capacity of the host cell to repair genomic lesions introduced by environmental injuries or resulting from normal cellular metabolism. Such lesions occur randomly throughout the genome and accumulate as a result of clonal expansion and selection of mutations that confer an advantage for proliferation and survival. This genomic instability may inactivate genes involved in DNA repair and cell cycle control, ultimately contributing to cellular transformation. In certain ATL cases, the transition from chronic to acute phase is marked by p53 mutation, underscoring the role of genomic mutations in ATL development.

2.C. Tax-Induced Genomic Instability

The 40 kDa Tax protein encoded by HTLV-I is a strong trans-activator of viral transcription and is the major transforming protein of HTLV-I. Although Tax affects a wide range of cellular functions through transcriptional modulation of cellular genes, protein–protein interactions and post-translational modification of cellular proteins, there is no evidence that Tax directly induces DNA damage [36]. Rather, Tax appears to inhibit the repair of DNA damage and allows replication of damaged DNA, thus indirectly leading to increased mutation frequency [37].

One of the first indications that Tax expression may induce genomic instability came from studies using the micronucleus formation assay [38]. Micronuclei are small nuclei-like bodies found in the cytoplasm, separated from the main cell nucleus and are formed as by-products of DNA damage [39,40]. The presence of micronuclei is widely used in mutagenicity testing as a sensitive indicator of genotoxicity [41]. Micronuclei containing whole chromosomes (kinetocore positive) are thought to result from mitotic defects (or treatment with aneuploidogenic agents), while those containing acentric chromosomal fragments (kinetocore negative) are a consequence of improper repair of DNA breaks (or treatment with clastogenic agents). The induction of micronuclei in Tax expressing cells correlates with the transcriptional activity of Tax [38,42]. Additionally, micronuclei observed in Tax expressing cells are both kinetocore positive and negative, and contain free 3'-hydroxyl DNA ends [42,36]. While the precise mechanism of MN formation in Tax-expressing cells remains unknown, these findings demonstrate both clastogenic and aneuploidogenic effects of Tax.

Gene amplification, which is thought to result from recombination events following the formation of DNA double-strand breaks, is an indicator of genomic instability [43]. Analysis of the gene encoding the trifunctional enzyme carbamyl phosphate synthetase/aspartate transcarbamylase/dihydro-orotase (CAD), a commonly used marker for gene amplification studies, was amplified five-fold in Tax-expressing cells compared to control cells, indicating that Tax expression contributes to genomic instability [44]. This result demonstrates that Tax-expressing cells are defective in recognition or repair of double-strand DNA breaks

2.D. Inhibition of DNA Repair Pathways by Tax

Despite constant genotoxic insults, the integrity of the cellular genome is maintained by DNA repair mechanisms including nucleotide excision repair (NER), base excision repair (BER), mismatch repair (MMR), and double-strand break repair (DSBR). Tax has been shown to interfere with several of these pathways by altering the transcription of certain critical factors or by direct protein-protein interactions.

Nucleotide excision repair NER was the first DNA repair pathway specifically shown to be suppressed by Tax [45]. One of the most versatile cellular repair systems, NER plays a major role in maintaining genome stability and defects in NER are responsible for several cancer predisposition syndromes. The inhibitory activity of Tax on NER correlates with its ability to activate transcription of the proliferating cell nuclear antigen (PCNA) promoter [46,47]. PCNA is a processivity factor of DNA polymerase δ (pol δ), an enzyme involved in both DNA replication and NER [48]. In the presence of DNA damage, elevated levels of the p21 CKI interact with PCNA to specifically interfere with its DNA synthesis function, but not its DNA repair function. Increased PCNA expression induced by Tax appears to inhibit NER by allowing cells to overcome the p21 mediated block in DNA replication and enabling pol δ to synthesize through template lesions [47]. As a result, DNA lesions induced by environmental mutagens are incorporated into the progeny genome inducing a "mutator phenotype" that can ultimately lead to cellular transformation.

Base excision repair The ability of Tax to suppress cellular DNA repair was first suggested by the observation that Tax repressed transcription of the human DNA polymerase β promoter [49]. DNA polymerase β. (pol. β) is involved in base excision and mismatch forms of DNA repair [50]. Interestingly, recent small scale studies suggest that approximately 30% of human tumors express mutant variants of pol β that either have a lower DNA synthesis fidelity than wild-type or interfere with BER in a dominant negative manner

[51,52,53]. These novel findings emphasize the role of BER in maintaining genomic stability and attribute functional significance to the repression of pol β of transcription by Tax. In addition, Tax proteins from HTLV-I, -II, and the related bovine leukemia virus (BLV), specifically suppress BER [54], however, more studies are necessary to determine if this effect is a direct consequence of pol β depletion.

DNA double-strand break repair Recent studies have been conducted to investigate the possible effects of Tax or HTLV-I infection on DNA double-strand break repair. These have been prompted by several anomalies observed in HTLV-I transformed cells, suggesting that this repair pathway may be affected by HTLV infection. As discussed previously, gross chromosomal abnormalities, micronuclei and gene amplification are typical features of HTLV-I transformed cells and can all arise as a result of improper DSB repair [55]. The next sections of this chapter will describe results from our lab and others that bring some insight into the mechanisms used by Tax to interfere with normal recognition and repair of DNA breaks.

3. Cellular Mechanisms for Repair of DNA Breaks

3.A. Role of DSB Repair in Maintaining Genomic Stability and Tumor Suppression

The efficient repair of DNA double-strand breaks is crucial in safeguarding the genomic integrity of cells and organisms. Responses to double-strand breaks include complex signal-transduction, cell-cycle-checkpoint and repair pathways. Defects in these pathways lead to several human disorders with pleiotropic clinical features [56]. DSB can arise from genotoxic insults and normal cellular processes such as DNA replication and are detected by sensor molecules that trigger the activation of transducing kinases. These transducers then phosphorylate effector proteins to initiate signaling cascades that control cell cycle checkpoints, activate the DNA repair machinery, or trigger apoptotic pathways. The primary transducers of the DNA damage response (DDR) are protein kinases members of the phosphatidylinositol 3-kinase related kinases (PIKKs) ataxia telangiectasia mutated (ATM) and ataxia telangiectasia and RAD3-related (ATR) [57]. The ataxia telangiectasia (AT) syndrome is characterized by unsteady posture (ataxia), dilated blood vessels (telangiectasia), growth retardation, progressive neurological degeneration, immune deficiencies, premature ageing and an approximately 100-fold increased incidence of cancer particularly lymphomas and leukemia [56]. . The cellular phenotype of AT cells include radiosensitivity, marked chromosomal instability and radioresistant DNA synthesis (RDS), which is indicative of the inability to fully induce an intra-S-phase checkpoint. The identification of the gene responsible for these defects in 1995 by Savitsky et. al. was an important milestone that paved the way for subsequent understanding of the molecular details of the DDR [58]. In addition to AT several cancer-prone syndromes have been described to be caused by mutations in other components of the DDR pathway. Hypomorphic mutations of MRE11 cause ataxia-telangiectasia-like disease (ATLD) and hypomorphic mutations of NBS1 cause Nijmegen breakage syndrome (NBS) [56]. Both disorders are phenotypically related to ataxia-telangiectasia. ATLD patients develop most of the hallmarks of AT, albeit at a later stage and with slower progression. NBS is characterized by immunodeficiency, small head size, mental deficiency, genomic instability, radiation sensitivity and acute predisposition to lymphoid malignancies. The NBS phenotype shows significant overlap with those of AT and ATLD, except that cerebellar degeneration does not occur.

3.B. The ATM Pathway

One of the first detectable events after induction of DSB by ionizing radiation treatment is the rapid relocalization of the MRE11–RAD50–NBS1 (MRN) complex to sites of DNA damage in the form of nuclear foci [59]. The highly conserved MRN complex is thought to have a key role in DSB repair, DNA replication, telomere maintenance and checkpoint signaling [60]. Although Nbs1 is a phosphorylation target of ATM and its phosphorylation is important for checkpoint activation, the binding of MRN to DNA ends appears to be independent of ATM. This suggests that MRN acts upstream of ATM in the DNA damage pathway [61]. Mre11/Rad50 complexes bind to DNA as a heterotetramers, tethering broken ends of a DSB [62].The binding appears to be mediated through the two DNA-binding motifs of Mre11 [63] (Figure 1). Within the Mre11/Rad50 tetramer, two coiled-coil regions in each of the two Rad50 molecules form two far-reaching arms that bridge the two DNA ends through inter-molecular interactions between the CXXC sequences located in the middle of Rad50. These sequences are displayed at the ends of the coiled-coil regions and appear to dimerize by coordinating a Zn^{2+} ion [64]. Association with Rad50 stimulates both the exonuclease and endonuclease activities of Mre11 [65,66], which are thought to contribute to DNA end processing that occurs before repair. Nbs1 binds to Mre11 and recruits activated ATM to the DNA end through a specific C terminal domain.

In unstressed cells ATM exists in the nucleus in inactive homodimers (or higher order oligomers). Studies using okadakic acid showed that ATM oligomers are maintained in the inactive form through the physical interaction with PP2A, which prevents intermolecular phosphorylation and activation [67]. Following DNA damage, ATM is activated by auto-phosphorylation at serine 1981 and other residues, followed by dissociation of the dimers into kinase active monomers [68]. Therefore, ATM activation requires both ATM kinase activity and intermolecular autophosphorylation of both ATM proteins on Ser 1981 [69]. While ATM can be activated by various forms of cellular stress, such as hypotonic swelling or chloroquine treatment, its activation and recruitment to DNA ends occurs by its interaction with the C terminus of Nbs1 [70,71]. Activated ATM phosphorylates a large number of cellular proteins including NBS1, Chk2, p53, BRCA1, H2AX and MDC1, which function to stop cell cycle progression, repair the DNA damage or induce apoptosis [72]. After initial phosphorylation of H2AX proximal to the DNA break by ATM, MDC1 binds to gH2AX through its BRCA1 C-terminal (BRCT) domain and rapidly relocalizes to sites of DNA damage. MDC1 also interacts with ATM through its forkhead-associated domain (FHA), of H2AX phosphorylation over megabase chromatin domains surrounding the break [73]. This extension of H2AX phosphorylation is believed to help maintain and amplify ATM activation, functioning as a positive feedback loop, and to facilitate the accumulation of DNA repair and checkpoint proteins close to the sites of DNA damage [74]. Absence of MDC1 leads to lack of recruitment of ATM to sites of DNA damage and defective checkpoint activation [73].

3.C. NHEJ – the Ku70/80 DNA-PK Pathway

After the DDR pathway is activated in response to DSBs the cell has to repair the broken DNA using homologous recombination or non-homologous end joining [75]. NHEJ appears to be the main pathway to repair DSBs and an important mechanism for preserving genomic integrity [76]. Homologous recombination is thought to repair a smaller number of DSBs, and is fully active only when the cell has replicated its genome in the S phase of the cell cycle. This pathway selection for repair of DSBs is explained by the high fraction of repetitive sequences present in mammalian genomes. Unless sister chromatids are closely aligned, the homology search process for repair of a DSB can be insurmountable and could lead to chromosomal translocations when the break occurs in a repeated sequence. Interestingly, repair of DSBs by homologous recombination is down-regulated during G0, G1 and early S phases of somatic cells in multicellular eukaryotes [77]. This means that NHEJ is the predominant — if not exclusive — mechanism for repairing DSBs during G0, G1, and early S phases, and that NHEJ continues to repair a minority of breaks during late S and G2 phases.

Repair of DSBs by NHEJ requires several proteins that capture both DNA ends, hold them together in a synaptic complex, and facilitate direct ligation of the DNA break [78]. The NHEJ core components include the DNA-dependent protein kinase (DNA-PK) complex, Artemis and the XRCC4/DNA ligase IV complex. DNA-PK is a large, trimeric protein kinase complex consisting of a DNA binding subunit, Ku and a kinase subunit, DNA-PKcs. Ku is a stable heterodimer of Ku70 and Ku80 that binds to the ends of dsDNA and, in vitro, can translocate along linear plasmid DNA in an ATP-independent manner. Ku70 and Ku80 have a similar three-dimensional structure [79], with regions of both subunits contributing to a channel structure that completely encircles the DNA molecule. In addition to their central DNA binding regions, which share similarities in amino-acid structure, both Ku80 and Ku70 possess unique amino- and carboxy- terminal regions that are required for distinct protein interactions. Of note, the C-terminal 12 amino acids of Ku80 are required for its interaction with DNA-PKcs. Ku appears to be the first protein to arrive at the DNA break and, upon binding to the end, it recruits DNA-PKcs to the complex through the Ku80 subunit. DNA-PKcs is a large (469 kDa), member of the PIKK family, which also includes ATM and ATR. DNA-PKcs contains a C-terminal catalytic domain and a number of putative protein interaction domains in its N-terminus, which are also found in the other members of the family.

Cells lacking DNA-PKcs, Ku70, Ku80 or Artemis are radiosensitive and defective in DSB repair. Animals carrying defects in DNA-PKcs gene have severe combined immunodeficiency due to a defect in V(D)J recombination [80]. Also mice lacking Ku70 or Ku80 show growth defects and premature senescence genomic instability and severe tumorigenesis when p53 is also absent [81]. In contrast, Ku80 appears to be essential for human cells, and therefore no human disease has been associated with inherited mutations in the Ku80 gene [82]. A recent study has linked polymorphism in the Ku70 and XRCC4 genes with an increased risk of breast cancer [83].

The current model for NHEJ describes a stepwise process, initiated by the binding of Ku dimers to the DNA ends on each side of a DSB. DNA-PKcs interacts with the end-bound Ku, to form the DNA-PK complex, which increases its kinase activity 10 fold. The two ends are held together by interactions between the DNA-PK complexes bound on each side of the break, in a process called synapsis. The nuclease Artemis is then recruited to the complex to perform the DNA end trimming and ligation is subsequently carried out by the by the XRCC4/DNA ligase IV complex. During break repair, DNA-PKcs phosphorylates itself, Ku70, Ku80, Artemis and XRCC4, however the precise mechanisms by which these phosphorylation events affect the function of the complex remains to be elucidated. Mutations of the DNA-PKcs phosphorylation target sites to alanine abrogate its function, as shown by complementation assays [84,85,86]. Recent studies suggest that phosphorylation of amino acid clusters 2609 and 2056 within DNA-PKcs cause it to be released from the synaptic complex, suggesting a model in which trans-phosphorylation of DNA-PKcs across the DNA break regulates the accessibility of other NHEJ components to the repair complex. Interestingly, one new study reported that phosphorylation of the 2609 and 2647 residues of DNA-PKcs is dependent on the ATM protein [87]. This allowed for refinement of the previous model, in which homotypic DNA-PK interaction and DNA end bridging, as well as the presence of ATM would regulate the progression of the rejoining process. This high level of control prevents premature degradation of the DNA ends and increases the repair fidelity.

4. HTLV-I Tax Interferes with Cellular DSB Repair

4.A. Tax Targets MDC1 to Prematurely Attenuate ATM Activation and Kinase Function

As discussed above, ATM is an important tumor suppressor protein and plays a central role in the DNA damage response. Importantly, individuals carrying homozygous inactivating mutations in the *ATM* gene have an increased risk of cancer, particularly leukemia and lymphoma. To investigate the effects of HTLV-I infection on the DNA damage response we analyzed the function of the ATM pathway in response to induction of DNA breaks. Our results showed that HTLV-I Tax compromises the ATM-mediated DNA damage response by allowing premature dephosphorylation of ATM at serine residue 1981 and attenuation of ATM kinase activity towards its cognate substrates NBS1 and Chk2. Tax does not bind ATM (unpublished data) therefore the effect of Tax on ATM dephosphorylation appears to be indirect and may be due to an inability of Tax-expressing cells to amplify and maintain the damage response.

Following IR, Tax-expressing cells show an initial robust phosphorylation of ATM at S1981 as well as phosphorylation of its cognate substrates NBS1 and Chk2, suggesting that Tax does not affect initial steps in the DNA damage response. However, phospho-ATM did not accumulate in nuclear foci, instead showing a more diffuse staining pattern in Tax-expressing cells. In addition, ATM did not associate with chromatin in Tax-expressing cells treated with the radiomimetic drug, Bleomycin. These results suggest that Tax interferes with the accumulation of ATM on chromatin surrounding DSBs.

Improper accumulation of ATM on chromatin compromises the extension of H2AX phosphorylation, preventing proper formation of repair foci. Indeed, γH2AX staining following IR treatment showed only weak, nascent foci in Tax-expressing cells, with no amplification over time. As discussed previously, the initial activation and recruitment of ATM to DNA ends depends on the Mre11/Rad50/NBS1 (M/R/N) complex [88,89,61,70,90], while the subsequent accumulation of ATM on chromatin is regulated by MDC1 [73], which bridges the interaction between ATM and γH2AX. We found that MDC1 did not colocalize with the nascent γH2AX foci, suggesting that Tax either blocks the BRCT domain of MDC1 or, alternatively, that Tax binds to γH2AX preventing its interaction with MDC1. However, Tax does not appear to alter the cellular amounts of MDC1 or its nuclear localization. Rather, we hypothesize that Tax interferes with the recruitment of MDC1 to chromatin, preventing stable accumulation of activated ATM into large repair foci and the subsequent amplification of γH2AX. In support of this hypothesis, co-immunoprecipitation experiments show that interactions between ATM, MDC1, and H2AX are disrupted in Tax-expressing cells following DNA damage (unpublished data). Therefore, we propose that Tax interferes with the ability of MDC1 to bridge the interaction between ATM and H2AX, thereby disrupting the positive feedback loop and promoting the return of ATM to an unphosphorylated, inactive state. Premature attenuation of the ATM mediated damage response allows cells to resume DNA synthesis, which translates in a partial RDS phenotype we observed in Tax expressing cells. Thus, sustained ATM activity, and not just its initial activation, is required to maintain an IR-induced S-phase checkpoint. Premature inactivation of this checkpoint occurs despite the presence of unrepaired DNA in Tax-expressing cells.

4.B. Ku80 Repression by Tax and its Implications for Repair of DSBs by NHEJ

Ku80 is a critical component of the NHEJ DNA repair pathway, which is thought to protect against chromosomal instability. Ku80 null cells show increased radiosensitivity and chromosomal breakage and introduction of Ku80 siRNA into human tumor cells increases their sensitivity to radiation and chemotherapeutic agents [91]. Studies by Majone et. al. using enzymatic labeling of DNA ends showed that expression of the HTLV-I Tax oncoprotein rapidly induces cytogenetic damage reflected in an increase in the prevalence of micronuclei (MN) containing free DNA ends [36]. The increase in MN formation induced by Tax expression was dependent on Ku80 protein expression. While Ku80 null cells displayed a high basal level of MN, Tax transfection did not have an additive effect in these cells [92]. This observation led to the hypothesis that Tax might target Ku80 to produce clastogenic DNA damage. To investigate this possibility we analyzed the expression of Ku and DNA-PKcs mRNA and protein levels in cells expressing Tax. We found that Tax represses the expression of Ku80 mRNA, which leads to a severe reduction in steady state levels of the Ku heterodimer. When assayed for DNA repair, HTLV-I infected cell lines showed a dramatic impairment of DSB rejoining as demonstrated by an increased number of residual chromosomal breaks detected by comet assays. We proposed that repression of Ku80 expression and attenuation of the ATM pathway by HTLV-I Tax causes a severe defect in DNA double strand break repair. Consequently, DNA breaks that occurr as a result of genotoxic agents or normal cellular metabolism will not be promptly repaired by non-mutagenic mechanisms. This would lead to loss of chromosomal fragments in micronuclei, degradation by endogenous nucleases or activation of mutagenic repair pathways, such as illegitimate recombination or single strand annealing. Altogether, inhibition of DNA double strand break repair by Tax creates a state of genomic instability that is thought to contribute to HTLV-I induced cellular transformation.

5. Role of the DNA Damage Response in Viral Infection and Tumor Suppression

5.A. ATM Mediated Signals Play Critical Roles in Viral Replication

Emerging evidence reveals a global role of the ATM pathway in recognizing various forms of cellular stress, such as oncogene-induced replicative stress (described in more detail in the next section), osmotic stress and alterations in chromatin structure induced by histone deacetylase inhibitors. Viruses can elicit some of these signals, either by replicating their DNA genomes, such as the Cytomegalovirus (CMV), Epstein Barr Virus (EBV), or Herpes Simplex Virus (HSV) , by integrating their DNA into the host genome, such as retroviruses, or by activating endogenous cellular oncogenes [93,94,95,96]. While some viruses evolved mechanisms to tolerate activation of this pathway and to benefit from it, others acquired ways to counteract it. Probably the best studied is the effect of retroviral infection and the host DNA damage response. Integration of retroviral DNA into the host cell genome generates a complex lesion in the host DNA. Interruption of existing chromatin conformation by the insertion of newly synthesized viral DNA as well as the two short single-stranded gaps in the host DNA flanking the integration site are likely to be sensed as major assaults on the genomic integrity of the cell [97]. Collision of a host cell replication fork with unrepaired gaps during S-phase could produce DSBs with free ends at the site of integration. Supporting this idea, a recent study showed that H2AX becomes phosphorylated at sites of retroviral integration [96]. In addition, unintegrated linear viral DNA molecules in the nucleus may be recognized by host DNA damage-sensing and repair pathways leading to self-ligation [98,99]. It seems likely, however, that mechanisms to limit such self-ligation have evolved, as this reaction could compete with productive viral integration. In contrast, post-integration repair is essential to maintain host DNA integrity as well as for the stable, heritable association of retroviral genome with host chromosomes. Indeed, recent studies have shown that the NHEJ pathway and ATM signaling are essential for cell survival after transduction by recombinant human immunodeficiency virus (HIV) vectors [100,101,102]. In one of these studies up to 90% of the NHEJ deficient cells were killed upon infection, in a process that was dependent on the presence of active integrase in the infecting virion [103]. Consequently, highly selective ATM kinase inhibitors have been shown to effectively suppress HIV infection and hold the promise of better therapy for HIV induced disease. While the same mechanisms might be involved in early stages of HTLV-I infection, following post-integration repair, activation of the DDR could be detrimental for the stable maintenance of infected cells, since Tax has acquired mechanisms to inhibit this pathway.

5.B. The DNA Damage Signaling Pathway in Protects Against Activated Oncogenes and Tumor Progression

Emerging evidence from cell culture and animal models as well as analyses of clinical specimens show that activation of oncogenes and loss of tumor suppressor genes result in DNA replication stress and DNA damage that alarm the cellular ATM kinase signaling pathway. Cell culture experiments demonstrated that that ectopic over-expression of some oncogenic factors including c-Myc, E2F1, cyclin E and cdc25A can induce ATM activation and phosphorylation of its downstream target p53. While the mechanism of oncogene-induced activation of the DDR is not fully understood, it is believed that de-regulation of cell cycle progression and DNA synthesis as well as over-production of reactive oxygen species (ROS) contribute to the induction of DNA breaks that are detected by the normal cellular repair machinery. Importantly, activation of the DDR network can lead to cellular senescence or apoptotic death of oncogene-transformed cells, resulting in delay or prevention of tumorigenesis. This outcome, however requires the integrity of the DDR pathway as inactivation of ATM kinase by siRNA transfection or treatment with small molecule inhibitors abolished oncogene-induced senescence in multiple in vitro studies. The relevance of this defense mechanism has recently been demonstrated by analyzing clinical specimens of various human tumors, which showed peak activation of the DDR, as evidenced by phosphorylation of ATM, Chk2 and H2AX in early stages of human tumors[4]. This led to the hypothesis that the ATM/ATR regulated DDR machinery acts as an inducible barrier to constrain early tumor development by inducing cellular senescence and death [4]. Chronic activation of checkpoint signaling has also been hypothesized to create an environment that selects for mutations or epigenetic silencing of critical genes involved in this pathway, ultimately leading to tumor escape and invasiveness [4]. Of note, the HTLV-I oncoprotein, Tax, induces the expression or function of endogenous oncogenes, including cyclin D2, E2F and NF-kB. The resulting deregulation of cellular homeostasis could induce DNA damage leading to oncogene-induced senescence in the presence of an uninhibited ATM-mediated DDR. It is likely that inhibition of ATM signaling imposed by Tax has evolved to surpass this cellular barrier to proliferation and to facilitate viral persistence. As a consequence, Tax expression eliminates this defense mechanism, and is likely to contribute to tumor progression from early stages of cellular dysplasia to overt leukemia.

Conclusion

The HTLV-I oncoprotein Tax is responsible for cellular transformation and is believed to play an important role in the development of ATL. Tax functions to enhance cellular proliferation, accelerate cell cycle progression, allow bypass of checkpoints imposed by the presence of DNA damage and inhibit specific DNA repair pathways. While all of these activities might contribute to cellular transformation, their primary role is to create an evolutionary advantage for viral replication and persistence in T-cells. Since cell to cell spread of HTLV-I is inefficient in maintaining a chronic infection, amplification and maintenance of HTLV-I provirus occurs mainly through Tax-induced clonal proliferation of infected cells. However, to achieve this goal, Tax ectopically activates growth stimulatory pathways such as E2F, CyclinD2 and NF-kB, all of which can act as oncogenes. The host cell is likely to detect this as an aggression to its internal homeostasis and engage mechanisms that limit oncogene-stimulated proliferation. Centered by ATM kinase and the p53 tumor suppressor gene, these mechanisms are designed to induce apoptosis or cellular senescence in cells that aberrantly express oncogenes. To counteract this potential impediment for the expansion of HTLV-I infected cells, Tax has developed a way to dampen ATM signaling. Targeting MDC1, Tax blocks the amplification of ATM activation, which allow cellular phosphatases to prematurely extinguish the DDR by removing activating phosphates from ATM and its targets. While this benefits the virus by eliminating an important checkpoint in cell proliferation and proviral expansion, impairment of the DNA damage signaling by Tax has dire effects for the host cell. ATM inactivation might cause improper DSB repair and defective signaling of oncogenic stress, leading to genomic instability and eliminating an important gatekeeper function, which ultimately contributes to the development of cancer.

References

[1]   Gatza, ML; Chandhasin, C; Ducu, RI;Marriott, SJ. Impact of transforming viruses on cellular mutagenesis, genome stability, and cellular transformation. *Environmental and Molecular Mutagenesis*, 2005 45, 304-325.

[2]   Endter, C;Dobner, T. Cell transformation by human adenoviruses. *Curr. Top Microbiol. Immunol*, 2004 273, 163-214.

[3]   Mallette, FA; Gaumont-Leclerc, MF;Ferbeyre, G. The DNA damage signaling pathway is a critical mediator of oncogene-induced senescence. *Genes. Dev*, 2007 21, 43-48.

[4]   Bartek, J; Bartkova, J;Lukas, J. DNA damage signalling guards against activated oncogenes and tumour progression. *Oncogene*, 2007 26, 7773-7779.

[5]   Yasunaga, J;Matsuoka, M. Human T-cell leukemia virus type I induces adult T-cell leukemia: from clinical aspects to molecular mechanisms. *Cancer Control*, 2007 14, 133-140.

[6]   Poiesz, BJ; Ruscetti, FW; Gadzar, AF; Bunn, PA; Minna, JD;Gallo, RC. Detection and isolation of type C retrovirus particles from fresh and cultured lymphocytes of a patient tropism of human T-cell leukemia virus type I. *Proc. Natl. Acad. Sci. USA*, 1980 77, 7415-7419.

[7]   Bangham, CR;Osame, M. Cellular immune response to HTLV-1. *Oncogene*, 2005 24, 6035-6046.

[8]   Proietti, FA; Carneiro-Proietti, AB; Catalan-Soares, BC;Murphy, EL. Global epidemiology of HTLV-I infection and associated diseases. *Oncogene*, 2005 24, 6058-6068.

[9]   Igakura, T; Stinchcombe, JC; Goon, PKC; Taylor, GP; Weber, JN; Griffiths, GM; Tanaka, Y; Osame, M;Bangham, CRM. Spread of HTLV-I between lymphocytes by virus-induced polarization of the cytoskeleton. *Science*, 2003 299, 1713-1716.

[10] Taylor, GP;Matsuoka, M. Natural history of adult T-cell leukemia/lymphoma and approaches to therapy. *Oncogene*, 2005 24, 6047-6057.

[11] Miyoshi, I; Yoshimoto, S; Taguchi, H; Kubonishi, I; Fujishita, M; Ohtsuki, M; Shiraishi, Y;Akagi, T. Transformation of rabbit lymphocytes with adult T-cell leukemia virus. *Jap. J. Cancer Res*, 1983 74, 1-4.

[12] Hoshino, H; Tanaka, H; Shimotohno, K; Miwa, M; Nagai, M; Shimoyama, M;Sugimura, T. Immortalization of peripheral blood lymphocytes of cats by human T-cell leukemia virus. *Int. J. Cancer*, 1984 34, 513-517.

[13] Tateno, M; Kondo, N; Itoh, T; Chubachi, T; Togashi, T;Yoshiki, T. Rat lymphoid cell lines with human T cell leukemia virus production. I. Biological and serological characterization. *J. Exp. Med*, 1984 159, 1105-1116.

[14] Ballard, DW; Bohnlein, E; Lowenthal, JW; Wano, Y; Franza, BR;Greene, WC. HTLV-1 Tax induces cellular proteins that activate the kB element in the IL-2 receptor gene. *Science*, 1988 241, 1652-1655.

[15] Uchiyama, T; Hori, T; Tsudo, M; Wano, Y; Umadome, H; Tamori, S; Yodoi, J; Maeda, M; Sawami, H;Uchino, H. Interleukin-2 receptor (Tac antigen) expressed on adult T cell leukemia cells. *Journal of Clinical Investigation*, 1985 76, 446-453.

[16] Hall, WW;Fujii, M. Deregulation of cell-signaling pathways in HTLV-1 infection. *Oncogene*, 2005 24, 5965-5975.

[17] Matsuoka, M;Jeang, KT. Human T-cell leukaemia virus type 1 (HTLV-1) infectivity and cellular transformation. *Nature Reviews Cancer*, 2007 7, 270-280.

[18] Matsuoka, M. Human T-cell leukemia virus type I and adult T-cell leukemia. *Oncogene*, 2003 22, 5131-5140.

[19] Taylor, GP; Goon, P; Furukawa, Y; Green, H; Barfield, A; Mosley, A; Nose, H; Babiker, A; Rudge, P; Usuku, K; Osame, M; Bangham, CR;Weber, JN. Zidovudine plus lamivudine in Human T-Lymphotropic Virus type-I-associated myelopathy: a randomised trial. *Retrovirology*, 2006 3, 63-

[20] Miyazato, P; Yasunaga, J; Taniguchi, Y; Koyanagi, Y; Mitsuya, H;Matsuoka, M. De novo human T-cell leukemia virus type 1 infection of human lymphocytes in NOD-SCID, common gamma-chain knockout mice. *J. Virol*, 2006 80, 10683-10691.

[21] Etoh, K; Tamiya, S; Yamaguchi, K; Okayama, A; Tsubouchi, H; Ideta, T; Mueller, N; Takatsuki, K;Matsuoka, M. Persistent clonal proliferation of human T-lymphotropic virus type I-infected cells in vivo. *Cancer Res*, 1997 57, 4862-4867.

[22] Whang-Peng, J; Bunn, PA; Knutsen, T; Kao-Shan, CS; Broder, S; Jaffe, ES; Gelman, E; Blattner, W; Lofters, W; Young, RC;Gallo, RC. Cytogenetic studies in human T-cell

lymphoma virus (HTLV)-positive leukemia-lymphoma in the United States. *Journal of the National Cancer Institute*, 1985 74, 357-369.

[23] Chieco-Bianchi, L; Saggioro, D; DelMistro, A; Montaldi, A; Majone, F;Levis, AG. Chromosome damage induced in cord blood T-lymphocytes infected in vitro by HTLV-I. *Leukemia*, 1988 2, 223s-232s.

[24] Itoyama, T; Sadamori, N; Tokunaga, S; Sasagawa, I; Nakamura, H; Yao, E; Jubashi, T; Yamada, Y; Ikeda, S;Ichimura, M. Cytogenetic studies of human T-cell leukemia virus type I carriers. A family study. *Cancer Genetics and Cytogenetics*, 1990 49, 157-163.

[25] Maruyama, K; Fukushima, T; Kawamura, K;Mochizuki, S. Chromosome and gene rearrangements in immortalized human lymphocytes infected with human T-lymphotropic virus type I. *Cancer Research*, 1990 50, 5697s-5702s.

[26] Kamada, N; Sakurai, M; Miyamoto, K; Sancar, A; Sadamori, N; Fukuhara, S; Abe, S; Shiraishi, Y; Abe, T; Kaneko, Y;Shimoyama, M. Chromosome abnormalities in adult T-cell leukemia/lymphoma: a karyotype review committee report. *Cancer Research*, 1992 52, 1482-1493.

[27] Fujimoto, T; Hata, T; Itoyama, T; Nakamura, H; Tsukasaki, K; Yamada, Y; Ikeda, S; Sadamori, N;Tomonaga, M. High rate of chromosomal abnormalities in HTLV-I-infected T-cell colonies derived from prodromal phase of adult T-cell leukemia: a study of IL-2-stimulated colony formation in methylcellulose. *Cancer Genet Cytogenet.*, 1999 109, 1-13.

[28] Okamoto, T; Ohno, Y; Tsugane, S; Watanabe, S; Shimoyama, M; Tajima, K; Miwa, M;Shimotohno, K. Multi-step carcinogenesis model for adult T-cell leukemia. *Jpn. J. Can. Res.*, 1989 80, 191-195.

[29] Nagai, H; Kinoshita, T; Imamura, J; Murakami, Y; Hayashi, K; Mukai, K; Ikeda, S; Tobinai, K; Saito, H; Shimoyama, M;Shimotohno, K. Genetic alteration of p53 in some patients with adult T-cell leukemia. *Jpn. J. Can. Res.*, 1991 82, 1421-1427.

[30] Sakashita, A; Hattori, T; Miller, CW; Suzushima, H; Asou, N; Takatsuki, K;Koeffler, HP. Mutations of the p53 gene in adult T-cell leukemia. *Blood*, 1992 79, 477-480.

[31] Yamato, K; Oka, T; Hiroi, M; Iwahara, Y; Sugito, S; Tsuchida, N;Miyoshi, I. Aberrant expression of the p53 tumor suppressor gene in adult T-cell leukemia and HTLV-1-infected cells. *Jap. J. Cancer Res*, 1993 84, 4-8.

[32] Hatta, Y; Yamada, Y; Tomonaga, M;Koeffler, HP. Extensive analysis of the retinoblastoma gene in adult T cell leukemia/lymphoma (ATL). *Leukemia*, 1997 11, 984-989.

[33] Suzuki, T; Narita, T; Uchida-Toita, M;Yoshida, M. Down-regulation of the INK4 family of cyclin-dependent kinase inhibitors by tax protein of HTLV-1 through two distinct mechanisms. *Virology*, 1999 259, 384-391.

[34] Hatta, Y;Koeffler, HP. Role of tumor suppressor genes in the development of adult T cell leukemia/lymphoma (ATLL). *Leukemia*, 2002 16, 1069-1085.

[35] Pombo-de-Oliveira, MS; Dobbin, JA; Loureiro, P; Borducchi, D; Maia, RC; Fernandes, MA; Cavalcanti, GB, Jr.; Takemoto, S;Franchini, G. Genetic mutation and early onset of T-cell leukemia in pediatric patients infected at birth with HTLV-I. *Leuk. Res*, 2002 26, 155-161.

[36] Majone, F;Jeang, KT. Clastogenic effect of the human T-cell leukemia virus type I tax oncoprotein correlates with unstabilized DNA breaks. *J. Biol. Chem*, 2000 275, 32906-32910.

[37] Miyake, H; Suzuki, T; Hirai, H;Yoshida, M. Trans-activator Tax of human T-cell leukemia virus type 1 enhances mutation frequency of the cellular genome. *Virology*, 1999 253, 155-161.

[38] Majone, F; Semmes, OJ;Jeang, KT. Induction of micronuclei by HTLV-I Tax: a cellular assay for function. *Virology*, 1993 193, 456-459.

[39] Parry, JM;Parry, EM. Comparison of tests for aneuploidy. *Mutation Research*, 1987 181, 267-287.

[40] Thomson, EJ;Perry, PE. The identification of micronucleated chromosomes: a possible assay for aneuploidy. *Mutagenesis*, 1988 3, 415-418.

[41] Arlett, CF; Ashby, J; Fielder, RJ;Scott, D. Micronuclei: origins, applications and methodologies-- a workshop sponsored by the Health and Safety Executive held in Manchester, May 23-25,1988. *Mutagenesis*, 1988 4, 482-485.

[42] Semmes, OJ; Majone, F; Cantemir, C; Turchetto, L; Hjelle, B;Jeang, KT. HTLV-1 and HTLV-II tax: Differences in induction of micronuclei in cells and transcriptional activation of viral LTRs. *Virology*, 1996 217, 373-379.

[43] Myllykangas, S;Knuutila, S. Manifestation, mechanisms and mysteries of gene amplifications. *Cancer Lett*, 2006 232, 79-89.

[44] Lemoine, FJ;Marriott, SJ. Genomic instability driven by the human T-cell leukemia virus type 1 (HTLV-I) oncoprotein, Tax. *Oncogene*, 2002 21, 7230-7234.

[45] Kao, SY;Marriott, SJ. Disruption of nucleotide excision repair by the human T-cell leukemia virus type 1 Tax protein. *Journal of Virology*, 1999 73, 4299-4304.

[46] Ressler, S; Morris, GF;Marriott, SJ. Human T-cell leukemia virus type 1 Tax transactivates the human proliferating cell nuclear antigen promoter. *Journal of Virology*, 1997 71, 1181-1190.

[47] Lemoine, FJ; Kao, SY;Marriott, SJ. Suppression of DNA Repair by HTLV-I Tax correlates with Tax transactivation of PCNA gene expression. *AIDS Research and Human Retroviruses*, 2000 16, 1623-1627.

[48] Kelman, Z. PCNA: Structure, functions and interactions. *Oncogene*, 1997 14, 629-640.

[49] Jeang, KT; Widen, SG; Semmes, OJ;Wilson, SH. HTLV-I trans-activator protein, Tax, is a trans-repressor of the human Ã¡-polymerase gene. *Science*, 1990 247, 1082-1084.

[50] Idriss, HT; Al Assar, O;Wilson, SH. DNA polymerase beta. *Int. J. Biochem. Cell Biol*, 2002 34, 321-324.

[51] Bhattacharyya, N; Chen, HC; Comhair, S; Erzurum, SC;Banerjee, S. Variant forms of DNA polymerase beta in primary lung carcinomas. *DNA Cell Biol*, 1999 18, 549-554.

[52] Miyamoto, H; Miyagi, Y; Ishikawa, T; Ichikawa, Y; Hosaka, M;Kubota, Y. DNA polymerase beta gene mutation in human breast cancer. *Int. J. Cancer*, 1999 83, 708-709.

[53] Starcevic, D; Dalal, S;Sweasy, JB. Is there a link between DNA polymerase beta and cancer? *Cell Cycle*, 2004 3, 998-1001.

[54] Philpott, SM;Buehring, GC. Defective DNA repair in cells with human T-cell leukemia bovine leukemia viruses: Role of tax gene. *Journal of the National Cancer Institute*, 1999 91, 933-942.

[55] Marriott, SJ;Semmes, OJ. Impact of HTLV-I Tax on cell cycle progression and the cellular DNA damage repair response. *Oncogene*, 2005 24, 5986-5995.

[56] Jeggo, A. DNA double strand repair and its relationship to human disease. *Febs. Journal*, 2006 273, 19-19.

[57] Durocher, D;Jackson, SP. DNA-PK, ATM and ATR as sensors of DNA damage: variations on a theme? *Curr. Opin. Cell Biol*, 2001 13, 225-231.

[58] Savitsky, K; Barshira, A; Gilad, S; Rotman, G; Ziv, Y; Vanagaite, L; Tagle, DA; Smith, S; Uziel, T; Sfez, S; Ashkenazi, M; Pecker, I; Frydman, M; Harnik, R; Patanjali, SR; Simmons, A; Clines, GA; Sartiel, A; Gatti, RA; Chessa, L; Sanal, O; Lavin, MF; Jaspers, NGJ; Malcolm, A; Taylor, R; Arlett, CF; Miki, T; Weissman, SM; Lovett, M; Collins, FS;Shiloh, Y. A Single Ataxia-Telangiectasia Gene with A Product Similar to Pi-3 Kinase. *Science*, 1995 268, 1749-1753.

[59] Maser, RS; Monsen, KJ; Nelms, BE;Petrini, JH. hMre11 and hRad50 nuclear foci are induced during the normal cellular response to DNA double-strand breaks. *Mol. Cell Biol*, 1997 17, 6087-6096.

[60] van den, BM; Bree, RT;Lowndes, NF. The MRN complex: coordinating and mediating the response to broken chromosomes. *EMBO Rep*, 2003 4, 844-849.

[61] Paull, TT;Lee, JH. The Mre11/Rad50/Nbs1 complex and its role as a DNA double-strand break sensor for ATM. *Cell Cycle*, 2005 4, 737-740.

[62] de Jager, M; van Noort, J; van Gent, DC; Dekker, C; Kanaar, R;Wyman, C. Human Rad50/Mre11 is a flexible complex that can tether DNA ends. *Mol. Cell*, 2001 8, 1129-1135.

[63] van den, BM; Bree, RT;Lowndes, NF. The MRN complex: coordinating and mediating the response to broken chromosomes. *EMBO Rep*, 2003 4, 844-849.

[64] Hopfner, KP; Craig, L; Moncalian, G; Zinkel, RA; Usui, T; Owen, BA; Karcher, A; Henderson, B; Bodmer, JL; McMurray, CT; Carney, JP; Petrini, JH;Tainer, JA. The Rad50 zinc-hook is a structure joining Mre11 complexes in DNA recombination and repair. *Nature*, 2002 418, 562-566.

[65] Paull, TT;Gellert, M. Nbs1 potentiates ATP-driven DNA unwinding and endonuclease cleavage by the Mre11/Rad50 complex. *Genes. Dev*, 1999 13, 1276-1288.

[66] Trujillo, KM;Sung, P. DNA structure-specific nuclease activities in the Saccharomyces cerevisiae Rad50*Mre11 complex. *J. Biol. Chem*, 2001 276, 35458-35464.

[67] Goodarzi, AA; Jonnalagadda, JC; Douglas, P; Young, D; Ye, R; Moorhead, GB; Lees-Miller, SP;Khanna, KK. Autophosphorylation of ataxia-telangiectasia mutated is regulated by protein phosphatase 2A. *EMBO J*, 2004 23, 4451-4461.

[68] Bakkenist, CJ;Kastan, MB. DNA damage activates ATM through intermolecular autophosphorylation and dimer dissociation. *Nature*, 2003 421, 499-506.

[69] Berkovich, E; Monnat, RJ, Jr.;Kastan, MB. Roles of ATM and NBS1 in chromatin structure modulation and DNA double-strand break repair. *Nat. Cell Biol*, 2007 9, 683-690.

[70] Lee, JH;Paull, TT. ATM activation by DNA double-strand breaks through the Mre11-Rad50-Nbs1 complex. *Science*, 2005 308, 551-554.

[71] You, Z; Chahwan, C; Bailis, J; Hunter, T;Russell, P. ATM activation and its recruitment to damaged DNA require binding to the C terminus of Nbs1. *Mol. Cell Biol*, 2005 25, 5363-5379.

[72] Lavin, MF;Kozlov, S. ATM activation and DNA damage response. *Cell Cycle*, 2007 6, 931-942.

[73] Lou, Z; Minter-Dykhouse, K; Franco, S; Gostissa, M; Rivera, MA; Celeste, A; Manis, JP; van Deursen, J; Nussenzweig, A; Paull, TT; Alt, FW;Chen, J. MDC1 maintains genomic stability by participating in the amplification of ATM-dependent DNA damage signals. *Mol. Cell*, 2006 21, 187-200.

[74] Stucki, M;Jackson, SP. gamma H2AX and MDC1: Anchoring the DNA-damage-response machinery to broken chromosomes. *Dna Repair*, 2006 5, 534-543.

[75] Kao, J; Rosenstein, BS; Peters, S; Milano, MT;Kron, SJ. Cellular response to DNA damage. *Ann. N. Y. Acad. Sci*, 2005 1066, 243-258.

[76] Burma, S; Chen, BP;Chen, DJ. Role of non-homologous end joining (NHEJ) in maintaining genomic integrity. *DNA Repair (Amst.)*, 2006 5, 1042-1048.

[77] Takata, M; Sasaki, MS; Sonoda, E; Morrison, C; Hashimoto, M; Utsumi, H; Yamaguchi-Iwai, Y; Shinohara, A;Takeda, S. Homologous recombination and non-homologous end-joining pathways of DNA double-strand break repair have overlapping roles in the maintenance of chromosomal integrity in vertebrate cells. *EMBO J*, 1998 17, 5497-5508.

[78] Lieber, MR; Ma, YM; Pannicke, U;Schwarz, K. Mechanism and regulation of human non-homologous DNA end-joining. *Nature Reviews Molecular Cell Biology*, 2003 4, 712-720.

[79] Rivera-Calzada, A; Spagnolo, L; Pearl, LH;Llorca, O. Structural model of full-length human Ku70-Ku80 heterodimer and its recognition of DNA and DNA-PKcs. *EMBO Rep*, 2007 8, 56-62.

[80] Lees-Miller, SP;Meek, K. Repair of DNA double strand breaks by non-homologous end joining. *Biochimie*, 2003 85, 1161-1173.

[81] Difilippantonio, MJ; Zhu, J; Chen, HT; Meffre, E; Nussenzweig, MC; Max, EE; Ried, T;Nussenzweig, A. DNA repair protein Ku80 suppresses chromosomal aberrations and malignant transformation. *Nature*, 2000 404, 510-514.

[82] Li, G; Nelsen, C;Hendrickson, EA. Ku86 is essential in human somatic cells. *Proc. Natl. Acad. Sci. U S A*, 2002 99, 832-837.

[83] Fu, YP; Yu, JC; Cheng, TC; Lou, MA; Hsu, GC; Wu, CY; Chen, ST; Wu, HS; Wu, PE;Shen, CY. Breast cancer risk associated with genotypic polymorphism of the nonhomologous end-joining genes: a multigenic study on cancer susceptibility. *Cancer Res*, 2003 63, 2440-2446.

[84] Chan, DW; Chen, BP; Prithivirajsingh, S; Kurimasa, A; Story, MD; Qin, J;Chen, DJ. Autophosphorylation of the DNA-dependent protein kinase catalytic subunit is required for rejoining of DNA double-strand breaks. *Genes. Dev*, 2002 16, 2333-2338.

[85] Soubeyrand, S; Pope, L; Pakuts, B;Hache, RJ. Threonines 2638/2647 in DNA-PK are essential for cellular resistance to ionizing radiation. *Cancer Res*, 2003 63, 1198-1201.

[86] Ding, Q; Reddy, YV; Wang, W; Woods, T; Douglas, P; Ramsden, DA; Lees-Miller, SP;Meek, K. Autophosphorylation of the catalytic subunit of the DNA-dependent protein kinase is required for efficient end processing during DNA double-strand break repair. *Mol. Cell Biol*, 2003 23, 5836-5848.

[87] Chen, BP; Uematsu, N; Kobayashi, J; Lerenthal, Y; Krempler, A; Yajima, H; Lobrich, M; Shiloh, Y;Chen, DJ. Ataxia telangiectasia mutated (ATM) is essential for DNA-PKcs phosphorylations at the Thr-2609 cluster upon DNA double strand break. *J. Biol. Chem*, 2007 282, 6582-6587.

[88] Carson, CT; Schwartz, RA; Stracker, TH; Lilley, CE; Lee, DV;Weitzman, MD. The Mre11 complex is required for ATM activation and the G2/M checkpoint. *EMBO J*, 2003 22, 6610-6620.

[89] Difilippantonio, S; Celeste, A; Fernandez-Capetillo, O; Chen, HT; San Martin, BR; Van Laethem, F; Yang, YP; Petukhova, GV; Eckhaus, M; Feigenbaum, L; Manova, K; Kruhlak, M; Camerini-Otero, RD; Sharan, S; Nussenzweig, M;Nussenzweig, A. Role of Nbs1 in the activation of the Atm kinase revealed in humanized mouse models. *Nature Cell Biology*, 2005 7, 675-U56.

[90] Uziel, T; Lerenthal, Y; Moyal, L; Andegeko, Y; Mittelman, L;Shiloh, Y. Requirement of the MRN complex for ATM activation by DNA damage. *EMBO Journal*, 2003 22, 5612-5621.

[91] Nimura, Y; Kawata, T; Uzawa, K; Okamura, J; Liu, C; Saito, M; Shimada, H; Seki, N; Nakagawara, A; Ito, H; Ochiai, T;Tanzawa, H. Silencing Ku80 using small interfering RNA enhanced radiation sensitivity in vitro and in vivo. *Int. J. Oncol*, 2007 30, 1477-1484.

[92] Majone, F; Luisetto, R; Zamboni, D; Iwanaga, Y;Jeang, KT. Ku protein as a potential human T-cell leukemia virus type 1 (HTLV-1) Tax target in clastogenic chromosomal instability of mammalian cells. *Retrovirology*, 2005 2,

[93] Luo, MH; Rosenke, K; Czornak, K;Fortunato, EA. Human cytomegalovirus disrupts both ataxia telangiectasia mutated protein (ATM)- and ATM-Rad3-related kinase-mediated DNA damage responses during lytic infection. *Journal of Virology*, 2007 81, 1934-1950.

[94] Kudoh, A; Fujita, M; Zhang, L; Shirata, N; Daikoku, T; Sugaya, Y; Isomura, H; Nishiyama, Y;Tsurumi, T. Epstein-Barr virus lytic replication elicits ATM checkpoint signal transduction while providing an S-phase-like cellular environment. *J. Biol. Chem*, 2005 280, 8156-8163.

[95] Shirata, N; Kudoh, A; Daikoku, T; Tatsumi, Y; Fujita, M; Kiyono, T; Sugaya, Y; Isomura, H; Ishizaki, K;Tsurumi, T. Activation of ataxia telangiectasia-mutated DNA damage checkpoint signal transduction elicited by herpes simplex virus infection. *J. Biol. Chem*, 2005 280, 30336-30341.

[96] Daniel, R; Ramcharan, J; Rogakou, E; Taganov, KD; Greger, JG; Bonner, W; Nussenzweig, A; Katz, RA;Skalka, AM. Histone H2AX is phosphorylated at sites of retroviral DNA integration but is dispensable for postintegration repair. *J. Biol. Chem*, 2004 279, 45810-45814.

[97] Skalka, AM;Katz, RA. Retroviral DNA integration and the DNA damage response. *Cell Death Differ*, 2005 12 Suppl 1, 971-978.

[98] Li, L; Olvera, JM; Yoder, KE; Mitchell, RS; Butler, SL; Lieber, M; Martin, SL;Bushman, FD. Role of the non-homologous DNA end joining pathway in the early steps of retroviral infection. *EMBO J*, 2001 20, 3272-3281.

[99] Jeanson, L; Subra, F; Vaganay, S; Hervy, M; Marangoni, E; Bourhis, J;Mouscadet, JF. Effect of Ku80 depletion on the preintegrative steps of HIV-1 replication in human cells. *Virology*, 2002 300, 100-108.

[100] Daniel, R; Katz, RA;Skalka, AM. A role for DNA-PK in retroviral DNA integration. *Science*, 1999 284, 644-647.

[101] Daniel, R; Katz, RA; Merkel, G; Hittle, JC; Yen, TJ;Skalka, AM. Wortmannin potentiates integrase-mediated killing of lymphocytes and reduces the efficiency of stable transduction by retroviruses. *Mol. Cell Biol*, 2001 21, 1164-1172.

[102] Daniel, R; Greger, JG; Katz, RA; Taganov, KD; Wu, X; Kappes, JC;Skalka, AM. Evidence that stable retroviral transduction and cell survival following DNA integration depend on components of the nonhomologous end joining repair pathway. *J. Virol*, 2004 78, 8573-8581.

[103] Lau, A; Swinbank, KM; Ahmed, PS; Taylor, DL; Jackson, SP; Smith, GC;O'Connor, MJ. Suppression of HIV-1 infection by a small molecule inhibitor of the ATM kinase. *Nat. Cell Biol*, 2005 7, 493-500.

In: New Research on DNA Damage   ISBN 978-1-60456-581-2
Editors: Honoka Kimura and Aoi Suzuki   © 2008 Nova Science Publishers, Inc.

Chapter 7

Genotoxicity and Biomonitoring: Micronuclei in Peripheral Blood and Epithelial Cells

Belinda C. Gómez-Meda [1,3,*], *Ana L. Zamora-Perez* [2,3] *and Guillermo M. Zúñiga-González* [3]

1. Instituto de Biología Molecular en Medicina y Terapia Génica, Departamento de Biología Molecular y Genómica, División de Disciplinas Básicas para la Salud, Centro Universitario de Ciencias de la Salud, Universidad de Guadalajara, Guadalajara, Jalisco, México
2. Instituto de Investigación en Odontología, Departamento de Clínicas Odontológicas Integrales, División de Disciplinas Clínicas, Centro Universitario de Ciencias de la Salud, Universidad de Guadalajara, Guadalajara, Jalisco, México
3. Laboratorio de Mutagénesis, Centro de Investigación Biomédica de Occidente, Instituto Mexicano del Seguro Social, Guadalajara, Jalisco, México

Abstract

The aim is to raise the importance of the study of genotoxicity, its effects and how to prevent it, as well as the use of a biomonitor to detect these agents. It will point out in a practical and applied manner the use of the micronucleus assay as an indicator of damage and how to detect DNA damage, considering new uses of this technique that are easy to implement and to interpret, as well as being, economical, and also a review of the most current information about this important subject. Addressed specifically in our research is our interest in about the search for new models to be used as biomonitors, taking into account our experience of working with peripheral blood erythrocytes from more than 150 different species, including humans, with an emphasis on the more suitable and feasible models, and to demonstrate their usefulness in different studies, considering the

---

* Correspondence should be addressed to: Dr. en C. Belinda C. Gómez-Meda, Centro de Investigación Biomédica de Occidente, Instituto Mexicano del Seguro Social, Sierra Mojada 800, Col. Independencia, C.P. 44340, Guadalajara, Jalisco, México, Tel: +(33) 36189410, Fax: +(33) 36181756, E-mail: mutagenesis95 @hotmail.com.

characteristics of the species to be tested, the advantages and disadvantages of each one, the influence of age, the applicability of the model in different areas of biomedical and clinic research, covering also the wide use of this test for detected genotoxic and/or the teratogenic potential, as well as damage marker and a tool to study the effects of diverse pathological conditions, and also to show the technical innovation for genotoxic study using amphibians and rat epithelial cells for genotoxicity studies in the laboratory and in the field by means of noninvasive and easy new proposals. It will also highlight the problem in the design of new methodological approaches and characteristics to be taken into account for a proper development of studies in the genotoxicity area.

1. Genotoxicity

All living organisms are constantly exposed to elements since their physical, chemical and/or biological properties, when ingested, inhaled, injected or applied topically, can cause functional alterations or even death [1,2]; such exposure could be inadvertent, accidental or intentional or even inevitable. Also, it is known that these agents could be not dangerous, but some of them can cause biological reactions with a pharmacological or toxic nature. Often these reactions depend on the conversion of the absorbed substances in an active metabolite, which can cause mutagenicity, carcinogenicity or teratogenicity [3-6].

The large numbers of pharmaceutical compounds that are released daily into the market obligate us to develop new methodologies and models for their study [3,7]; a wide variety of tests are commonly used to determine the toxicity of compounds, and more than one test is required to evaluate the genotoxic potential of any single compound [7], since genotoxicity can occur through a variety of mechanisms and is often expressed in particular tissues. Therefore, assays that detect genotoxic agents that cause DNA damage are of great importance, since genotoxic compounds have the capacity to alter the genetic material in all living organisms, including humans, may have teratogenic effects, may cause germ cell mutation, inducing cardiac disease, may influence aging processes [8], and may induce mutations in somatic cells that may contribute to carcinogenesis [9-11], therefore it is important to implement alternative tests.

Toxicology studies have undergone a significant evolution during the past decades, with much greater emphasis being placed on chronic toxicity, carcinogenesis, teratology, and mutagenesis. Several *in vivo* tests, among a battery of assays, have been proposed to identify mutagens and carcinogens [12]. Included in these tests are chromosome analysis as karyotype, mitotic index, sister chromatid exchange, Ames test, apoptosis, cometa assay and the micronucleus test [12,13].

1.1. The Micronucleus Assay

Micronuclei are chromosome fragments or whole chromosomes that remain out of the nucleus in mitosis [14-16] and the *in vivo* micronucleus test can assess the genotoxic effects of environmental and occupational carcinogenic compounds [13,17-22].

The *in vivo* micronucleus test is a widely used assay for measuring damage to chromosomes and spindle fibers, and it can be adapted to assess the effects of compounds and their metabolites in multiple tissues [23].

The micronucleus test is based on the observation that mitotic cells with chromatid breaks or chromatid exchanges suffer from disturbances in the anaphase distribution of their chromatin and that, after telophase, a sizable proportion of such displaced chromatin is not included in the nuclei of the daughter cells but forms single or multiple micronuclei in the cytoplasm of these cells [24].

The micronucleus test *in vivo* is a method devised primarily for screening chemicals for chromosome-breaking effects. The test substances are normally applied sub-acutely to small mammals, and the effect is read in direct smears from bone marrow. This testing procedure, developed by Schmid and coworkers [14], has a number of important advantages over the analysis of bone marrow metaphase chromosomes. In technique of preparation as well as the reading of the slides, it is simpler and faster than chromosome analysis in the same material, but not at the expense of accuracy. In the monitoring of chromosome breakage, the test is at least as sensitive as the metaphase method; in addition it includes effects on the spindle apparatus. All these properties render the micronucleus test highly suitable for routine toxicological screening [14].

The method is based on the following principles and observations (Figure 1): in anaphase, acentric chromatid and chromosome fragments lag behind when the centric elements move toward the spindle poles. After telophase the undamaged chromosomes, as well as the centric fragments, give rise to regular daughter nuclei. The lagging elements are included in the daughter cells, too, but a considerable proportion is transformed into one or several secondary nuclei which are, as a rule, much smaller than the principal nucleus and are therefore called micronuclei. Similar events occur if the functioning of the spindle apparatus is impaired, e.g. under the influence of colchicine, taxol, vinblastine; in this event, however, the main nucleus is often replaced by a whole group of small nuclei, which, in general, are considerably larger than typical micronuclei [14]. In bone marrow smears from mammals treated with chromosome-breaking agents, micronuclei are found in numerous cell types (Figure 2), always provided that these cells have completed-under the influence of the mutagen- one or a few mitoses. In cell types with little cytoplasm they are not always easily distinguishable from normal lobes or projections [14,15].

In vivo cytogenetic analysis and the micronucleus test have been proposed for screening chemicals for their clastogenic potential [12]. Any assay that is considered for use as a mutagen-screening procedure should undergo a rigorous validation process with mutagens that have different mechanisms of action; ideally, the test should be subjected to various classes of known mutagens and structurally related non-mutagens to evaluate the effectiveness of the test system to predict carcinogenic/mutagenic potential [12].

A particular virtue of the micronucleus test resides in its permitting a fast comparison of a test result in any number of different mammalian species. Number and morphology of the chromosomes do not pose limitations to this technique [14].

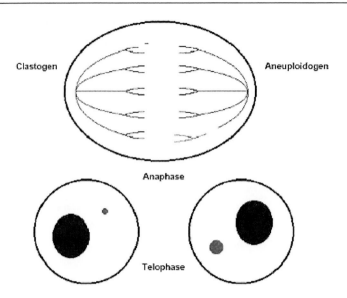

Figure 1. Micronuclei formation.

The micronucleus test is preferred over *in vivo* chromosome analysis since it requires less time to score and is technically easier to run [12]. The scored elements are the micronucleated cells and not the number of micronuclei [14], with this assay the obtained results are very informative and decisive since what it is observed in the micronucleus assay is DNA damage.

1.1.1. Clastogenic or Aneugenic Origin of Micronuclei

The micronucleus test [14] is a simple *in vivo* assay used to detect cytogenetic damage induced by chemical and physical mutagens [25]. Micronuclei are produced after chromosome breakage (clastogenic damage) or spindle disturbance (aneugenic damage); in the first case, the micronucleus contains a chromosome fragment, in the second case a whole chromosome [25]. A major strength of the assay is its ability to detect both clastogenic and aneugenic effects of genotoxic agents, being able to differentiate from each other by the size of micronuclei [26] and the presence of centromere [27,28]. The observed micronuclei can be formed from either acentric fragments or entire chromosomes lagging in mitosis. Micronuclei containing whole chromosomes were first characterized by their large size [26], by C-banding [29] or by measurement of DNA content [30]. Because conventional microscopic analysis, however, cannot discriminate micronuclei for their aneugenic or clastogenic origin, more recently, two molecular cytogenetics methods were developed to identify he presence of centromeres in micronuclei and tereby diferentiate between micronuclei according to their origin [31]. This can be achieved detecting the presence or absence of centromere proteins, through immunofluorescent staining with CREST antibodies [32,33] or with fluorescence *in situ* hybridization with pancentromeric DNA probes [31].

When only its required to detect DNA damage, no matter the mechanism of action of a compound or their clastogenic or aneugenic origin, or when such mechanism of action is already known, the stains that can be used would be varied, although it is certainly preferable and recommended the use of specific nucleic acid staining in order to discriminate clearly artefacts or RNA granules from a real micronuclei [31].

The use of a DNA specific stain (e.g., acridine orange [34] or Hoechst 33258 plus pyronin Y [35]) can eliminate most of the artefacts associated with using a non-DNA specific stain. For mice, DNA specific stains are preferred, but non-specific staining (e.g., May-Grünwald Giemsa or Giemsa only) is also acceptable. For rats, a DNA specific stain should be used to distinguish mast cell granules from micronuclei [31].

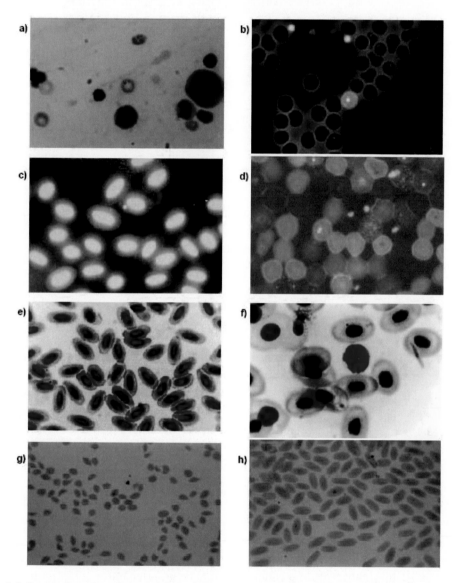

Figure 2. Micronucleated erythrocytes from different species (100×). a) mouse bone marrow (*Mus musculus*; Giemsa-Wrigth stain); b) dolphin (*Tursiops truncatus*; acridine orange stain); c) parrot (*Aratinga canicularis*; acridine orange stain); d) newborn rat (*Rattus norvergicus*; acridine orange stain); e) common ground-dove (*Scartasella inca*; Giemsa-Wrigth stain); f) toad (*Buffo horribilis*; Giemsa-Wrigth stain); g) temazate deer (*Tamazate americana*; Giemsa-Wrigth stain), h) llama (*Lama glama glama*; Giemsa-Wrigth stain).

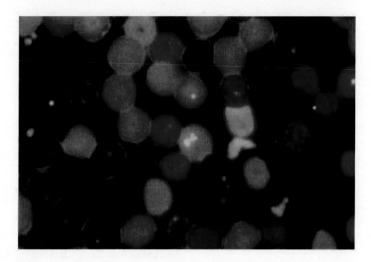

Figure 3. Micronucleated erythrocytes from newborn rabbit (100× / acridine orange stain). Polychromatic erythrocytes are stained in red and micronuclei in yellow.

The *in vivo* micronucleus assay is one of the most widely used *in vivo* screening tests in genotoxicity testing [36]. Among the advantages, micronucleus test is easy and fast, the abundance of cells in different cell cycle periods that can be analyzable, and the fact that the micronuclei formed during cell division persist for at least the next interphase [14,37].

1.1.2. Mechanisms by which Micronuclei Can Arise

Since the formation of micronuclei from acentric chromosomal fragments is so easily and widely understood, it may be useful to emphasize some of the uncertainties that remain. There are, in fact, four recognized mechanisms by which micronuclei and micronucleus-like structures can arise: 1) mitotic loss of acentric fragments, the classic mechanism, 2) a variety of mechanical consequences of chromosomal breakage and exchange, 3) mitotic loss of whole chromosomes, and 4) apoptosis. In the bone marrow micronucleus test it is assumed that only the first three are important and thus that the induction of micronuclei indicates a genetic hazard [37].

Micronuclei can arise from chromosomal aberrations in a variety of cell types *in vivo* and *in vitro*. Also there is interest in using the frequency of micronuclei as a measure of chromosomal damage in a variety of cell types besides bone marrow. In such situations it is important to be able to distinguish among the mechanisms that generate micronuclei. For the formation of micronuclei that are indicative of cytogenetic damage, as opposed to cell death by apoptosis, cell division is essential. Cells containing micronuclei arising from cytogenetics events will contain a normal nucleus and one micronucleus, rarely more (Figure 3) [37].

1.1.3. Normochromatic and Polychromatic Erythrocytes

Micronuclei are counted separately in normochromatic and polychromatic erythrocytes. The polychromatic cell type lends itself to this test in a most advantageous way: a few hours after their last mitoses, erythroblasts expel their nuclei (in mammals, occurs after 5 hours of the last mitosis). For unknown reasons micronuclei remain behind and are easily detected.

For a minimum of 24 hours the young erythrocytes have the advantage of staining differently from older forms [14,24,38].

Micronuclei in polychromatic erythrocytes are characteristic and obtrusive elements which can be scored by personnel without special training in cytogenetics. In haematological routine these micronuclei have long been known as Howell-Jolly bodies [14].

Anucleated polychromatophilic erythrocytes are normally less than 30 hours old and stain differently than normochromatophilic erythrocytes. This easily recognized population that is of a defined age readily facilitates the observation of micronuclei [12].

On the other hand, to determine cytotoxicity the parameter used is the proportion of polychromatic erythrocytes in relation to normochromatic erythrocytes in peripheral blood, due to this cell proportion must be constant, but could be altered if the individual receives cytotoxic compounds (reaching zero polychromatic erythrocytes count value) which indicates bone marrow depression. Because polychromatic erythrocytes do not lose their ribosomes approximately 24 hours after they enter the circulation, they are stained with giemsa, colored blue-grey [38] and with acridine orange stain, colored red or orange (Figure 4) [34,39,40], making microscopic analysis easy in short-term exposure assays, since these cells after 24 hours become normochromatic erythrocytes, so a micronucleus test option is to count micronucleated polychromatic erythrocytes, since these cells reflect the most recent damage, that occur 24 hours before the exposure with a genotoxic compound [14,41].

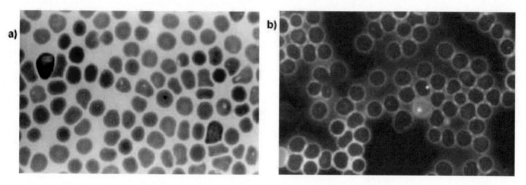

Figure 4. Erythrocytes from mouse peripheral blood (100×). a) Giemsa-Wright stained; b) Acridine orange stained.

1.2. Micronuclei in Peripheral Blood

An important step in the evolution of the micronucleus assay was the recognition that it could provide reliable data if the scoring of micronuclei was limited to those cells that had completed one nuclear division, which allows micronuclei to form [42].

This assay can be adapted to virtually all dividing cells [14,38,43-46], however, the simplest way is to use a drop of blood, in the cases that this tissue option is feasible.

1.2.1. Micronuclei in Lymphocytes
The micronucleus test can be achieved in peripheral blood cells as lymphocytes and erythrocytes. In lymphocytes the assay is carry out *in vitro*, using lymphocytes culture.

The use of micronuclei as a measure of chromosome damage in peripheral blood lymphocytes was first proposed by Countryman and Heddle [47] and subsequently improved with the development of the cytokinesis-block micronucleus method [42], which allowed micronuclei to be scored specifically in cells that had completed nuclear division. As a consequence the assay has been extensively used to evaluate the presence and the extent of chromosome damage in human populations exposed to genotoxic agents in various occupational settings, in the environment, or as a consequence of lifestyles. Subgroups of the general population considered at risk because of their genetic make-up or because they are affected by certain diseases have also been evaluated, to validate this biomarker as a predictor of adverse health effects [48]. An important step in the evolution of the micronucleus assay was the recognition that it could provide reliable data if the scoring of micronuclei was limited to those cells that had completed one nuclear division, which allows micronuclei to form [42]. The cytokinesis-block technique using cytochalasin-B which arrests division of cytoplasm or cytokinesis without inhibiting nuclear division enabled such cells to be recognised by their binucleate appearance. The simplicity of this approach led to its adoption for both *in vitro* genotoxicity testing and human population monitoring [42,49,50]. In this variant of the micronucleus test proliferating lymphocytes appear as binucleated cells and provide an optimal reference for determining micronuclei frequencies. This approach can be used for all *in vitro* applications of the micronucleus test and is now the standard technique [51,52]. An *ex vivo/in vitro* analysis of lymphocytes in the presence of cytochalasin-B (added 44 hours after the start of cultivation), an inhibitor of actins, allows to distinguish easily between mononucleated cells which did not divide and binucleated cells which completed nuclear division during *in vitro* culture. Indeed, in these conditions the frequencies of mononucleated cells provide an indication of the background level of chromosome/genome mutations accumulated *in vivo* and the frequencies of binucleated cells with micronuclei a measure of the damage accumulated before cultivation plus mutations expressed during the first *in vitro* mitosis [51]. The combination of the micronucleus assay with fluorescence *in situ* hybridization with a probe labeling the pericentromeric region of the chromosomes (fluorescence *in situ* hybridization assay) allows discrimination between micronuclei containing a whole chromosome (centromere positive micronucleus) and an acentric chromosome fragment (centromere negative micronucleus) [51,52]. The criteria for selecting binucleated cells to score are the following: Score binucleated cells with main nuclei that are separate and of approximately equal size, main nuclei that touch and even overlap as long anuclear boundaries are able to be distinguished, and main nuclei that are linked by nucleoplasmic bridges [42,53]. Do not score: trinucleated, quadranucleated, or multinucleated cells or cells where main nuclei are undergoing apoptosis (because micronuclei may be gone already or may be caused by apoptotic process). In the absence of cytochalasin B, mononucleated cells are analyzed for the presence of micronuclei. In the presence of cytochalasin B, mononucleated cells are recommended to be harvested at 24 hours post-phitohemaglutinin stimulation as there can be no doubt at this time-point that micronuclei within such a cell are a result of *in vivo* rather than *ex vivo* division. Binucleated cells are recommended to be harvested at 72 hours post-phitohemaglutinin. Moreover, 24 hour post-phitohemaglutinin time-point may be the right time to count apoptotic/necrotic cells [52].

The cytokinesis-block micronucleus assay was originally described for cultures of isolated lymphocytes [49,50]. Subsequently, most laboratories adapted the method to whole blood cultures using a variety of culture media. Although the original method recommended 3.0 micrograms/ml of cytochalasin-B for optimal cytokinesis-blocking it was subsequently shown that the optimal concentration for whole-blood cultures was 6.0 micrograms/ml [54].

Cell harvesting methods used in different laboratories vary from direct transfer of cells from the culture of isolated lymphocytes, to preparation of slides using a cytocentrifuge, to treatment of whole blood cultures with hypotonic and fixative before dropping the cell suspension onto slides. A less frequently used variation is the isolation of lymphocytes from whole blood cultures by density gradient methods followed by cytocentrifuge preparation of slides [42].

It has recently been suggested that some micronuclei may already exist in lymphocytes before culture as a result of induction and expression *in vivo* in dividing cell populations such as the bone-marrow [55]. Furthermore, micronuclei observed in cytokinesis-blocked cultured lymphocytes may originate not only from DNA breaks and centromere/kinetochore defects generated *in vivo* in lymphocytes but they possibly could also be derived from pre-existing micronuclei. Some of the lymphocytes collected from blood may contain a micronucleus that was expressed *in vivo* during the last cell division before collection. However, during the time between this last division and the time the blood was collected, the lymphocytes may have accumulated additional DNA lesions in cells in that would not be expressed until after o they are stimulated to divide in culture. It should be possible to distinguish between those two events by scoring micronuclei in lymphocytes before they divide in culture and those that appear only after *in vitro* nuclear division [42].

1.2.2. Micronuclei in Erythrocytes

In the case of using peripheral blood erythrocytes, this alternative may be performed *in vivo* without cell culture, which makes it a good alternative to realize this assay.

The micronucleus test in erythrocytes of peripheral blood is an easy, fast and economical assay for detecting genotoxic compounds, that gives clear and accurate results being able to implement and apply anywhere without economic limitans that might be present with the use of very sophisticated and expensive tests [2,13,19,41,56]. This test is highly informative, furthermore, it is possible to apply the test *in vivo* and just a drop of blood is needed to carry out the study, without the necessity of sacrificing the animals for making measurements, or could be used in field studies to detect genotoxicity in different environments, before they endangered the survival of the species.

The technique is very simple, for sample preparation and micronucleated erythrocytes analysis is need to count blood smears from the species tested, that are make on pre-cleaned and pre-coded microscope slides. In animal models, a drop of peripheral blood is taken from the tip of the tail, the tip of the paw, or by venous puncture of each animal immediately before the first treatment (0 hr or basal value) and daily until 24 or 48 hr later after the last drug administration or xenobiotic exposition [57]. The smears are air-dried, fixed in absolute ethanol for 10 min, and stain with acridine orange [2,34,39,58]. The micronucleated erythrocytes in each sample are score manually using a microscope equipped with epifluorescence and a 100× objective. For each individual of the various species, the micronucleated erythrocytes frequency is establish from the number of micronuclei in 10,000 total erythrocytes (normochromatic and polychromatic erythrocytes). In micronuclei experiments induction, the number of micronucleated erythrocytes in 10,000 total erythrocytes, the number of micronucleated polychromatic erythrocytes in 1,000 polychromatic erythrocytes, and the proportion of polychromatic erythrocytes in 1,000 total erythrocytes are evaluated [56]. The simplicity and non-invasive nature of this technique (allows working with a few quantity blood samples), makes it an attractive alternative for genotoxic monitoring.

Likewise, it has been accepted for some time that bone marrow and peripheral blood are acceptable tissues for analysis in studies with mice. However, when blood is the tissue sampled, the absence of spleen function should have been demonstrated in the mouse strain being used. The simplest procedure for assessing spleen function is to determine the relative (micronucleated immature erythrocytes)/(micronucleated mature erythrocytes) ratio in peripheral blood of control animals; this ratio should equal approximately 1 when micronucleated cells are not removed selectively. When there is selective removal of micronucleated cells, the steady state level of micronucleated mature erythrocytes is lower than that in immature erythrocytes due to the much longer residence time of mature erythrocytes in the circulation. This expectation is supported by the available data, which show that species that do select against micronucleated cells (rat, dog, and human) have the highest frequency of micronucleated cells in bone marrow, with lower frequencies in peripheral blood immature erythrocytes, and the lowest in peripheral blood mature erythrocytes [57-61] whereas mice have similar micronucleus frequencies in all three cell types at steady state [62].

1.2.3. Control Over Micronuclei Presence in Peripheral Blood

The reticuloendothelial system is responsible for eliminating erythrocytes with alterations, including micronucleated erythrocytes (normochromatic and polychromatic erythrocytes) [63,64].

The spleen, as part of the reticuloendothelial system, filters the blood, remove particles by phagocytic cells, and destroy old red blood cells or their fragments. When erythrocytes get old, certain changes occur that reduce its flexibility, this makes difficult its way through the microcirculation of the spleen and in some moments cell lysis occurs or phagocytosis and elimination by the reticuloendothelial system. Even that all reticuloendothelial cells are involved in the destruction of old red blood cells, spleen cells are located anatomically, that make then the most sensitive detectors of any erythrocytic abnormality [65-67].

Some species have spleens that remove micronuclei from the peripheral circulation, making such measurements problematical [25]. In contrast, micronucleated erythrocytes can be observed at any time during the lifetime of species with a less efficient reticuloendothelial system [38,64,68]. In general, mammals have the potential to spontaneously produce micronucleated erythrocytes and their presence might increase when organisms are exposed to genotoxic compounds [41,69,70]. However, they are not detected in the peripheral blood of all species [63,64,71].

In this concept, there are species that have high efficiency of its reticuloendothelial system for removing abnormal erythrocytes, which makes no possible to observed micronucleated erythrocytes in peripheral blood, while in others such structures can be observed at any time in their lives [64].

In humans, the number of micronucleated erythrocytes in peripheral blood is virtually zero [60], but they can be observed if the individual present spleen malfunction [14,16,72,73], or when it has been splenectomized [63,73,74]. In this last condition is how it can be obtained data about the possible genotoxicity effect of any drugs administered to patients [63,75]. However, when the requirement is to test a new drug, obvious ethical reasons exclude this possibility and it is when the bioassays give us the opportunity to test these compounds.

Since the presence of micronuclei is translated for the DNA loss, this assay is a very effective alternative for monitoring genotoxic in an easily, quickly and with definitive results. In addition, the micronucleus test leaves no doubt about the DNA damage that have occur, since it is clear that the micronuclei number increase when organisms are exposed to genotoxic compounds with micronucleogenic effect [2,20,41,70], also, this test is widely used for the evaluation of the possible genotoxicity effect of new drugs, since this assay can be performance *in vivo*, which gives the opportunity to observe the effect of their metabolites.

2. Biomonitoring

The monitoring of pollution by direct analysis of the chemical compounds requires great precision and a well knowledge of the compound and its evaluation is limited by the sensitivity and specificity of the method used. Instead, biomonitors allow us to study the compound, as well as their metabolites which sometimes can be more toxic than the original compound [23,76]. It is important to mention that many mutagenic substances or oncogenic own their action to a product after its metabolism in the liver [77]. Numerous environmental and industrial chemicals, as well as some drugs, could produce genetic damage in experimental animals, and is obvious the potential for similar effects in humans [38], so studies about the genotoxic effects of the compounds in animals is a very useful tool.

It is also known that in genetic toxicology a single assay or model is not sufficient to determine the genotoxic potential of a compound, which justifies the use of the largest number of test and models to obtained more evidence [7]. Experiments with animals, therefore, may suggest that similar effects are likely to occur in humans. If a drug or chemical substance presents genotoxic effects in two or more species, it must be consider that the risk probability in humans is high; however, it must be important to estimate the drug dose [78]. In addition, health institutions indicate that to provide adequate protection of public health both tests in laboratory animals and the monitoring of human population are requires. Research with laboratory animals are conducted both by regulatory requirements for pharmaceuticals and chemicals marketing and, with the objective to understand the basic mechanisms of toxicity, of diseases and compounds that are used in chemical therapies [79].

2.1. Micronuclei and Biomonitoring

The micronucleus assay can be realized in a wide number of different species, since the essential condition is that the tissue going through division. This test can be applied in humans [18,74,80], laboratory animals and wildlife [27,38,56,64,69-71,81,82], and a large variety of tissues, such as bone marrow, peripheral blood erythrocytes [14,69-71,83], lymphocytes [15,84], hepatocytes [45], germ cells [43], oral mucosa epithelial cells [17,44], rats vaginal cells [20], or even in salamander shed cells [21]. In the case of laboratory animals, the most common are rat [12], mouse [2,15,34] and hamster [38], and others not to common as the cat [70] and some primates, apes and monkeys [56,81]. Therefore, the use of organism as biomonitors, which naturally can give information about the possible genotoxic effect of any compound; it is a very economical alternative of great benefit to human health.

Taking this advantage, many groups have been given the task of finding organisms that can be used as bioindicators of genotoxic damage. It has been described the spontaneous micronuclei from a great number of species, with the aim to have the alternative to select the ones with the highest spontaneous micronucleated erythrocytes number to propose them as models for genotoxicity studies [41,56,64,69-71,82]. For micronucleus assay, these organisms should respond forming a high frequency of spontaneous micronucleated erythrocytes, so that when this organisms be exposed to a probably genotoxic agent a significant increase in the number of micronucleated erythrocytes will be observed [82]. The approach is that if a species present high spontaneous micronucleated erythrocytes number, it means 6 micronucleated erythrocytes in 10,000 erythrocytes cells, is due to that the reticuloendothelial system, which is responsible for removed this structure from the circulation, does not have a good control over them and as a result variation in their basal micronucleated erythrocytes values can be observed in peripheral blood erythrocytes to their accumulation. Therefore, if these organisms are exposed to a genotoxic agent, the micronucleated erythrocytes number will be increased [63,70]. This will allow detecting genotoxic micronucleogenic compounds by means of comparative study of micronucleated erythrocytes in peripheral blood of these species before and after genotoxic exposure.

The micronucleus test can be done in a large number of species, thus the used of living organisms that give us information, it is very inexpensive and valuable since research may be conducted in the laboratory or in their natural environment.

While there are a number of species that can be used for genotoxic studies (mostly lab animals), it is known that in genetic toxicology is accepted that a single assay does not allow to conclude about the possible genotoxic effect of a compound, since there are drugs that respond species-specific or tissue-specific [73], so it becomes important to have different options.

In one occasion, some one asked us the reason of this search, taking into account that the extrapolation of results obtained from animals to humans was difficult to carry out. To which we responded that if, for example, at that time a cat enters to the room where we were and ate some of the food that we were ate and the animal instantly fell dead in that, none of us would take that food, even when literature most recognized that support the idea of the difficulty of the extrapolations.

Another question that should be under these circumstances is what readers would prefer? Take a new drug which has been tested only in mice or that the drug has been tested in a large number of species before being used in humans. Regardless of this, "bioindicators" or "biomonitoring" organisms can also give us information on the effect of new veterinary drugs that will be used in our pets, as well as they would give information about the pollution status of their natural habitat, in a simple, fast and powerful way, carrying out a micronucleus analysis.

2.1.1. Searching New Models to be Proposed as Bioindicators by Means of the Micronucleus Assay

For more than a decade some research groups have been working to obtain the spontaneous micronucleated erythrocytes values from different species, especially mammals, but also including some reptiles and birds. As a result of these investigations, a micronuclei database have been obtained that describes these values in erythrocytes of peripheral blood of more than 150 different species with the aim to looking for those that can be suitable as bioindicators even for laboratory analysis or to environmental researches [64,69,71,82]. From these species that have been described as potential bioindicators, some of then have proved for as models for genotoxicity studies, like domestic species as the cat [70] that allows to assess pollutants in urban environments where people cohabit, other species as squirrels [41], could be used to evaluate forests habitats, pigs for evaluating compounds for veterinary use and/or quality of meat for human consumption, aquatic mammal like dolphins [22] as useful as a biomonitor in marine environments or aquariums and even monkeys, as common marmosets, squirrel monkeys or capuchin monkeys, as models for pharmaceutical industry studies to evaluate drugs for human use with the advantage of their phylogenetic relationship with human species [56].

2.2. Spontaneous Micronucleated Erythrocytes of Peripheral Blood from Species Chosen to be Proposed as Bioindicators for Genotoxicity Assays

As it was mentioned before, a species must present certain characteristics to be used as a bioindicator of genotoxic compound by means of micronucleus assay in peripheral blood erythrocytes. Among these characteristic, the most important is the presence of spontaneous micronucleated erythrocytes, since this indicate that the system which is responsible for removing them from circulation is not effective, and these structures could be observed due to its accumulation when the organism is exposed to a genotoxic compound.

It has been analyzed blood samples from more than 150 different species and many of them present high spontaneous micronucleated erythrocytes number [56,64,69,71,82]. It is interesting to note that as a result of this analysis it has been establish a phylogenetic relationship that occurs in some groups. For example, felines group, which was developed from a single common ancestor, and all the species of this group present spontaneous MNE. In addition, primates group have several phylogenetic origins, and those primates who belong to the New World present spontaneous micronucleated erythrocytes and in at least one species of lemur.

The spontaneous micronucleated erythrocytes values observed in samples from selected species as biomonitor are show in Table 1.

Table 1. Spontaneous micronucleated erythrocytes from selected species [82]

SPECIES	sampled animals	micronucleated erythrocytes in 10,000 total erythrocytes
MAMMALS		
Carnivores		
Leopard (*Panthera pardus*)	1	57.0
Binturong (*Arctictis binturong*)	1	32.0
Bengal tiger (*Panthera tigris*)	7	20.5
Puma (*Puma concolor*)	2	18.5
Ferret (*Mustela putorius*)	3	18.0
Ocelote (*Felis pardalis*)	1	13.5
Lynx (*Lynx ruffus*)	4	11.9
Jaguar (*Panthera onca*)	1	10.0
Domestic cat (*Felis catus*)	9	9.3
Cetaceans		
Dolphin (*Tursiops truncatus*)	12	24.3
Insectivores		
Hedgehog (*Erinaceus sp.*)	5	15.4
Marsupials		
Wallaby (*Macropus sp.*)	1	11.0
Primates		
Capuchin monkey (*Cebus sp.*)	4	20.5
Common marmoset (*Callithrix jacchus*)	18	16.3
Squirrel monkey (*Saimiri sciureus*)	3	12.3
Pygmy marmoset (*Cebuella pygmaea*)	1	10.0
Lemur (*Lemur catta*)	2	8.5
Rodents		
Squirrel (*Sciurus aureogaster*)	10	9.1
Ungulates		
Barbary Sheep (*Ammotragus lervia*)	1	35.0
Pig (*Sus scrofa*)	25	11.8
Collared Peccary (*Tayassu tajacu*)	2	9.5
White-tailed Deer (*Odocoileus virginianus*)	11	6.3
Nilgai antelope (*Boselaphus tragocamelus*)	1	6.0
BIRDS		
Owl (*Otus sp.*)	2	15.8

Spontaneous micronucleated erythrocytes values are show in micronucleated erythrocytes mean in 10,000 total erythrocytes for each species.

These species that were selected, have the potential to be used as bioindicators of genotoxic compounds basically micronucleogenic [64,82]. This group of species with spontaneous micronucleated erythrocytes it could be used for genotoxicity studies by means of micronucleus assay. From this selection various species were able to be prove, such as the domestic cat, gray squirrel and common marmoset [41,56,70], all with positive results. The advantage to use the domestic cat as a biomonitor, is that the cat is a territorial animal that allow to realize monitoring study in confined areas, obtaining result from the area that the cat live, and with the possibility to use this species in laboratories research. Other species of felines, like siamese cat, bengal tiger, puma, ocelote, lynx, jaguars and leopards, although present higher spontaneous micronucleated erythrocytes values that the domestic cat and they are also considered as species potentially suitable to be biomonitors.

In the case of rodents [85], the squirrel results to be a good model and even that this species is difficult to reproduce in captivity, their adaptation to laboratory conditions is extraordinary.

In the Ungulates it was found potential species to be considered as biomonitors [64,69,71,82], as is the case of the pig, a species already used for research purposes with a wide variety of races and therefore large number of alternatives for work. The peccary, like other Ungulates, such as white-tailed deer, barbary sheep and nilgai antelope are species that definitively could be used for genotoxic studies in their natural habitats due to the difficulty in handling them.

Within domesticated species, it have been described the hedgehog and ferret [86-88], which have been used in biomedical research due to of its size, easy maintenance, captive breeding and easy adaptation, because they are docile and are adapted to being handled. Another animal easy handle is the wallaby, which could be the first marsupial used for genotoxicity studies by means of micronucleus assay.

A species little known is the binturong, which has the characteristic to present high spontaneous micronucleated erythrocytes number and therefore to be species to be study as potentially biomonitor. Birds present nucleated erythrocytes and in some occasions nuclear protrusions that can be confusing when the cells are analyze for micronucleus test, so if a species with nucleated erythrocytes is chosen, it will be convenient to be careful to identify micronucleus from this structures, for example the owl could be a candidate with nucleated erythrocytes to be proved as biomonitor of micronucleogenic compounds [64].

The dolphin has already been used as a biomarker of DNA damage by means of micronucleus assay in lymphocytes of peripheral blood [89]. However, we identified the presence of spontaneous micronuclei in erythrocytes from peripheral blood, making this marine mammal a potential sentinel for marine environment [21,82].

Of greater importance was the identification of primates with high number of spontaneous micronuclei [56,64,69,71,82], since until now the micronucleus assay was conducted mainly in mouse peripheral blood and bone marrow, which is located phylogenetically in an Order not to close from humans, while species like capuchin monkeys, squirrel monkeys, pygmy and common marmoset, even that these are not related closer with humans as the great apes, whether they are in the same Order that humans belongs, it mean that once it has been demonstrated its feasibility as biomonitors, the results obtained from trails of drugs for human use will have greater validity than others assays realized in other species [64,82].

It should be emphasized that micronucleus assay using this species may be the most simple and inexpensive described until now, since just a drop of blood, slides and a microscope will be required, which is a technique that in any kind of laboratory can be realized.

Having exotics organisms with the potential to be used as biomonitors for environmental genotoxic, as well as the alternative to work with them in the laboratory, lead us to have the option to study them in their natural habitat and with this, knowing how contaminated could be, and just left to choose correctly the species to be use.

It is shows that there are exotic species or not conventional laboratory species that can be used as biomonitors, due to its high spontaneous micronucleated erythrocytes number, that could increase micronuclei number in erythrocytes from peripheral blood when are exposed to a genotoxic compound, which made them potential indicators of agents that affects directly the genetic material, measured by means of micronucleus assay [82].

2.3. Factors Affecting on Micronuclei Frequencies

The literature described that the sensitivity for micronuclei induction taking into account gender can be attributed to enzyme and/or hormonal differences found between males and females [76,90].

Also, it has been described that the variability in the micronucleated erythrocytes number is influenced by age [28,91,92]; splenectomized patients adults and children, showed differences in the number of micronucleated erythrocytes in peripheral blood, being higher in adults compared with children [63,75]. Studies in rodents support this observation, since it has been found that the micronuclei frequency in old mice and hamster spermatid is higher compared with younger [93,94]. On the other hand, it has been described differences in the number of spontaneous micronucleated erythrocytes due to the immaturity of the reticuloendothelial system in juvenile stages, which make then unable to withdraw these structure from circulation and conforming the organism matures their system becomes more efficient, such that can remove them from circulation until it was almost imperceptible in their adult stage [41,63,64,69].

In previous studies, it has been described high values of spontaneous micronucleated erythrocytes in newborn or young animals, while in adult members of these same species, low or near-zero values of micronucleated erythrocytes were observed [64]. These differences in the micronucleated erythrocytes number reflected the maturity of the reticuloendothelial system.

Some of the species that are reported in the micronuclei database have been assessed at different ages to identify differences in the number of micronuclei according with age (Table 2) and we have found species that in early stages of their lives presented higher micronucleated erythrocytes frequency and this frequency decreases as the organism mature, as is the case of humans too [41,64], since it has been observed that although they are not detectable values of micronucleated erythrocytes in adult human [60], preterm newborn present micronuclei in their erythrocytes of peripheral blood, but not children even in full term neonates [64]. This allows to conducted genotoxicity studies in juvenile stages and/or to verify xenobiotic exposition in prenatal stages, and even to detect in a simple way the harmful effects that could be affecting to the fetus due to maternal pathologies present during pregnancy [95,96].

In the case of laboratory animals with these characteristics, adult rats have very few micronucleated erythrocytes in peripheral blood [64,69], and therefore the micronucleus assay must be performed using bone marrow and/or by counting micronucleated polychromatic erythrocytes in peripheral blood. Our results show that newborn rats have a relatively high spontaneous micronucleated erythrocytes frequency. This value is significantly higher than we previously reported for seven-day-old rats and adult rats [64,69]. Therefore, the developing spleen of neonatal rats may not efficiently remove micronucleated erythrocytes from circulation and it is possible that the micronucleus test can be performed directly using the peripheral blood of newborn rats.

Table 2. Spontaneous micronucleated erythrocytes in 10,000 total erythrocytes in young and adult animals [64]

Species	Young (X±SD)	N	Reference	Adult (X±SD)	n	Reference
HUMAN (*Homo sapiens*)	6.2±6.7 (27-35 weeks gestation)	14	[64]	0.0	6	[60]
LION (*Panthera leo*)	6.5±1.3 (unknown age)	3	[71]	0.6±0.1	2	[69]
PUMA (*Puma concolor*)	18.5±0.7 (2 months old)	2	[64]	No data	---	------------
BENGAL TIGER (*Panthera tigris*)	20.5±2.9 (2-8 weeks old)	7	[64]	No data	---	------------
CAT (*Felis domesticus*)	23.2±9.3 (6-8 weeks old)	50	[70]	8.4±2.5	61	[69]
DOG (*Canis familiaris*)	27.0±2.9 (10 days old)	5	[64]	1.0±1.1 1.1±1.2	12 7	[69] [73]
RAT (*Ratus norvegicus*)	26.3±8.7 (7 days old)	15	[64]	2.2±0.7	10	[69]
GRAY SQUIRREL (*Sciurus aureogaster*)	12.8±3.8 (unknown age)	6	[71]	3.5±1.7	4	[71,41]
GUINEA PIG (*Cavia porcellus*)	0.2±0.4 (1-5 days old)	5	[64]	0.3±2.8	10	[69]
RABBIT (*Oryctolagus canniculus*)	15.7±14.3 (5-18 days old)	8	[64]	1.4±0.1 3.1±0.6	8 4	[69] [73]
PIG (*Sus scrofa*)	19.1±7.9 (30-45 days old)	10	[64]	6.9±4.0	15	[69]
GIRAFFE (*Giraffa camelopardalis*)	18.0 (newborn)	1	[69]	0.0	1	[64]
WHITE-TAILED DEER (*Odocoileus virginianus*)	8.0±3.6 (unknown age)	3	[64]	2.3±1.5	5	[69]
OPOSSUM (*Didelphis virginiana*)	3.7±1.5 (unknown age)	15	[64]	1.3±1.5	3	[71]

Moreover, the peripheral blood of newborn rats has recently been described as a new model to evaluate the genotoxic and teratogenic potential of compounds administered during pregnancy [68].

In adult rabbits, micronucleus test are carried out on bone marrow samples, because the spleen quickly removes damaged erythrocytes from the peripheral blood [64]. This species present a sinusal spleen so the adult rabbit is not an appropriate mammalian species for conducting the micronucleus assay on peripheral blood erythrocytes [25]. Indeed, even after splenectomy, spontaneous micronuclei number in adult rabbits did not reach that of other species [69,73]. However, rabbits from 5 days of age, present a mean of 15 spontaneous micronucleated erythrocytes in 10,000 total erythrocytes and in rabbits from 13 days old, the mean spontaneous micronucleated erythrocytes is 6 in 10,000 total erythrocytes [64].

On the other hand, other species present this behaviour too but by its nature, size or handle may not be appropriate for laboratory studies but would be adequate in field studies or in veterinary studies specific for each species. Thus, the perinatal stages of this species could be a useful biomonitor.

2.4. Teratogenic Potential: Micronuclei in Neonates Affected During Gestational Period

There are an increasing number of new chemicals and pharmaceutical products that are used and could have the potential for inducing birth defects, and there are many other agents in the process of being evaluated for possible effects during the human perinatal period [97]. Many compounds that are classified as genotoxic have "teratogenic potential", and various mechanisms of teratogenesis could involve micronucleus induction [97,98]. Thus, micronuclei have been used in a number of studies investigating teratogenicity [31]. For example, micronuclei frequency has been measured in fetal rodent liver cells [99-102], mouse fetal blood [103], mouse newborn blood [104], lymphocyte cultures from cord blood [105], and in studies of teratogenic potential in peripheral blood erythrocytes from newborn rats [68].

Any compound that is transferred across the placental barrier and induces the formation of micronucleated erythrocytes in the fetus may be considered a potential teratogen [68]. Thus, the micronucleus assay in newborn animals could be useful to identify compounds with teratogenic potential or genotoxicity effects during gestation [68,106], with the advantage that the micronucleus test is performed *in vivo*, so that any effects due to the metabolism of the original compound to even more toxic substances will also be observed [23]. This alternative of the micronucleus test in newborn rats could be useful for identifying compounds with teratogenic potential without the necessity of observing malformations, which can result complicated if the observer do not have experience.

To realize the study of the teratogenic potential of a compound, female wistar rats that are mated with males are used. Each female rat is flushed daily with a vaginal wash of 0.1 ml of water using an adjustable-volume pipettor and the contents are smeared onto clean slides. The presence of sperm indicates that mating had occurred and established the first day of pregnancy. With these rats different groups are formed, which must have a negative and a positive control groups and at least 3 experimental groups [107].

The female rats are housed in individual cages. Groups of five pregnant rats are give daily oral doses of the vehicle, 0.5 ml of water, and served as the negative control. Micronucleated erythrocytes are induce by transplacental treatment with cyclophosphamide [102,108-113], then positive control group receives 10 mg/kg of cyclophosphamide, this dose produce a strong increase in micronucleated erythrocytes and micronucleated polychromatic erythrocytes frequency, while the three experimental groups will receive the compound to be tested at three different concentrations. To minimize toxicity to the developing fetuses, the cyclophosphamide, water and the compound to be tested, must be administered to the pregnant rats after organogenesis [114], daily at days 16 to 20 of gestation. All compounds are adjusted to a final volume of 0.5 ml with the vehicle.

At birth, six pups (3 males and 3 females) are select randomly from each dam and used for the analysis of micronucleated erythrocytes. A drop of peripheral blood it is taken from the tip of the tail of each newborn rat, immediately after birth. Two smears are made on pre-cleaned microscope slides. The smears are air-dried, fixed in absolute ethanol for 10 min, and then stain with acridine orange for its subsequent analysis to the microscope as is described for peripheral blood erythrocytes samples.

A very important point is that newborn rats and premature humans have relatively high spontaneous micronucleated erythrocytes frequencies in their peripheral blood. The micronucleated erythrocytes frequency diminishes with age to be virtually undetectable in adults [64,69]. The relatively high micronucleated erythrocytes frequency in human neonates, particularly in premature infants, could be useful for evaluating the genotoxicity of drugs administered to the mother during pregnancy. With regard to predictive tests in model species, species-specific differences in the teratogenicity of compounds have been reported [115]. Thus, more than one test may be required for adequately evaluating the developmental toxicity of any compound [7], making it important to implement alternative tests [99]. It has been observed previously that the neonates of 12 different animal species have relatively high frequencies of micronucleated erythrocytes [64], and therefore these species may provide alternative tools for evaluating teratogenic potential by counting micronucleated erythrocytes in the peripheral blood of newborns.

As it was described above, we also have studied the response of the rabbit for evaluating teratogenic potential of compounds and the results were also positive, which suggests that other species identified with similar behavior to the rat and rabbit about the micronucleated erythrocytes presence at birth, could be good indicators of teratogenic potential through this study design.

2.5. Micronuclei in Epithelial Cells

Exfoliated cells from the intermediate and superficial layers of the epithelium have been widely used in cytology to detect abnormal morphology, premalignant changes, and cancer [116].

Since to carry out the micronucleus assay, as it was mention before, a high proliferation tissue is required, epithelial tissues in general are good candidate. For example the oral mucosa cell micronucleus assay, is useful as a biomarker of genetic damage caused by life-style habits, exposures to environmental pollutants, medical procedures, as well as, inherited genetic defects in DNA repair. The non-invasive nature of this technique makes it an attractive candidate for the biomonitoring of human populations or individuals. Other epithelia also used such as the nasal mucosa, epithelial cells from and even cells from the root of the hair. Moreover, as it will be mentioned below, different types of epithelial cells from other species have also been good alternative to carry out the micronucleus assay, as alternative tissues to assess genotoxicity by means of the micronucleus test.

In oral mucosa cells, this test has been applied to the biological monitoring of human populations exposed to mutagenic and carcinogenic agents (Figure 5).

Micronuclei in exfoliated cells reflect genotoxic events that occurred in the dividing basal cell layer 1 to 3 weeks earlier [116]. The technique involves examination of epithelial smears to determine the prevalence of cells containing micronuclei, and it has been used to evaluate the effect of exposure to different xenobiotics which are capable of inducing cancer. Therefore, the micronucleus test in exfoliated cells from oral mucosa can be used as a tool in studies aimed at assessing the potential genotoxicity of different drugs used to the treatment of some diseases.

The exfoliated cell micronucleus assay has advantages over another. It is a non invasive technique and repeated sampling is acceptable. Contrasting to blood sampled obtained by puncture (which involves invasive procedures). To carry out the micronucleus assay in oral mucosa cells, the universe of study is widely, since it can include the whole population, because in this case the spleen has no control over this kind of cells.

To obtain oral smear samples, subjects are asked to rinse their mouths with water, then polished slide is used to collect cells from the oral mucosa of the right and left cheeks; the samples are spread directly into two separate pre-cleaned slides. The smears are air dried and fixed in 80% methanol for 48 hours and then stain using orcein and green fast or it is preferred it can be use a DNA specific stain as acridine orange [96]. After this procedure with acridine orange, the nucleus and micronuclei were stained in yellow and the cytoplasm in dark green.

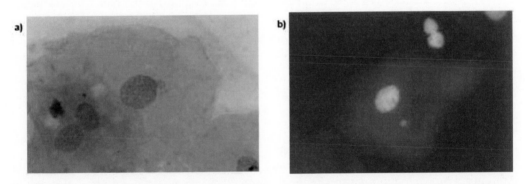

Figure 5. Micronucleated cells from oral mucosa (100×). a) orcein and fast green stain; b) acridine orange stain.

The slides were observed in a light microscope at 100× magnifications using a microscope equipped with epifluorescence and scoring is perform according to the criteria established by Tolbert *et al.* [44], with the results presented as micronucleated cells in 2,000 cells [17,44].

A disadvantage of the manual analysis of micronuclei in oral mucosa cells is that the analysis time from a sample is 4 to 6 times higher than in blood samples and the number of cells analyzable is also lower due to the sample is obtained from a gently scraped from the inside of the mouth. This also means that the smear should be made correctly to obtain enough analyzable cells.

An important step in the evolution of the micronucleus assay was the recognition that it could provide reliable data about the screening of the genotoxicity of drugs from medical procedures such as chemotherapy. In previous studies the micronucleogenicity of the drugs used in anticancer therapies were determined considering the number of micronucleated cell produced, and the most genotoxic micronucleogenic drugs were cyclophosphamide and arabinose-c, while busulfan was the less. In general, to know the micronucleogenicity of drugs used in chemotherapy sooner or later may allow to the doctor to choose the less micronucleogenic compound, in the cases that may be possible.

At the same time, it is well know that the anticancer therapies are mostly genotoxics and micronucleogenic. Moreover, the test can also be used to identify those patients resistent to these kind of drugs used in anticancer therapy, it mean that even though this patients received antineoplastic drugs that in theory might produced increased of micronuclei, and for inherited genetic defects in the metabolism of these compounds that are not metabolized and the micronuclei number did not increased [18].

Also the micronucleus test could be used to identify the "genotoxic" effects of some human diseases, it mean that some diseases have the potential to increase the micronuclei number *per se*, such as cancer [117], or rheumatoid arthritis that frequencies of micronuclei are 3 times higher compared with healthy population [116], which could be a possible explanation of why these patients develop leukaemia more frequently than healthy individuals.

Another pathology that has been identified as micronucleogenic *per se* is the diabetes mellitus which the increase in the micronuclei basal values is approximately doubled compared to non-diabetic population [96].

Finally, the test can be used for the opposite objective that was designed, and a lot of works have been realized with the aim to determine the protective effect of compounds as antioxidant such as vitamin C, vitamin E, folic acid [96,118-122].

However, other alternatives to realize genotoxicity study using epithelial cells from living organism as biomonitors have been developed, techniques that have allowed us to avoid the sacrifice of the animals to obtained the sample, as it was required in the original techniques, in addition it to use alternative tissues with the possibility to carry out laboratory studies and in field studies to the assessment of both drugs and toxic environment compounds. Among these new proposals to realize the micronucleus test are salamanders shed skin and proestrus vaginal rat cells [20,21].

2.5.1. Micronuclei in Epithelial Cells of the Shed Skin of Salamanders (Ambystoma sp.)

The micronucleus assay can be used to detect the genotoxic effects of chemical agents in virtually any cell that divides frequently. Salamanders (*Ambystoma sp.*), are amphibians that can be easily maintained and bred in the laboratory, and spontaneously shed their skin every 2.5–4 days. In this part, we show the usefulness of this shed skin for the micronucleus assay.

The use of non-human organisms to study genotoxic agents is increasing [41,56,64,70,81,123-127], and amphibians are of special interest in this regard due to their ecological niche [128-132]. Urodela, which includes salamanders and newts, is one of the three surviving orders of the amphibian class. Their skin is glandular; induration of the skin is not present, and it lacks characteristic epidermal structures of other tetrapods such as scales, feathers, and hair [133]. Urodela slough their skin very frequently, either in patches or in one large piece (Figure 6).

To perform this assay, it can be used as positive controls aneugenic compound as colchicine and/or a clastogen as cyclophosphamide, and salamanders from the genus Ambystoma (*Ambystoma sp.*) are exposed to different concentrations of the compound to be tested (compound that must be water soluble) and to determine the frequency of micronucleated cells in their shed skin.

The animals used as adults, when animals arrived in the laboratory in the larval stage, metamorphosis is induced [133-135] because larvae do not slough their skins suitably (Figure 6). The animals are settled individually in fish bowls filled with tap water and are feed daily with bloodworms.

The sheds are collected, and the date of each shed is recorded. Sloughs occurred every 2.5-4 days. Fragments from the ventral part of the shed are placed on clean slides, air dried, fixed, stain, and the frequency of micronucleated cells in 2000 cells is determined using a microscope [17]. Micronucleated cells are confirmed using acridine orange stain.

The model of the salamander skid shed allows to made intra-group or inter-group comparisons [21]. The scoring of micronucleated cells start with the last shed before beginning the treatment period, and this shed is used as the basal value for the individual salamander. The micronucleated cells frequencies in the subsequent are determined, and both intra-group comparisons in order to determine if shed salamander skin could be used in controlled laboratory experiments to detect genotoxic compounds, or inter-group comparisons to verify that the assay could be used to compare the genotoxicity of populations from different aquatic environments are done.

The presence of micronucleated cells in the shed skin and the speed of sloughing lead us to propose that the sheds of *Ambystoma sp.*, or other amphibians that slough their skin, are suitable alternative models for detecting genotoxic exposures relevant to aquatic environments.

In our experience, the assay detects the genotoxicity of cyclophosphamide (a clastogen) and colchicine (an aneugen) administered in both single and multiple doses. The groups that received multiple doses of the compounds, however had the greatest micronucleated cell frequencies and had significant responses in almost all the post-treatment sheds, also, intra-group comparisons generally were more sensitive than inter-group comparisons, especially for the colchicine-treated animals [21].

As a positive control, the recommended doses are a single administration of the colchicine 0.774 mg or the same doses of the compound for 5 consecutive days, and for cyclophosphamide, a single administration of the compound at 112.5 mg or the same doses for 5 consecutive days. Both compounds dissolved in the water of their fish bowls.

The mean basal micronucleated cells frequency in *Ambystoma sp.* is 0.44±0.79 micronucleated cells/2000 cells. The timing of the appearance of micronucleated cells in the skin sheds may be partially explained by the biology of salamander skin. Different layers compose the salamander epidermis. The outermost layer of the epidermis, the stratum corneum, consists of a single layer of flattened cells. Underlying the stratum corneum is the stratum germinativum, which normally are 4-8 cells thick. The stratum corneum is sloughed. Micronuclei formation probably occurs in the stratum germinativum, and thus to observe the genotoxicity of a compound, it is necessary that the stratum corneum present at treatment be sloughed (first shed). Micronucleated cells then would be observed in the cells of this stratum that appear in subsequent sheds [21].

Although greater sample size appeared to increase the sensitivity of the assay, our results indicate that short treatments with relatively potent genotoxicants were capable of inducing significant increases in micronucleated cells frequency in shed salamander skin, even with a sample size of 5 animals. Previous assays that used blood erythrocytes from some amphibians required treatments that lasted over 2–3 months [128,130,132], and thus animals had a greater chance of dying during the long exposure period, and more test compound was required for the assay [128,130,132,136], which increases the cost of the trial. Furthermore, in this assay, it was not necessary to sacrifice the animal to obtain the sample [21].

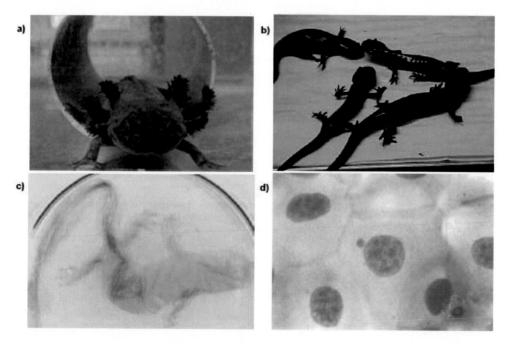

Figure 6. *Ambystoma sp.* a) salamander larvae; b) adult salamanders; c) shed skin; d) micronucleated cell of the shed skin of salamander (100× / fast grifols stain: Giemsa-Wright stain modified).

Urodeles can easily adapt to captivity which makes them suitable subjects for use in research [133]. In our experience, Urodeles slough their skin frequently, and with animals in captivity, it is possible to recover the complete shed. Using a microscope, we found that the shed was composed of a monolayer of cells, making the scoring of micronuclei unambiguous (Figure 6d). Variations in the schedule of water changes did not influence slough frequency; however, previous observations in our laboratory indicate that the frequency of skin shedding is affected by water temperature, and can vary from every 2.5 days to every 4 days with a range of water temperature of 14 to 29°C. It was also important that the animals were located in the same place during the course of the experiment. We observed that sloughing ceased for up to 15 days after animals (without treatments) were moved, for example, from one laboratory to another.

Amphibians possess macro- and micro-chromosomes, with Ambystoma having a diploid number of 28 macrochromosomes [133]. Micronucleated cells can be easily observed owing to the large size of the chromosomes and the presence of large chromosome fragments [26].

In conclusion, this is an alternative model for evaluating genotoxic agents in amphibians by means of the micronucleus test in epithelial cells. Because of the high rate of cellular proliferation in Urodela skin, we were able use shed skin to measure micronucleated cells frequencies induced by treating *Ambystoma sp.* with both an aneugenic and a clastogenic compound. Salamander shed skin may be useful as a laboratory model, without the necessity of sacrificing the animals for making measurements, or could be used in field studies to detect genotoxicity in aquatic environments [21].

2.5.2. Micronuclei in Proestrus Vaginal Rat Cells

As it mentioned, a highly proliferative tissue is required for conducting the micronucleus test, and desquamating vaginal cells of the rat have this characteristic. The sexual cycle of the rat is complete in four to five days [137] and has four phases (diestrus, proestrus, estrus, and metestrus), which are very easily identified by vaginal cytology [134,137,138]. During diestrus (60 to 70 h), leukocytes and a few basal-type cells (small and nucleated) are observed. In proestrus (approximately 12 h), intermediate-type cells occur; the cells are rounded or navicular and have large nuclei. Estrus (9 to 15 h) is the sexually receptive phase, during which many mitotic cells are present in the vaginal mucosa, together with superficial angular cells with or without small nuclei. During metestrus (10 to 14 h), leukocytes and cornified cells are the most important cells types observed [134,138]. Also, it has been described the micronucleus assay in proestrus cells from the rat [20]. Proestrus cells were chosen for analysis because of their size and numbers, their homogeneous nuclei, and the intact and well-defined borders of their cytoplasm (Figure 7a).

To carry out the assay, a group of rats are sampled daily to identify the first proestrus subsequently; the rats are assigned to one of five groups, all with 5 rats/group. Animals will be group as follow: a negative control group who receives just the vehicle in which the compound to be tested is dissolves, a positive control group who receives a dose of 80 mg/kg of cyclophosphamide in a single administration, dose that produced significant increases in proestrus micronucleated cells frequency in the first and second proestrus.

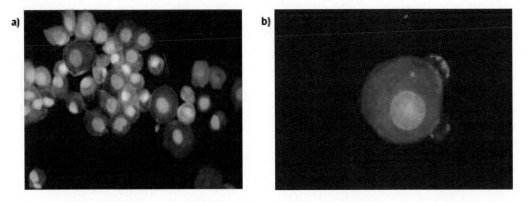

Figure 7. Proestrus vaginal rat cells (acridine orange stain). a) proestrus cells (40×); b) proestrus micronucleated cell (100×).

Animals could be dosed orally with 20 mg/kg cyclophosphamide for five consecutive days; in this way it is obtained had significantly elevated frequencies of proestrus micronucleated cells in the three proestrus periods following the treatment. If the dose administration is in just one occasion or subsequently is determine as the type of study design. Finally, a minimum of 3 groups exposed to the compound that will be tested (low, medium and high dose) [107].

Daily cell samples are taken (see below), and cells from the first identified proestrus are used to establish basal micronucleus frequencies. All doses are adjusted to a final volume of 200 μl. Cell samples are taken daily until four cycles of estrus are completed for all groups. The samples in proestrus are identified cytologically, and used for counting micronucleated cells [20].

The daily sampling is conducted with a vaginal wash of 100 μl of sterile water containing 10-25% calf serum using an adjustable-volume pipettor, higher concentrations of calf serum are not recommended because serum fluorescence may interfere with the observation of micronucleated cells. The 200 μl plastic pipette tips are flattened beforehand to minimize injury to the animals. Smears are made on each of two coded slides. 100 μl water are used to wash the remaining serum from the vagina. The smears are air-dried and fixed in absolute ethanol for 48 h, then stain as described by Tice *et al.* [58], with modifications [20]. The concentration of acridine orange used for stain the samples is 0.02 mg/ml of phosphate buffer (pH, 7.4). The slides are observed with a microscope equipped with epi-fluorescence and a 100× objective. Two thousand cells of each proestrus sample are examined for micronuclei [20].

Proestrus cells are counted only when the cytoplasmic borders and the nuclei are intact, defined, and homogeneous [20]. The results are presented as proestrus micronucleated cells per 2,000 proestrus cells [17,20]. Micronucleated cells are counted only when the micronuclei is clearly separated from the main nucleus or, in the case of the binucleated cells that are commonly observed in this tissue after exposure to colchicine or cyclophosphamide, clearly separated from both nuclei (Figure 7b).

Also, the rats should be handled gently, because daily and repeated vaginal manipulation could induce pseudopregnancy. If this should occur, the rat's sexual cycle is interrupted for about 12 days. Similarly, factors such as light, temperature, nutritional status, and social relations can influence the duration of the cycle [134,138,139].

Zúñiga-González et al. [20] explain that rat proestrus micronucleated cells could be useful as an alternative tissue for the micronucleus assay 1) when an alternative tissue is required to demonstrate a genotoxic effect or when the compound is tissue-specific [31]; 2) when the period of exposure to the test agent is prolonged, and/or counting micronucleated polychromatic erythrocytes is inadequate [24] because newly formed erythrocytes remain polychromatic for approximately 1-2 days before maturing into normochromatic cells; 3) when the size of blood samples taken periodically is large enough to disturb the proportion of polychromatic erythrocytes [140]; 4) when automated equipment is not available for counting the large numbers of erythrocytes [31,141] required because the rat spleen is highly efficient in removing micronucleated erythrocytes [31,63,64,73,142,143]; 5) or when killing the rat is not desirable, as is required for the bone-marrow micronucleus assay [12].

The desquamating vaginal cells in proestrus could be an alternative tissue for performing the micronucleus test in rats [20]. Because it is a relatively non-invasive procedure, other measurements may be made in the same animals, which could reduce the number of animal used and the overall cost for evaluating suspected genotoxins [20,37].

2.6. Automated Micronucleus Scoring Methods

The quantification of DNA damage, both *in vivo* and *in vitro*, can be very time consuming, since large amounts of samples need to be scored. Additional uncertainties may arise due to the lack of documentation or by scoring biases [144]. The relative rarity of the micronucleated cells makes microscopy based scoring a tedious and time-consuming process. In this era where human and material resources must be used most efficiently, the labor-intensive nature of microscopic enumeration of rare events is clearly undesirable. Because mammalian erythrocytes are ordinarily devoid of DNA, it has been assumed that cells containing micronuclei could be accurately recognized and scored by image analysis or flow cytometric systems. A number of automated scoring techniques based on these technologies have been proposed to improve the throughput capacity, objectivity, and sensitivity of the assay [31,141,145-157]. Image analysis automation is a possible strategy to cope with these difficulties and to generate a new quality of reproducibility. The automated scoring for dicentric chromosomes, for micronuclei, and for comet assay cells produce reliable and reproducible results, which prove the usability of automated scanning in some research fields as radiation research, biological dosimetry, DNA repair research and environmental mutagenesis studies [144]. An advantage of flow cytometric scoring over manual scoring and image analysis is its extremely high analysis rates. Modern flow cytometers are able to evaluate tens of thousands of immature and hundreds of thousands of mature erythrocytes for micronuclei in several minutes [31]. Erythrocytes from peripheral blood and bone marrow are the easiest to score with automated systems. Using specimens, the instrument is capable of scoring a few hundred cells per minute using smears of purified bone marrow erythrocytes. Standard transmission light microscopy is utilized for scoring these Giemsa-stained cells. This instrument is being developed to score primarily fluorescent-stained (acridine orange) samples of erythrocytes. There is general agreement that the key to automation is sample preparation. This includes cell purification or smear preparation (as needed), appropriate dilution, and careful staining. Cell purification, at least for erythrocytes, may be advantageous as it would simplify scoring. Purification must be free of technical artefacts and not be biased with respect to the micronucleated cells. In the case of flow measurements, new staining methods may improve discrimination between reticulocytes and mature erythrocytes. In nucleated cell cultures, binucleated cells are scored and these must be distinguished from cells with one, three, or four nuclei. Validation of automated methods will be an important part of their final development. Users must be confident that the instruments accurately measure micronuclei. The most direct method of validation would be to compare the results obtained using an automated approach with that of manual scoring, first at the level of individual cells and eventually with coded samples. The use of kinetochore staining would permit discrimination between micronuclei containing whole chromosomes and those containing acentric fragments, and would permit the measurement of events pertinent to aneuploidy [154,158,159].

3. General Considerations

The micronucleus assay, in its different modifications, present many advantages over other genotoxicity tests, including that it can be carried out in at least any tissue that presents high proliferation rate. It is cheap, especially if performed *in vivo* and its results are fast and simple, with the added advantage that the results are easy to interpret.

For the interpretation of micronucleus test results, positive results in this assay indicate that a substance induces micronuclei, which are the result of chromosomal damage or damage to the mitotic apparatus in the erythroblasts of the test species, under the treatment condition used. Negative results indicate that under the test conditions, the test substance does not induce chromosomal or spindle damage leading to the formation of micronuclei in the immature erythrocytes of the test species. When the assay is incorporated into the other toxicological studies, data of the other end points should be taken into consideration when interpreting the results [31].

In this chapter we have shown some alternatives an application of the micronucleus assay trying to be very descriptive so the reader gets a clear idea of what is needed and how you can use this assay.

References

[1] Córdoba, D. Toxicología. 4ª ed. Bogotá, Colombia: Manual Moderno; 2001.

[2] Zúñiga-González, GM; Torres-Bugarín, O; Zamora-Perez, A; Gómez-Meda, BC; Ramos-Ibarra, ML; Gallegos-Arreola, MP; Flores-García, A; López-Uribe, A. Induction of micronucleated erythrocytes in mouse peripheral blood after cutaneous application of 5-Fluorouracil. *Archives of Medical Research*, 2003; 34, 141–144.

[3]   Pariza, MW. *Mutagens and carcinogens in the diet.* New York, USA: Wiley-Liss; 1990.

[4]   Katzung, BG. Farmacología Básica y Clínica. 4ª ed. México, D.F.: Manual Moderno; 1991.

[5]   Montoya-Cabrera, MA. Toxicología Clínica. México: Ed. Francisco Méndez Cervantes; 1992.

[6]   Gibson, GG; Skett, P. Pathways of Drug Metabolism. In: *Introduction to Drug Metabolism.* 2ª ed. London, Glasgow, New York, Tokyo, Melbourne, Madras: Blackie Academic and Professional An Imprint of Chapman and Hall; 1994.

[7]   Shelby, MD; Erexson, GL; Hook, GJ; Tice, RR. Evaluation of a three-exposure mouse bone marrow micronucleus protocol: results with 49 chemicals. *Environmental and Molecular Mutagenesis,* 1993; 21, 160–179.

[8]   Plewa, MJ; Gentile, JM. The activation of chemicals into mutagens by green plants. In: Hollander A. *Series Chemical Mutagens, Principles and Methods for their Detection.* New York: Plenum Press; 1982.

[9]   Ames, BN. The detection of chemical mutagens with enteric bacteria. In: *Microbial test for Mutagenicity/Carcinogenicity.* New York: Ed. by Traul KA. Van Nostrand Reinhold Company; 1985.

[10]   Quillardet, P; Hofnung, M. The SOS chromotest, a colorimetric bacterial assay for genotoxins procedures. *Mutation Research,* 1985; 147, 65–78.

[11]   Kier, LD. The Salmonella typhimurium/mammalian-microsomal assay. A report of the U.S. Environmental Protection Agency Gene-Tox Program. *Mutation Research,* 1986; 168, 69–240.

[12]   Trzos, RJ; Petzold, GL; Brunden, MN; Swenberg, JA. The evolution of sixteen carcinogens in the rat using the micronucleus test. *Mutation Research,* 1978; 58, 79–86.

[13]   Zúñiga-González G. Sistemas de detección de daño genético. In: *Genética, Ambiente y Salud.* Álvarez Moya C. 2ª ed. México: Universidad de Guadalajara; 2001.

[14]   Schmid, W. The micronucleus tests. *Mutation Research,* 1975; 31, 9–15.

[15]   Heddle, JA; Lue, CB; Saunder, F; Benz, D. Sensitivity to five mutagens in Fanconi´s anemia as measured by the micronucleus method. *Cancer Research,* 1978; 38, 2983–2988.

[16]   Corazza, GR; Ginaldi, L; Zoli, G; Frisoni, M; Lalli, G; Gasbarrini, G; Quaglino, D. Howell-Jolly body counting as a measure of splenic function. A ressesment. *Clinical Laboratory Haematology,* 1990; 12, 269–275.

[17]   Torres-Bugarín, O; De Anda-Casillas, A; Ramírez-Muñoz, MP; Sánchez-Corona, J; Cantú, JM; Zúñiga, G. Determination of diesel genotoxicity in firebreathers by micronuclei and nuclear abnormalities in buccal mucosa. *Mutation Research,* 1998; 413, 277–281.

[18]   Torres-Bugarín, O; Ventura-Aguilar, A; Zamora-Perez, A; Gómez-Meda, BC; Ramos-Ibarra, ML; Morgan-Villela, G; Gutiérrez-Franco, A; Zúñiga-González, G. Evaluation of cisplatin + 5-FU, carboplatin + 5-FU, and ifosfamide + epirubicine regimens using the micronuclei test and nuclear abnormalities in the buccal mucosa. *Mutation Research,* 2004; 565, 91–101.

[19] Zúñiga-González, GM; Gómez-Meda, BC. La prueba de micronúcleos. *La Ciencia y el Hombre*, 2006; 19(1), 13–16.

[20] Zúñiga-González, G; Gómez-Meda, BC; Zamora-Perez, A; Ramos-Ibarra, ML; Batista-González, CM; Espinoza-Jiménez, S; Gallegos-Arreola, MP; Álvarez-Moya, C; Torres-Bugarín, O. Induction of micronuclei in proestrus vaginal cells from colchicine- and cyclophosphamide-treated rats. *Environmental and Molecular Mutagenesis*, 2003; 42, 306–310.

[21] Zamora-Perez, A; Zúñiga-González, G; Gómez-Meda, BC; Ramos-Ibarra, ML; Batista-González, CM; Torres-Bugarín, O. Induction of micronucleated cells in the shed skin of salamanders (*Ambystoma sp.*) treated with colchicine or cyclophosphamide. *Environmental and Molecular Mutagenesis*, 2004; 44(5), 436–440.

[22] Zamora-Perez, A; Camacho-Magaña, C; Gómez-Meda, B; Ramos-Ibarra, M; Batista-González, B; Zuñiga-González, G. Importance of spontaneous micronucleated erythrocytes in bottlenose dolphin *Tursiops truncatus* to marine toxicology studies. *Acta Biologica Hungarica*, 2006; 57(4), 441–448

[23] Rodríguez-Ariza, A; Abril, N; Navas, JI; Dorado, G; López-Barea, J; Pueyo, C. Metal mutagenicity and biochemical studies on bivalve molluscs from Spanish coasts. *Environmental and Molecular Mutagenesis*, 1992; 19, 112–124.

[24] Von Ledebur, M; Schmid, W. The micronucleus test. Methodological aspects. *Mutation Research*, 1973; 19, 109–117.

[25] Udroiu, I; Cristaldi, M; Ieradi LA; Bedini, A; Giuliani, L; Tanzarella, C. Clastogenicity and aneuploidy in newborn and adult mice exposed to 50 Hz magnetic fields. *International Journal of Radiation Biology*, 2006; 82, 561–567.

[26] Yamamoto, KI; Kikuchi, YA. Comparison of diameters of micronuclei induced by clastogens and by spindle poisons. *Mutation Research*, 1980; 71, 127–131.

[27] Caria, H; Chaveca, T; Laires, A; Rueff, J. Genotoxicity of quercetin in the micronucleus assay in mouse bone marrow erythrocytes, human lymphocytes, V79 cell line and identification of kinetochore-containing (CREST staining) micronuclei in human lymphocytes. *Mutation Research*, 1995; 343, 85–95.

[28] Odagiri, Y; Uchida, H. Influence of serum micronutrients on the incidence of kinetochore-positive or –negative micronuclei in human peripheral blood lymphocytes. *Mutation Research*, 1998; 415, 35–45.

[29] Verschaeve, L; Vanderkerken, K; Kirsch-Volders, M. 1988. C-banding as a simple tool to discriminate between micronuclei induced by clastogens and aneugens. *Stain Technology*, 1988; 63, 351–354.

[30] Vanderkerken, K; Vanparys, Ph; Verschaeve, L; Kirsch-Volders, M. 1989. The mouse bone marrow micronucleus assay can be used to distinguish aneugens from clastogens. *Mutagenesis*, 1989; 4, 6–11.

[31] Hayashi, M; MacGregor, JT; Gatehouse, DG; Adler, ID; Blakey, DH; Dertinger, SD; Krishna, G; Morita, T; Russo, A; Sutou, S. *In vivo* rodent erythrocyte micronucleus assay. II. Some aspects of protocol design including repeated treatments, integration with toxicity testing, and automated scoring. *Environmental and Molecular Mutagenesis*, 2000; 35, 234–252.

[32] Degrassi, F; Tanzarella, C. Immunofluorescent staining of kinetochores in micronuclei: A new assay for the detection of the aneuploidy. *Mutation Research*, 1988; 203, 339–345.

[33] Miller, BM; Adler, ID. Application of antikinetochore antibody staining (CREST staining) to micronuclei in erythrocytes induced *in vivo*. *Mutagenesis*, 1990; 5, 411–415.

[34] Hayashi, M; Morita, T; Ishidate, M. An application of acridine orange fluorescent staining to the micronucleus test. *Mutation Research*, 1983; 120, 241–247.

[35] MacGregor, JT; Wher, CM; Langlois, RG. A simple fluorescent staining procedure for micronuclei and RNA in erythrocytes using Hoechst 33258 and Pyronin Y. *Mutation Research*, 1983; 120, 269–265.

[36] Hayashi, M; Tice, RR; MacGregor, JT; Anderson, D; Blakey, DH; Kirsch-Volders, M; Oleson, FB; Pacchierotti, F; Romagna, F; Shimada, H; Sutou, S; Vannier, B. 1994b. *In vivo* Rodent Erythrocyte Micronucleus Assay. *Mutation Research*, 1994; 312, 293–304.

[37] Heddle, JA; Cimino, MC; Hayashi, M; Romagna, F; Shelby, MD; Tucker, JD; Vanparys, P; MacGregor, JT. Micronuclei as an index of cytogenetic damage: past, present and future. *Environmental and Molecular Mutagenesis*, 1991; 18, 277–291.

[38] Heddle, JA; Hite, M; Kirthart, BK; Mavournin, JT; MacGregor, G; Newll, W; Salamone, MF. The induction of micronuclei as a measure of genotoxicity. A report of the U.S. Environmental Protection Agency Gene-Tox Program. *Mutation Research*, 1983; 123, 61–118.

[39] Hayashi, M; Morita, T; Kodama, Y; Sofuni, T; Ishidate, M. The micronuclei assay with mouse peripheral blood reticulocytes using acridine orange-coated slides. *Mutation Research*, 1990; 245, 245–249.

[40] Schreinemachers, DM; Everson, RB. Effect of residual splenic function and folate levels on the frequency of micronucleated red blood cells in splenectomized humans. *Mutation Research*, 1991; 263, 63–67.

[41] Zúñiga-González, G; Torres-Bugarín, O; Ramos-Ibarra, ML; Zamora-Perez, A; Gómez-Meda, BC; Ventura-Aguilar, AJ; Ramos-Mora, A; Ortiz, GG; Álvarez-Moya, C; González-Rodríguez, A; Luna-Aguirre, J; Gallegos-Arreola, MP. Variation of micronucleated erythrocytes in peripheral blood of *Sciurus aureogaster* in relation to age: an increment of micronucleated polychromatic erythrocytes after the administration of colchicine. *Environmental and Molecular Mutagenenesis*, 2001; 37, 173–177.

[42] Fenech, M; Holland, N; Chang, WP; Zeiger, E; Bonassi, S. The HUMNproject: an international collaborative study on the use of the micronucleus technique for measuring DNA damage in humans. *Mutation Research*, 1999; 428, 271–283.

[43] Russo, A; Levis, AG. Further evidence for the aneuploidogenic properties of chelating agents: induction of micronuclei in mouse male germ cells by EDTA. *Environmental and Molecular Mutagenesis*, 1992; 19, 125–131.

[44] Tolbert, PE; Shy, CM; Allen, JW. Micronuclei and other nuclear anomalies in buccal smears: methods development. *Mutation Research*, 1992; 271, 69–77.

[45] Schmezer, P; Pool, BL; Lefevre, PA; Callander, R; Ratpan, F; Tinwell, H; Ashby, J. Assay-Specific genotoxicity of n-nitrosodibenzylamine to the rat liver *in vivo*. *Environmental and Molecular Mutagenesis*, 1990; 15, 190–197.

[46] Suzuki, Y; Shimizu, H; Nagae, Y; Fukumoto, M; Okonogi, H; Kadokura, M. Micronucleus test and erythropoiesis: effect of cobalt on the induction of micronuclei by mutagens. *Environmental and Molecular Mutagenesis*, 1993; 22, 101–106.

[47] Countryman, PI; Heddle, JA. The production of micronuclei from chromosome aberrations in irradiated cultures of human lymphocytes. *Mutation Research*, 1976; 41, 321–332.

[48] Fenech, M. The cytokinesis-block micronucleus technique: a detailed description of the method and its application to genotoxicity studies in human populations. *Mutation Research*, 1993; 285, 35–44.

[49] Fenech, M; Morley, AA. Solutions to the kinetic problem in the micronucleus assay. *Cytobios*, 1985; 43(172-173), 233–246.

[50] Fenech, M; Morley, AA. Cytokinesis-block micronucleus method in human lymphocytes: effect of *in vivo* ageing and low-dose X-irradiation. *Mutation Research*, 1986; 161, 193–198.

[51] Fenech, M; Chang, WP; Kirsch-Volders, M; Holland, N; Bonassi, S; Zeiger, E. HUman MicronNucleus project.HUMN project: detailed description of the scoring criteria for the cytokinesis-block micronucleus assay using isolated human lymphocyte cultures. *Mutation Research*, 2003; 534(1-2), 65–75.

[52] Kirsch-Volders, M; Fenech, M. Inclusion of micronuclei in non-divided mononuclear lymphocytes and necrosis/apoptosis may provide a more comprehensive cytokinesis block micronucleus assay for biomonitoring purposes. *Mutagenesis*, 2001; 16(1), 51–58.

[53] Fenech, M; Bonassi, S; Turner, J; Lando, C; Ceppi, M; Chang, WP; Holland, N; Kirsch-Volders, M; Zeiger, E; Bigatti, MP; Bolognesi, C; Cao, J; De Luca, G; Di Giorgio, M; Ferguson, LR; Fucic, A; Lima, OG; Hadjidekova, VV; Hrelia, P; Jaworska, A; Joksic, G; Krishnaja, AP; Lee, TK; Martelli, A; McKay, MJ; Migliore, L; Mirkova, E; Müller, WU; Odagiri, Y; Orsiere, T; Scarfi, MR; Silva, MJ; Sofuni, T; Surralles, J; Trenta, G; Vorobtsova, I; Vral, A; Zijno, A. HUman MicroNucleus project. Intra- and inter-laboratory variation in the scoring of micronuclei and nucleoplasmic bridges in binucleated human lymphocytes. Results of an international slide-scoring exercise by the HUMN project. *Mutation Research*, 2003; 534(1-2), 45–64.

[54] Surrales, J; Antoccia, A; Creus, A; Degrassi, F; Peris, F; Tanzarella, C; Xamena, N; Marcos, R. The effect of cytochalasin-B concentration on the frequency of micronuclei induced by four standard mutagens. Results from two laboratories. *Mutagenesis*, 1994; 9, 347–353.

[55] Fenech, M. The advantages and disadvantages of the cytokinesis-block micronucleus method. *Mutation Research*, 1997; 392, 11–18.

[56] Zúñiga-González, GM; Gómez-Meda, BC; Zamora-Perez, A; Ramos-Ibarra, ML; Batista-González, CM; Lemus-Varela, ML; Rodríguez-Ávila, JL; Gallegos-Arreola, MP. Micronucleated erythrocyte frequencies in old and new world primates: measurement of micronucleated erythrocyte frequencies in peripheral blood of

Callithrix jacchus as a model for evaluating genotoxicity in primates. *Environmental and Molecular Mutagenesis*, 2005; 46(4), 253–259.

[57] Vanparys, P; Deknudt, G; Vermeiren, F; Sysmans, M; Marsboom, R. Sampling times in micronucleus testing. *Mutation Research*, 1992; 282, 191–196.

[58] Tice, RR; Erexson, GL; Hilliard, CJ; Huston, JL; Boehm, RM; Gulati, D; Shelby, MD. Effect of treatment protocol and sample time on the frequencies of micronucleated polychromatic erythrocytes in mouse bone marrow and peripheral blood. *Mutagenesis*, 1990; 5, 313–321.

[59] Schlegel, R; MacGregor, JT. The persistence of micronucleated erythrocytes in the peripheral circulation of normal and splenectomized Fischer 344 rats: implications for cytogenetic screening. *Mutation Research*, 1984; 127, 169 –174

[60] Schlegel, R; MacGregor, JT; Everson, RB. Assessment of cytogenetic damage by quantitation of micronuclei in human peripheral blood erythrocytes. *Cancer Research*, 1986; 46, 3717–3721.

[61] MacGregor, JT; O'Loughlin, KG; Hill, JR. Micronucleated erythrocytes in bone marrow and peripheral blood of the beagle dog. *Environmental and Molecular Mutagenesis*, 1992; 19(S20), 38.

[62] MacGregor, JT; Wehr, CM; Henika, PR; Shelby, MD. The *in vivo* erythrocyte micronucleus test: measurement at steady state increases assay efficiency and permits integration with toxicity studies. *Fundamental and Applied Toxicology*, 1990; 14, 513–522.

[63] Zúñiga, G; Torres-Bugarín, O; Ramírez-Muñoz, MP; Delgado-Lamas, JL; De Loza-Saldaña, R; Cantú, JM. Micronucleated erythrocytes in splenectomized patients with and without chemotherapy. *Mutation Research*, 1996; 361, 107–112.

[64] Zúñiga-González, G; Torres-Bugarín, O; Zamora-Perez, A; Gómez-Meda, BC; Ramos-Ibarra, ML; Martínez-González, S; González-Rodríguez, A; Luna-Aguirre, J; Ramos-Mora, A; Ontiveros-Lira, D; Gallegos-Arreola, MP. Differences in the number of micronucleated erythrocytes among young and adult animals including humans. Spontaneous micronuclei in 43 species. *Mutation Research*, 2001; 494, 161–167.

[65] Schalm, OW; Schalm, DVM. Hematología Veterinaria. México: UTEHA; 1964.

[66] Hillman, RS; Finch, CA. El eritrocito. 5a ed. México: Manual Moderno; 1987.

[67] Hillman, RS; Finch, CA, Boggs DR, Winkelstein A, Harper LA. Manual de Hematología. 1a ed. México: Manual Moderno; 1990.

[68] Gómez-Meda, BC; Zúñiga-González, GM; Zamora-Perez, A; Ramos-Ibarra, ML; Batista-González, CM; Torres-Mendoza, BM. Folate supplementation of cyclophosphamide-treated mothers diminishes micronucleated erythrocytes in peripheral blood of newborn rats. *Environmental and Molecular Mutagenesis*, 2004; 44(2), 174–178.

[69] Zúñiga, G; Torres-Bugarín, O; Ramírez-Muñoz, MP; Ramos, A; Fanti-Rodríguez, E; Portilla, E; García-Martínez, D; Cantú, JM; Gallegos-Arreola, MP; Sánchez-Corona, J. Spontaneous micronuclei in peripheral blood erythrocytes from 35 species. *Mutation Research*, 1996; 369, 123–127.

[70] Zúñiga-González, G; Ramírez-Muñoz, MP; Torres-Bugarín, O; Pérez-Jiménez, J; Ramos-Mora, A; Zamora-Perez, A; Gallegos-Arreola, MP; Sánchez-Corona, J.

Induction of micronuclei in the domestic cat (*Felis domesticus*) peripheral blood by colchicine and cytosine-arabinoside. *Mutation Research*, 1998; 43, 187–189.

[71]   Zúñiga-González, G; Torres-Bugarín, O; Luna-Aguirre, J; González-Rodríguez, A; Zamora-Perez, A; Gómez-Meda, BC; Ramos-Ibarra, ML; Ramos-Mora, A; Ortiz, GG; Gallegos-Arreola, MP. Spontaneous micronuclei in peripheral blood erythrocytes from 54 animal species (mammals, reptiles and birds): Part two. *Mutation Research*, 2000; 467, 99–103.

[72]   Williams, WJ; Beutler, E; Erslev, AJ; Lichtman, MA. Hematology. 4th ed. USA: McGraw Hill; 1990.

[73]   Ramírez-Muñoz, MP; Zúñiga, G; Torres-Bugarín, O; Portilla, E; García-Martínez, D; Ramos, A; Cantú, JM; Sánchez-Corona, J. Evaluation of the micronucleus test in peripheral blood erythrocytes by use of the splenectomized model. *Laboratory Animal Science*, 1999; 49, 418–420.

[74]   Pearson, HA; Johnston, D; Smith, KA; Touloukian, RJ. The born-again spleen. Return of splenic function after splenectomy for trauma. *The New England Journal of Medicine*, 1978; 298, 1389–1392.

[75]   Torres-Bugarín, O; Zamora Perez, AL; Esparza-Flores, A; López-Guido, B; Feria-Velasco, A; Cantú, JM; Zúñiga, G. Eritrocitos micronucleados en niños esplenectomizados con y sin quimioterapia. *Boletín Médico del Hospital Infantil de México*, 1999; 56, 212–217.

[76]   Nagae, Y; Miyamoto, H; Suzuki, Y; Shimizu, H. Effect of estrogen on induction of micronuclei by mutagens in male mice. *Mutation Research*, 1991; 263, 21–26.

[77]   Miguel, AG; Daisey, JM; Sousa, JA. Comparative study of the mutagenic and genotoxic activity associated with inhalable particulate matter in Rio de Janeiro air. *Environmental and Molecular Mutagenesis*, 1990; 15, 36–43.

[78]   Moore, KL; Persaud, TVN. Embriología Clínica. México: McGraw-Hill Interamericana; 1999.

[79]   Casarett and Doull. Toxicología. 5ª ed. USA: McGraw Hill; 1999.

[80]   Montero, R; Serrano, L; Dávila, V; Segura, Y; Arrieta, A; Fuentes, R; Abad, I; Valencia, L; Sierra, P; Camacho, R. Metabolic polymorphisms and the micronucleus frequency in buccal epithelium of adolescents living in an urban environment. *Environmental and Molecular Mutagenesis*, 2003; 42, 216–222.

[81]   Choy, WN; Willhite, CC; Cukierski, MJ; Book, SA. Primate Micronucleus study of L-Selenomethionine. *Environmental and Molecular Mutagenesis*, 1989; 14, 123–125.

[82]   Zúñiga-González, G; Gómez-Meda, BC; Zamora-Perez, A; Ramos-Ibarra, ML; Batista-González, CM; González-Rodríguez, A; Luna-Aguirre, J; Rodríguez-Ávila, JL. Especies exóticas con micronúcleos espontáneos: alternativa para estudios de genotoxicidad. *Nowet*, 2002; 1, 5–9.

[83]   Tice, RR; Luke, CA; Shelby, MD. Methyl isocyanate: an evaluation of *in vivo* cytogenetic activity. *Environmental and Molecular Mutagenesis*, 1987; 9, 37–58.

[84]   Herrera, A; Barrueco, C; Caballo, C; Peña, E. Effect of permethrin on the induction of sister chromatid exchanges and micronuclei in cultured human lymphocytes. *Environmental and Molecular Mutagenesis*, 1992; 20, 218–228.

[85] Meier, JR; Wernsing, P; Torsella, J. Feasibility of micronucleus methods for monitoring genetic damage in two feral species of small mammals. *Environmental and Molecular Mutagenesis*, 1999; 33, 219–225.

[86] Gregoryst, MW; Stocker, L. Erizos, In: *Manual de Animales Exóticos*, Beynon PH, Cooper JE. España: Hartcourt Brace; 1999.

[87] Larsen, RS; Carpenter, JW. Husbandry and medical management of African hedgehogs. *Veterinary Medicine*, 1999; 94, 877–888.

[88] Oxenham, M. Hurones. In: *Manual de Animales Exóticos*, Beynon PH, Cooper JE. España: Hartcourt Brace; 1999.

[89] Gauthier, JM; Dubeau, H; Rassart, É; Jarman, WM; Wells, RS. Biomarkers of DNA damage in marine mammals. *Mutation Research,* 1999; 444, 427–439.

[90] Meyne, J; Legator, MS. Sex-related differences in cytogenetic effects of benzene in the bone marrow of Swiss mice. *Environmental Mutagenesis,* 1980; 2, 43–50.

[91] Peace, BE; Succop, P. Spontaneous micronucleus frequency and age: what are normal values? *Mutation Research*, 1999; 425, 225–230.

[92] Wojda, A; Witt, M. Manifestations of ageing at the cytogenetic level. *Journal of Applied Genetics*, 2003; 44, 383–399.

[93] Lowe, X; Collins, B; Allen, J; Titenko-Holand, N; Breneman, J; van Beek, M; Bishop, J; Wyrobeck, AJ. Aneuploidies and micronuclei in the germ cells of male mice of advanced age. *Mutation Research*, 1995; 338, 59–76.

[94] Allen, JW; Collins, BW; Setzer, RW. Spermatid micronucleus analysis of ageing effects in hamster. *Mutation Research*, 1996; 316, 261–266.

[95] Batista-González, CM; Corona-Rivera, JR; Gómez-Meda, BC; Zamora-Perez, AL; Ramos-Ibarra, ML; Zúñiga-González, GM. Micronucleated erythrocytes in preterm newborns in relation to maternal pathology. *Revista Biomedica*, 2006; 17(1), 11–16.

[96] Zúñiga-González, GM; Batista-González, CM; Gómez-Meda, BC; Ramos-Ibarra, ML; Zamora-Perez, AL; Muñoz-Magallanes, T; Ramos-Valdés, C; Gallegos-Arreola, MP. Micronuclei in diabetes: folate supplementation diminishes micronuclei in diabetic patients but not in an animal model. *Mutation Research*, 2007; 634(1-2), 126–134.

[97] Shepard, TH. Catalog of teratogenic agents. Tenth edition. Baltimore and London: The John Hopkins University Press; 2001.

[98] Ferguson, LR; Ford, JH. Overlap between mutagens and teratogens. *Mutation Research*, 1997; 396, 1–8.

[99] Alaoui-Jamali, MA; Rossignol, G; Schuller, HM; Castonguay, A. Transplacental genotoxicity of a tobacco-specific N-nitrosamine, 4-(methylnitrosamino)-1-(3-pyridyl)-1-butanone, in Syrian golden hamster. *Mutation Research*, 1989; 223, 65–72.

[100] Nakamura, M; Fort, FL; Kikuchi, Y. Fetal liver micronucleus assay in mice of 5-fluorouracil and related compounds. *Mutation Research*, 1993; 291, 29–34.

[101] Maura, A; Pino, A; Gardella, A; Falugi, C. Micronucleus formation in fetal maternal rat erythroblasts after norfloxacin transplacental administration. *Mutation Research*, 1994; 312, 127–130.

[102] Chorvatovicova, D; Ujhazy, E. Transplacental effect of stobadine on cyclophosphamide induced micronucleus frequency in mice. *Mutagenesis*, 1995; 10, 531–534.

[103] Abraham, SK. Inhibitory effects of coffee on transplacental genotoxicity in mice. *Mutation Research*, 1995; 347, 45–52.

[104] Balansky, RM; Blagoeva, PM. Tobacco smoke-induced clastogenicity in mouse fetuses and in newborn mice. *Mutation Research*, 1989; 223, 1–6.

[105] Henderson, LM; Aghamohammadi, SZ; Arlett, CF; Cole, RJ. Lack of discernible effect of diagnostic ultrasound on the chromosomes of cord blood lymphocytes exposed *in utero. The British Journal of Radiology*, 1986; 59, 499–503.

[106] Gómez-Meda, BC; Zúñiga-González, GM. Genotoxicidad y potencial teratógeno. *La Ciencia y el Hombre*, 2007; 20(3), 57–62.

[107] Hayashi. M; Sofuni T. The need of three dose levels to detect genotoxic chemicals in *in vivo* rodent assays. *Mutation Research*, 1995; 327, 247–251.

[108] Greenaway, JC; Fantel, AG; Shepard, TH; Juchau, MR. The *in vitro* teratogenicity of cyclophosphamide in rat embryos. *Teratology*, 1982; 25, 335–343.

[109] Gilani, SH; Chatzinoff, M. Embryopathic effects of cyclophosphamide. *Environmental Research*, 1983; 31, 296–301.

[110] Porter, AJ; Singh, SM. Transplacental teratogenesis and mutagenesis in mouse fetuses treated with cyclophosphamide. *Teratogenesis, Carcinogenesis, and Mutagenesis*, 1988; 8, 191–203.

[111] Harper, BL; Ramanujam, VM; Legator, MS. Micronucleus formation by benzene, cyclophosphamide, benzo(a)pyrene, and benzidine in male, female, pregnant female, and fetal mice. *Teratogenesis, Carcinogenesis, and Mutagenesis*, 1989; 9, 239–252.

[112] Zemlickis, D; Lishner, M; Erlich, R; Koren, G. Teratogenicity and carcinogenicity in a twin exposed in utero to cyclophosphamide. *Teratogenesis, Carcinogenesis, and Mutagenesis*, 1993; 13, 139–143.

[113] Krishna, G; Petrere, J; Anderson, J; Theiss, J. Use of cyclophosphamide as a positive control in dominant lethal and micronucleus assay. *Mutation Research*, 1995; 335, 331–337.

[114] Komae, N; Sanzen, T; Kozaki, T; Furubo, E; Kawamura, Y; Kodama, T. Reproductive and developmental toxicity study of T-3762 in rats administered intravenously during the period of organogenesis. *The Japanese Journal of Antibiotics*, 1998; 51, 682–708.

[115] Nau, H. Species differences in pharmacokinetics and drug teratogenesis. *Environmental Health Perspectives*, 1986; 70, 113–129.

[116] Ramos-Remus, C; Dorazco-Barragán, G; Aceves-Ávila, FJ; Alcaraz-López, F; Fuentes-Ramírez, F; Michel-Díaz, J; Torres-Bugarín, O; Ventura-Aguilar, A; Zúñiga-González, G. Genotoxicity assessment using micronuclei assay in rheumatoid arthritis patients. *Clinical and Experimental Rheumatology*, 2002; 20, 208–212.

[117] Bonassi, S; Znaor, A; Ceppi, M; Lando, C; Chang, WP; Holland, N; Kirsch-Volders, M; Zeiger, E; Ban, S; Barale, R; Bigatti, MP; Bolognesi, C; Cebulska-Wasilewska, A; Fabianova E; Fucic, A; Hagmar, L; Joksic, G; Martelli, A; Migliore, L; Mirkova, E; Scarfi, MR; Zijno, A; Norppa, H; Fenech, M. An increased micronucleus frequency in peripheral blood lymphocytes predicts the risk of cancer in humans. Carcinogenesis, 2007; 28(3), 625-631.

[118] Shankel, DM; Hartman, PE; Kada, T; Hollaender A. Synopsis of the first international conference on antimutagenesis and anticarcinogenesis: Mechanisms. *Environmental and Molecular Research*, 1987; 9, 87–103.

[119] Hartman, PE; Shankel, DM. Antimutagens and Anticarcinogens: A survey of putative interceptor molecules. *Environmental and Molecular Research*, 1990; 15, 145–182.

[120] Hartmann, A; Nieβ, AM; Grünert-Fuchs, M; Poch, B; Speit, G. Vitamin E prevents exercise-induced DNA damage. *Mutation Research*, 1995; 346, 195–202.

[121] Vijayalaxmi, KK; Venu, R. *In vivo* anticlastogenic effects of L-ascorbic acid in mice. *Mutation Research*, 1999; 438, 47–51.

[122] Lohman, PHM; Gentile, JM; Gentile, G; Ferguson, LR. Antimutagenesis/anticarcino-genesis 2001: screening, methods and biomarkers. *Mutation Research*, 2001; 496, 1–4.

[123] Ruiz, EF; Valtierra, RE; Lecona, SU; Perez, AB; Ma, TH. Tradescantia micronucleus (Trad-MCN) bioassay on clastogenicity of wastewater and *in situ* monitoring. *Mutation Research*, 1992; 270, 45–51.

[124] Al-Sabti, K; Metcalfe, CD. Fish micronuclei for assessing genotoxicity in water. *Mutation Research*, 1995; 343, 121–135.

[125] Burgeot, T; His, E; Galgani, F. The micronucleus assay in *Crassostrea gigas* for the detection of seawater genotoxicity. *Mutation Research*, 1995; 342, 125–140.

[126] Jena, GB; Bhunya, SP. Use of chick, Gallus domesticus, as an *in vivo* model for the study of chromosome aberration: a study with mitomycin C and probable location of a hot spot. *Mutation Research*, 1995; 334, 167–174.

[127] Ma, TH; Xu, Z; Xu, Ch; McConnell, H; Arreola, GA; Zhang, H. The improved Allium/Vicia root tip micronucleus assay for clastogenicity of environmental pollutant. *Mutation Research*, 1995; 334, 185–195.

[128] Jaylet, A; Deparis, P; Ferrier, V; Grinfeld, S; Siboulet, R. A new micronucleus test using peripheral blood erythrocytes of the newt Pleurodeles waltl to detect mutagens in fresh-water pollution. *Mutation Research*, 1986; 164, 245–257.

[129] Krauter, PW; Anderson, SL; Harrison, FL. Radiation induced micronuclei in peripheral erythrocytes of Rana catesbeiana: an aquatic animal model for *in vivo* genotoxicity studies. *Environmental and Molecular Mutagenesis*, 1987; 10, 285–296.

[130] Le, CF; Marzin, D; Erb, F. Genotoxic activity of three carcinogens in peripheral blood erythrocytes of the newt Pleurodeles waltl. *Mutation Research*, 1992; 283, 157–160.

[131] Rudek, Z; Rozek, M. Induction of micronuclei in tadpoles of *Rana temporaria* and *Xenopus leavis* by the pyrethroid fastac 10 EC. *Mutation Researh*, 1992; 298, 25–29.

[132] Fernandez, M; I'Haridon, J. Effects of light on the cytotoxicity and genotoxicity of benzo(a)pyrene and an oil refinery effluent in the newt. *Environmental and Molecular Mutagenesis*, 1994; 24, 124–136.

[133] Duellman, W; Trueb, L. Biology of amphibians. Baltimore, MD: Johns Hopkins University Press; 1994.

[134] Turner, CD. General endocrinology. Philadelphia: WB Saunders; 1966.

[135] Barrington, EJW. An introduction to general and comparative endocrinology. Oxford: Clarendon Press; 1975.

[136] Siboulet, R; Grinfeld, S; Deparis, P; Jaylet, A. Micronuclei in red blood cells of the newt Pleurodeles waltl Michah: induction with X-rays and chemicals. *Mutation Research*, 1984; 125, 275–281.

[137] Salas-Valdés A. A quick and inexpensive staining method for vaginal smears. *Archivos de Investigación Médica*, 1979; 10, 147–150.

[138] Poole TB, Robinson R. The UFAW handbook on the care and management of laboratory animals. London: Longman Scientific Technical; 1994.

[139] Frye, CA; Erskine, MS. 1990. Influence of time of mating and paced copulation on induction of pseudopregnancy in cyclic female rats. *Journal of Reproduction and Fertility*, 1990; 90, 375–385.

[140] Suzuki, Y; Shimizu, H; Nagae, Y; Fukumoto, M; Okonogi, H; Kadokura, M. 1993. Micronucleus test and erythropoiesis: effect of cobalt on the induction of micronuclei by mutagens. *Environmental and Molecular Mutagenesis*, 1993; 22, 101–106.

[141] Romagna, F; Staniforth, CD. The automated bone marrow micronucleus test. *Mutation Research*, 1989; 213, 91–104.

[142] Hayashi, M; Kodama, Y; Awogi, T; Suzuki, T; Asita, AO; Sofuni, T. The micronucleus assay using peripheral blood reticulocytes from mitomycin-C and cyclophosphamide-treated rats. *Mutation Research*, 1992; 278, 209–213.

[143] Henderson, L; Fedyk, J; Windebank, S; Smith, M. Induction of micronuclei in rat bone marrow and peripheral blood following acute and subchronic administration of azathioprine. *Mutation Research*, 1993; 291, 79–85.

[144] Schunck, C; Johannes, T; Varga, D; Lörch, T; Plesch, A. New developments in automated cytogenetic imaging: unattended scoring of dicentric chromosomes, micronuclei, single cell gel electrophoresis, and fluorescence signals. *Cytogenetics and Genome Research*, 2004; 104(1-4), 383–389.

[145] Hutter, KJ; Stöhr, M. Rapid detection of mutagen induced micronucleated erythrocytes by flow cytometry. *Histochemistry*, 1982; 75, 353–362.

[146] Hayashi, M; Norppa, H; Sofuni, T; Ishidate, M Jr. Mouse bone marrow micronucleus test using flow cytometry. *Mutagenesis*, 1992; 7, 251–256.

[147] Hayashi, M; Norppa, H; Sofuni, T; Ishidate, M Jr. Flow cytometric micronucleus test with mouse peripheral erythrocytes. *Mutagenesis*, 1992; 7, 257–264.

[148] Grawé, J; Zetterberg, G; Amneus, H. Flow-cytometric enumeration of micronucleated polychromatic erythrocytes in mouse peripheral blood. *Cytometry*, 1992; 13, 750–758.

[149] Krishna, G; Brott, D; Urda, G; McKeel, M; Zandee, J; Theiss, J. Comparative micronucleus quantitation in pre- and post-column fractionated mouse bone marrow by manual and flow methods. *Mutation Research*, 1993; 302, 119–127.

[150] Krishna, G; Criswell, K; Zielinski, D; Urda, G; Juneau, P; Bleavins, M; Theiss, J. Validation of micronucleus evaluation in the rat using flow cytometry with five model compounds. *Environmental and Molecular Mutagenesis*, 1998; 31(S29), 46.

[151] Krishna, G; Urda, G; Theiss, J. Principles and practices of integrating genotoxicity evaluation into routine toxicology studies: a pharmaceutical industry perspective. *Environmental and Molecular Mutagenesis*, 1998; 32, 115–120.

[152] Tometsko, AM; Torous, DK; Dertinger, SD. Analysis of micronucleated cells by flow cytometry. 3. Advanced technology for detecting clastogenic activity. *Mutation Research*, 1993; 292, 145–153.

[153] Dertinger, SD; Torous, DK; Tometsko, KR. Simple and reliable enumeration of micronucleated reticulocytes with a single-laser flow cytometer. *Mutation Research*, 1996; 371, 283–292.

[154] Parton, JW; Hoffman, WP; Garriott, ML. Validation of an automated image analysis micronucleus scoring system. *Mutation Research*, 1996; 370, 65–73.

[155] Asano, N; Katsuma, Y; Hironobu, T; Higashikuni, N; Hayashi, M. An automated new technique for scoring rodent micronucleus assay: computerized image analysis of acridine orange supravitally stained peripheral blood cells. *Mutation Research*, 1998; 404, 149–154.

[156] Criswell, K; Krishna, G; Zielinski, D; Urda, G; Theiss, J; Juneau, P; Bleavins, M. Use of acridine orange in flow cytometric evaluation of erythropoietic cytotoxicity. *Mutation Research*, 1998; 414, 49–61.

[157] Criswell, K; Krishna, G; Zielinski, D; Urda, G; Theiss, J; Juneau, P; Bleavins, M. Use of acridine orange in flow cytometric assessment of micronuclei induction. *Mutation Research*, 1998; 414, 63–75.

[158] Tucker, JD; Heddle, JA; MacGregor, JT; Oleson, FB. Automated Micronucleus Scoring Workshop Report. *Environmental and Molecular Mutagenesis*, 1989; 14, 6243.

[159] Thierens, H; Vral, A; Scheerder, F; Ridder, L; Tates, A. Semi-automated micronucleus scoring in cytokinesis-blocked lymphocytes after irradiation. *International Journal of Radiation Biology*, 1997; 72, 319–324.

In: New Research on DNA Damage
Editors: Honoka Kimura and Aoi Suzuki

ISBN 978-1-60456-581-2
© 2008 Nova Science Publishers, Inc.

Chapter 8

Assays for the Quantitative Characterization of Genomic, Mitochondrial and Plasmid DNA

Christos D. Georgiou,[*] *Ioannis Papapostolou, Nikolaos Patsoukis, and Konstantinos Grintzalis*

Department of Biology, Section of Genetics, Cell Biology and Development,
University of Patras, Greece

Abstract

This chapter presents four ultrasensitive methods (as Hoechst and PicoGreen versions) for the accurate quantification of non-repairable and repairable dsDNA damage, as well as for the concentration of dsDNA. The assays can be applied to genomic, mitochondrial and plasmid dsDNA. The first assay provides an accurate quantification of dsDNA irrespective of size, and the following assays quantify (a) non-repairable and (b) repairable dsDNA damage: for case (a), two assays, one for the direct quantification of small-sized (0–1000 bp) fragmented necrotic/apoptotic DNA, and the other for the quantification of the 0-23 Kb smearing seen in a typical DNA agarose gel electrophoresis; for case (b), a fourth assay that quantifies the percentage of DNA nicks present in DNA samples.

Introduction

Characterizing the structural integrity of dsDNA (genomic, mitochondrial, plasmid) is very important in a wide variety of biological applications. Since DNA damage is a consequence of oxidative stress and many other related biological alterations, pathogenic or

---

[*] Corresponding author: Christos D. Georgiou, University of Patras, 26100-Patras, Greece, Tel.: +3061-997227, fax: +3061-997840, E-mail: c.georgiou@upatras.gr.

not (e.g., carcinogenesis, mutagenesis, ageing, etc.) it is of great importance to develop methods for the quantification of this damage. DNA damage (e.g. nicks, fragmentation, sugar/base modifications) can originate from oxidative attack of reactive oxygen species to DNA, from nuclease action during DNA repair, or during early or late events in apoptosis or necrosis [1]. Thus, DNA integrity can be easily disturbed leading to repairable as well as to non-repairable damage.

Repairable DNA damage includes formation of nicked DNA and oxidative modifications of DNA bases (e.g., 8-oxodeoxyguanosine), which do not give a definitive picture of oxidative stress-induced genotoxicity. Most attempts to monitor repairable DNA damage have been focused on the quantification of DNA oxidation adducts by HPLC [1] and DNA nicks by various assays [2-6]. The non-repairable dsDNA breakage is qualitatively evaluated as DNA fragmentation by DNA agarose electrophoresis [7] and the Comet assay [8, 9]. However, both methods do not measure DNA fragments that are stacked with intact DNA during their migration through the agarose gel, and cannot assess small-sized fragmented DNA (25–200 bp) resulting from telomere shortening in mammalian cells approaching senescence [10]. Another qualitative method applied only for the estimation of breakages in chromatin of large size, is the micronuclei detection assay [11, 12]. The non-repairable dsDNA breakage is also assessed quantitatively by the diphenylamine assay [13] and by the quantification of the smearing on a DNA agarose electrophoresis gel using the Hoechst dye [14]. The first assay is not specific because the cytoplasm may contain free or bound sugars (other than ribose), and cannot discriminate fragmented DNA if the genome size is small, while the second assay (a) does not measure the fragmented DNA that is stacked with the >23 Kb intact DNA band on the agarose gel, and (b) does not take into account the fact that the measurement of the concentration of dsDNA with size 23 to 0 Kb by the use of Hoechst, is underestimated by 0 to 70%, respectively [15].

From the above it can be concluded that the accurate quantification of non-repairable and repairable dsDNA damage as well as the concentration of dsDNA irrespective of size is of great importance. This chapter presents a method for the accurate quantification of dsDNA and the following methods for the quantification of non-repairable and repairable dsDNA damage: The first DNA damage category includes (a) an assay for the direct quantification of small-sized (0–1000 bp) fragmented necrotic/apoptotic DNA, and (b) an assay for the direct quantification of the 0-23 Kb smearing observed in a typical DNA agarose electrophoresis gel without using electrophoresis. The second DNA damage category includes an assay that quantifies the percentage of DNA nicks present in DNA samples. All assays were developed as Hoechst and PicoGreen (more sensitive) versions, and under certain conditions they can be applied to genomic, mitochondrial and plasmid dsDNA.

Assay for Quantification of Genomic, Mitochondrial and Plasmid DNA

Introduction

Any attempt to characterize dsDNA (genomic, mitochondrial, plasmid) requires first its accurate quantification. Traditionally, dsDNA is quantified by its UV absorbance at 260 nm, using appropriate standard curves of known quantities of genomic DNA. This assay is independent of dsDNA size but is of limited use mainly by its low sensitivity due to its relatively high extinction coefficient (EC) at 260 nm ($EC_{260\ nm} = 0.02\ \mu g^{-1}.ml.cm^{-1}$) [16] and by the purity of the DNA sample (possible presence of protein contaminants). Alternative assays of much higher sensitivity use the Hoechst and PicoGreen dyes, which bind preferably on dsDNA of various sizes. We have already shown that these assays are not accurate because their binding with dsDNA strongly depends on its size. Specifically, if dsDNA size is <23 Kb (i.e. it is not 'intact') its quantification cannot be done accurately by these assays [15]. Traditionally, as 'intact' dsDNA is arbitrarily defined the DNA that is stacked as a >23 Kb band in a typical DNA agarose electrophoresis gel, and this is due to the inability of the gel (~>0.7%) to resolve it in more size bands. Based on this criterion, as 'intact' DNA is considered a >23 Kb fragment of an intact genomic DNA with size >23 Kb. Nevertheless, intact dsDNA can exist even in sizes <23 Kb given the fact that genomic, mitochondrial and plasmid dsDNA have size <23 Kb in some organisms [17, 18]. The present assay avoids the differential binding of Hoechst and PicoGreen dyes on variably sized dsDNA by totally fragmenting the dsDNA of an unknown sample to small pieces (<1 Kb) and quantifies it as such with either Hoechst or PicoGreen (for even higher sensitivity) using standard curves with known quantities of dsDNA similarly fragmented. This assay can be used for the accurate quantification of genomic, mitochondrial and plasmid dsDNA irrespective of size.

Materials and Methods

Materials

DNA (from calf thymus), DMSO and Hoechst 33258 were obtained from Sigma-Aldrich. Na$_2$EDTA and Tris-HCl were obtained from Merck. Quant-iT™ PicoGreen was obtained from Invitrogen (Molecular Probes).

Methods

The accurate quantification of a previously isolated dsDNA is performed by the following steps:

1. Place the isolated dsDNA sample in a 1.5-ml eppendorf tube, immerse it in an ice-water bath and sonicate it for 15 s at 350 W cm^{-2} by placing the sonicator tip in the

center of the DNA solution at 1.5 cm depth. A suggested sonicator is the Dr. Hielscher UP- 50 H (Dr. Hielscher GmbH, Teltow, Germany) supplied with a MS2 microtip.

2. Prepare the Hoechst and PicoGreen working solutions needed for the measurement of the totally fragmented DNA sample as follows:

    a) The fresh Hoechst working solution (1 µM) is prepared by serial dilutions of a Hoechst stock solution, which is prepared by dissolving 1 mg Hoechst in 0.4 ml 100% DMSO, followed by centrifugation at 15000 g for 5 min. The resulting stock solution (the supernatant) is stable at -80°C for at least 6 months when stored amber vial. Specifically, the 1 µM Hoechst working solution (in final 1% DMSO) is made after 3 serial dilutions of the Hoechst stock as follows: Mix 3 µl of this stock solution with 27 µl dH$_2$O (1st dilution), then mix 3 µl from 1st dilution with 24 µl dH$_2$O and 3 µl 10% DMSO (2nd dilution), and mix 22 µl of the 2nd dilution with 0.86 ml dH$_2$O and 9 µl 100% DMSO (3rd dilution).

    b) For preparing the PicoGreen working solution, mix 10 µl of the commercial reagent stock (exists in 100% DMSO) with 0.99 ml TE buffer (10 mM Tris-HCl, 1 mM EDTA, pH 8.0). For preparing e.g. 100 ml TE buffer, dissolve 0.121 g Tris-HCl and 0.037 g EDTA in deionized-distilled water (ddH$_2$O) and vapour sterilize at 121°C, 1.1 atm.

3. Prepare the DNA Hoechst and PicoGreen fragmented dsDNA standard curves needed for the conversion of the fluorometric measurement (fluorescent units) of a totally fragmented DNA unknown sample to its concentration as follows:

    a) Firstly, prepare a 0.25 mg ml^{-1} DNA (calf thymus) working standard solution by weighing accurately and dissolving 1 mg calf thymus genomic DNA (overnight in an ice-cold bath) in 4 ml sterile TE buffer. In order to construct the Hoechst and PicoGreen dsDNA standard curves, totally fragmented dsDNA standard solution has to be prepared by placing 0.5 ml of the 0.25 mg ml^{-1} calf thymus DNA working standard solution in a 1.5-ml eppendorf tube and following the procedure described in step 1 of this section.

    b) For constructing a Hoechst fragmented dsDNA standard curve, prepare a series of 0.1 ml TE solutions containing different quantities (0-60 ng) of the totally fragmented DNA (prepared in sub-step a), and to each of them add 3 µl 100% DMSO, 0.05 ml Hoechst working solution and 0.15 ml TE (final volume ~0.3 ml). Measure the fluorescence value (FU) of the resulting solutions against a reagent blank (without DNA) at ex/em 353/451 nm (e.g. in a 0.5 ml quartz microcuvette, using a Shimadzu RF-1501 spectrofluorometer, set at 10 nm excitation/emission slit width and at high sensitivity). From this, the fluorescence extinction coefficient (FEC) of fragmented dsDNA using Hoechst can be determined.

c) For constructing a PicoGreen fragmented dsDNA standard curve, prepare a series of 0.1 ml TE solutions containing different quantities (0-90 pg) of the totally fragmented DNA (prepared in sub-step *a*), and to each of them add 3 µl 100% DMSO, 0.075 ml PicoGreen working solution and 0.125 ml TE (final volume ~0.3 ml). Measure fluorescence of the resulting solutions against a reagent blank (without DNA) at ex/em 480/530 nm (as in sub-step *b*). From this, the FEC of fragmented dsDNA using PicoGreen can be determined.

4. Measure the FU of the sonicated unknown dsDNA sample (diluted with TE buffer, if necessary) at the appropriate ex/em wavelengths for Hoechst and PicoGreen (as stated in step 3, sub-steps *b* and *c*), and convert this fluorescence value to dsDNA concentration using the appropriate FEC (determined in step 3, sub-steps *b* and *c*).

Conclusion

The sensitivity of the assay is 10 ng ml^{-1} or 15 pg ml^{-1} DNA with Hoechst or PicoGreen, respectively. Therefore, it is far more sensitive than the UV-based DNA quantification assay (~0.5 µg ml^{-1}).

Assay for Quantification of The Necrotic/Apoptotic (0-1000 bp) Fragmented Genomic, Mitochondrial and Plasmid dsDNA

Introduction

This assay is used for the direct quantification of small-sized (0–1000 bp) fragmented DNA, irrespective of size and dsDNA type (genomic, mitochondrial, plasmid). For genomic DNA, the small size fragmented DNA is an indicator of permanent DNA damage and results from necrotic or apoptotic events associated with normal and abnormal biological conditions. The fact that this assay can be also applied to mitochondrial DNA renders it very important because mitochondria, which are a potential source of reactive oxygen species and play a key role in apoptosis activation, are very vulnerable to DNA damage. Moreover, the assay can be used to evaluate the toxicity levels of many xenobiotic substances causing DNA breaks and to even assess possible DNA fragmentation caused by methods that isolate intact DNA. The assay is a modification of a previous assay [19] and is based on the differential separation of the small size dsDNA from total dsDNA by polyethylene glycol (PEG) precipitation. This DNA ends up in the supernatant fraction, and its quantification (after PEG removal) is based on the ability of the fluorescent DNA probes Hoechst and PicoGreen to form stable and intensely fluorescent complexes with dsDNA.

Materials and Methods

Materials

DNA (from calf thymus), DMSO and Hoechst 33258 were obtained from Sigma-Aldrich. Na_2EDTA, Na_2HPO_4, NaCl and Tris-HCl were obtained from Merck. Quant-iT™ PicoGreen was obtained from Invitrogen (Molecular Probes). PEG-6000 was from Serva, and NucleoSpin® Extract II kit was from Macherey-Nagel (Duren, Germany).

Methods

The quantification of a necrotic/apoptotic (0-1000 bp) fragmented genomic, mitochondrial and plasmid isolated dsDNA sample is performed by the following steps:

1. Quantify total dsDNA in the unknown sample as described in the 'Assay for quantification of genomic, mitochondrial and plasmid dsDNA'.
2. In a 1.5-ml eppendorf tube add 0.16 ml of the isolated DNA sample (obtained usually in sterilized TE buffer and containing at least 2.5 µg ml^{-1} DNA) and 0.34 ml PEG-NaCl solution prepared as follows. For 20 ml fresh PEG-NaCl solution, weigh 2.822 g PEG with the maximum possible accuracy and dissolve it in 12.35 ml ddH$_2$O. Then, add to it 1.47 ml 0.2 M sterilized phosphate buffer, pH 7.0, and 4.05 ml 4 M sterilized NaCl (made in 10 mM phosphate buffer, pH 7.0). Due to the small PEG-NaCl solution/DNA sample volumes used in this assay, accurate pipetting of the required volumes of this viscous PEG-NaCl solution needs to be done without immersing the pipette deep in the solution as to avoid transferring the extra solution adhering on the outside of the tip.
3. Incubate the mixture PEG-NaCl solution/DNA sample for minimum 12 hrs (or overnight) in an ice-water bath.
4. Centrifuge at 15000 g for 5 min and collect the supernatant (which contains the 0-1000 bp fragmented DNA) in a 1.5-ml eppendorf tube.
5. Dilute the collected supernatant 2x with TE buffer (the resulting volume is 1 ml), purify its fragmented DNA with the Nucleospin Extract II kit (following its instructions). The resulting purified small size fragmented DNA exists concentrated in 0.05 ml of the kit's elution buffer (NE buffer).
6. To 0.05 ml purified fragmented DNA (appropriately diluted with TE buffer if needed) add 0.2 ml TE buffer, 0.003 ml 100% DMSO and 0.05 ml Hoechst working solution (see 'Methods' section, step 2, sub-step a, of 'Assay for quantification of genomic, mitochondrial and plasmid DNA'). For even higher sensitivity (~600 fold), add to the 0.05 ml purified fragmented DNA, 0.175 ml TE buffer, and 0.075 ml PicoGreen working solution (see 'Methods' section, step 2, sub-step b, of 'Assay for quantification of genomic, mitochondrial and plasmid DNA').
7. Measure its FU and convert it to dsDNA concentration as stated in step 4 of the 'Methods' section of the 'Assay for quantification of genomic, mitochondrial and

plasmid dsDNA'. This DNA concentration represents the total amount of 0-1000 bp DNA fragments in the initially isolated DNA sample. DNA quantification can be expressed as % w/w fragmented small-sized DNA per total DNA (quantified in step 1).

Conclusion

This is a very simple assay for the quantification of 0-1 Kp fragmented DNA that can be applied to genomic, mitochondrial and plasmid dsDNA samples as low as 2.5 µg ml^{-1} and has very low DNA detection limit (10 ng ml^{-1} or 15 pg ml^{-1} 0- to 1000-bp fragmented DNA with Hoechst or PicoGreen, respectively). The fact that this assay quantifies fragments below 1000 bp is very important because their presence implies a non-repairable DNA damage associated with normal and abnormal biological conditions.

Assay for the Quantification of the Fragmentation Smearing in DNA Agarose Electrophoresis

Introduction

This assay is a quantitative replacement of the qualitative agarose gel electrophoresis dsDNA smearing assay. The reason being that, this assay quantifies the 0-23 Kb size range DNA smearing of the DNA agarose gel electrophoresis assay, and it can be applied to genomic DNA, mitochondrial and plasmid dsDNA with size >23 Kb, given the fact that in some organisms their size is <23 Kb [17, 18]. The assay is a replacement of the non-specific - and restricted to very large genome size- diphenylamine assay [13], and also represents a quantitative alternative to the single cell-based genomic DNA Comet assay [8, 9]. The assay, besides being quantitative, it overcomes another major drawback of the agarose gel electrophoresis and Comet assays which arises from the stacking of DNA fragments with 'intact' (>23 Kb) dsDNA during their migration through the agarose gel. Furthermore, these assays cannot assess small-sized fragmented DNA (25–200 bp) resulting from telomere shortening in mammalian cells approaching senescence [10]. The present assay is a modification of a previous assay [15], and in its Hoechst and PicoGreen version discriminates quantitatively dsDNA in two dsDNA size ranges >23 and <23Kb by taking advantage of the fact that the commonly used Hoechst- and PicoGreen-based assays underestimate by 0 to 70% the concentration of dsDNA with size 23 to 0 Kb, respectively.

Materials and Methods

Materials

DNA (from calf thymus), DMSO and Hoechst 33258 were obtained from Sigma-Aldrich. Na_2EDTA and Tris-HCl were obtained from Merck. Quant-iT^{TM} PicoGreen was obtained from Invitrogen (Molecular Probes).

Methods

The fragment sizes of a DNA sample as fractionated by agarose electrophoresis can be classified in three fragmentation statuses: (a) dsDNA sizes are <23 Kb, or (b) are all >23 Kb, or (c) they exist as a mixture of <23 Kb and >23 Kb (in unknown proportions). The present assay discriminates in which of the three fragmentation statuses the unknown DNA sample exists and quantifies them either with Hoechst or PicoGreen (the two alternative versions of the assay). In the fragmentation status case (c) in particular, the assay quantifies both <23 Kb and >23 Kb DNA size fractions, with the <23 Kb fraction representing the DNA smearing in the agarose electrophoresis method.

In order to be able to find in which of the thee fragmentation statuses the unknown dsDNA sample exists, it is initially divided into two equal portions, designated DNA sample portion A (sonicated) and portion B (unsonicated), and treated as follows:

1. DNA sample portion A: Sonicate portion A (under the sonication conditions stated in step 1 of the 'Methods' section of the 'Assay for quantification of genomic, mitochondrial and plasmid dsDNA') in order to convert it to totally fragmented DNA. Then, measure its FU value ($FU_{sonicated}$) as stated in step 4 of the 'Methods' section of the 'Assay for quantification of genomic, mitochondrial and plasmid dsDNA'.

2. DNA sample portion B: Measure the FU value ($FU_{unsonicated}$) of portion and B (not sonicated sample) as stated in as stated in step 4 of the 'Methods' section of the 'Assay for quantification of genomic, mitochondrial and plasmid dsDNA'.

3. The resulting FU values $FU_{sonicated}$ and $FU_{unsonicated}$ of the DNA sample portion A and B, respectively, are compared to each other in order to distinguish the fragmentation status of the unknown sample as follows:

    a. The FU values of the DNA sample portions A and B are identical (with S.E. ±3%). This means that the DNA sample is composed only of totally fragmented DNA with sizes <23 Kb. Therefore, the concentration of this DNA sample is estimated from the $FU_{sonicated}$ as stated in step 4 of the 'Methods' section of the 'Assay for quantification of genomic, mitochondrial and plasmid dsDNA'.

    b. The FU values of the DNA sample portions A and B differ by 70% (with S.E. ±3%). This means that the DNA sample is composed only of DNA having sizes >23 Kb. Therefore, the concentration of this DNA sample portion B is estimated again from its $FU_{sonicated}$ value as stated in step 4 of the 'Methods' section of the 'Assay for quantification of genomic, mitochondrial and plasmid dsDNA'.

c.   The FU values of the DNA sample portions A and B differ between 1 and 70% (with S.E. ±3%). This means that the unknown DNA sample is composed of a mixture of DNA size fractions >23 Kb and <23 Kb of unknown proportions, which are estimated by the following sub-steps:

     i.   The $FU_{sonicated}$ value of the DNA sample portion A (measured in step 1) is used to determine the total DNA concentration of this sample (>23 Kb size fraction plus <23 Kb size fraction) as stated in step 4 of the 'Methods' section of the 'Assay for quantification of genomic, mitochondrial and plasmid dsDNA'.

     ii.   The following sub-steps *ii*, *iii* and *iv* are used to estimate the % proportions of >23 Kb and <23 Kb size fractions in the unknown DNA sample:

     iii.   Multiply the $FU_{unsonicated}$ value of the DNA sample portion B (measured in step 2) by 3.333 (=100%/30%) to convert it to the FU value ($FU_{>23\ Kb}$) it would give if it were >23 Kb.

     iv.   Express the $FU_{unsonicated}$ (of the DNA sample portion B measured in step 2) as % value (using as 100% the $FU_{>23\ Kb}$ value calculated in sub-step *ii*) and designate it as y%.

     v.   Enter this y% value in the equation x% = (100% − y%)/0.7 to calculate the x% value. This value represents the % proportion of the <23 Kb size fraction, which in turn represents the <23 Kb DNA smearing seen in the agarose gel electrophoresis. The % of the dsDNA >23 Kb size fraction is calculated as 100-x%.

     vi.   The so estimated percentages of the >23 Kb and <23 Kb size fractions in the unknown DNA sample are converted to their corresponding concentrations using as 100% the total concentration of the DNA sample (determined in sub-step *i*).

Conclusion

Under the stated fluorescence measurement conditions, the required minimum concentration of the unknown dsDNA sample for quantifying the fragmentation statuses *a*, *b*, and *c* is as follows: (a) 10 ng/15 pg ml^{-1} for Hoechst/PicoGreen, respectively, (b) 3 ng/5 pg ml^{-1} for Hoechst/PicoGreen, respectively, and (c) (i) for being able to measure the presence of a minimum 5% >23 Kb DNA size fraction (in the presence of 95% <23 Kb DNA size fraction), the corresponding minimum concentration (3 ng/5 pg ml^{-1} >23 Kb DNA for Hoechst/PicoGreen, respectively) can be determined if the total DNA concentration of the sample is ≥60 ng ml^{-1} and ≥100 pg ml^{-1} for Hoechst and PicoGreen, respectively. (ii) for being able to measure the presence of a minimum 10% <23 Kb DNA size fraction (in the presence of 90% >23 Kb DNA size fraction), the corresponding minimum concentration (10 ng/15 pg ml^{-1} <23 Kb DNA for Hoechst/PicoGreen, respectively) can be determined if the total DNA concentration of the sample is ≥ 90 ng ml^{-1} and ≥ 135 pg ml^{-1} for Hoechst and PicoGreen, respectively. Even lower than the minimum 5%/10% proportions of >23 Kb/<23 Kb DNA, respectively, can be measured by further increasing the stated total concentrations of the DNA sample.

Assay for the Quantification of dsDNA Nicks

Introduction

The principle of this assay is based on the determination of the annealing degree of DNA under alkaline conditions, which depends on the number of nicks present in dsDNA. The assay represents an extensive modification of a previous method [4], which is based on the differential binding of Hoechst with ssDNA and dsDNA (to which it binds preferably). The assay's concept is that the ssDNA is resulting more readily from the alkaline annealing of nicked than intact dsDNA. The weak point of this and other similar methods (using ethidium) [3] is that they do not take into account the facts that (a) the dsDNA in the unknown sample may exist also as a mixture of nicked and fragmented DNA, and (b) that Hoechst (and PicoGreen) binds differentially to fragmented and intact dsDNA; that is, Hoechst binds 70-0% less to fragmented dsDNA with size 0-23 Kb, respectively, in comparison to 'intact' dsDNA with size >23 Kb [15], thus resulting in an underestimation of the nicked DNA. The present assay has optimized the alkaline DNA unwinding conditions of the initial method, introduces an additional more sensitive PicoGreen version (as alternative to the Hoechst version), and uses a more accurate determination of the total dsDNA (see also 'Assay for quantification of genomic, mitochondrial and plasmid DNA') in order to increase the accuracy of the estimated % nicked dsDNA (and % not nicked dsDNA).

Materials and Methods

Materials

DNA (from calf thymus), DMSO and Hoechst 33258 were obtained from Sigma-Aldrich. Na$_2$EDTA, NaOH and Tris-HCl were obtained from Merck. Quant-iT^{TM} PicoGreen was obtained from Invitrogen (Molecular Probes).

Methods

The assay proceeds by splitting the unknown dsDNA sample in 3 equal fractions (0.075 ml each, appropriately diluted to contain ≥ 150 ng DNA) in three 1.5-ml eppendorf tubes (designated as Fractions A, B and C) and treats them as follows:

1. (i) Hoechst assay version:

    a. Fraction A: In tube A add 0.125 ml NaOH/HCl mixture solution (composed of 0.063 ml 0.06 N NaOH and 0.063 ml 0.06 N HCl), and completely fragment it by sonication as described in step 1 of the procedure section of 'Assay for quantification of genomic, mitochondrial and plasmid dsDNA'. Then add to it 0.05 ml 1 µM Hoechst working stock solution (for preparation see 'Methods' section, step 2, sub-step *a*, of 'Assay for quantification of genomic, mitochondrial and plasmid DNA'). Record the FU of the resulting solution at ex/em 353/451 nm (e.g. in a 0.5 ml quartz microcuvette, using a Shimadzu RF-1501 spectrofluorometer, set at 10 nm excitation/emission slit width and at high sensitivity). Then, multiply the resulting FU value of the sonicated DNA by 3.333 in order to convert it to the FU value it would have if it were 'intact' (>23 Kb) [15], and designate it as FU = A.

    b. Fraction B: In tube B add 0.063 ml 0.06 N NaOH, incubate exactly for 5 min at RT, followed by the addition of 0.063 ml 0.06 N HCl and 0.05 ml 1 µM Hoechst working stock solution. Record the FU value (=B) of the resulting solution at ex/em 353/451 nm, which represents the dsDNA in the sample that was not annealed after alkaline pH exposure (for 5 min).

    c. Fraction C: In tube C add 0.063 ml 0.06 N NaOH, incubate at 80°C for at least for 5 min, followed by the addition of 0.063 ml 0.06 N HCl and 0.05 ml 1 µM Hoechst working stock solution. Record the FU value (=C) of the resulting solution at ex/em 353/451 nm, which represents the background fluorescence of the ssDNA sample resulting from the complete annealing (by alkaline pH and heating to 80°C) of the dsDNA in the unknown sample.

    (ii) PicoGreen assay version (600 fold higher sensitivity than Hoechst version):

    a. Fraction A: In tube A add 0.15 ml NaOH/HCl mixture solution (composed this time of 0.075 ml 0.05 N NaOH plus 0.075 ml 0.05 N HCl), and completely fragment it by sonication (as described in step 1 of the procedure section of 'Assay for quantification of genomic, mitochondrial and plasmid dsDNA'). Then, add to it 0.075 ml PicoGreen working stock solution (for preparation see 'Methods' section, step 2, sub-step *b*, of 'Assay for quantification of genomic, mitochondrial and plasmid DNA'). Record the FU of the resulting solution at ex/em 480/530 nm. Then, multiply the resulting FU value of the sonicated DNA by 3.333 and designate it as FU = A.

    b. Fraction B: In tube B add 0.075 ml 0.05 N NaOH first, incubate exactly for 5 min at RT, and to that add 0.075 ml 0.05 N HCl and 0.075 ml PicoGreen working stock solution. Record the FU value (=B) of the resulting solution at ex/em 480/530 nm.

    c. Fraction C: In tube C add 0.075 ml 0.05 N NaOH first, incubate at 80°C for at least for 5 min, followed by the addition of 0.075 ml 0.05 N HCl and 0.075 ml

PicoGreen working stock solution. Record the FU value (=C) of the resulting solution at ex/em 480/530 nm.

2. Insert the FU values A, B and C in the formula $F = (B-C)/(A-C)$ and multiply the resulting F number (ranging between 0 and 1) by 100 to get the % of not nicked dsDNA, while the $(1-F) \times 100$ represents the % of nicked dsDNA. Thus, the more nicks in dsDNA the smaller the F will be; $1-F = 0$ when DNA is 100% undamaged, and $1-F = 1$ when DNA is 100% nicked.

Conclusion

This assay can assess nicks, a repairable dsDNA damage, in genomic, mitochondrial and plasmid dsDNA with size >23 Kb [17].

Acknowledgments

This work was financially supported by the Greek Ministry of Education, University of Patras, Greece.

References

[1]   De Bont, R; van Larebeke N. Endogenous DNA damage in humans: a review of quantitative data. *Mutagenesis*, 2004 19, 169-185.

[2]   Gavrieli, Y; Sherman, Y; Ben-Sasson SA. Identification of programmed cell death *in situ* via specific labeling of nuclear DNA fragmentation. *J. Cell Biol.*, 1992 119, 493-501.

[3]   Birnboim, CH. Fluorometric analysis of DNA unwinding to study strand breaks and repair in mammalian cells. In: Packer L, Glazer AN, editors. *Methods in Enzymology*. 186. San Diego: Academic Press; 1990; 550-555.

[4]   Kanter, MP; Schwartz, SH. A fluorescence enhancement assay for cellular DNA damage. *Mol. Pharmacol.*, 1982 22, 145-151.

[5]   Jones, DP; Maellaro, E; Jiang, S; Slater, GFA; Orrenius, S. Effects of N-acetyl-L-cysteine on T-cell apoptosis are not mediated by increased cellular glutathione. *Immunol. Lett.*, 1995 45, 205-209.

[6]   Jonas, RC; Ziegler, RT; Gu, HL; Jones, PD. Extracellular thiol/disulfide redox state affects proliferation rate in a human colon carcinoma (Caco2) cell line. *Free Rad. Biol. Med.*, 2002 33, 1499-1506.

[7]   Lelli, LJJ; Becks, LL; Dabrowska, IM; Hinshaw, BD. ATP converts necrosis to apoptosis in oxidant-injured endothelial cells. *Free Rad. Biol. Med.*, 1998 25, 694-702.

[8]   Collins, AR; Dobson, VL; Dusinska, M; Kennedy, G; Stetina, R. The Comet assay: what can it really tell us? *Mutat. Res.*, 1997 375, 183-193.

[9]   Singh, NP; McCoy, MT; Tice, RR; Schneider, EL. A simple technique for quantitation of low levels of DNA damage in individual cells. *Exp. Cell Res.*, 1988 175, 184-191.

[10] Halliwell, B; Gutteridge, CMJ. Free Radicals in Biology and Medicine. Oxford: Oxford University Press; 1999.

[11] Fenech, M; Holland, N; Chang, WP; Zeiger, E; Bonassi, S. The human micronucleus project - An international collaborative study on the use of the micronucleus technique for measuring DNA damage in humans. *Mut. Res.*, 1999 428, 271-283.

[12] Fenech, M. The in vitro micronucleus technique. *Mut. Res.*, 2000 455, 81-95.

[13] Arita, K; Yamamoto, Y; Takehara, Y; Utsumi, T; Kanno, T; Miyaguchi, C; Akiyama, J; Yoshioka, T; Utsumi, K. Mechanisms of enhanced apoptosis in HL-60 cells by UV-irradiated N-3 and N-6 polyunsaturated fatty acids. *Free Rad. Biol. Med.*, 2003 35, 189-199.

[14] Ohyama, K; Enn, P; Uchide, N; Bessho, T; Yamakawa, T. Improvement of separation method of fragmented DNA from an appoptotic cell DNA sample for the quantitation using agarose gell electrophoresis. *Biol. Pharm. Bull.*, 2001 24, 342-346.

[15] Georgiou, DC; Papapostolou, N. Assay for the quantification of intact/fragmented genomic DNA. *Anal. Biochem.*, 2006 358, 247-256.

[16] Sambrook, J; Fritsch, FE; Maniatis, T. Molecular cloning. New York: Cold Spring Harbor Lab Press; 1989.

[17] Brown, TA. Gene cloning and DNA analysis: An introduction. Malden: Blackwell Publishing; 2001.

[18] Griffiths, AJF; Miller, JH; Suzuki, DT; Lewontin, RC; Gelbart, WM. An introduction to genetic analysis. New York: W. H. Freeman; 2000.

[19] Georgiou, DC; Patsoukis, N; Papapostolou, I. Assay for the quantification of small-sized fragmented genomic DNA. *Anal. Biochem.*, 2005 339, 223-230.

In: New Research on DNA Damage
Editors: Honoka Kimura and Aoi Suzuki

ISBN 978-1-60456-581-2
© 2008 Nova Science Publishers, Inc.

Chapter 9

DNA Damage through Photo-induced Electron Transfer and Photosensitized Generation of Reactive Oxygen Species

Kazutaka Hirakawa[*]

Department of Basic Engineering (Chemistry), Faculty of Engineering, Shizuoka University, Japan

Abstract

DNA damage via photosensitized reaction such as photo-induced electron transfer and photosensitized reactive oxygen formation contributes to solar carcinogenesis and phototoxic effect. Furthermore, DNA damage by photosensitized reaction is important mechanism of photodynamic therapy, which is a promising treatment of cancer and other non-malignant conditions. The mechanism of photosensitized DNA damage strongly depends on the excitation energy of photosensitizer, i.e. the wavelength is important. In general, ultra-violet photosensitizer induces DNA damage via the electron transfer, whereas photosensitized singlet oxygen generation is important for the mechanism by visible-light photosensitizer. Guanine residue is the important target of the two mechanisms, electron transfer and singlet oxygen generation. The consecutive guanines are selectively oxidized through electron transfer, because these sites act as hole-trap. Singlet oxygen induces base oxidation at every guanine residues. Rarely, superoxide anion radical, which is formed through photo-induced electron transfer from excited photosensitizer to molecular oxygen, contributes to DNA damage. Superoxide itself hardly damages DNA, but hydrogen peroxide and hydroxyl radical formed from superoxide are important reactive species for DNA damage.

[*] Shizuoka University, Johoku 3-5-1, Naka-ku, Hamamatsu, Shizuoka 432-8561, Japan.

1. Introduction

DNA damage via photosensitized reaction contributes to solar carcinogenesis and phototoxic effect. In addition, this mechanism is closely related to the process of photodynamic therapy (PDT), which is a relatively new modality of treatment of diseases involving uncontrolled cell proliferation [1-3]. In general, the excited photosensitizer damages cellular components, including DNA via the generation of reactive oxygen species such as singlet oxygen ($^1O_2$) in the presence of oxygen or electron transfer, leading to cell death or carcinogenesis. As a minor mechanism, ultra-violet (UV) A induces the formation of cyclobutane pyrimidine-dimers as the likely result of the triplet energy transfer from excited photosensitizers to pyrimidine bases [4-7]. DNA damage via photo-induced electron transfer is called the type I mechanism, whereas the reactive oxygen mediated damage is called the type II (Figure 1). The type I mechanism does not absolutely require oxygen for induction of DNA damage, whereas type II mechanism proceeds only in the presence of oxygen.

In the type I mechanism, one electron is transferred from guanine to photoexcited sensitizers, resulting in damage at the consecutive G sequence in double-stranded DNA [8, 9]. Various endogenous and exogenous photosensitizers mediate DNA photodamage via this mechanism. The major type II mechanism involves the generation of $^1O_2$ from photoexcited sensitizers, resulting in damage to guanines without preference for consecutive guanines. In the minor type II mechanism, superoxide anion radical ($O_2^{\cdot-}$) is generated, and then DNA damage is induced by reactive species generated through the interaction of hydrogen peroxide (H_2O_2), which is formed from the dismutation of $O_2^{\cdot-}$, with metal ions.

Exposure to solar UV radiation is undoubtedly linked to skin carcinogenesis [10]. It has been well demonstrated in early studies that UVB radiation, which constitutes about 5 % of the solar UV radiation that reaches the surface of the earth, directly activates the DNA molecule to generate dipyrimidine photoproducts such as cyclobutane pyrimidine dimers and pyrimidine (6-4) pyrimidone photoadducts, resulting in mutations and carcinogenesis.

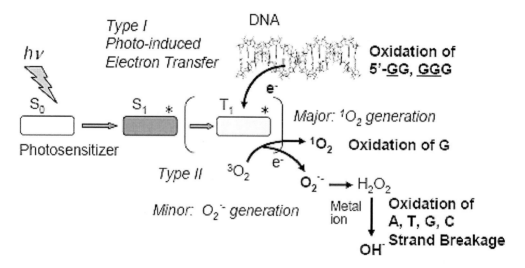

Figure 1. Mechanism of photosensitized DNA damage.

However, recent studies have provided sufficient evidence that UVA radiation, which accounts for the major portion of the solar UV radiation, is also mutagenic and carcinogenic, although it is unlikely that UVA directly activates DNA bases to produce dipyrimidine photoproducts [11, 12]. It is, therefore, generally recognized that solar UVA carcinogenesis involves a mechanism by which UVA radiation indirectly induces DNA damage through photosensitized reactions mediated by intracellular chromophores. Accordingly, a variety of cellular compounds have been considered to be potential endogenous photosensitizers. In addition, certain drugs may act as exogenous photosensitizers. For example, psolarens have been used for treatment of skin diseases, particularly psoriasis, in combination with UVA irradiation (PUVA therapy), and it is known that the incidence of skin tumor is increased by PUVA therapy [10]. In this chapter, the mechanism of DNA damage by various photosensitizers is described especially from the energetically point of view.

2. Type I Mechanism: Photo-induced Electron Transfer

The type I mechanism involves electron transfer from DNA base to excited photosensitizer. This mechanism is dependent on the energy of the molecular orbital (MO) of photosensitizer (Sens), its excited state (Sens*), and nucleobase, namely the oxidation potential of the DNA base and the reduction potential of the excited photosensitizer (Figure 2). Guanine has the lowest oxidation potential among the four DNA bases, that is, guanine is most likely to be oxidized. Formed guanine radical cation through the electron transfer reacts with water or molecular oxygen, leading to the formation of oxidized product of guanine. These photoproducts cause mutation and cancer.

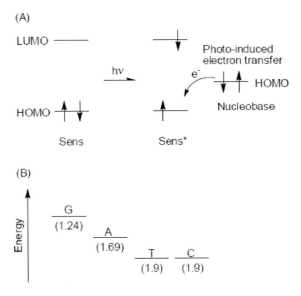

Figure 2. Photo-induced electron transfer from the highest occupied MO (HOMO) of nucleobase to the excited photosensitizer (A). The HOMO energy of nucleobases and their redox potentials of one-electron oxidation (V vs. SCE in acetonitrile) (B).

2.1. Physical Chemistry of Electron Transfer Mechanism

According to basic Marcus theory [13], the electron transfer rate constant (k_{et}) is expressed as follows:

$$k_{et} \propto \exp\left(-\frac{(\Delta G + \lambda)^2}{4\lambda RT}\right) \tag{1}$$

where ΔG represents the free energy of reaction, λ the reorganization energy, R the gas constant, and T is the absolute temperature. The ΔG depends on the redox potentials of one electron reduction of the sensitizer ($E_{red}(S/S^{\bullet-})$) and the oxidation of nucleobase ($E_{ox}(N/N^{\bullet+})$), and can be estimated using the Rehm-Weller relationship [14]:

$$\Delta G = E_{ox}(N/N^{\bullet+}) - E_{red}(S/S^{\bullet-}) - E(Sens^*)$$

$$\approx E_{ox}(N/N^{\bullet+}) - E_{ox}(S/S^{\bullet+}) \tag{2}$$

where $E(Sens^*)$ and $E_{ox}(S/S^{\bullet+})$ are the excitation energy (first excited singlet srtate) and the one-electron oxidation potential of the photosensitizer. Since guanine has the lowest oxidation potential (1.24 V vs. SCE in acetonitorile) among the four DNA bases [15], the type I photosensitizers are required to have larger oxidation potential than that of guanine. This equation indicates that the electron transfer is enhanced depending on the value of $-\Delta G$ up to the value of λ; the larger $E_{red}(S/S^{\bullet-})$ and $E(Sens^*)$ increase the value of $-\Delta G$. But the large $E_{red}(S/S^{\bullet-})$ is not favored for the stability of the photosensitizer. Therefore, relatively large excitation energy is required. Indeed, DNA damage through the type I mechanism was observed in the case of large $E(Sens^*)$ (Table 1). However, in the case of large energy gap, the Marcus equation indicates that the electron transfer is rather suppressed. In many cases, k_{et} become maximum at $-\Delta G \sim 1$ eV and the value of $E_{red}(S/S^{\bullet-})$ of stable photosensitizer is about $-1 \sim -2$ V; the $E(Sens^*)$ value about UVA region ($3 \sim 4$ eV) is suitable for DNA photooxidation through electron transfer.

2.2. Hole Transfer along DNA Strand and Guanine Oxidation

Formed radical cation of certain nucleobase (hole) by the photo-induced electron transfer to Sens* migrates the hole-trapping site. A hole has been demonstrated to migrate through DNA by hopping between guanines [25-34]. The rate constant of this hopping is $\sim 10^8$ s^{-1} [35-38]. Guanine oxidation is induced by this DNA-mediated charge hopping over 200 Å [32]. The base pair stack within double helical DNA provides an effective medium for charge transfer. The DNA π-stack mediates oxidative DNA damage over long molecular distances in a reaction that is sensitive to the sequence-dependent conformation and dynamics of DNA. Further, it has been revealed that adenine, the second most easily oxidized base, acts as the hole carrier in DNA [39-41]. This adenine hopping proceeds with a rate constant faster than

10^8 s^{-1} over a distance of 30 Å [42, 43]. The adenine hopping as well as the hole hopping through guanines should play an important role in the photosensitized DNA damage.

Table 1. DNA-damaging mechanism by photosensitizers

Photosensitizer	Absorption	E(Sens*) / eV	DNA-damaging mechanism	Reference
Xanthone	UVA	3.6	ET[a]	[16]
NADH	UVA	3.6	$O_2^{\cdot-}$	[9]
Pteridine (PCA[b])	UVA	3.4	ET	[17]
Pteridine (DHP[c])	UVA	3.4	ET	[18]
TiO$_2$ (Anatase, Rutile)	UVA	3.3[d]* 3.1[e]*	$O_2^{\cdot-}$ (major), •OH (minor)	[19]
Riboflavin	Vis[f] (Blue)	2.7	ET	[16, 20]
Sb(V)porphyrin	Vis (Red)	2.1	$^1O_2$ (major), ET (minor)	[21]
P(V)porphyrin	Vis (Red)	2.1	$^1O_2$ (major), ET (minor)	[22]
TMPyP[g]	Vis (Red)	1.9	$^1O_2$	[23]
Methylene blue	Vis (Red)	1.9	$^1O_2$	[24]

a: electron transfer, b: pterine-6-carboxylic acid, c: 2,4-diamino-6-hydroxymethylpteridine,
d: anatase, e: rutile, f: visible light, g: tetrakis-(*N*-methyl-4-pyridyl)porphyrin, *: band gap energy.

Oxidative cleavage at guanine displays sequence selectivity, depending on the identity of the neighboring base in the π-stacked array [15, 44]. The type I photosensitizers damage DNA at consecutive guanine site such as at the underlined G of 5'-GG, 5'-GGG, and 5'-GGGG in double-stranded DNA [8, 9]. Since consecutive guanine residues act as a hole trap, this site is specifically damaged by the type I mechanism. It was performed that *ab initio* MO calculations on stacked DNA bases to explain the mechanism of sequence-specific guanine photodamage [45]. The energy level of the HOMO of guanine is highest among the four DNA bases, and therefore, guanine is most likely to be oxidized. More detailed calculations have revealed that a large part of HOMO is concentrated and electron-loss centers are localized on the 5'-G of GG doublets in the B-form double-stranded DNA, and that stacking of two guanine bases significantly lowers the ionization potential [45]. Therefore, electron transfer occurs specifically at this site to produce the guanine radical cation. In GGG triplets, HOMO is mainly distributed on the 5'-G, and therefore, this guanine is easily oxidized by electron transfer. However, the guanine radical cation formed at the 5'-G is reduced by electron transfer from the middle guanine, because the radical on the middle G is estimated to be the most stable in certain GGG triplets [46]. Therefore, the middle G is most likely to be damaged. The radical cation on the consecutive G sequence arises from either initial electron abstraction of this guanine by photoexcited sensitizer or through hole transfer from a relatively distant one-electron oxidized nucleobase [47]. On the other hand, when denatured single-stranded DNA was used, DNA damage can be hardly induced via the type I mechanism due to the inhibition of the charge transfer through DNA strand [8, 9].

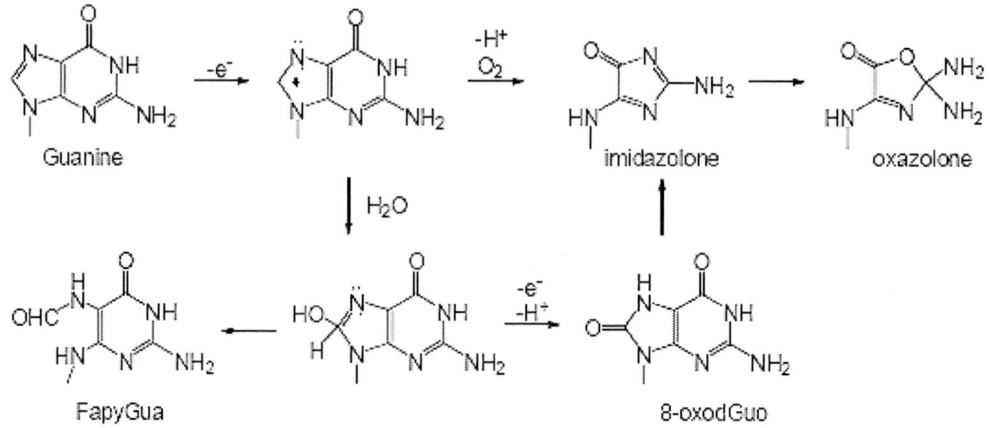

Figure 3. Oxidation of guanine moiety via photo-induced electron transfer.

2.3. Formation of Oxidized Product of Guanine via Electron Transfer

The formed guanine radical cations react with a water molecule to form the 8-hydroxy-7,8-dihydroguanyl radical (C-8 OH adduct radical) (Figure 3) [23, 48]. This radical is converted into a 2,6-diamino-4-hydroxy-5-formamidopyrimidine (FapyGua) residue through a reducing process [23, 48, 49]. FapyGua site is alkali-labile and can be detected by an electrophoresis after cleavage of DNA strand at this site by hot piperidine treatment. This FapyGua formation is a minor process. On the other hand, competitive oxidation of the C-8 OH adduct radical, which may be achieved by molecular oxygen, gives rise to 8-oxo-7,8-dihydro-2'-deoxyguanosine (8-oxodGuo) [23, 50-52]. 8-OxodGuo site is piperidine resistant and the enzyme treatment is necessary for the detection by an electrophoresis. The formation of 8-oxodGuo causes DNA misreplication that may lead to mutations such as G-C $\rightarrow$ T-A transversion [53, 54]. 8-OxodGuo undergoes further oxidation, resulting in the formation of piperidine-labile oxidized products (e.g. imidazolone, oxazolone) [23, 55, 56]. Imidazolone and oxazolone can also be primary oxidation products that arise from the conversion of the deprotonated form of the guanine radical cation after O_2 or $O_2^{\cdot-}$ addition [23, 57, 58]. It has been reported that imidazolone and oxazolone are major oxidized products of guanine by the type I mechanism [23, 57, 58]. Imidazolone forms a stable base pair with guanine comparable with the Watson-Click G-C base pair [55, 56] and may cause G-C $\rightarrow$ C-G transversion [59, 60].

3. Type II Mechanism: Generation of Reactive Oxygen Species

DNA damage can be induced indirectly by the excited photosensitizer via the type II mechanism. This process can be mediated by reactive oxygen species, especially $^1O_2$, and $O_2^{\cdot-}$ also contributes to DNA damage.

3.1. Singlet Oxygen Generation

The type II mechanism (major type II mechanism) involves energy transfer from an excited photosensitizer to molecular oxygen to produce $^1O_2$. Molecular oxygen has two low-lying singlet excited states, $^1\Delta_g$ and $^1\Sigma_g^+$, 0.98 eV (95 kJ mol^{-1}) and 1.63 eV (158 kJ mol^{-1}) above the ground triplet state ($^3\Sigma_g^-$), respectively [61]. Since the lifetime of $^1\Sigma_g^+$ is very short, the contribution of $^1\Sigma_g^+$ to DNA damage is negligible and $^1\Delta_g$ is important reactive species ($^1O_2$ indicates $^1\Delta_g$ in the below part of this chapter). The energy transfer reaction can be expressed as follows:

$$^1Sens + h\nu \rightarrow {}^1Sens^* \tag{3}$$

$$^1Sens^* \rightarrow {}^3Sens^* \tag{4}$$

$$^3Sens^* \,({}^1Sens^*) + {}^3O_2 \rightarrow {}^1Sens + {}^1O_2 \,({}^1\Sigma_g^+ \text{ or } {}^1\Delta_g) \tag{5}$$

$$^1O_2 \,({}^1\Sigma_g^+) \rightarrow {}^1O_2 \,({}^1\Delta_g) \tag{6}$$

where ^1Sens represents the ground state photosensitizer, $^1Sens^*$ the excited singlet state photosensitizer, and $^3Sens^*$ is the excited triplet state photosensitizer. The spin multiplicity of molecular oxygen (triplet state) changes into the singlet state via this energy transfer. Since this process must proceed through electron exchange (Dexter mechanism) [62], contact between the excited photosensitizer and molecular oxygen is important for $^1O_2$ generation. $^1O_2$ is unstable excited state and undergoes physical quenching by surroundings. The lifetime of $^1O_2$, which is relatively short (2 ~ 3 μs) [63] in H_2O, is greatly elongated in D_2O (~ 70 μs). Consequently, DNA damage via the type II mechanism can be enhanced in D_2O compared with that in H_2O. The lifetime of $^1O_2$ is markedly shortened in cell (0.01 ~ 0.2 μs) [64], indicating that the binding interaction of photosensitizer with DNA is important in the damaging mechanism.

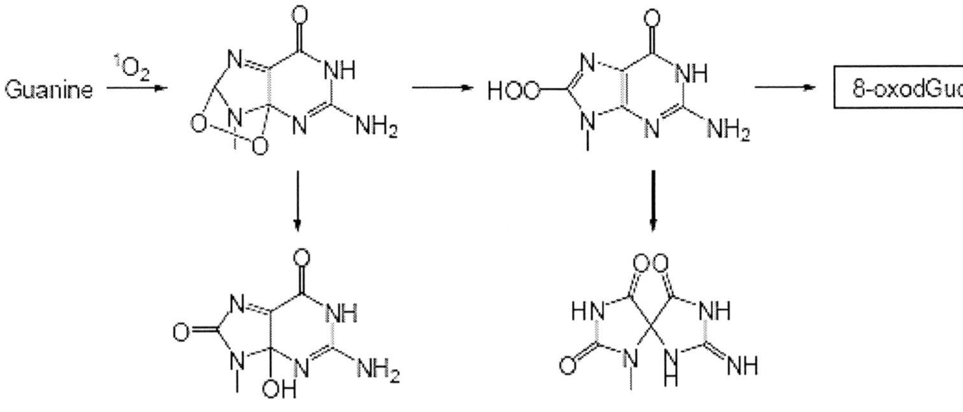

Figure 4. Oxidation of guanine by $^1O_2$.

3.2. Guanine Oxidation by Singlet Oxygen

Oxygen is *ca.* 1 V more oxidizing in its singlet excited state and is therefore significantly more electrophilic, reacting rapidly with unsaturated carbon-carbon bonds, neutral nucleophiles [61]. Indeed, various compounds have been shown to generate $^1O_2$ during photo-irradiation and cause DNA oxidation (Figure 4). In this type II mechanism, guanines are specifically oxidized, whereas other nucleobases are hardly damaged by $^1O_2$ [8, 9]. This guanine specific oxidation is markedly enhanced in single-stranded DNA compared with that in double-stranded DNA. The interaction of guanine with $^1O_2$, which is similar to the Diels–Alder reaction, leads to the formation of [4 + 2] cycloaddition product with the imidazole ring to produce an unstable endoperoxide, which undergoes subsequent proton transfer to form 8-hydroperoxyguanine [65, 66]. Formed 8-hydroperoxyguanine can be converted into 8-oxodGuo followed by subsequent reduction [23].

3.3. DNA Damage Mediated by the Formation of Superoxide

On the other hand, the minor type II mechanism is also confirmed [8, 9]. This mechanism is mediated by the formation of $O_2{}^{\bullet-}$ by electron transfer from an excited photosensitizer to molecular oxygen. This reaction is followed by dismutation to H_2O_2. $O_2{}^{\bullet-}$ may also be generated by the interaction of oxygen with the sensitizer anion radical produced by the type I mechanism. Therefore, $O_2{}^{\bullet-}$ may contribute to the DNA damage as a secondary effect of the type I mechanism other than the minor type II mechanism. Although $O_2{}^{\bullet-}$ and H_2O_2 are not capable of DNA damage by themselves, H_2O_2 can cause DNA damage in the presence of metal ions. Free hydroxyl radical ($\bullet OH$) is generated by the reaction of H_2O_2 with Fe^{2+} ion (the Fenton reaction). $\bullet OH$ is known to cause DNA damage at every nucleotide with little or no site selectivity [67]. In contrast, H_2O_2 induces site-specific DNA damage particularly at thymine and guanine residues in the presence of Cu^{2+}, and the primary reactive species causing DNA damage appears to be copper-oxygen complexes [68]. This $O_2{}^{\bullet-}$ mechanism requires relatively large reduction potential. According to the Marcus theory [13], the electron transfer rate depends on the λ (above described), and the λ is expressed as follows:

$$\lambda = \frac{e^2}{4\pi\varepsilon_0}\left(\frac{1}{n^2} - \frac{1}{\varepsilon}\right)\left(\frac{1}{2r_D} + \frac{1}{2r_A} - \frac{1}{d}\right) \tag{7}$$

where e represents the electric charge, ε_0 the vacuum dielectric constant, n the refractive index of medium, ε the dielectric constant of medium, r_D the radius of the electron donor, r_A the radius of the electron acceptor, and d is the donor-acceptor distance. The equations (1) and (7) indicate that the electron transfer to small molecule requires large energy gap between the electron donor and the acceptor. Because molecular oxygen is small, relatively high energy photon such as ultra-violet ray is favored in this mechanism. Indeed, it is reported that visible-light photosensitizers can hardly reduce molecular oxygen into $O_2{}^{\bullet-}$ [69, 70].

4. DNA Damage and Photomutagenisity and Photocarcinogenisity

In type I mechanism, DNA damage is induced specifically at the consecutive guanine sequences, whereas major type II mechanism mediates damage to every guanine residue without specificity for consecutive guanines. It is presumed that 8-oxodGuo accounts for a large part of damaged guanines. The formation of 8-oxodGuo through the type I and the major type II mechanisms may lead to DNA misreplication, resulting in mutation, particularly G $\rightarrow$ T transversions [53, 54]. A recent study has demonstrated that G $\rightarrow$ T transversions occur particularly in the stratum basale of human skin squamous cell carcinomas [71]. The mutations at consecutive guanines, such as GGT $\rightarrow$ TGT and GGC $\rightarrow$ TGC in *ras* oncogenes were observed in human skin cancer [72]. These mutations may be induced by 8-oxodGuo formation through the type I mechanism. The mutational spectra induced by other oxidative DNA lesions have been investigated. Imidazolone and oxazolone can be generated by oxidation of guanine and 8-oxodGuo (above described). Similarly to 8-oxodGuo, oxazolone induced G $\rightarrow$ T transversions [73], whereas imidazolone induced G $\rightarrow$ C transversions [74]. DNA damage induced through minor type II mechanism is dependent on metal ions. It has shown that reactive species generated in the presence of copper ion, probably copper-oxygen complex, induce piperidine-labile damage especially at thymines in the 5'-GTC-3' sequences. UVA-induced mutations were observed at thymines in rodent and human cells [11, 75]. Although it is known that UV radiation induces the formation of thymine dimers, UVA-induced DNA photodamage at thymines would be mainly due to the formation of oxidized products of thymine. Although UVB has been believed to be responsible for solar carcinogenesis, UVA-induced DNA damage in the presence of endogenous and exogenous photosensitizers may play an important role in solar carcinogenesis.

5. Ultra-violet A Photosensitizer

Exposure to solar UV radiation is undoubtedly linked to skin carcinogenesis [10]. Photosensitized reaction by UV radiation, especially UVA radiation, is considered to cause cancer through oxidative DNA damage. Photosensitizer should be located in the vicinity of DNA for DNA photodamage to occur. And when the photosensitizer is bound to DNA, the type I mechanism is favored, because the electron transfer rate from DNA to the sensitizer in the singlet excited state is faster than that of the intersystem crossing which leads to the formation of the triplet excited state and subsequent $^1O_2$ generation. In addition, the type I mechanism requires relatively large oxidative power, and in general, HOMO-LUMO gap of sensitizer become larger, the oxidation potential become larger. Photochemical reaction mediated by UV ray occurs with larger driving force compared with that by visible light. Consequently, the type I mechanism is favored in DNA damage by UVA photosensitizer. Indeed, various UVA photosensitizers induce DNA damage via electron transfer (Table 1).

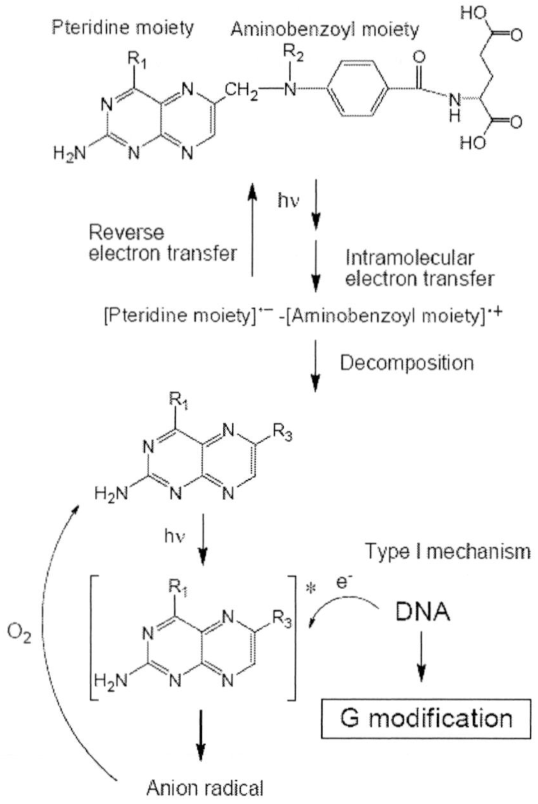

Figure 5. Mechanism of photosensitized DNA damage via photodecomposition of folic acid analogues. Methotrexate: $R_1=NH_2$, $R_2=CH_3$, $R_3=CH_2OH$. Folic acid: $R_1=OH$, $R_2=H$, $R_3=COOH$.

5.1. Exogenous and Endogenous Photosensitizers

The photosensitized DNA damage has been extensively studied using various chemical compounds including exogenous and endogenous photosensitizers. In this section, several examples of DNA damage by exogenous and endogenous photosensitizers are presented. Methotrexate has been used for chemotherapy of many types of cancer. This compound is one of the folic acid analogues and consists of pteridine moiety and aminobenzene-L-glutamic acid moiety (Figure 5). Pteridine absorbs UVA region and this compound also acts as UVA photosensitizer. It is demonstrated that photo-irradiated methotrexate caused piperidine-sensitive DNA cleavage specifically at the underlined G in 5'-GG-3' and 5'-GGG-3' sequences in double-stranded DNA [18]. fluorescence measurement, high-pressure liquid chromatography, and mass spectrometry have demonstrated that photoexcited methotrexate undergoes photohydrolysis to yield 2,4-diamino-6-(hydroxymethyl)pteridine (DHP), which is a strong photosensitizer to damage DNA via the type I mechanism. The kinetic studies on DNA photodamage and the DHP formation by the photo-irradiated methotrexate led to conclusion that photoexcited methotrexate produces DHP, which causes DNA damage through photo-induced electron transfer from guanine.

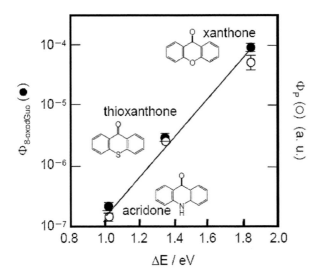

Figure 6. Relationship between the DNA-damaging abilities of photosensitizers and their HOMO energies. $\Phi_{\text{8-oxodGuo}}$: the quantum yield of 8-oxodGuo formation. Φ_P: the quantum yield of piperidine-sensitive photoproduct. ΔE: the energy gap between HOMO energy of photosensitizer and that of G. HOMO energies of photosensitizers were estimated from *ab intio* MO calculation at Hatree-Fock 6-31G* level.

In 1993, it has been firstly demonstrated that DNA damage by UVA radiation with riboflavin, an endogenous photosensitizer, occurs at the 5' site of GG sequences in double-stranded DNA [20]. These studies demonstrated that the DNA double helix could serve as a medium for the hole migration over long distances in UVA-mediated guanine oxidation. The radical cation on the consecutive guanines can react with water to form the 8-hydroxy-7,8-dihydroguanyl radicals (above described). Riboflavin has absorption maximum in the blue color region and is exactly not the UVA sensitizer. This result indicates that blue color visible light, other than UV ray, can induce DNA damage via the type I mechanism.

Folic acid is one of the B vitamins essential for human nutrition. Supplement of folic acid is useful for prevention of cancer [76, 77]. Folic acid is easily decomposed by sunlight and UV light [17] and photodegradation in human skin [78]. UVA-irradiated folic acid generates pterine-6-carboxylic acid (PCA) via intramolecular electron transfer and subsequent reactions (Figure 5) [17]. UVA-irradiated folic acid or PCA caused DNA cleavage specifically at consecutive guanine residues in double-stranded DNA through electron transfer [17]. Kinetic studies demonstrated that DNA damage is caused mainly by photoexcited PCA rather than by folic acid itself. Therefore, folic acid appears to induce DNA photooxidation in a similar manner to methotrexate [18]. The formation of the oxidative products of guanine through the type I mechanism would play the key role in carcinogenesis induced by endogenous photosensitizers.

5.2. HOMO Energy of Photosensitizer and DNA Damaging Activity

The DNA-damaging activity of UVA photosensitizers via the type I mechanism depends on their redox potential of the one electron oxidation (oxidation potential). This value is practically determined by the HOMO energy. Xanthone analogues, UVA photosensitizers, induce DNA damage through the type I mechanism and their DNA-damaging activities depend on their HOMO energy (Figure 6) [16]. This figure shows the plots of the quantum yields of DNA damage against the energy gaps of HOMO energy (ΔE) between the photosensitizers and guanine. The plots have shown an increase of the extent of DNA damage exponentially, almost depending on ΔE. This result suggests that the simple calculation of the HOMO energy can be applied to predict the DNA-damaging activity of UVA photosensitizers and their photo-carcinogenicity might be evaluated.

5.3. Reactive Oxygen Formation by UVA Radiation

Sepiapterin, an endogenous dihydropterin, induced DNA photodamage at the 5'-G of the 5'-<u>GG</u>-3' sequences, whereas in the presence of Cu^{2+} ion, DNA damage was induced preferably at thymine of the 5'-G<u>T</u>C-3' sequence [79]. Catalase and bathocuproine, a Cu^+-specific chelating agent, inhibited DNA photolesions, suggesting that DNA damage involved H_2O_2 and Cu^+ ion, which may be produced via the reduction of Cu^{2+} ion through photosensitized reaction. It is speculated that photoexcited sepiapterin reacts with oxygen to form $O_2^{\cdot-}$, which is dismutated to H_2O_2, and reactive species generated from the reaction of H_2O_2 with Cu^+ ion played the key role in DNA photodamage. A similar result was observed with nicotinamide adenine dinucleotide (NADH), an endogenous reductant [9]. These photosensitizers have relatively large S_1 energy and absorb UVA. The minor type I mechanism rarely contributes to DNA damage in the case of highly reductive UVA photosensitizer.

5.4. Titanium Dioxide Photocatalyst

Titanium dioxide (TiO_2) is a well-known photocatalyst [80]. The two crystaline forms of TiO_2, anatase and rutile, are semiconductors with band gap energies of 3.26 and 3.06 eV, respectively. When exposing to UVA light, the reduction-oxidation activity of TiO_2 has a significant biological impact, as is exemplified by its bactericidal activity. Moreover, the photocatalytic effect of TiO_2 has been studied for medical application, such as PDT [80-82]. TiO_2 catalyses the generation of $O_2^{\cdot-}$, H_2O_2, and $\cdot OH$ during UVA irradiation.

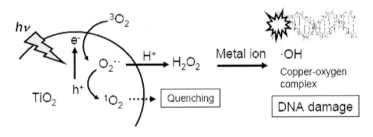

Figure 7. Mechanism of the generation of reactive oxygen species and DNA damage photocatalyzed by TiO_2.

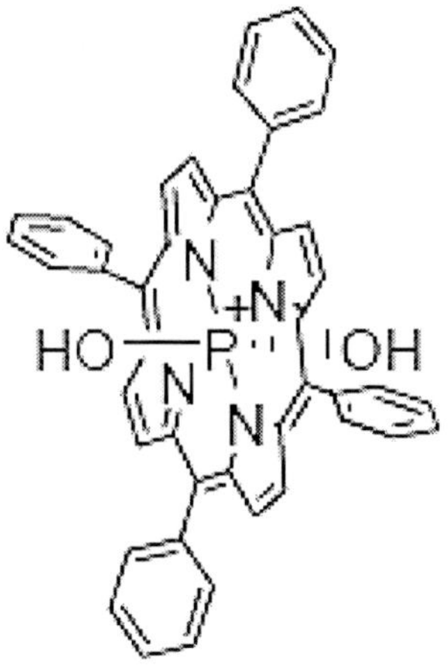

Figure 8. Structure of P(V)TPP.

It has been reported that H_2O_2, which can be generated from the dismutation of $O_2^{\cdot-}$, is important reactive oxygen species, because the lifetime of H_2O_2 is long and H_2O_2 easily diffuses in cell to incorporate into nucleus (Figure 7) [19]. DNA damage photocatalyzed by TiO_2 is markedly enhanced in the presence of Cu^{2+} ion similarly to the above mentioned mechanism. Photo-irradiated anatase and rutile induce the Cu^{2+}-mediated damage at guanine and thymine residues via H_2O_2 generation. In addition, the photocatalytic •OH formation directly from water partially contributes to DNA damage by TiO_2 as a minor mechanism (Table 1). Recently, $^1O_2$ generation by TiO_2 photocatalysis via re-oxidation of $O_2^{\cdot-}$ has been reported [83, 84]. But the generated $^1O_2$ is easily deactivated on TiO_2 surface and hardly damages DNA.

6. Visible-light Photosensitizer

Visible light photosensitizer mainly induces DNA damage via the type II mechanism (major type II mechanism). $^1O_2$ generation can be induced by photons with relatively small energy. Since the carcinogenisity of visible-light itself has not been demonstrated, the visible-light photosensitizers have an importance in the application such as the drug for PDT rather than their photo-carcinogenisity.

6.1. Application of the Visible-light Photosensitizer: Photodynamic Therapy

PDT, which is a relatively new treatment for cancer, employs a photosensitizer and visible light to produce an oxidative stress in cells and ablate cancerous tumors [1-3]. PDT is also used for treating some non-malignant conditions that are generally characterized by the overgrowth of unwanted or abnormal cells. The human tissue has relatively high transparency for visible-light, especially red color light, and visible-light hardly demonstrates side-effect. Because $^1O_2$ can be easily generated by visible-light due to the above mentioned reason, $^1O_2$

is considered as important reactive species of PDT. Critical sites of the generated $^1O_2$ include mitochondria and lipid membranes [1-3, 85]. Moreover, DNA is also an important target biomolecule of photosensitized reactions [86-89].

6.2. Porphyrins

Porphyrins and their analogues are important as endogenous photosensitizer, further the most commonly administered photosensitizers in PDT [90]. Cellular DNA damage photosensitized by porphyrin derivatives has been reported [91, 92]. With regard to porphyrinoid photosensitizers, various reports have indicated the involvement of the type II mechanism [8, 9, 90], whereas other mechanisms have rarely been reported to be involved in DNA damage [21, 22]. In the case of the type II mechanism, hematoporphyrin has been reported to induce DNA damage specifically at guanine residues through the generation of $1O2$ [93]. DNA damage including 8-oxodGuo formation induced by photoexcited hematoporphyrin was enhanced in D2O, because the lifetime of $1O2$ is markedly elongated in D2O [63].

On the other hand, a few study demonstrated DNA damage by porphyrins via the type I mechanism [21, 22]. Photoexcited high-valent metalloporphyrins have high oxidation ability compared with low-valent metalloporphyrins or free-base porphyrins [94, 95]. For example, the oxidation potential of tetraphenylporphyrin P(V) complexes (1.4-1.8 V vs. SCE in acetonitrile) [95-97] is higher than that of guanine (1.24 V) [15], indicating that photoexcited P(V)porphyrins have the potential to oxidize DNA through photo-induced electron transfer. Therefore, P(V)porphyrin may potentially damage DNA through dual mechanisms (the type I and type II mechanisms) [22]. It was reported that photosensitized DNA damage by dihydroxoP(V)tetraphenylporphyrin (P(V)TPP, Figure 8) was examined using an isolated DNA fragment [22]. Because P(V)TPP is water-soluble and a cationic sensitizer, it is considered that P(V)TPP could bind to DNA through electrostatic interaction. In the PDT process, a photosensitized reaction occurs in a complex biological environment, since the administered sensitizer necessarily interacts with the biomaterials [90]. The examination of the photosensitized reaction of porphyrins under a binding interaction with biomolecules should yield important information for the development of PDT photosensitizers. P(V)TPP photosensitizes guanine selective oxidation in single-stranded DNA mainly through $1O2$ generation under aerobic condition. On the other hand, for double-stranded DNA, photoexcited P(V)TPP selectively damages consecutive guanines. Because the consecutive guanines act as a hole trap, this DNA-damaging pattern suggests the involvement of the type I mechanism. Fluorescence quenching of P(V)TPP by DNA also supported the photo-induced electron transfer from DNA to the photoexcited P(V)TPP. Since the oxygen concentration in cancerous cell is low, the oxygen-independent type I mechanism should be advantageous for PDT.

6.3. Control of Singlet Oxygen Generating Activity of Photosensitizer

The microenvironmental effect of the DNA strand should be one of the key factors in controlling the activity of photosensitizers, of which the target biomolecule is DNA [98]. The effect of the interaction between DNA and the photosensitizer on photosensitized $^1O_2$ generation was investigated using DNA-binding alkaloids, berberine and palmatine [99]. These photosensitizers were bound to DNA by electrostatic force. Near-infrared luminescence measurement demonstrated that the photoexcited alkaloids can generate $^1O_2$ only when the photosensitizers are bound to DNA (Figure 9). A fluorescence decay study showed significant enhancement of the lifetime of their photoexcited state with the DNA binding. A calculation study suggested that the electrostatic interaction with DNA inhibits the quenching of the photoexcited state of these alkaloids via intramolecular electron transfer, leading to the prolongation of the lifetime of their excited state [100]. This effect should enhance their intersystem crossing and the yield of energy transfer to molecular oxygen. These results showed that the electrostatic interaction with DNA significantly affects the $^1O_2$ generating activity of a photosensitizer. In addition, this interaction may be applied to the control and the design of photosensitizers for medical applications such as PDT.

6.4. Near-infra Red Photosensitizer

Recently, it has been reported that DNA damaging activity above 700 nm is possible in the presence of (L-lysine) (dppz) Cu^{2+} complex, where L-lysine is a potential photosensitizer in the metal bound form and N,N-donor heterocyclic bases (dppz) are DNA grove binders [101]. This experiment demonstrated the effect of the DNA damage efficiency on the excitation wavelengths within the d-d transition bands through $^1O_2$ formation, and showed significant DNA cleavage between 700 and 755 nm in the presence of that complex which satisfies the basic requirements for a sensitizer to be useful in PDT. Since the maximum transmittance of skin tissue is in the 700 ~ 800 nm region, these wavelengths are better suited for PDT applications. This result has shown that near-infra red photon as well as visible-light can be used to generate $^1O_2$ and the medical application of photosensitized reaction.

7. Conclusion

Various compounds including exogenous and endogenous materials induce DNA damage via photosensitized reaction. The important mechanisms of photosensitized DNA damage are the one-electron oxidation of nucleobase via photo-induced electron transfer (the type I mechanism) and DNA oxidation by $^1O_2$ generated through photo-energy transfer from excited photosensitizer to molecular oxygen (the type II mechanism). In addition, $O_2^{\cdot-}$ generated via photosensitized reduction of molecular oxygen rarely contributes to DNA damage. These mechanisms are strongly dependent on the driving force, i.e. the excitation energy of the photosensitizers. The type I mechanism requires relatively strong oxidation

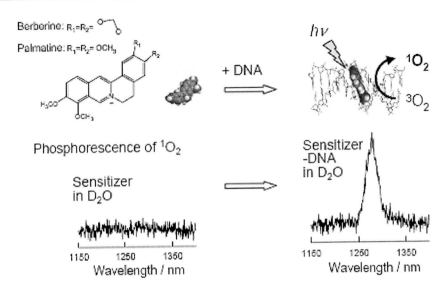

Figure 9. The off-on switching phenomenon in which binding of the photosensitizers to DNA facilitates the photosensitized $^1O_2$ generation.

activity of the excited photosensitizer; UVA sensitizer is favored to this mechanism. The $O_2^{\cdot -}$ generation also rarely occurs in the UVA photoreaction. This reaction requires relative strong reductive power and a few strong reductive photosensitizer induces DNA damage via this mechanism. Since carcinogenisity of UVA is demonstrated and visible-light is notcarcinogenisity, UVA photosensitizer should contribute to solar carcinogenesis. The photo-induced electron transfer is considered to play an important role in the solar carcinogenesis from the energetically point of view. On the other hand, $^1O_2$ can be easily generated by visible-light energy, because the excitation energy of molecular oxygen ($\sim 1eV$) is relatively small. Since the human tissue has high transparency against the red color visible-light and visible-light is not harmful for human, this $^1O_2$-mediated mechanism is important in the medical application of the photosensitized DNA damage, such as PDT. The control of the activity of the photosensitizers is important theme of this medical application. In addition, visible-light photosensitizer rarely induces DNA damage via the type I mechanism. Since the oxygen concentration in cancerous cell is low, the oxygen-independent type I mechanism should be advantageous for PDT. This result suggests that the novel photosensitizer can be designed by the control of the excitation energy and the redox potential.

References

[1]   Dolmans, D. E.; Fukumura, D. and Jain, R. K. (2003). Photodynamic therapy for cancer. *Nat. Rev. Cancer, 3,* 380-387.

[2]   Ackroyd, R.; Kelty, C.; Brown, N. and Reed, M. (2001). The history of photodetection and photodynamic therapy. *Photochem. Photobiol., 74,* 656-669.

[3]   Moan, J. and Peng, Q. (2003). An outline of the hundred-year history of PDT. *Anticancer Res., 23,* 3591-3600.

[4]   Applegate, L. A.; Scaletta, C.; Panizzon, R.; Niggli, H. and Frenk, E. (1999). In vivo induction of pyrimidine dimers in human skin by UVA radiation: initiation of cell damage and/or intercellular communication?. *Int. J. Mol. Med., 3*, 467-472.

[5]   Douki, T.; Reynaud-Angelin, A.; Cadet, J. and Sage, E. (2003). Bipyrimidine photoproducts rather than oxidative lesions are the main type of DNA damage involved in the genotoxic effect of solar UVA radiation. *Biochemistry, 42*, 9221-9226.

[6]   Rochette, P. J.; Therrien, J. P.; Drouin, R.; Perdiz, D.; Bastien, N.; Drobetsky, E. A. and Sage, E. (2003). UVA-induced cyclobutane pyrimidine dimmers form predominantly at thymine-thymine dipyrimidines and correlate with the mutation spectrum in rodent cells. *Nucleic Acids Res., 31*, 2786-2794.

[7]   Cadet, J.; Sage, E. and Douki, T. (2005). Ultraviolet radiation-mediated damage to cellular DNA. *Mutat. Res., 571*, 3-17.

[8]   Kawanishi, S.; Hiraku, Y. and Oikawa, S. (2001). Sequence-specific DNA damage induced by UVA radiation in the presence of endogenous and exogenous photosensitizers. *Curr. Probl. Dermatol. 29*, 74-82.

[9]   Hiraku, Y.; Ito, K.; Hirakawa, K. and Kawanishi, S. (2007). Photosensitized DNA damage and its protection via a novel mechanism. *Photochem. Photobiol., 83*, 205-212.

[10] IARC Working Group (1992). IARC Monographs on the Evaluation of the Carcinogenic Risk of Chemicals to Humans, Vol. 55, IARC, Lyon.

[11] Drobetsky, E. A.; Turcotte, J. and Chateauneuf, A. (1995). A role for ultraviolet A in solar mutagenesis. *Proc. Natl. Acad. Sci. USA, 92*, 2350-2354.

[12] Besaratinia, A.; Synold, T. W.; Chen, H. H.; Chang, C.; Xi, B.; Riggs, A. D. and Pfeifer, G. P. (2005). DNA lesions induced by UV A1 and B radiation in human cells: comparative analyses in the overall genome and in the p53 tumor suppressor gene. *Proc. Natl. Acad. Sci. USA, 102*, 10058-10063.

[13] Marcus, R. A. and Sutin, N. (1985). Electron transfers in chemistry and biology. *Biochim. Biophys. Acta, 811*, 265–322.

[14] Weller, A. (1982). Photoinduced electron transfer in solution. *Z. Phys. Chem. Noue Folge, 133*, 93-98.

[15] Lewis, F. D. and Wu, Y. (2001). Dynamics of superexchange photoinduced electron transfer in duplex DNA. *J. Photochem. Photobiol. C: Photochemistry Rev., 2*, 1-16.

[16] Hirakawa, K.; Yoshida, M.; Oikawa, S. and Kawanishi, S. (2003). Base oxidation at 5' site of GG sequence in double-stranded DNA induced by UVA in the presence of xanthone analogues: relationship between the DNA-damaging abilities of photosensitizers and their HOMO energies. *Photochem. Photobiol., 77*, 349-355.

[17] Hirakawa, K.; Suzuki, H.; Oikawa, S. and Kawanishi, S. (2003). Sequence-specific DNA damage induced ultraviolet A-irradiated folic acid via its photolysis product. *Arch. Biochem. Biophys., 410*, 261-268.

[18] Hirakawa, K.; Aoshima, M.; Hiraku, Y. and Kawanishi, S. (2002). Photohydrolysis of methotrexate produces pteridine, which induces poly-G-specific DNA damage through photoinduced electron transfer. *Photochem. Photobiol., 76*, 467-472.

[19] Hirakawa, K.; Mori, M.; Yoshida, M.; Oikawa, S. and Kawanishi, S. (2004). Photo-irradiate titanium dioxide catalyzes site specific DNA damage via generation of hydrogen peroxide. *Free Radic. Res., 38*, 439-447.

[20] Ito, K.; Inoue, S.; Yamamoto, K. and Kawanishi, S. (1993). 8-Hydroxydeoxyguanosine formation at the 5' site of 5'-GG-3' sequences in double-stranded DNA by UV radiation with riboflavin. *J. Biol. Chem., 268,* 13221-13227.

[21] Hirakawa, K.; Kawanishi, S.; Matsumoto, J.; Shiragami, T. and Yasuda, M. (2006). Guanine-specific DNA damage photosensitized by the dihydroxo (tetraphe-nylporphyrinato) antimony (V) complex. *J. Photochem. Photobiol. B: Biol., 82,* 37-44.

[22] Hirakawa, K.; Kawanishi, S.; Hirano, T. and Segawa, H. (2007). Guanine-specific DNA oxidation photosensitized by the tetraphenylporphyrin phosphorus(V) complex via singlet oxygen generation and electron transfer. *J. Photochem. Photobiol. B: Biol., 87,* 209-217.

[23] Burrows, C. J. and Muller, J. G. (1998). Oxidative nucleobase modifications leading to strand scission. *Chem. Rev., 98,* 1109-1151.

[24] Tuite, E. M. and Kelly, J. M. (1993). New trends in photobiology: Photochemical interactions of methylene blue and analogues with DNA and other biological substrates. *J. Photochem. Photobiol. B: Biol., 21,* 103-124.

[25] Bixon, M.; Giese, B.; Wessely, S.; Langenbacher, T.; Michel-Beyerle, M. E. and Jortner, J. (1999). Long-range charge hopping in DNA. *Proc. Natl. Acad. Sci. USA, 96,* 11713–11716.

[26] Giese, B. (2000). Long distance charge transport in DNA: the hopping mechanism, *Acc. Chem. Res., 33,* 631–636.

[27] Meggers, E.; Michel-Beyerle, M. E. and Giese, B. (1998). Sequence dependent long range hole transport in DNA. *J. Am. Chem. Soc., 120,* 12950–12955.

[28] Jortner, J.; Bixon, M.; Langenbacher, T. and Michel-Beyerle, M. E. (1998). Charge transfer and transport in DNA. *Proc. Natl. Acad. Sci. USA, 95,* 12759–12765.

[29] Schuster, G. B. (2000). Long-range charge transfer in DNA: transient structural distortions control the distance dependence. *Acc. Chem. Res., 33,* 253–260.

[30] Henderson, P. T.; Jones, D.; Hampikian, G.; Kan, Y. Z. and Schuster, G. B. (1999). Long-distance charge transport in duplex DNA: the phonon-assisted polaron-like hopping mechanism. *Proc. Natl. Acad. Sci. USA, 96,* 8353–8358.

[31] Barnett, R. N.; Cleveland, C. L.; Joy, A.; Landman, U. and Schuster, G. B. (2001). Charge migration in DNA: ion-gated transport. *Science, 294,* 567–571.

[32] Nunez, M. E.; Noyes, K. T.; Gianolio, D. A.; McLaughlin, L. W. and Barton, J. K. (2000). Long-range guanine oxidation in DNA restriction fragments by a triplex-directed naphthalene diimide intercalator. *Biochemistry, 39,* 6190–6199.

[33] Nakatani, K.; Dohno, C. and Saito, I. (1999). Chemistry of sequence-dependent remote guanine oxidation: photoreaction of duplex DNA containing cyanobenzophenone-substituted uridine. *J. Am. Chem. Soc., 121,* 10854–10855.

[34] Kawai, K.; Takada, T.; Tojo, S.; Ichinose, N. and Majima, T. (2001). Observation of hole transfer through DNA by monitoring the transient absorption of pyrene radical cation. *J. Am. Chem. Soc., 123,* 12688–12689.

[35] Lewis, F. D.; Liu, J.; Zuo, X.; Hayes, R. T. and Wasielewski, M. R. (2003). Dynamics and energetics of single-step hole transport in DNA hairpins. *J. Am. Chem. Soc., 125,* 4850–4861.

[36] Lewis, F. D.; Liu, J.; Weigel, W.; Rettig, W.; Kurnikov, I. V. and Beratan, D. N. (2002). Donor-bridge-acceptor energetics determine the distance dependence of electron tunneling in DNA. *Proc. Natl. Acad. Sci. USA, 99*, 12536–12541.

[37] Lewis, F. D.; Letsinger, R. L. and Wasielewski, M. R. (2001). Dynamics of photoinduced charge transfer and hole transport in synthetic DNA hairpins. *Acc. Chem. Res., 34*, 159–170.

[38] Lewis, F. D.; Liu, X. Y.; Liu, J. Q.; Miller, S. E.; Hayes, R. T. and Wasielewski, M. R. (2000). Direct measurement of hole transport dynamics in DNA. *Nature, 406*, 51–53.

[39] Giese, B.; Amaudrut, J.; Kohler, A. K.; Spormann, M. and Wessely, S. (2001) Direct observation of hole transfer through DNA by hopping between adenine bases and by tunneling. *Nature, 412*, 318–320.

[40] Giese, B. and Biland, A. (2002). Recent developments of charge injection and charge transfer in DNA. *Chem. Commun.*, 667–672.

[41] Kendrick, T. and Giese, B. (2002). Charge transfer through DNA triggered by site selective charge injection into adenine. *Chem. Commun.*, 2016–2017.

[42] Kawai, K.; Takada, T.; Tojo, S. and Majima, T. (2003). Kinetics of weak distance-dependent hole transfer in DNA by adenine-hopping mechanism. *J. Am. Chem. Soc., 125*, 6842–6843.

[43] Takada, T.; Kawai, K.; Fujitsuka, M. and Majima, T. (2004) Direct observation of hole transfer through double-helical DNA over 100 Å. *Proc. Natl. Acad. Sci. USA, 101*, 14002–14006.

[44] Hickerson, R. P.; Prat, F.; Muller, J. G.; Foote, C. S. and Burrows, C. J. (1999). Sequence and stacking dependence of 8-oxoguanine oxidation: comparison of one-electron vs singlet oxygen mechanisms. *J. Am. Chem. Soc., 121*, 9423-9428.

[45] Sugiyama, H. and Saito, I. (1996). Theoretical studies of GG-specific photocleavage of DNA via electron transfer: significant lowering of ionization potential and 5'-localization of HOMO of stacked GG bases in B-form DNA. *J. Am. Chem. Soc. 118*, 7063-7068.

[46] Yoshioka, Y.; Kitagawa, Y.; Takano, Y.; Yamaguchi, K.; Nakamura, T. and Saito, I. (1999). Experimental and theoretical studies on the selectivity of GGG triplets toward one-electron oxidation in B-form DNA. *J. Am. Chem. Soc., 121*, 8712-8719.

[47] Ravanat, J. L.; Douki, T. and Cadet, J. (2001). Direct and indirect effects of UV radiation on DNA and its components. *J. Photochem. Photobiol. B: Biol., 63*, 88-102.

[48] Steenken, S. (1989). Purine bases, nucleoside, and nucleotides: aqueous solution redox chemistry and transformation reactions of their radical cation and e⁻ and OH adducts. *Chem. Rev., 89*, 503-520.

[49] Pouget, J. P.; Douki, T.; Richard, M. J. and Cadet, J. (2000). DNA damage induced in cells by gamma and UVA radiation as measured by HPLC/GC/-MS and HPLC-EC and Comet assay. *Chem. Res. Toxicol., 13*, 541-549.

[50] Douki, T. and Cadet, J. (1999). Modification of DNA bases by photosensitized one-electron oxidation. *Int. J. Radiat. Biol., 75*, 571-581.

[51] Kasai, H.; Yamaizumi, Z.; Berger, M. and Cadet, J. (1992). Photosensitized formation of 7,8-dihydro-8-oxo-2'-deoxyguanosine (8-hydroxy-2'-deoxyguanosine) in DNA by riboflavin: a nonsinglet oxygen-mediated reaction. *J. Am. Chem. Soc., 114*, 9692-9694.

[52] Cullis, P. M.; Malone, M. E. and Merson-Davies, L. A. (1996). Guanine radical cations are precursors of 7,8-dihydro-8-oxo-2'-deoxyguanosine but are not precursors of immediate strand breaks in DNA. *J. Am. Chem. Soc., 118,* 2775-2788.

[53] Shibutani, S.; Takeshita, M. and Grollman, A. P. (1991). Insertion of specific bases during DNA synthesis past the oxidation-damaged base 8-oxodG. *Nature, 349,* 431-434.

[54] Bruner, S. D.; Norman, D. P. G. and Grollman, A. P. (2000). Structural basis for recognition and repair of the endogenous mutagen 8-oxoguanine in DNA. *Nature, 403,* 589-866.

[55] Kino, K.; Saito, I. and Sugiyama H. (1998). Product analysis of GG-specific photooxidation of DNA via electron transfer: 2-aminoimidazolone as a major guanine oxidation product. *J. Am. Chem. Soc., 120,* 7373-7374.

[56] Kino, K. and Sugiyama, H. (2001) Possible cause of GC→CG transversion mutation by guanine oxidation product, imidazolone. *Chem. Biol., 8,* 369-378.

[57] Cadet, J.; Berger, M.; Buchko, G. W.; Joshi, P. C.; Raoul, S. and Ravabnat, J. L. (1994). 2,2-diamino-4-[(3,5-di-*o*-acetyl-2-deoxy-β-D-erythro-pentofuranosyl)amino]-5-(2H)-oxazolone: a novel and predominant radical oxidation product 3',5'-di-*o*-acetyl-2'-deoxyguanosine. *J. Am. Chem. Soc., 116,* 7403-7404.

[58] Gasparutto, D.; Ravanat, J. L.; Gerot, O. and Cadet, J. (1998). Characterization and chemical stability of photooxidized oligonucleotides that contain 2,2'-diamino-4-[(2-deoxy-D-erythro-pentofuranosyl)amino]-5(2H)-oxazolone. *J. Am. Chem. Soc., 118,* 10283-10286.

[59] McBride, T. J.; Schneider, J. E., Floyd, R. A. and Loeb, L. A. (1992). Mutation induced by methylene blue plus light in single-stranded M13mp2. *Proc. Natl. Acad. Sci. USA, 89,* 6866-6870.

[60] Negishi, K. and Hao, W. (1992). Spectrum of mutations in single-stranded DNA phage M13mp2 exposed to sunlight: predominance of G-to-C transversion. *Carcinogenesis, 13,* 1615-1618.

[61] DeRosa, M. C. and Crutchley, R. J. (2002). Photosensitized singlet oxygen and its applications. *Coord. Chem. Rev., 233-234,* 351-371.

[62] Dexter, D. L. (1953). A theory of sensitized luminescence in solids. *J. Chem. Phys., 21,* 836-850.

[63] Baier, J.; Fuβ, T.; Pöllmann, C.; Wiesmann, C.; Pindl, K.; Engl, R.; Baumer, D.; Maier, M.; Landthaler, M. and Bäumler, W. (2007). Theoretical and experimental analysis of the luminescence signal of singlet oxygen for different photosensitizers. *J. Photochem. Photobiol. B: Biol., 87,* 163-173.

[64] Niedre, M.; Patterson, M. S. and Wilson, B. C. (2002). Direct near-infrared luminescence detection of singlet oxygen generated by photodynamic therapy in cells in vitro and tissues in vivo. *Photochem. Photobiol., 75,* 382-391.

[65] Shu, C.; Kang, P.; Khan, S. and Foote, C. S. (2002). Low-temperature photosensitized oxidation of a guanosine derivative and formation of an imidazole ring-opened product. *J. Am. Chem. Soc., 124,* 3905-3913.

[66] Kang, P. and Foote, C. S. (2002). Formation of transient intermediates in low-temperature photosensitized oxidation of an 8-(13)C-guanosine derivatives. *J. Am. Chem. Soc., 124*, 4865-4873.

[67] Celander, D. W. and Cech, T. R. (1990). Iron(II)-ethylenediaminetetraacetic acid catalyzed cleavage of RNA and DNA oligonucleotides: similar reactivity toward single- and double-stranded forms. *Biochemistry, 29*, 1355-1361.

[68] Yamamoto, K. and Kawanishi, S. (1989). Hydroxyl free radical is not the main active species in site-specific DNA damage induced by copper (II) ion and hydrogen peroxide. *J. Biol. Chem., 264*, 15435-15440.

[69] Kikuchi, K.; Sato, C.; Watabe, M.; Ikeda, H.; Takahashi, Y. and Miyashi, Y. (1993). New aspects on fluorescence quenching by molecular oxygen. *J. Am. Chem. Soc., 115*, 5180-5184.

[70] Sato, C.; Kikuchi, K.; Okamura, K.; Takahashi, Y. and Miyashi, T. (1995). New aspects on fluorescence quenching by molecular oxygen. 2. inhibition of long-distance electron transfer in acetonitrile. *J. Phys. Chem., 99*, 16925-16931.

[71] Agar, N. S.; Halliday, G. M.; Barnetson, R. S.; Ananthaswamy, H. N.; Wheeler, M. and Jones, A. M. (2004). The basal layer in human squamous tumors harbors more UVA than UVB fingerprint mutations: a role for UVA in human skin carcinogenesis. *Proc. Natl. Acad. Sci. USA, 101*, 4954-4959.

[72] Ananthaswamy, H. N. and Pierceall, W. E. (1990). Molecular mechanisms of ultraviolet radiation carcinogenesis. *Photochem. Photobiol., 52*, 1119-1136.

[73] Henderson, P. T.; Delaney, J. C.; Gu, F.; Tannenbaum, S. R. and Essigmann, J. M. (2002). Oxidation of 7,8-dihydro-8-oxoguanine affords lesions that are potent sources of replication errors in vivo. *Biochemistry, 41*, 914-921.

[74] Neeley, W. L.; Delaney, J. C.; Henderson, P. T. and Essigmann, J. M. (2004). In vivo bypass efficiencies and mutational signatures of the guanine oxidation products 2-aminoimidazolone and 5-guanidino-4-nitroimidazole. *J. Biol. Chem., 279*, 43568-43573.

[75] Robert, C.; Muel, B.; Benoit, A.; Dubertret, L.; Sarasin, A. and Stary, A. (1996). Cell survival and shuttle vector mutagenesis induced by ultraviolet A and ultraviolet B radiation in a human cell line. *J. Invest. Dermatol., 106*, 721-728.

[76] Young, K. J. and Lee, P. N. (1999). Intervention studies on cancer. *Eur. J. Cancer Prev., 8*, 91-103.

[77] Giacosa, A.; Filiberti, R.; Hill, M. J. and Faivre, J. (1997). Vitamins and cancer chemoprevention. *Eur. J. Cancer Prev., 6 Suppl 1*, S47-54.

[78] Cohn, B. A. (2002). Sunlight, skin color, and folic acid. *J. Am. Acad. Dermatol., 46*, 317-318.

[79] Ito, K. and Kawanishi, S. (1997). Photoinduced hydroxylation of deoxyguanosine in DNA by pterins: sequence specificity and mechanism. *Biochemistry, 36*, 1774-1781.

[80] Fujishima, A.; Rao, T. N. and Tryk, D. A. (2000). Titanium dioxide photocatalyst. *J. Photochem. Photobiol. C: Photochemistry Rev., 1*, 1-21.

[81] Cai, R.; Hashimoto, K.; Ito, K.; Kubota, Y. and Fujishima, A. (1991). Photokilling of malignant cells with ultrafine TiO$_2$ powder. *Bull. Chem. Soc. Jpn., 64*, 1268-1273.

[82] Cai, R.; Kubota, Y.; Shuin, T.; Sakai, H.; Hashimoto, K. and Fujishima, A. (1992). Induction of cytotoxicity by photoexcited TiO$_2$ particles. *Cancer Res.*, *52*, 2346-2348.

[83] Nosaka, Y.; Daimon, T.; Nosaka, A. Y. and Murakami, Y. (2004). Singlet oxygen formation in photocatalytic TiO$_2$ aqueous suspension. *Phys. Chem. Chem. Phys.*, *6*, 2917-2918.

[84] Hirakawa, K. and Hirano, T. (2006). Singlet oxygen generation photocatalyzed by TiO$_2$ particles and its contribution to biomolecule damage. *Chem. Lett.*, *35*, 832-833.

[85] Ji, Z.; Yang, G.; Vasovic, V.; Cunderlikova, B.; Suo, Z.; Nesland, J. M. and Peng, Q. (2006). Subcellular localization pattern of protoporphyrin IX is an important determinant for its photodynamic efficiency of human carcinoma and normal cell lines. *J. Photochem. Photobiol. B: Biol.*, *84*, 213-224.

[86] Ravanat, J. L.; Sauvaigo, S.; Caillat, S.; Martinez, G. R.; Medeiros, M. H.; Di Mascio, P.; Favier, A. and Cadet, J. (2004). Singlet oxygen-mediated damage to cellular DNA determined by the comet assay associated with DNA repair enzymes. *Biol. Chem.*, *385*, 17-20.

[87] Cadet, J.; Ravanat, J. L.; Martinez, G. R.; Medeiros, M. H. and Di Mascio, P. (2006). Singlet oxygen oxidation of isolated and cellular DNA: product formation and mechanistic insights. *Photochem. Photobiol.*, *82*, 219-225.

[88] Kawai, K.; Osakada, Y.; Fujitsuka, M. and Majima, T. (2006). Effects of reaction rate of radical anion of a photosensitizer with molecular oxygen on the photosensitized DNA damage. *Chem. Commun.*, 3918-3920.

[89] Kawai, K.; Osakada, Y.; Fujitsuka, M. and Majima, T. (2007). Hole transfer in DNA and photosensitized DNA damage: importance of adenine oxidation. *J. Phys. Chem. B*, *111*, 2322-2326.

[90] Lang, K.; Mosinger, J. and Wagnerová, D. M. (2004). Photophysical properties of porphyrinoid sensitizers non-covalently bound to host molecules; models for photodynamic therapy. *Coord. Chem. Rev.*, *248*, 321-350.

[91] Besaratinia, A.; Bates, S. E.; Synold, T. W. and Pfeifer, G. P. (2004). Similar mutagenicity of photoactivated porphyrins and ultraviolet A radiation in mouse embryonic fibroblasts: involvement of oxidative DNA lesions in mutagenesis. *Biochemistry*, *43*, 15557-15566.

[92] Woods, J. A.; Traynor, N. J.; Brancaleon, L. and Moseley, H. (2004). The effect of photofrin on DNA strand breaks and base oxidation in HaCaT keratinocytes: a comet assay study. *Photochem. Photobiol.*, *79*, 105-113.

[93] Kawanishi, S.; Inoue, S.; Sano, S. and Aiba, H. (1986). Photodynamic guanine modification by hematoporphyrin is specific for single-stranded DNA with singlet oxygen as a mediator. *J. Biol. Chem.*, *261*, 6090-6095.

[94] Inoue, H.; Okamoto, T.; Kameo, Y.; Sumitani, M.; Fujiwara, A.; Ishibashi, D. and Hida, M. (1994). Photochemical epoxidation of cyclohexene sensitized by tetraphenylporphyrinatoantimony(V) in the presence of water acting both as an electron and an oxygen donor. *J. Chem. Soc. Perkin Trans.*, *1*, 105-111.

[95] Hirakawa, K. and Segawa, H. (1999). Excitation energy transfer and photo-induced electron transfer in axial bispyrenyl phosphorus porphyrin derivatives: factors governing the competition between energy and electron transfer processes under the

existence of intramolecular π-π interaction. *J. Photochem. Photobiol. A: Chem., 123,* 67-76.

[96] Marrese, C. A. and Carrano, C. J. (1983). Synthesis, characterization, and electrochemistry of (5,10,15,20-tetraphenylporphinato)dichlorophosphorus(V) chloride. *Inorg. Chem., 22,* 1858-1862.

[97] Takeuchi, Y.; Hirakawa, K.; Susumu, K. and Segawa, H. (2004). Electrochemical determination of charge transfer direction of center-to-edge phosphorus(V) porphyrin arrays. *Electrochemistry, 7,* 449-451.

[98] Cló, E.; Snyder, J. W.; Ogilby, P. R. and Gothelf, K. V. (2007). Control and selectivity of photosensitized singlet oxygen production: challenges in complex biological systems. *ChemBioChem, 8,* 475-481.

[99] Hirakawa, K.; Kawanishi, S. and Hirano, T. (2005). The mechanism of guanine specific photo-oxidation in the presence of berberine and palmatine: activation of photosensitized singlet oxygen generation through DNA-binding interaction. *Chem. Res. Toxicol., 18,* 1545-1552.

[100] Hirakawa, K. and Hirano, T. (2008). The microenvironment of DNA switches the activity of singlet oxygen generation photosensitized by berberine and palmatine. *Photochem. Photobiol., 84,* 202-208.

[101] Fortner, A.; Wang, S.; Darbha, G. K.; Ray, A.; Yu, H.; Ray, P. C.; Kalluru, R. R.; Kim, C. K.; Rai, V. and Singh, J. P. (2007). Near infrared photo-induced DNA damage in the presence of copper-dppz complex: evidence for the involvement of singlet oxygen. *Chem. Phys. Lett., 414,* 127-132.

In: New Research on DNA Damage
Editors: Honoka Kimura and Aoi Suzuki

ISBN 978-1-60456-581-2
© 2008 Nova Science Publishers, Inc.

Chapter 10

Consecutive Adenine Sequences Serve as Potential Targets in Photosensitized Oxidative DNA Damage

Kiyohiko Kawai[*] *and Tetsuro Majima*[†]

The Institute of Scientific and Industrial Research (SANKEN), Osaka University, Japan

Abstract

Upon exposure of our skin to solar UV radiation, the photosensitized DNA damage takes place through two major pathways, i.e., formation of the mutagenic pyrimidine dimmers via excitation of the pyrimidine bases, and one-electron oxidation of nucleobases triggered by electron transfer from the nucleobase to the excited photosensitizer. This chapter shed light on the latter process. In the initial step of the photosensitized DNA damage by one-electron oxidation, a positive charge "a hole" is generated in DNA which can subsequently migrate along DNA. Though a number of kinetic and theoretical studies have been performed, the biological relevance between the charge transfer in DNA and photosensitized DNA damage are still not clear. Herein, the kinetic mechanisms of the photosensitized one-electron oxidation of DNA was assayed both by the direct spectroscopic measurements of the charge transfer in DNA and by quantification of the yield of the guanine oxidative damage. Consecutive adenine sequences were found to be a good launching site for the photosensitizers to inject a hole in DNA, where the following rapid hole transfer through adenines causes a long-lived charge-separated state leading to DNA oxidative damage. It was clearly demonstrated that the consecutive adenine sequences serve as a good target in the photosensitized DNA damage, or G adjacent to such sequences may be a potential hot spot of oxidative DNA damage. The essential requisites for the efficient and/or harmful photosensitizer are given as follows: be able to oxidize adenine, and react rapidly with molecular oxygen

[*] Mihogaoka 8-1, Ibaraki, Osaka 567-0047, Japan, Tel: (+81)6-6879-8496, Fax: (+81)6-6879-8499, E-mail: kiyohiko@sanken.osaka-u.-ac-jp.

[†] Mihogaoka 8-1, Ibaraki, Osaka 567-0047, Japan.Tel: (+81)6-6879-8495, Fax: (+81)6-6879-8499, E-mail: majima@sanken.osaka-u.-ac-jp.

following its reduction avoiding the charge recombination and making the reaction irreversible. Elucidation of the kinetic mechanisms of the photosensitized one-electron oxidation of DNA allowed us to know the effective target DNA sequences and the essential requisites for the efficient photosensitizer, which will greatly help the understanding of the harmful compound for health and the improvement of the photosensitizer for therapeutic and biochemical applications.

1. Introduction

The photosensitized oxidative DNA damage has been extensively studied because it leads to the formation of oxidative lesions that causes carcinogenesis and aging [1, 2]. It has also received attention from a therapeutic point of view since DNA is one of the potential targets of photodynamic therapy [3, 4]. To either suppress or to promote photosensitized DNA damage, it is important to understand the involved kinetic mechanisms [5-7].

Following the absorption of light, photosensitizers (Sens) are activated to be in the singlet excited state, which may convert to be in the triplet excited state. The mechanisms of the photosensitized oxidative DNA damage involve oxidation through electron transfer from DNA to the Sens in the singlet or triplet excited state (mechanism Type I), as well as oxidation mediated by singlet oxygen (mechanism Type II), which is formed through energy transfer from the Sens in the triplet excited state to the molecular oxygen (O_2) [8]. Since the lifetimes of Sens in the excited state or singlet oxygen are usually short in living cells, Sens should be located in the vicinity of DNA for the photosensitized DNA damage to occur. Therefore, the Sens targeting the DNA were commonly designed to have a high affinity to DNA. And when the Sens is bound to DNA, the Type I process will be favored because, for many of the well studied DNA-damaging Sens, the electron transfer rates from DNA to the Sens in the singlet excited state is faster compared to the rates of the intersystem crossing which leads to the formation of the Sens in the triplet excited state and subsequent singlet oxygen genration [7, 9-13]. Hence, it is important to understand the kinetic mechanisms of the photosensitized one-electron oxidation of DNA, the Type I process [5, 6].

Among the double-helical DNA structure, the electron-rich nucleobases are prime targets for one-electron oxidation. The photoirradiation of DNA-bound Sens triggers electron transfer from nucleobases to the excited Sens to produce the radical anion of the Sens (Sens$^{\bullet-}$) and radical cation of the nucleobase (hole) as the charge-separated state. Since guanine (G) exhibits the lowest oxidation potential among the four DNA bases as shown in Figure 1, the radical cation of G (G$^{\bullet+}$) is formed, of which reaction with water and O_2 leads to oxidative DNA damage. As a consequence, one-electron oxidation of DNA exclusively leads to the loss or damage of G and the formation of G oxidative products [1, 14-16]. Apparently, it seems likely that the efficiency of the photosensitized one-electron oxidation of DNA is low since the process leading to the DNA damage, such as the reaction of G$^{\bullet+}$ with water ($k_G \sim 5$ s^{-1} or slower: discussed below) [17-19], is much slower than the charge recombination which typically occurs with rate constants $> 10^9$ s^{-1} [9-13]. Here, a hole can migrate through DNA by hopping between G's,[20-31] and if the hole transfer rate is fast enough to escape from the charge recombination, it may promote photosensitized DNA damage (Figure 1). However, the rate constants of hole transfer between G's across A-T base-pairs have been determined by Lewis *et al.* to be smaller than 10^8 s^{-1}, [9-12] which is also too slow to compete with charge recombination. Though the hole transfer between consecutive G's may proceed fast, a hole will localize in the consecutive G's since a hole cannot get over the A-T bridge, which results in the fast charge recombination. However, photosensitized DNA damage actually occurs [14, 15].

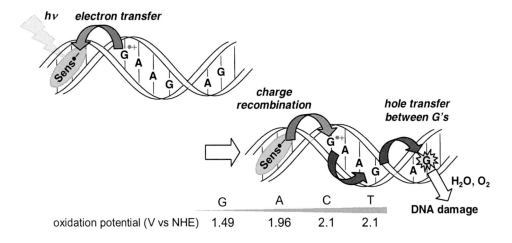

Figure 1. Oxidation potentials of nucleobases and schematic representation of charge-transfer through DNA and photo-sensitized oxidative DNA damage.

In 2001, Giese et al. revealed the role of adenine (A), the second most easily oxidized base, as the charge carriers of hole transfer in DNA [32-34]. Recently, we found that hole transfer between A's proceeds with a rate constant faster than 10^8 s^{-1} over a distance of ~30 Å [35, 36]. And more recently, the hole transfer rate between A's was measured by Lewis and co-workers to be approximately 10^9 s^{-1}.[37] These findings prompted us to suggest that this fast hole transfer between A's may help to separate the Sens$^{\bullet-}$ and a hole in the initial step of the photosensitized one-electron oxidation of DNA before a hole is trapped at G and thus promote photosensitized DNA damage by providing sufficiently long time for the irreversible reaction to take place. Consequently, consecutive A sequences may serve as potential targets in photosensitized DNA damage. To assess this hypothesis, we performed a combination of a laser flash photolysis transient absorption measurements and quantitative HPLC analyses of DNA damage using Sens modified oligodeoxynucleotides (ODNs).

2. Photosensitized Oxidation of NDI-Modified DNA

First, naphthaldiimide (NDI) was selected as a Sens since NDI in the singlet excited state (^{1}NDI*) can oxidize A to promote fast hole transfer between A's.[38] When NDI was attached at the consecutive A sequences, the excitation of the NDI produces the NDI radical anion (NDI$^{\bullet-}$) and A radical cation (A$^{\bullet+}$), followed by the fast hole hopping between A's, and then a hole is trapped at G to yield G$^{\bullet+}$ [4, 36, 38-41]. Several ODNs with different distances between the NDI and G's with intervening A-T sequences (NDn) were synthesized [41, 42] and the effect of the hole transfer on the DNA damage was investigated (Figure 2a). The excitation of NDI-modified ODN with the 355-nm laser (5 ns, 5 mJ pulse^{-1}) produced NDI$^{\bullet-}$ and one-electron oxidized ODN (ODN$^{\bullet+}$) charge-separated state through the photoinduced electron transfer, and the charge separation and recombination process were examined by monitoring the formation and decay of NDI$^{\bullet-}$ as shown in Figure 2b. In the case of NDn (n = 0-2) where G's are near the NDI, no transient absorption was observed due to the fast charge separation and charge recombination which proceeds within the laser flash duration of 5 ns. In NDn (n = 3-5) where the G's are separated from NDI by more than three base pairs, the formation of the transient absorption with a maximum peak at 495 nm was observed immediately after the flash excitation, which was assigned to NDI$^{\bullet-}$. The yield of the formed NDI$^{\bullet-}$ was similar for NDn (n = 3-5). In contrast, the lifetime of the charge-separated state (τ) significantly increased with the increasing distance between NDI and G's, i.e., the charge recombination process is strongly distance dependent. These results are consistent with the charge separation by the hopping between the A's and charge recombination by the super-exchange mechanism between NDI$^{\bullet-}$ and G$^{\bullet+}$ as previously reported.[32-35, 43, 44] The charge-separation yield (Φ) is small at about 2% [41] owing to the fast charge recombination from the contact radical ion pair.[45] Therefore, charge-separated state is generated by occasional escape from the charge recombination by the hole shift process. However, once a hole escapes from the Coulombic interaction, it efficiently migrates through DNA by hole hopping between A's. [41]

Insertion of a single G in the An sequence between NDI and G's significantly diminished the transient absorption of NDI$^{\bullet-}$ (NDG) since the inserted G serves as a hole trap on the hole shift process causing inhibition of consecutive A-hopping in which a hole migrates to G's.[7, 46]. To investigate the effect of the hole transfer on the DNA damage during the photosensitized one-electron oxidation of DNA, NDn was photoirradiated and the consumption of G was quantified by HPLC (Figure 2a). Interestingly, the consumption of G increased with the increasing distance between NDI and G's. In the case of NDG, where most of the generated holes recombine within the laser duration because of the inserted G in the An sequence, the consumption of G was small even though the remaining G's locate far from NDI.[47] Thus, not the distance between the NDI and G's, but the τ determines the efficiency of the DNA damage. In other words, the yield of the DNA damage increases with the increase in the τ.

The combination of the transient absorption measurement and DNA damage quantification provide the data for the effects of the hole transfer on the DNA damage during the photosensitized one-electron oxidation of DNA. For the Sens, which can only oxidize G, the close distance between the photosensitizer and G is crucial for the efficient DNA damage.[23, 30] In contrast, in the case of Sens, which can also oxidize A to promote the fast hole transfer between A's, the shorter distance between the Sens and G is not necessary for the efficient DNA damage. This is also true in the case of Schuster's work where anthraquinone was used as the Sens which can also oxidize A.[26, 48] These results strongly suggest that the fast hole transfer between A's plays an important role in separating Sens$^{\bullet-}$ and G$^{\bullet+}$ during the photosensitized one-electron oxidation of DNA, providing a sufficiently long time for G$^{\bullet+}$ and Sens$^{\bullet-}$ to react with water or O$_2$, avoiding the charge recombination and making the reaction irreversible.

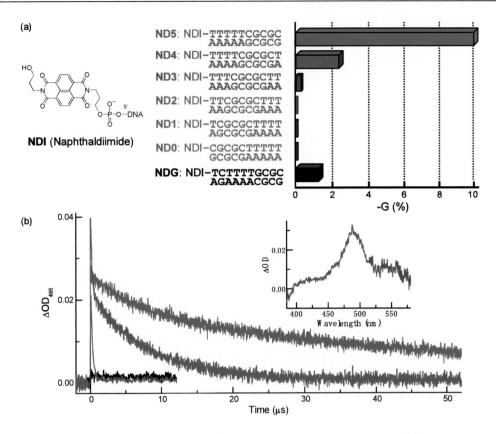

Figure 2. (a) Chemical structure of 5'-end labeled NDI, sequences of NDI-modified DNA, and consumption of G upon photo-irradiation of NDI-modified ODNs. (b) Time profiles of the transient absorption of NDI$^{\bullet-}$ monitored at 495 nm during the 355-nm laser flash photolysis of Ar-saturated aqueous solution of NDI-modified ODNs: ND3 (red), ND4 (green), ND5 (blue), and NDG (black). The inset shows the transient absorption spectrum of NDI$^{\bullet-}$ obtained at 100 ns after 355 nm flash excitation of ND3.

3. Photosensitized Oxidation of NI-Modified DNA

To further elucidate the key kinetic processes which determine the efficiency of the photosensitized DNA damage by the Type I process, ODNs modified with naphthalimide (NI) and 2'-deoxybromocytidine (^{br}C) were synthesized (Figure. 3).[49] Similar to NDI, NI in the singlet excited state (^{1}NI*) can oxidize A to promote hole transfer between A's to produce a long-lived charge-separated state, and charge-separation and charge-recombination processes were examined by monitoring the formation and decay of NI$^{\bullet-}$ with a peak maximum at 400 nm. The Φ decreased with the increasing distance between NI and G, but are weakly dependent upon the distance because the charge separation proceeds by a hopping mechanism. On the other hand, the charge-recombination rates are strongly distance dependent since once G$^{\bullet+}$ is generated far from NI$^{\bullet-}$, the charge recombination proceeds by a strongly distance dependent super-exchange mechanism. Hence τ significantly increases with the increasing number of A's between NI and G's. Before the completion of the charge recombination, the hole can migrate to the more distal G's, where the difference in the oxidation potential of G causes the shift in the hole equilibrium between the G's leading to the change in τ. Previously, we demonstrated that bromine substitution of the cytosine C5 hydrogen in the C:G base-pair causes a 24 mV increase in the oxidation potential of G which resulted in a change in τ during the photosensitized one-electron oxidation of DNA.[40, 50] Here, in order to investigate the τ dependence of the photosensitized DNA damage in more detail, ^{br}C was incorporated into the ODNs to construct ODNs which show various τ values. As shown in Figure 4a, the τ systematically varied depending on the number of A bases between NI and G, and the incorporation sites of ^{br}C. To investigate the effect of τ on the DNA damage during the photosensitized one-electron oxidation of DNA, these ODNs were photoirradiated and the consumption of G was quantified by HPLC (Figure 4b). When the τ was shorter than 1 μs, the yield of the DNA damage increased with the τ, showing again that hole transfer do promote photosensitized DNA damage by producing a long-lived charge-separated state. Interestingly, for the ODNs with longer τ, DNA damage did not simply increase with the increasing τ but rather depended both on τ and Φ which was in strong contrast to the NDI-modified ODNs.

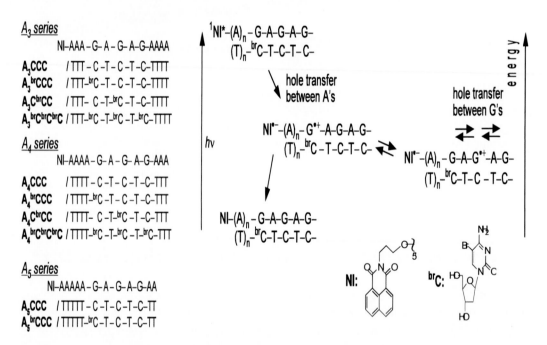

Figure 3. Sequences of NI- and ^{br}C-modified ODNs, and kinetic scheme for photo-induced one-electron oxidation of A and subsequent hole transfer through DNA.

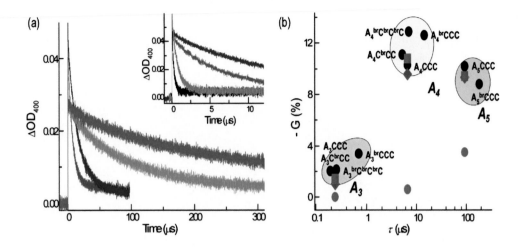

Figure 4. (a) Lifetime of the charge-separated state monitored by the transient absorption of NI$^{\bullet-}$ at 400 nm during the 355-nm laser flash photolysis of Ar-saturated aqueous solution of NI- and ^{br}C-modified ODNs: A$_3$CCC (black), A$_3$^{br}CCC (cyan), A$_4$CCC (red), A$_4$^{br}CCC (blue), A$_5$CCC (orange), and A$_5$^{br}CCC (green). (b) Correlation between the lifetimes of the charge-separated state (τ) and the yields of photosensitized DNA damage (–G %/min).

4. The Role of O$_2$

Before the charge recombination takes place, DNA damage can occur through two pathways, i.e., the reaction of G$^{\bullet+}$ with water and the reaction of the Sens$^{\bullet-}$ with O$_2$ (Figure 5). As for the reaction of G$^{\bullet+}$ with water, pioneering work has been done by Giese et al. in which the k_G value was calculated to be ~ 6×10^4 s^{-1} based on the assumption that the hole transfer between G's in the GTTG sequence proceeds with the rate constant of 2.5×10^6 s^{-1}.[43] After their report, this hole transfer rate was experimentally demonstrated to be slower than 1.7×10^5 s^{-1} by Lewis et al. [9], and measured as 3.6×10^4 s^{-1} by our group.[39]. Hence, the k_G value should be much smaller than the value estimated by Giese et al. In line with this, the lifetime of G$^{\bullet+}$ or the deprotonated G$^{\bullet+}$ (G$^{\bullet}$) was experimentally measured by Hildenbrand et al. to be as long as ~5 s^{-1} in calfthymus DNA,[19] and measured by Shafirovich et al. to be 0.2 s or longer in duplex DNA.[17, 18] Therefore, the reaction of G$^{\bullet+}$ with water occurs on a much slower time scale than the τ measured in this study ($\tau < 200$ μs). In contrast, though the importance of the reaction of Sens$^{\bullet-}$ with O$_2$ was pointed out by Schuster [48, 51] and has been often discussed in the literature,[14, 15, 21] there have been only few reports addressing the reaction rate of Sens$^{\bullet-}$ in the vicinity of DNA. To measure the bimolecular reaction rate of NI$^{\bullet-}$ and NDI$^{\bullet-}$ with O$_2$, transient absorptions were measured under air (Figure 6, red) and compared with those measured under Ar (Figure 6, black).[52] The decay rate of NI$^{\bullet-}$ was accelerated by the presence of O$_2$, showing that NI$^{\bullet-}$ reacts with O$_2$ rapidly with a rate constant of $k_{O2} = 1.2 \times 10^9$ M^{-1} s^{-1}, which is close to the diffusion controlled rate in H$_2$O (Figure 6a). In contrast, the presence of O$_2$ only slightly affected the decay of NDI$^{\bullet-}$ (Figure 6b); that is, NDI$^{\bullet-}$ reacts with oxygen only slowly ($k_{O2} = 4.2 \times 10^7$

$M^{-1}\ s^{-1}$). The difference in the reaction rates was explained by the difference in the redox potentials between NI (-1.0 V vs NHE) and NDI (-0.22 V vs NHE),[53] where the former is more negative and the latter is more positive than the reduction potential of O_2 (-0.32 V vs NHE). As a consequence, the quantum yield of photosensitized DNA damage (Φ_{-G}) was much higher for NI-modified DNA than that for NDI-modified DNA as shown in Figure 6.

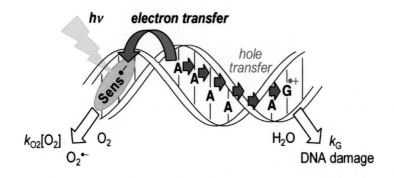

Figure 5. Schematic representation of the formation of the charge-separated state via hole transfer between A's and photosensitized DNA damage.

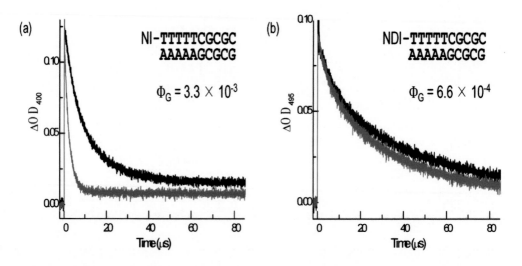

Figure 6. Time profiles of the transient absorption of $NI^{\bullet-}$ monitored at 400 nm (a), $NDI^{\bullet-}$ monitored at 495 nm (b) during the 355-nm laser flash photolysis of Ar-saturated aqueous solution (black) and aerobic condition (red).

Thus, in the case of NI, not the reaction of $G^{\bullet+}$ with water, but the reaction between $NI^{\bullet-}$ and O_2 was suggested to be the major process that produces DNA damage, and this proves to be the very reason that, when bound to DNA, NI is much better photosensitizer than NDI in which the radical anion reacts with O_2 only very slowly. According to the bimolecular reaction rate constant of $NI^{\bullet-}$ and O_2, the reaction of $NI^{\bullet-}$ and O_2 occurs at 2.9 μs under aerated conditions ([O_2] = 290 μM [54]). Therefore, for the ODNs having τ longer than 2.9

μs, the DNA damage yield depends on Φ which decreases with the number of A's (Figure 4a). Taking into account that k_G is much slower than $k_{O2}[O_2]$, DNA damage yield can be depicted by Eq. (1).

$$[\text{DNA damage}] = (\text{const.}) \times \Phi \times k_{O2}[O_2]/(k_{O2}[O_2] + 1/\tau) \qquad (1)$$

According to Eq. (1), theoretical plots for the DNA damage for A_3CCC, A_4CCC, and A_5CCC were obtained, and good agreement between the experimental and theoretical plots was found where DNA damage yield was highest for A_4 sequences (Figure 4b, green square). Under Ar-bubbling conditions, consumption of G was lower than 1%/min for A_4CCC and was 2%/min for A_5CCC, respectively, which is consistent with the much smaller value of k_G compared to $k_{O2}[O_2]$ in aerated conditions, and to $1/\tau$ measured in this study. Therefore, it can be concluded that when NI was used as the Sens, the reaction between $\text{Sens}^{\bullet-}$ and O_2 is the dominant pathway for irreversible DNA damage to take place. Escaping from the charge recombination, $G^{\bullet+}$ can react with water or $O_2^{\bullet-}$ which eventually leads to DNA damage [17]. Thus in general, a good photosensitizer for DNA damage should have a reduction potential more negative than O_2, and this is the case for NI, but not for NDI where much longer τ or lager number of consecutive A bases (A_5 or longer) is needed for the irreversible DNA damage reactions to take place [38]. However, it is important to keep in mind that $[O_2]$ is lower in the living cell,[55] especially in the nuclei. The theoretical plots showing the DNA damage efficiency obtained for the cell ($[O_2]$ = 200 μM: red diamond),[55] and that for nuclei (assuming $[O_2]$ = 5 μM: cyan circle) are also shown in Figure 4b. These plots give a good approximation of the essential number of A's in the target sequences in the cell (A_4) and that in the nuclei (A_5 or longer).

4. Sequence Specificity of Photosensitized DNA Damage

To actually show that the consecutive A sequences serve as potential targets in photosensitized DNA damage, the consumption of G during the photosensitized DNA oxidation for ODN-A7 having seven consecutive A's, was compared with that for ODN-A3, and ODN-A21 and ODN-A22, with three and two consecutive As, respectively, and ODN-A1 without consecutive A's (Figure 7).[56] Since Sens are usually not covalently bound to DNA in the living cell, the effect of A oxidation and subsequent fast hole transfer between A's on the photosensitized DNA damage was investigated for Sen non-covalently bound or unbound to DNA. NI and NDI derivatives (NIN, NDIN) having cationic side chains and electrostatically binding to DNA due to favorable electrostatic interactions between the negatively charged phosphate groups of DNA and cationic groups, and NIP and NDIP which possess phosphate groups and do not bind to DNA were synthesized and used as a Sens. Photosensitized DNA damage by NI and NDI can be induced by oxidation through electron transfer from DNA to $^1\text{Sens}^*$ or to $^3\text{Sens}^*$. In the case of NIN and NDIN, the one-electron oxidation of DNA mainly proceeds through the DNA-bound Sens in the singlet excited state ($^1\text{NI}^*$ and $^1\text{NDI}^*$) that can oxidize both G and A. When Sens are not bound to DNA, the reaction occurs through collisions between DNA and Sens in the triplet excited state. NDI in the triplet excited state (^{3}NDI*) can oxidize both A and G, while NI in the triplet excited state (^{3}NI*) oxidizes only G. Therefore, NIN, NDIN, and NDIP can oxidize both A and G while NIP can oxidize only G. Interestingly, NIN, NDIN, and NDIP caused significant DNA damage and was the highest for DNA-A7 and decreased as the number of A's in a row decreased (Figure 7). In contrast, NIP which oxidize only G via its triplet state caused only moderate damage to DNA and showed no preference for the consecutive A sequences (Figure 7c). These results clearly demonstrate the importance of A-oxidation especially in consecutive A sequences which triggers the rapid hole transfer between A's, and that conscutive A sequences are the potential targets in photosensitized DNA damage via one-electron oxidation pathway.

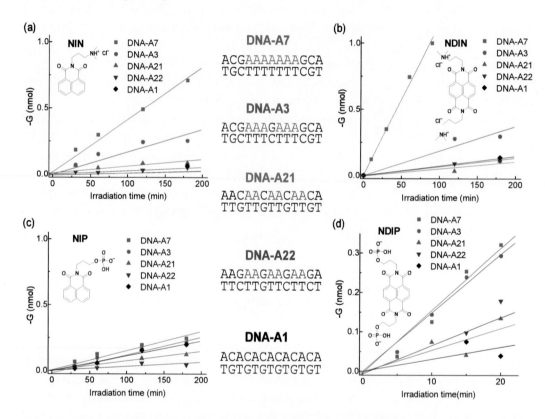

Figure 7. Sequence specificity of the photosensitized one-electron oxidation of DNA.

Sequence selectivity for DNA-A7 was the highest for NDIN, and NDIN caused only moderated DNA damage for DNA having sequences with three or fewer A's are in a row. As mentioned above, the reaction rate of Sens$^{\bullet-}$ with O_2 is an important factor determining the efficiency of photosensitized DNA damage especially when the length of consecutive A sequence or the lifetime of the charge-separated state is not long enough.[57] Since the reaction rate between NDI$^{\bullet-}$ and O_2 is much slower compared to that between NI$^{\bullet-}$ and O_2, longer consecutive A sequences that produce a longer lifetime of the charge-separated states are required for the irreversible reaction to occur efficiently in the case of NDI. Interestingly,

NDIP which oxidize A via its triplet excited state showed the highest DNA damage among the four NI and NDI derivatives studied here even though it is not bound to DNA. It is generally believed that Sens should be bound to DNA to maximize the DNA damage through the one-electron oxidation mechanism, and so far, many DNA-targeting Sens were designed so as to bind to DNA.[14, 15] These results pointed out that the efficiency of photosensitized DNA damage strongly depends on the nature of the interaction between the Sens and DNA according to the redox properties of the Sens, and that it is not always the Sens bound to DNA that causes the higher DNA damage.

When NDIP was used as the Sens, sequence specificity for DNA-A7 was not as high compared to NIN and NDIN, and a high degree of DNA damage was observed also for DNA-A3 (Figure 7d). This is probably because the charge recombination rate is slower for the ion-pair formed via ^{3}Sens* than that formed via ^{1}Sens*, requiring a shorter lifetime of the charge-separated state or the fewer A's in a row for the DNA damage to occur. In the case of NIP and NDIP, G damage may also be caused by singlet oxygen ($^1O_2$) which is formed by the reaction between ^{3}Sens* and O_2 (Type II process). This is especially the case for DNA-A1, where NIP induced a similar or even higher extent of DNA damage compared with NIN and NDIN. However, it has been well documented that $^1O_2$ shows no sequence specificity for G damage reactions.[14] Therefore, it can be concluded that the efficient DNA damage observed for DNA having consecutive A sequences is mainly due to the one-electron oxidation pathway.

5. Conclusions and Remarks

The mechanism of photosensitized DNA damage via one-electron oxidation mechanism was investigated on the basis of the direct spectroscopic measurements of the hole transfer in DNA and quantification of the yield of the DNA oxidative damage. Our results clearly demonstrate that the consecutive A sequences serve as a good target in the photosensitized DNA damage, or G adjacent to such sequences may be a potential hot spot of oxidative DNA damage. During the photosensitized one-electron oxidation of DNA, the reaction becomes irreversible when either the reaction of $G^{\bullet+}$ with water or the reaction of the Sens$^{\bullet-}$ with O_2 occurs faster than the charge recombination. In this report, the latter pathway was proven to be critically important. The best DNA-binding photosensitizer for DNA damage or the most harmful to human health is the photosensitizer powerful enough to oxidize A but weak enough to give up an electron to oxygen from its radical anion. Our results clearly showed that the hole transfer between A's promotes photosensitized DNA damage, which may provide one answer for the biological consequences of the hole transfer in DNA.

6. Acknowledgement

We are deeply indebted to Ms. Yasuko Osakada and Dr. Mamoru Fujitsuka for their contributions to this study. This work has been partly supported by a Grant-in-Aid for

Scientific Research (Projects 18750148, 17105005, and others) from the Ministry of Education, Culture, Sports, Science and Technology (MEXT) of Japanese Government.

References

[1]   Kino, K., and Sugiyama, H. (2001). Possible cause of G•C -> C•G transversion mutation by guanine oxidation product, imidazolone. *Chem. Biol. 8*, 369-378.

[2]   Mouret, S., Baudouin, C., Charveron, M., Favier, A., Cadet, J., and Douki, T. (2006). Cyclobutane pyrimidine dimers are predominant DNA lesions in whole human skin exposed to UVA radiation. *Proc. Natl. Acad. Sci. U S A 103*, 13765-13770.

[3]   Dolmans, D.E.J.G.J., Fukumura, D., and Jain, R.K. (2003). Photodynamic therapy for cancer. *Nat. Rev. Cancer 3*, 380-387.

[4]   Kawai, K., Cai, X., Sugimoto, A., Tojo, S., Fujitsuka, M., and Majima, T. (2004). Two-color two-laser DNA damaging. *Angew Chem, Int Ed 43*, 2406-2409.

[5]   Williams, T.T., Dohno, C., Stemp, E.D.A., and Barton, J.K. (2004). Effects of the photooxidant on DNA-mediated charge transport. *J. Am. Chem. Soc. 126*, 8148-8158.

[6]   Delaney, S., Yoo, J., Stemp, E.D.A., and Barton, J.K. (2004). Charge equilibration between two distinct sites in double helical DNA. *Proc. Natl. Acad. Sci. U S A 101*, 10511-10516.

[7]   Dohno, C., Stemp, E.D.A., and Barton, J.K. (2003). Fast back electron transfer prevents guanine damage by photoexcited thionine bound to DNA. *J. Am. Chem. Soc. 125*, 9586-9587.

[8]   Sharman, W.M., Allen, C.M., and van Lier, J.E. (2000). Role of activated oxygen species in photodynamic therapy. *Methods Enzymol 319*, 376-400.

[9]   Lewis, F.D., Liu, J., Zuo, X., Hayes, R.T., and Wasielewski, M.R. (2003). Dynamics and energetics of single-step hole transport in DNA Hairpins. *J. Am. Chem. Soc. 125*, 4850-4861.

[10]   Lewis, F.D., Liu, J., Weigel, W., Rettig, W., Kurnikov, I.V., and Beratan, D.N. (2002). Donor-bridge-acceptor energetics determine the distance dependence of electron tunneling in DNA. *Proc. Natl. Acad. Sci. U S A 99*, 12536-12541.

[11]   Lewis, F.D., Letsinger, R.L., and Wasielewski, M.R. (2001). Dynamics of photoinduced charge transfer and hole transport in synthetic DNA hairpins. *Acc. Chem. Res. 34*, 159-170.

[12]   Lewis, F.D., Liu, X.Y., Liu, J.Q., Miller, S.E., Hayes, R.T., and Wasielewski, M.R. (2000). Direct measurement of hole transport dynamics in DNA. *Nature 406*, 51-53.

[13]   Lewis, F.D., Kalgutkar, R.S., Wu, Y.S., Liu, X.Y., Liu, J.Q., Hayes, R.T., Miller, S.E., and Wasielewski, M.R. (2000). Driving force dependence of electron transfer dynamics in synthetic DNA hairpins. *J. Am. Chem. Soc. 122*, 12346-12351.

[14]   Burrows, C.J., and Muller, J.G. (1998). Oxidative nucleobase modifications leading to strand scission. *Chem. Rev. 98*, 1109-1151.

[15]   Armitage, B. (1998). Photocleavage of nucleic acids. *Chem. Rev. 98*, 1171-1200.

[16]   Kawai, K., and Majima, T. (2002). Effect of hydrogen bonding on the photo-oxidation of DNA. *J. Photochem. Photobiol. C 3*, 53-66.

[17] Misiaszek, R., Crean, C., Joffe, A., Geacintov, N.E., and Shafirovich, V. (2004). Oxidative DNA damage associated with combination of guanine and superoxide radicals and repair mechanisms via radical trapping. *J. Biol. Chem. 279*, 32106-32115.

[18] Shafirovich, V., Dourandin, A., Huang, W.D., and Geacintov, N.E. (2001). The carbonate radical is a site-selective oxidizing agent of guanine in double-stranded oligonucleotides. *J. Biol. Chem. 276*, 24621-24626.

[19] Hildenbrand, K., and Schulte-Frohlinde, D. (1990). ESR spectra of radicals of single-stranded and double-stranded DNA in aqueous solution. Implications for hydroxyl radical-induced strand breakage. *Free Rad. Res. Commun. 11*, 195-206.

[20] Barton, J.K., Carell, T., Giese, B., Kawai, K., Lewis, F.D., Majima, T., Saito, I., Schuster, G.B., Shafirovich, V., and Wagenknecht, H.A. (2005). *Charge Transfer in DNA*. (Wagenknecht H.-A.) (Weinheim, Wiley-VCH).

[21] Barton, J.K., Cadet, J., Carell, T., Giese, B., Kawai, K., Lewis, F.D., Majima, T., Saito, I., Schuster, G.B., Shafirovich, V., Angelov, D., Behrens, C., Cichon, M.K., Grolle, F., and Hennecke, U. (2004). *Long-Range Charge Transfer in DNA I and II. Vol 236, 237*, (Schuster G. B.) (New York, Springer-Verlag).

[22] Bixon, M., Giese, B., Wessely, S., Langenbacher, T., Michel-Beyerle, M.E., and Jortner, J. (1999). Long-range charge hopping in DNA. *Proc. Natl. Acad. Sci. U S A 96*, 11713-11716.

[23] Giese, B. (2000). Long distance charge transport in DNA: The hopping mechanism. *Acc. Chem. Res. 33*, 631-636.

[24] Meggers, E., Michel-Beyerle, M.E., and Giese, B. (1998). Sequence dependent long range hole transport in DNA. *J. Am. Chem. Soc. 120*, 12950-12955.

[25] Jortner, J., Bixon, M., Langenbacher, T., and Michel-Beyerle, M.E. (1998). Charge transfer and transport in DNA. *Proc. Natl. Acad. Sci. U S A 95*, 12759-12765.

[26] Schuster, G.B. (2000). Long-range charge transfer in DNA: Transient structural distortions control the distance dependence. *Acc. Chem. Res. 33*, 253-260.

[27] Henderson, P.T., Jones, D., Hampikian, G., Kan, Y.Z., and Schuster, G.B. (1999). Long-distance charge transport in duplex DNA: The phonon-assisted polaron-like hopping mechanism. *Proc. Natl. Acad. Sci. U S A 96*, 8353-8358.

[28] Barnett, R.N., Cleveland, C.L., Joy, A., Landman, U., and Schuster, G.B. (2001). Charge migration in DNA: Ion-gated transport. *Science 294*, 567-571.

[29] Nunez, M.E., Noyes, K.T., Gianolio, D.A., McLaughlin, L.W., and Barton, J.K. (2000). Long-range guanine oxidation in DNA restriction fragments by a triplex-directed naphthalene diimide intercalator. *Biochemistry 39*, 6190-6199.

[30] Nakatani, K., Dohno, C., and Saito, I. (1999). Chemistry of sequence-dependent remote guanine oxidation: Photoreaction of duplex DNA containing cyanobenzophenone-substituted uridine. *J. Am. Chem. Soc. 121*, 10854-10855.

[31] Kawai, K., Takada, T., Tojo, S., Ichinose, N., and Majima, T. (2001). Observation of hole transfer through DNA by monitoring the transient absorption of pyrene radical cation. *J. Am. Chem. Soc. 123*, 12688-12689.

[32] Giese, B., Amaudrut, J., Kohler, A.K., Spormann, M., and Wessely, S. (2001). Direct observation of hole transfer through DNA by hopping between adenine bases and by tunnelling. *Nature 412*, 318-320.

[33] Giese, B., and Biland, A. (2002). Recent developments of charge injection and charge transfer in DNA. *Chem. Commun*, 667-672.

[34] Kendrick, T., and Giese, B. (2002). Charge transfer through DNA triggered by site selective charge injection into adenine. *Chem. Commun*, 2016-2017.

[35] Kawai, K., Takada, T., Tojo, S., and Majima, T. (2003). Kinetics of weak distance-dependent hole transfer in DNA by adenine-hopping mechanism. *J. Am. Chem. Soc. 125*, 6842-6843.

[36] Takada, T., Kawai, K., Fujitsuka, M., and Majima, T. (2004). Direct observation of hole transfer through double-helical DNA over 100 Å. *Proc Natl Acad Sci U S A 101*, 14002-14006.

[37] Lewis, F.D., Zhu, H., Daublain, P., Fiebig, T., Raytchev, M., Wang, Q., and Shafirovich, V. (2006). Crossover from superexchange to hopping as the mechanism for photoinduced charge transfer in DNA hairpin conjugates. *J. Am. Chem. Soc. 128*, 791-800.

[38] Kawai, K., Takada, T., Nagai, T., Cai, X., Sugimoto, A., Fujitsuka, M., and Majima, T. (2003). Long-lived charge-separated state leading to DNA damage through hole transfer. *J. Am. Chem. Soc. 125*, 16198-16199.

[39] Takada, T., Kawai, K., Fujitsuka, M., and Majima, T. (2005). Contributions of the distance-dependent reorganization energy and proton-transfer to the hole-transfer process in DNA. *Chem. Eur. J 11*, 3835-3842.

[40] Kawai, K., Osakada, Y., Takada, T., Fujitsuka, M., and Majima, T. (2004). Lifetime regulation of the charge-separated state in DNA by modulating the oxidation potential of guanine in DNA through hydrogen bonding. *J. Am. Chem. Soc. 126*, 12843-12846.

[41] Takada, T., Kawai, K., Cai, X., Sugimoto, A., Fujitsuka, M., and Majima, T. (2004). Charge separation in DNA via consecutive adenine hopping. *J. Am. Chem. Soc. 126*, 1125-1129.

[42] 5'-Linked-NDI are considered to associate with the 5'-terminus by end-capping. Rahe, N., Rinn, C., and Carell, T. (2003). Development of donor-acceptor modified DNA hairpins for the investigation of charge hopping kinetics in DNA. *Chem. Commun*, 2120-2121.

[43] Giese, B., and Spichty, M. (2000). Long distance charge transport through DNA: Quantification and extension of the hopping model. *ChemPhysChem 1*, 195-198.

[44] Dohno, C., Ogawa, A., Nakatani, K., and Saito, I. (2003). Hole trapping at N6-cyclopropyldeoxyadenosine suggests a Direct contribution of adenine bases to hole transport through DNA. *J. Am .Chem. Soc. 125*, 10154-10155.

[45] Lewis, F.D., Liu, X., Miller, S.E., Hayes, R.T., and Wasielewski, M.R. (2002). Formation and decay of localized contact radical Ion pairs in DNA hairpins. *J. Am. Chem. Soc. 124*, 14020-14026.

[46] Yoo, J., Delaney, S., Stemp, E.D.A., and Barton, J.K. (2003). Rapid radical formation by DNA charge transport through sequences lacking intervening guanines. *J. Am. Chem. Soc. 125*, 6640-6641.

[47] The higher consumption of G for NDG compared to that of ND3 can be explained by the existence of some long-lived component in the case of NDG as can be seen in Figure 1a because of the hole transfer from the inserted G to the Gs.

[48] Sanii, L., and Schuster, G.B. (2000). Long-distance charge transport in DNA: Sequence-dependent radical cation injection efficiency. *J. Am. Chem. Soc. 122*, 11545-11546.

[49] Kawai, K., Osakada, Y., Fujitsuka, M., and Majima, T. (2005). Consecutive adenine sequences are potential targets in photosensitized DNA damage. *Chem. Biol. 12*, 1049-1054.

[50] Kawai, K., Wata, Y., Hara, M., Tojo, S., and Majima, T. (2002). Regulation of one-electron oxidation rate of guanine by base pairing with cytosine derivatives. *J. Am. Chem. Soc. 124*, 3586-3590.

[51] Breslin, D.T., and Schuster, G.B. (1996). Anthraquinone photonucleases: Mechanisms for GG-selective and nonselective cleavage of double-stranded DNA. *J. Am. Chem. Soc. 118*, 2311-2319.

[52] Kawai, K., Osakada, Y., Fujitsuka, M., and Majima, T. (2006). Effects of reaction rate of radical anion of a photosensitizer with molecular oxygen on the photosensitized DNA damage. *Chem. Commun*, 3918-3920.

[53] Rogers, J.E., and Kelly, L.A. (1999). Nucleic acid oxidation mediated by naphthalene and benzophenone imide and diimide derivatives: Consequences for DNA redox chemistry. *J. Am. Chem. Soc. 121*, 3854-3861.

[54] Murov, S.L., Carmichael, I., and Hug, G.L. (1993). *Handbook of photochemistry*. (2nd Edn.) (New York, Marcel Dekker, Inc.).

[55] Chiarotto, J.A., and Hill, R.P. (1999). A quantitative analysis of the reduction in oxygen levels required to induce up-regulation of vascular endothelial growth factor (VEGF) mRNA in cervical cancer cell lines. *Br. J. Cancer 80*, 1518-1524.

[56] Kawai, K., Osakada, Y., Fujitsuka, M., and Majima, T. (2007). Hole transfer in DNA and photosensitized DNA damage: importance of adenine oxidation. *J. Phys. Chem. B. 111*, 2322-2326.

[57] Kawai, K., Osakada, Y., Fujitsuka, M., and Majima, T. (2006). *Chem. Commun*, 3918-3920.

In: New Research on DNA Damage
Editors: Honoka Kimura and Aoi Suzuki

ISBN 978-1-60456-581-2
© 2008 Nova Science Publishers, Inc.

Chapter 11

A Novel Methodology to Characterize DNA Damage Utilizing Phosphodiesterase I Function

Ken Akamatsu[*]

Radiation Effect Analysis Group, Nuclear Science and Engineering Directorate,
Japan Atomic Energy Agency

Abstract

We have developed a new-conceptual analytical methodology to estimate the DNA damage spectrum on natural DNA without radioisotope and fluorescent labeling.

DNA damage is generally classified into two categories: one is 'strand break', the other is 'nucleobase lesion'. There are two kinds of termini in the strand break pattern: the termini with or without phosphate. We have developed the protocols to quantify 3'termini without phosphate (site 1), 3'termini with phosphate (site 2), and nucleobase lesions (site 3). An enzyme, phosphodiestrase I (snake venom phosphodiesterase (SVPD)), can recognize a 3'terminus without phosphate followed by production of DNA monomers (2'-deoxynucleoside-5'-phosphate) sequentially from the 3'terminus (3' → 5' exonuclease function). Then, the yield of 'site 1' can be quantified since the amount of the DNA monomers produced during incubation for a given period is proportional to that of 'site 1'. In addition, pre-treatment of irradiated DNA by another enzyme, calf intestine alkaline phosphatase (CIAP) enables 'site 2' to be recognized by SVPD, because CIAP removes phosphate at 'site 2' to convert into 3'OH terminus categorized in 'site 1'. Furthermore, pre-treatment of irradiated DNA by a chemical, piperidine, can covert most electron-withdrawing nucleobase lesions into 'site 2', which can become recognizable by SVPD after CIAP pre-treatment as mentioned above. As a result, in the case of ^{60}Co γ-irradiated dry DNA, the yields of total 3'termini, 3'termini without phosphate, 3'termini with phosphate, and piperidine-labile nucleobase lesions, are estimated to be 0.102, 0.024, 0.078, and 0.084, respectively. The de novo analytical protocol is unique in the

[*] Japan Atomic Energy Agency (JAEA), 2-4 Shirakatashirane, Tokai-mura, Naka-gun, Ibaraki 319-1195, Japan,
E-mail: akamatsu.ken@jaea.go.jp.

idea itself, and future analyses based on the methodology will elucidate unknown DNA damage spectrum using a variety of combinations of enzymes.

1. Introduction

The environmental factors stimulating a living body, such as ionizing radiations, ultraviolet, and chemicals, can injure DNA. Particularly, ionizing radiations have ability to produce a variety of damage on DNA. They are classified into *e.g.*, γ-rays, X-rays, ion particles, and neutron. Each of radiations would have individual DNA damage spectrum. During this half century, more than a hundred oxidized nucleobases initiated by hydroxyl radial and one-electron oxidative agents have been characterized [1]. A lot of sugar lesions, moreover, have also been discovered [2]. However, there would actually be more lesions that can be induced by inner-shell electron excitation and ionization as has recently been investigated, *e.g.*, using ultrasoft X-rays [3-10]. Each yield of lesions would be fairly different. In addition, it has been important that relative distances among the lesions are taken into consideration when investigating repairbility of a lesion. Thus, particularly in case of ionizing radiations, it is quite significant for understanding upstream of radiation-biological processes to clarify each spectrum of DNA lesions produced by a variety of radiations and the differences among the spectra.

So far, there have been three categories in the detection methods: the first one is (1) a method using an antibody to a specific damage, the second one is (2) that using a chemical agent reactive to a specific functional group on the damage, and the other one is (3) that using a super-coiled plasmid DNA which can be conformationally-changed to its linear form directly or via its open-circular form by strand scission.

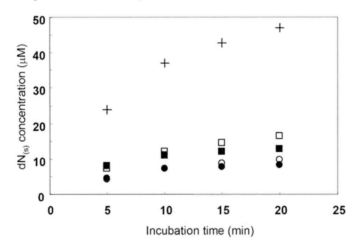

Figure 1. Time courses of concentration of dNs cut away from the 3'OH termini (68.4 μM) of pUC19/*Sau*3AI fragments by SVPD (0.01 unit/mL) and excess CIAP treatment in buffer (pH 8.0) at 31.4°C: (○) dC, (●) dG, (□) dT, (■) dA, and (+) total dNs. Similar curves were also obtained with different 3'OH termini concentrations of 3.4, 8.6, 17.1, 25.7, and 34.2 μM. Each of dNs production rates increased with increasing concentrations of the 3'OH termini.

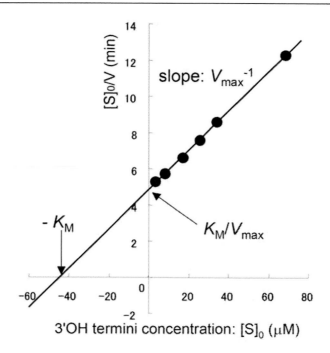

Figure 2. Kinetic analysis dNs production from 3'OH termini in pUC19/*Sau*3AI fragments incubated with SVPD (0.01 unit/mL) and excess CIAP in buffer (pH 8.0) at 31.4°C. This plot of $[S]_0/V$ versus $[S]_0$ is derived from a transformed Michaelis-Menten equation: $[S]_0/V = 1/V_{max} \cdot [S]_0 + K_M/V_{max}$, where $[S]_0$: initial concentration of the substrate (3'OH termini), V: initial velocity of pdN (or dN) production, V_{max} : maximum velocity of pdN (or dN) production, K_M: Michaelis-Menten constant. The equation of the regression line, which was obtained by a least square fit, is given by $y = 0.108 x + 4.806$ (correlation coefficient: 0.999).

Several antibodies to oxidized DNA bases, in relation to (1) have been developed as reviewed previously [11]. An aldehyde reactive probe with a biotin moiety (ARP) [12] is one of a chemical agent covalently reactive to the lesion with a carbonyl carbon, *e.g.*, AP site (2). In addition, other biotinylated probes, reactive to so-called 'oxidized AP-sites' are also developed [13, 14]. However, few agents, *e.g.*, ARP and antibodies to 7,8-dihydro- 8-oxoguanine or 5,6-dihydroxy- 5,6-dihydrothymine for the methodologies (1) and (2) are commercially available. Although these are useful to detect known lesion, it is difficult to be aware of their overall spectrum containing unknown ones. On the other hand, the methodology (3) is effective to know the overall spectrum of lesions, some of which are unknown and/or (immuno-) chemically undetectable at present. The yields of single or double strand breaks (SSB or DSB) and the lesions cleavable with a base excision repair enzyme can be quantified by (3). However, in principle, the calculated yield could often be underestimated, *i.e.*, in case of existence of interspersed SSBs from each other in an open-circular plasmid DNA. The new methodology introduced here will be a worthful technique to give us another point of view in DNA damage spectrum comparable with the conventional methodology.

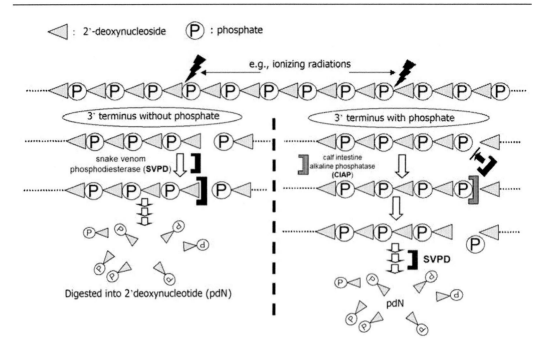

Figure 3. Central procedure to analyzing DNA strand-break termini using SVPD. The pdNs obtained are HPLC-analyzed as 2'-deoxynucleosides (dNs) by excess CIAP treatment. This procedure is also available for nucleobase lesions. Some nucleobase lesions can be removed by piperidine treatment. The lesions are cleaved, leaving a terminus with phosphate. Then, it is possible to estimate the yield of the lesions using the increase in the amount of termini with phosphate in piperidine treated irradiated DNA.

2. Methods

2.1. Overall Strategy for DNA Damage Analyses Using Phosphodiesterase I

Phosphodiesterase I, snake venom phosphodiesterase (SVPD) derived from *clotalus adamanteus*, plays a principal role in the analytical methodology. SVPD is one of 3' → 5'-exonucleases, whose general function is the sequential digestion 3' OH termini or 3' termini without phosphate of DNA to produce DNA monomers (2'-deoxynucleosides -5'-phosphate (pdN)). Figure 1 shows time course of each of pdNs cut away from the recessed 3'OH termini of Sau 3AI digests of pUC19 plasmid DNA (2686 base pairs; GC: 51.3 %, TA: 48.7 %)) by SVPD. This indicates, fortunately, that pdNs have been accumulated during incubation with SVPD though the digestion rates for the purine nucleotides (A, G) are somewhat lower than those for pyrimidine nucleotides (T, C). In this connection, the digestion kinetics follows the Michaelis-Menten-type conventional theory (Figure 2). Thus, the function of SVPD is available for quantification of the 3'-termini in consideration of their chemical structures.

The central procedure of this methodology is shown in figure 3. Here, it is assumed that strand-break termini produced by a stimulating factor are divided into two categories: the termini *without* phosphate and the termini *with* phosphate.

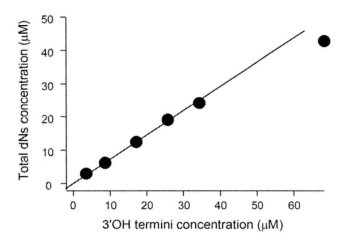

Figure 4. Relationship between the 3'OH termini concentration in the pUC19/Sau3AI fragments and total dNs produced by SVPD (0.01 unit/mL) and excess CIAP treatment in buffer (pH 8.0) for 15 min at 31.4°C [15]. The slope of the regression line, which was obtained by a least square fit without the data point at the 3'OH terminus concentration of 68.4 μM, is 0.723 (correlation coefficient: 0.999).

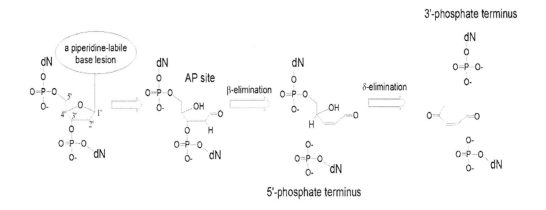

Figure 5. Strand-break formation at piperidine-labile base lesions. Generally, the β-elimination and the δ-elimination reactions occur completely at 25 °C for 30 min and 90 °C for 30 min in 1 M piperidine, respectively [20]. Those elimination reactions also occur by formamidopyrimidine N-glycosylase (Fpg) [30].

The former can directly be recognized by SVPD, while the latter cannot be recognized by SVPD without previous dephosphorylation by a phosphatase (In the strict sense, there could be 'a dirty terminus' which cannot be recognized by SVPD even by the phosphatase pre-treatment.). As a consequence, most 3' strand-break termini in damaged DNA become recognizable by SVPD by the pre-treatment. A calibration curve constructed by pUC19/Sau 3AI double-stranded DNA fragments, which have thirty recessed 3' termini without phosphate (3' OH) in total, allows the amount of pdNs to be converted into that of 3' termini without phosphate.

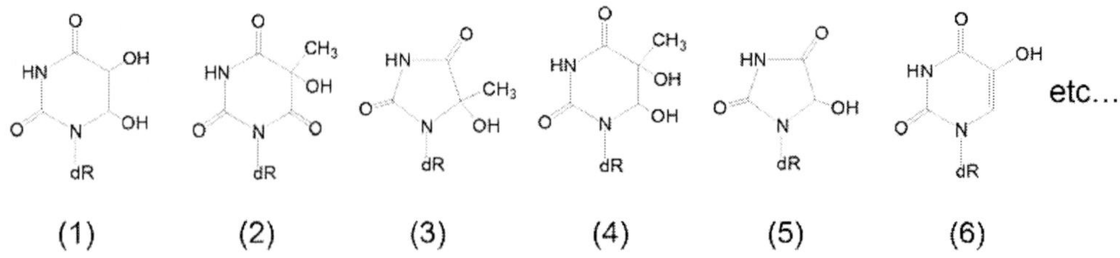

Figure 6. Known piperidine-labile sites [17]. (1) uracil glycol, (2) 5-hydroxy-5-methylbarbituric acid, (3) 5-hydroxy-5-methylhydantoin, (4) thymine glycol, (5) 5-hydroxyhydantoin, (6) 5-hydroxyuracil. dR: 2'-deoxy-*D*-ribose.

It is noted that there will not be a little alkaline- and/or heat-labile lesion in damaged DNA. Moreover, the enzyme activity, in general, gradually depleted during turnover at a high temperature. Thus, the optimal enzymatic reaction condition was determined by taking these into account (: ~ pH 8, ~ 30°C, for 15 min), though optimal pH for SVPD function is around ten. Moreover, as a DNA sample for exposing to a DNA damaging agent, the linear-formed pUC19 plasmid DNA cleaved at the CCCGGG site by Sma I has been used in order to avoid effect of steric hindrance on the enzyme reaction kinetics. The following analytical procedures are described base on the previous report [15].

2.2. Equipments, Tools, and Buffers

- A high-performance liquid chromatograph (HPLC) equipped with a reverse-phase column
- A centrifugal separator (for 1.5-mL microtube, 6000 *g*, ~ 0 °C)
- An incubator (0 ~ 90°C)
- A freeze-dryer
- A UV-VIS spectrometer
- A microtube equipped with a 10-kDa molecular-weight cutoff filter
- 1 × TE buffer (10 mM Tris-HCl (pH 8.0) + 1 mM EDTA-Na (pH.8.0))
- 2 × enzyme reaction buffer (0.2 M Tris-HCl (pH 8.0) + 0.2 M NaCl + 28 mM $MgCl_2$)

2.3. Enzymes

SmaI (*Serratia marcescens* Sb, 12 units/µL), Sau3AI (*Staphylococcus aureus* 3A, 10 units/µL), snake venom phosphodiesterase (SVPD, *Crotalus adamanteus*, 39.0 units/mg solid, 1.29 A_{280}/mg/mL), and calf intestinal alkaline phosphatase (CIAP) were purchased from Amersham-Pharmacia Biotech (Piscataway, NJ). The unit definitions of the nucleases are as follows: SmaI – 1 unit is defined as the amount of enzyme required to completely digest 1 µg of λ DNA in 1 h at pH 7.5 and 30°C in 50 µL of assay buffer; Sau3AI – 1 unit is defined as the amount of enzyme required to completely digest 1 µg of λ DNA in 1 h at pH

7.5 and 30°C in 50 μL of assay buffer; SVPD – 1 unit is defined as the amount of enzyme required to hydrolyze 1 μmole of *p*-nitrophenyl thymidine 5'-phosphate per minute at pH 8.9 and 25°C; CIAP – 1 unit is defined as the amount of enzyme required to hydrolyze 1 μmole of *p*-nitrophenyl phosphate per minute at pH 8.0 and 37°C.

2.4. Preparation of pUC19/Sma I

pUC19 plasmid DNA (1 mg/mL in TE at pH 8.0) is purified by ethanol precipitation. The EDTA-free pUC19 is incubated in buffer (10 mM Tris-HCl at pH 7.5, 7 mM $MgCl_2$, 20 mM KCl, and 7 mM 2-mercaptothanol) with SmaI (84 units, 7 μL) at 30°C for 7 h (~250 μg of DNA/200 μL of reaction buffer). The reaction mixture is phenol extracted to remove the enzyme, and the DNA is purified by ethanol precipitation. The concentration of the aqueous solution of SmaI-digested pUC19 (pUC19/SmaI) is determined by measuring the OD_{260}. The purity of the samples of pUC19/SmaI is confirmed by calculating the OD_{260}/OD_{280} ratio; samples of pUC19/SmaI with a ratio greater than 1.8 are used in this study. Finally, one makes sure that most pUC19 has been digested by means of agarose electrophoresis (1% agarose gel).

2.5. Preparation of pUC19/Sau 3AI

The preparation process is similar to that of pUC19/Sma I. In brief, the pUC19 (~175 μg) is incubated in 200 μL of reaction buffer (10 mM Tris-HCl at pH 7.5, 10 mM $MgCl_2$, 50 mM NaCl, and 1 mM DTT) with Sau 3AI (50 units, 5 μL) at 37°C for 2 h. An additional 50 units of the enzyme is added to the reaction mixture and the sample is incubated at 37°C for 4 h to complete the digestion reaction. Finally, one makes sure the fragments by the electrophoresis.

2.6. Quantification of 3′ Strand-Break Termini

2.6.1. Collection of 2′deoxynucleosides (dNs) from 3′ Strand-Break Termini without Phosphate

The brief procedure is seen in the left side of figure 3. A flow chart diagram of the procedure is shown below:

1. Prepare 0.32-μg/μL of a solution dissolving damaged DNA in water (HPLC grade) or 1/10 TE buffer (pH ~8). Transfer 10-μL of the DNA solution to 0.5-mL microtube on an incubator. Moreover, add 10-μL of 2 × enzyme reaction buffer (pH 8.0) and 29-μL of 1 × enzyme reaction buffer (pH 8.0) in the microtube. The resulting solution, as a consequence, contains 3.2-μg of the damaged DNA in 49-μL of 1 × enzyme reaction buffer (pH 8.0). All of the process should be performed at ~ 0°C. ---------soln.I

2. Add 1-µL of SVPD solution (0.005 unit/µL) in soln.I at ~ 0°C, and homogenize by light stirring. Keep the solution at a constant temperature around 30°C for 15 min. ---------soln.II

3. Transfer the tube with soln.II into liquid nitrogen to terminate the enzyme reaction immediately after the incubation. Melt the solidified soln.II, and keep it at 0°C. Subsequently, transfer the soln.II to a 10 kDa-cutoff filter cartridge set in a 1.5-mL microtube at ~ 0°C. Wash the tube used in the enzyme reaction by 50-µL of cold water, and add the washing also to the filter cartridge.

4. Centrifuge the reaction mixture at 6000 g until complete filtration at ~ 0°C. Add 100- µL of cold water on the filter and filtrate again. The filter-washing processes should be repeated at lease three times for complete recovery of low-molecular fractions in the reaction mixture containing pdNs. Finally, approximately 400-µL of the filtrate is obtained. --------soln.III

5. Freeze-dry the soln.III completely. Dissolve the residue again with 50-µL of cold water.----soln.IV

6. Add 2-µL of CIAP solution (2 units / µL) in the soln.IV, and incubate the mixture for 30 min at 37°C. ----soln.V

7. Transfer the soln.V to a 10 kDa-cutoff filter cartridge set in a 1.5-mL microtube at ~ 4°C. Wash the tube used in the enzyme reaction by 50-µL of cold water, and add the washing also to the filter cartridge.

8. Centrifuge the reaction mixture at 6000 g until complete filtration at ~ 4°C. Add 100-µL of cold water on the filter and filtrate again. The filter-washing processes should be repeated at lease three times for complete recovery of low-molecular fractions in the reaction mixture containing dNs. Finally, approximately 400-µL of the filtrate is obtained. --------soln.VI

9. Freeze-dry the soln.VI. Dissolve the residue again with 30-µL of cold water.----soln.VII

10. Analyze 20-µL of the soln.VII by HPLC to quantify each dN.

2.6.2. Collection of dNs from all 3' Strand-Break Termini

The brief procedure is shown in figure 3 (both sides). Here, all 3'-termini can be recognized by SVPD as well as the 3'-termini without phosphate as mentioned previously. A flow chart diagram of the procedure is shown below:

1. Prepare 0.32-µg/µL of a solution dissolving damaged DNA in water (HPLC grade) or 1/10 TE buffer (pH ~8). Transfer 10-µL of the DNA solution to 0.5-mL microtube on an incubator. Moreover, add 10-µL of 2 × enzyme reaction buffer (pH 8.0) and 27-µL of 1 × enzyme reaction buffer (pH 8.0) in the microtube. The resulting solution, as a consequence, contains 3.2-µg of the damaged DNA in 47-µL of 1 × enzyme reaction buffer (pH 8.0). All of the process should be performed at ~ 0°C. ---------soln.IX

2. Add 2-µL of CIAP solution (2 units / µL) in the soln.IX, and incubate the mixture for 30 min at 30°C. ----soln.X

3. Add 1-μL of SVPD solution (0.005 unit/μL) in the soln.X at 30 °C. Keep the solution at a constant temperature around 30°C for 15 min. ---------soln.XI

4. Transfer the tube with soln.XI into liquid nitrogen to terminate the enzyme reaction immediately after the incubation. Melt the solidified soln.XI, and keep it at 0°C. Subsequently, transfer the soln.XI to a 10 kDa-cutoff filter cartridge set in a 1.5-mL microtube at ~ 0°C. Wash the tube used in the enzyme reaction by 50-μL of cold water, and add the washing also to the filter cartridge.

5. Centrifuge the reaction mixture at 6000 g until complete filtration at ~ 4°C. Add 100-μL of cold water on the filter and filtrate again. The filter-washing processes should be repeated at lease three times for complete recovery of low-molecular fractions in the reaction mixture containing dNs. Finally, approximately 400-μL of the filtrate is obtained. --------soln.XIII

6. Freeze-dry the soln.XII completely. Dissolve the residue again with 30-μL of cold water.----soln.XIII.

7. Analyze 20-μL of the soln.XIII by HPLC to quantify each dN.

2.6.3. Conversion of dNs Concentration into 3′ Termini Concentration

A calibration curve to convert dNs concentration into 3′ termini concentration should be constructed as mentioned at section 2.1. One gram of pUC19/Sau 3AI fragments has 18.134 μmole 3'OH termini. The data for the curve are obtained using, *e.g.*, 0.2, 0.5, 1.0, 1.5, 2.0, and 4.0 g/L pUC19/Sau 3AI solution according to the procedure shown in section 2.6.2. A sample calibration curve is shown in figure 4.

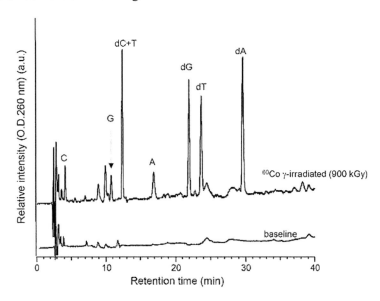

Figure 7. An HPLC chromatogram of 900 kGy-irradiated pUC19/*Sma*I treated with SVPD (0.01 unit/mL) and excess CIAP in buffer (pH 8.0) at 31.4°C for 15 min [15]. The peaks corresponding to dC and T often cannot be separated. If so, the peak area corresponding to dC can be calculated using the chromatogram data obtained for irradiated pUC19/*Sma*I without any enzymatic treatments. These unaltered base release events generally also occur in dry DNA exposed to ionizing radiations [32] as well as in case of using aqueous DNA [31].

2.7. Quantification of Piperidine-Labile DNA Lesions

2.7.1. About Piperidine-Labile Sites in Damaged DNA

As one of the application of the methodology, piperidine-labile DNA lesions can be quantified according to the protocols above. It is originally well-known that piperidine is available for cleaving at the upstream of 7-methyl-2'-deoxyguanosine in Maxam-Gilbert DNA sequencing method [16]. Hence, piperidine, as a nucleophile, reacts to C1' carbon with an electron-withdrawing atom or molecule by a nucleophilic substitution reaction, followed by strand scission by β,δ-elimination via an intermediate: apurinic/ apyrimidinic (AP) site [17] (Figure 5). This reaction mechanism is considered to be similar to that of a base excision repair enzyme. Some known examples of piperidine-labile sites are listed in figure 6. It appears that highly-oxidized pyrimidine nucleobases generally are vulnerable by piperidine, while oxidized purines, especially 7,8-dihydro-8-oxo-adenosine, are stable to the nucleophile.

2.7.2. Strategy for Quanification of Piperidine-Labile Sites

Fortunately, as shown in figure 5, such a piperidine-labile site leaves a 3'-terminus with phosphate after sufficient piperidine treatment. Thus, piperidine-labile sites can be quantified as the amount of newly produced 3'-terminus by the SVPD method. Here, the damage DNA sample treated with piperidine is used in the SVPD procedure as mentioned previously in the section 2.6.

2.7.3. Preparation Of Piperidine-Treated Damaged DNA Sample

1. Prepare 0.32-μg/μL of a solution dissolving damaged DNA in water (HPLC grade) or 1/10 TE buffer (pH ~8). Transfer 10-μL of the DNA solution to 0.5-mL microtube.----soln.XIV
2. Add 10-μL of 2 M piperidine aqueous solution in the soln. XIV.----- soln.XV
3. Incubate the soln.XV at 90°C for 30 min, and freeze-dry it.
4. Dissolve the residue of (3) either in 49 or in 47-μL of 1 × enzyme reaction buffer for the protocol in the section 2.6.1 or 2.6.2, respectively.
5. The procedures after (4) are the same as those after (2) shown in the sections 2.6.1 and 2.6.2.

2.8. HPLC Analytical Condition

Any analytical conditions are available as long as each dN can be completely separated. For example:

- Column: a reverse-phase C18 or C30 column for analysis
- Column temperature: 40 °C
- Flow rate of eluent: 0.8 mL/min
- Mobile phase: A: 0.05 M ammonium acetate, B: acetonitrile

- Gradient: 0 – 40 min (B 0% → B 20%), 40 – 45 min (B 20%), 45 – 50 min (B 20% → B 0%)
- Detection: 260 nm

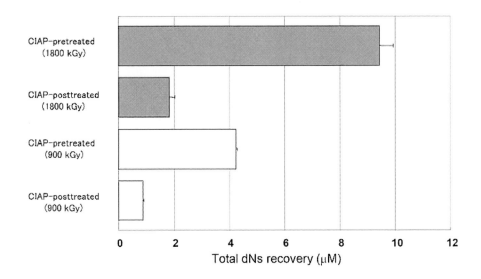

Figure 8. dNs produced by SVPD (0.01 unit/mL) treatment (15 min at 31.4°C and pH 8.0) from pUC19/*Sma*I irradiated with 900 and 1800 kGy of ^{60}Co γ-rays with or without CIAP pretreatment. The bars and error bars represent the mean ± 1 SD from two independent experiments.

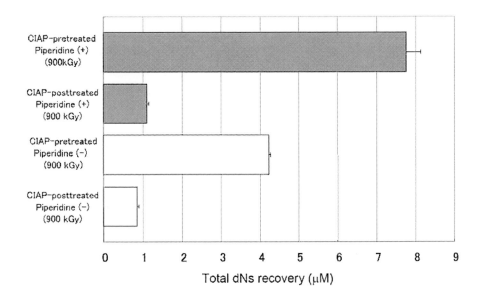

Figure 9. Effect of piperidine pretreatment on the levels of dNs recovered following SVPD treatment (15 min at 31.4°C and pH 8.0) from pUC19/*Sma*I irradiated with 900 kGy of ^{60}Co γ-rays with or without CIAP pretreatment. The bars and error bars represent the mean ± 1 SD from two independent experiments. The piperidine (-) data are same as the 900 kGy data in Figure 8.

Table 1 Strand break yields (μmol/J) in ^{60}Co γ-irradiated pUC19/*Sma* I based on SVPD digestion kinetics to 3'OH termini in pUC19/*Sau* 3AI fragments.

Category of 3'-terminus	Yield (μmol / J)	
	piperidine (-)	piperidine (+)
Without phosphate	0.024	0.026
With phosphate	0.078	0.160
Total	0.102	0.186

A HPLC result analyzed under the condition above is shown in figure 7. The quantification of each dN was performed using each calibration curve constructed from a chromatogram of purchased standard dNs.

3. Example

Then, we will here demonstrate the results of ^{60}Co γ-irradiated dry pUC19/Sma I plasmid DNA. The detailed DNA sample preparation processes for irradiation are explained in the previous report [15]. Figures 8 and 9 show total amount of dNs collected by the SVPD procedure and by the same one accompanying with piperidine pre-treatment, respectively. In figure 8, total amount of dNs in case without CIAP pre-treatment clearly larger than that in case with CIAP pre-treatment. This suggests that ~ 20% of total prompt strand breaks in DNA induced by the direct radiation effect have no phosphate residue at the 3' termini. In addition, the amount of dNs with CIAP pre-treatment when using piperidine treated irradiated DNA (figure 9) is twice larger than that when using the irradiated DNA without piperidine treatment (figure 8) at 900 kGy. This means that piperidine-labile sites, as exemplified in figure 6, are produced to the same extent as the prompt strand breaks produced. Moreover, these dNs' values can be converted into 'yields' (*e.g.*, μmol/J) using a calibration curve as shown previously (figure 4). The converted results are seen in Table 1. The yield of piperidine-labile sites can be estimated as the difference between the yields of 3'-phosphate termini pretreated with and without piperidine: 0.082 μmol/J.

4. Discussion

We have described a new-conceptual methodology for DNA damage spectrum analysis using 3' → 5' exonuclease activity of SVPD. One can perform the proposed protocol in a conventional laboratory for biochemistry without radioisotope labeling, though not a few processes to be done are needed at present. More amounts of dNs collected and/or a UV spectrometer equipped with a microcell may make HPLC analytical processes to be omitted.

One of distinctive results from the protocol is quantitative and qualitative information about strand break 3'termini on damaged plasmid DNA. As mentioned in the introduction section, it should be noted that we assume that the 3'termini can be distinguished between those *without* phosphate and those *with* phosphate. However, to be accurate, they had better be categorized into three: (1) the termini recognizable by SVPD *without* CIAP, (2) those recognizable by SVPD *with* CIAP, and (3) those *not* recognizable even with CIAP. Thus, those without or with phosphate are a part of the strict category (1) or (2), respectively. Some SVPD reactivity to DNA lesions are known: terminal 5,6-dihydroxy-5,6-dihydrothymidine can removed by SVPD comparable to intact nucleobases, while terminal 5,6-dihydrothymidine cannot be recognized by the enzyme at all [18], and while a 'tandem damage', in which two lesions are immediately adjacent to each other on the same DNA strand, hardly be refractory to the enzyme [19]. In addition, interestingly, the enzyme is not able to remove a 3'terminal AP site (β-eliminated) (r'), but hydrolyze the penultimate phosphodiester bond to release a pdNpr' [20]. Thus, the 3' → 5' exonuclease activity of SVPD works on also the 'abnormal' 3' termini as well as the intact pdN termini. However, as shown in figure 7, any other fragments hardly detectable at 260 and 210 nm (not shown) except for dNs and Ns (unaltered released nucleobases). This implies that (i) most terminal dNs or dNps remain intact, otherwise (ii) not a few damaged terminal dNs or dNps refractory to SVPD are produced since it seems that a plane (an intact nucleobase) or sub-plane molecule (*e.g.*, 5,6-dihydrothymine) on C1' carbon is needed as a scaffolding to catalyze hydrolysis of a phosphodiester bond. If (ii), the 3' termini without phosphate may be underestimated. However, the lesion such as case (ii), a base lesion adjacent to a strand-break side, is so-called 'tandem lesion', that should be stochastically infrequent. The other point to be noted is the recognition to a 3'terminal pdN dangling a sugar residue, *e.g.*, 3'-phosphoglycolate and 3'-phosphoglycaldehyde [2], by SVPD. These can also be removed by the same manner as above-mentioned fragment: dNpr'.

On the other hand, piperidine-labile sites, which are removed leaving 3'termini with phosphate, unambiguously become SVPD-recognizable site with CIAP pretreatment. We have no information about piperidine-lability of 3'-phosphoglycolate or 3'-phosphoglycaldehyde terminus. It is, however, likely that these termini with sugar fragment are hydrolyzed under the alkaline condition to be 3'-phosphate termini, leaving hydroxyacetate or hydroxyacetaldehyde, respectively.

Then, the results obtained by the new method should be compared with the other conventional methods. A sample experiment was performed using dry pUC19/Sma I plasmid DNA irradiated with ^{60}Co γ-rays (figures 7 – 9 and Table 1). This is one of our studies to clarifying 'direct effect' to DNA in radiation biology. The 'direct effect' is defined as the effect of direct energy transfer from radiation to a target molecule, whereas the other, 'indirect effect' is defined as that of a radical product, *e.g.*, hydroxylradical (•OH) [21]. The possibility and the importance of 'direct effect' in living cell as comparison with those of 'indirect effect' have been controversial [22]. Apart from the details, Razskanovskiy *et al.* have been investigated the strand-break termini induced by 70 keV X-rays in a crystal duplex oligodeoxynucleotide by direct HPLC analysis of irradiated sample. According to their results, it appears that the yields of fragments with 3' or 5'-phosphate termini are generally independent on the sequence of the DNA. In the sequence of d(CG)n duplexes, the yield of the 3'-phosphate were clearly lower than those of 5'-phosphates [23, 24]. The similar results were obtained using dry oligonucleotide irradiated with vacuum UV [25, 26]. However, no information about termini with neither 3'phosphate nor 3'OH is contained in these results. On the other hand, figure 8 suggests that the yields of 3'-phosphate termini are predominant. It is noted that the values of 3'-phosphate termini as shown in Table 1 is estimated *indirectly* as difference between the values with and without CIAP pre-treatment. By the way, total yield of 3'termni (Table 1) is consistent with a prompt strand break yield predicted [27] as ~ 0.1 μmol/J. As mentioned previously, the yield of 3'termini without phosphate could be underestimated using the SVPD method proposed. Henner *et al.* actually found 3' termini with neither a hydroxyl nor a phosphoryl group, though this is a case of aqueous DNA irradiated with ^{60}Co γ-rays [28]. Considering from these results for the 3' termini, it seems that the damage spectrum of them cannot be determined only by a method.

Now, super coiled plasmid DNA method, as mentioned in the introduction section, is discussed. This method generally gives us not only prompt SSB and DSB yields, but also base excision repair (BER) enzyme site as additional SSB or DSB. In fully dry DNA irradiated with ^{60}Co γ-rays, the yields of the prompt SSB and DSB are 0.054 and 0.0053, respectively [29]. The yield of total strand breaks is two-fold lower than that obtained by other methods using the linear DNA (~ 0.1 μmol/J), even if taking contribution of DSB into account. This difference may be the results of more SSB on the open circular DNA by a SSB. Moreover, the SSB yield increases twice as much as that of prompt SSB by pre-treatment by a BER enzyme, Nth, which can remove a variety of pyrimidine lesions and AP site (~ 0.1 μmol/J), some of which correspond to piperidine-labile sites. The increase ratio to the yield of prompt strand breaks is consistent with the results of the SVPD method (figures 8, 9). On the other hand, there were also another BER enzyme (Fpg) sites comparable to Nth sites in the γ-irradiated dry DNA [29]. Although piperidine-labile sites are considered to be some of oxidized pyrimidine lesions and not to be oxidized purine lesions, purine lesions induced by 'direct' radiation effect also would not be piperidine-labile sites. Thus, it is quite important for finding the truth of DNA damage to consider both obtainable information and not obtainable one by each method to study DNA damage.

Some applications based on the methodology proposed can be considered. The fundamental of this methodology is to convert the amount of a lesion into that of DNA monomers collected by an exonuclease. Since there are several commercially-available nucleases, a variety of applications will have been developed. For example, it is interesting that one treats BER enzyme (e.g., Nth, Fpg) sites by SVPD. Phosphodiesterase II is a 5' → 3' exonuclease that can cleave 2'-deoxynucleoside-3-phosphate monomer (dNp) sequentially from 5'-OH termini of DNA. Hence, it is expected that the use of phosphodiesterase II clarifies features of the 5'-termini. Moreover, exonuclease III, that is a 3' → 5' exonuclease which cannot recognize protruding 3'OH termini but blunt and recessed ones, would be available for investigating feature of DSB termini. Thus, a variety of combinations of a exonuclease with a BER enzyme or a chemical will give us a lot of information about DNA damage spectrum particularly induced by ionizing radiations.

5. Conclusion

We have proposed a new methodology using an exonuclease, phosphodiesterase I, to quantify and qualify the 3' termini of damaged DNA with neither radioisotope nor fluorescent labeling, and one of the application utilizing piperidine to study the nucleobase lesions. The results are worthful enough to relativize those obtained by a conventional methodology. A variety of combinations of an exonuclease with a BER enzyme or a chemical will have given us information about distribution of lesions as well as their individual qualities and quantities in a damaged DNA.

6. Aknowledgments

We gratefully thank Dr. Y. Kobayashi (JAEA) for supporting ^{60}Co γ-irradiation experiments, and acknowledge the valuable advices by Dr. A. Yokoya (JAEA), Dr. N. Shikazono (JAEA), Dr. K. Fujii, and Dr. K. Saito. This research was supported by a Grant-in-Aid for Science Research for Young Scientists (No. 15710048) from the Japan Society for Promotion Science.

References

[1] Cadet, J., Douki, T., Ravanat, J.-L. (2007). Radiation chemistry of DNA in cells. In: *Abstract book of 13th international congress of radiation research* (pp. 8). Lawrence, KS: Radiation Research Society.

[2] Pogozelski, W. K. and Tullius, T. D. (1998). Oxidative strand scission of nucleic acids: Routes initiated by hydrogen abstraction from the sugar moiety. *Chem. Rev.*, 98, 1089-1107.

[3] Kobayashi, K., Hieda, K., Maezawa, H., Furusawa, Y., and Ito, T. (1991). Effects of K-shell X-ray absorption of intracellular phosphorus on yeast cells. *Int. J. Radiat. Biol.*, 59, 643-650.

[4] Hieda, K. (1994). DNA damage induced by vacuum and soft X-ray photons from synchrotron radiation. *Int. J. Radiat. Biol.*, 66, 561-567.

[5] Yokoya, A., Watanabe, R., and Hara, T. (1999). Single- and double-strand breaks in solid pBR322 DNA induced by ultrasoft X-rays at photon energies of 388, 435 and 537 eV. *J. Radiat. Res.*, 40, 145-158.

[6] Akamatsu. K., Fujii, K., and Yokoya, A. (2003). Infrared spectral change in 2-deoxy-D-ribose by irradiation with monochromatic photons around oxygen K-edge. *Nucl. Instr. Met. Phys. Res. B* 199, 328-331.

[7] Fujii, K., Akamatsu, K., and Yokoya, A. (2004). The measurement of molecular fragments from DNA components using synchrotron radiation. *Surface Sci.* 528, 249-254.

[8] Akamatsu. K., Fujii, K., and Yokoya, A. (2004). Qualitative and quantitative analyses of the decomposition products that arise from the exposure of thymine to

monochromatic ultrasoft X rays and ^{60}Co gamma rays in the solid state. *Radiat. Res.*, 161, 442-450.

[9]   Fujii, K., Akamatsu, K., and Yokoya, A. (2004). Ion desorption from DNA components irradiated with 0.5 keV ultrasoft X-ray photons. *Radiat. Res.* 161, 435-441.

[10] Yokoya, A., Akamatsu, K., Fujii, K., and Ukai, M. (2004). "In situ" observation of guanine radicals induced by ultrasoft X-ray irradiation around the K-edge regions of nitrogen and oxygen. *Int. J. Radiat. Biol.*, 80, 833-839.

[11] Melamede, R. J., Kow, Y. W., Bespalov, I. A., and Wallace, S. S. (1996). Detection of oxidative DNA base damages: Immunochemical and electrochemical approaches. In: Pfeifer, G. P. (Ed.), Technologies for detection of DNA damage and mutations (pp. 103-115). New York, NY: Plenum Press.

[12] Ide, H., Akamatsu, K., Kimura, Y., Michiue, K., Makino, K., Asaeda, A., Takamori, Y, and Kubo, K. (1993). Synthesis and damage specificity of a novel probe for the detection of abasic sites in DNA. *Biochemistry*, 32, 8276-8283.

[13] Sato, K and Greenberg, M. M. (2005). Selective detection of 2-deoxyribonolactone in DNA. *J. Am. Chem. Soc.*, 127, 2806-2807.

[14] Dhar, S., Kodama, T., and Greenberg, M. M. (2007). Selective detection and quantification of oxidized abasic lesions in DNA. *J. Am. Chem. Soc.*, 129, 8702-8703.

[15] Akamatsu, K. (2007). A novel methodology for characterizing strand-break termini and damaged bases in plasmid DNA exposed to ionizing radiation. *Anal. Biochem.*, 362, 229-235.

[16] Maxam, A. M. and Gilbert, W. (1977). A new method for sequencing DNA. *Proc. Natl. Acad. Sci. USA*, 74, 560-564.

[17] Burrows, C. J. and Muller, J. G. (1998). Oxidative nucleobase modifications leading to strand scission. *Chem. Rev.*, 98, 1109-1151.

[18] Weinfeld, M., Soderlind, K. M., and Buchko, G. W. (1993). Influence of nucleic acid base aromaticity on substrate reactivity with enzymes acting on single-stranded DNA. *Nucleic Acids Res.*, 21, 621-626.

[19] Bowman, K. J., Le Pla, R., Guichard, Y., Farmer, P. B., and Jones, G. D. D. (2001). Evaluation of phosphodiesterase I-based protocols for the detection of multiply damaged sites in DNA: the detection of abasic, oxidative and alkylative tandem damage in DNA oligonucleaotides. *Nucleic. Acids Res.* 29, e101.

[20] Stuart, G. R. and Chambers, R. W. (1987). Synthesis and properties of oligodeoxynucleotides with an AP site at a preselected position. *Nucleic Acids Res.*, 18, 7451-7462.

[21] Becker, D. and Sevilla, M. D. (1993). The chemical consequences of radiation damage to DNA. Avd. Radiat. Biol., 17, 121-180.

[22] Douki, T., Ravanat, J.-L., Pouget, J.-P., Testard, I., and Cadet, J. (2006). Minor contribution of direct ionization to DNA base damage induced by heavy ions. *Int. J. Radiat. Biol.*, 82, 119-127.

[23] Debije, M. G., Razskazovskiy, Y., and Bernhard, W. A. (2001). The yield of strand breaks resulting from direct-type effects in crystalline DNA X-irradiated at 4 K and room temperature. *J. Am. Chem. Soc.*, 123, 2917-2918.

[24] Razskazovskiy, Y., Debije, M. G., Howerton, S. B., Williams, L. D., and Bernhard, W. A. (2003). Strand breaks produced in X-irradiated crystalline DNA: Influence of base sequence. *Radiat. Res.*, 160, 334-339.

[25] Ito, T. and Saito, M. (1991). Effects of vacuum ultraviolet radiation on deoxyoligonucleotides in solids in the wavelength region around and above ionization potential– with special reference to the chain scission. *Radiat. Phys. Chem.*, 37, 681-690.

[26] Ito, T. and Saito, M. (1998). Degradation of oligonucleotides by vacuum-UV radiation in solid: Roles of the phosphate group and bases. *Photochem. Photobiol.*, 48, 567-572.

[27] Bernhard, W. A. and Close, D. M. (2004). DNA damage dictates the biological consequences of ionizing radiation: The chemical pathways. In: Mozumder, A. and Hatano, Y. (Eds.), Charged particle and photon interactions with matter (pp. 431-470). New York, NY : Marcel Dekker Inc..

[28] Henner, W. D., Grunberg, S. M., and Haseltine, W. A. (1982). Site and structure of γ radiation-induced DNA strand breaks. *J. Biol. Chem.*, 257, 11750-11754.

[29] Yokoya, A, Cunniffe, S. M. T., and O'Neill, P. (2002). Effect of hydration on the induction of strand breaks and base lesions in plasmid DNA films by γ-radiation. *J. Am. Chem. Soc.*, 124, 8859-8866.

[30] Bhagwat, M. and Gerlt, J. A. (1996). 3'- and 5'-strand cleavage reactions catalyzed by the Fpg protein from Escherichia coli occur via successive β- and δ-elimination mechanism, respectively. *Biochemistry*, 35, 659-665.

[31] Henle, E. S., Roots, R., Holley, W. R., and Chatterjee, A. (1995). DNA strand breakage is correlated with unaltered nase release after gamma irradiation. *Radiat. Res.*, 143, 144-150.

[32] Swarts, S. G., Sevilla, M. D., Becker, D., Tokar, C. J., and Wheeler, K. T. (1992). Radiation-induced DNA damage as a function of hydration. I. Release of unaltered bases. *Radiat. Res.*, 129, 333-344.

In: New Research on DNA Damage
Editors: Honoka Kimura and Aoi Suzuki

ISBN 978-1-60456-581-2
© 2008 Nova Science Publishers, Inc.

Chapter 12

Factors Governing the Recurrence and Breakpoint Distribution of Chromosomal Translocations in Human Tumors

Francisco J. Novo[*]

Department of Genetics, University of Navarra., Spain

Abstract

Chromosomal translocations, a frequent finding in cancer cells, are the result of double-strand breaks that are repaired via non-homologous end-joining in somatic cells. Since many translocations are recurrent and the breakpoints are non-randomly distributed, a widely held view posits that local sequence factors are responsible for the appearance of double-strand breaks at specific genomic sites. However, efforts to identify such factors are complicated by their widespread occurrence throughout the genome. Thus, establishing a convincing direct causal link between specific sequence elements and nearby breakpoints has been difficult.

Other potential factors that could account for the recurrence of chromosomal translocations are frequently overlooked. For instance, the importance of chromosome localization inside the cell nucleus, and the relative positions of chromosomes with respect to each other, could determine which genes participate in specific translocations. Therefore, studies that aim to identify the causes of recurrence of chromosomal translocations should take into account factors responsible for the nuclear co-localization of specific genes.

Likewise, little attention has been given to the power of functional selection in determining the identity of the genes translocated and the localization of breakpoints within those genes. However, careful analysis of reciprocal translocations that create chimeric fusion proteins could show whether recurrence is the result of strong cellular selection pressures for the functions encoded by specific genes. Furthermore, the

---

[*] 31080 Pamplona, e-mail: fnovo@unav.es.

requirement to keep the reading frame in the fusion product could explain, in these cases, the non-random distribution of translocation breakpoints across those genes.

I propose that the generation of DNA double-strand breaks might be widespread throughout the genome, resulting in a relatively high number of potential translocation events. Most of these would never take place because the genes involved are far apart within the nuclear space. Of those rearrangements that would be allowed, only a small subset could generate an in-frame fusion product with oncogenic potential. Thus, the non-random genomic distribution of translocation breakpoints in tumor samples might be due to the fact that these samples contain the limited collection of rearrangements that were able to survive distinct functional requirements imposed by cellular selection pressures.

Non-Random Chromosomal Translocations in Cancer

Most cancer cells display some type of chromosomal rearrangement. It is not always clear whether such genetic aberrations are the cause of the disease, or "passenger" mutations acquired during tumor development. Solid tumors, for instance, contain numerous chromosomal rearrangements (deletions, translocations, duplications) and it is unlikely that all of them are causally related to tumor progression [1]. Hematological malignancies and some sarcomas, on the other hand, display only one or a few aberrations, usually balanced chromosomal translocations, many of which have been shown to be the initiating event in tumor development [2][3]. Extensive analysis of chromosomal translocations in human malignancies over the past three decades has revealed two main outcomes by which such rearrangements drive cancer progression: i) promoter exchange (mainly in lymphoid neoplasms) and ii) generation of chimaeric genes that are translated as fusion proteins (myeloid leukemias and solid tumors) [4].

The clinical relevance of chromosomal translocations, their causal association with cancer initiation and their high prevalence in human tumors, have led to intensive research on the mechanisms responsible for the generation of this type of rearrangement. The consensus derived from these studies is that chromosomal translocations are the result of misrepaired DNA double-strand breaks (DSB) in somatic cells [5-8]. DSBs are repaired mainly by homologous recombination and by non-homologous end-joining, depending on the phase of the cell cycle in which the DSB is present. Given the relatively high number of endogenous DSBs created per cell per cell cycle [9], a slight decrease in the rate of correct repair of these lesions will increase the likelihood of incorrect joining, creating new opportunities for the appearance of reciprocal translocations.

Some of the balanced chromosomal translocations found in tumors are recurrent, in the sense that they are present in different patients with the same tumor type, or even in different tumor types [10]. Furthermore, characterization of fusion sequences at the molecular level in different patient samples has shown that, at least for a few genes, breakpoints tend to cluster in specific regions. As a result, the distribution of translocation breakpoints found in tumor samples follows a non-random pattern, with a few sites in which breakpoints are more frequent than expected by chance. In this context, the DSB repair model described above, which is fairly well established by experimental data, is frequently invoked to explain the non-random distribution of translocation breakpoints throughout the genome. Given the proven link between DSB repair and chromosomal translocations, it is tempting to speculate that local sequence features responsible for the generation of DSBs will also lead to the presence of translocation breakpoints at specific genomic locations.

In this regard, various sequence motifs and structures have been implicated in the localization of translocation breakpoints in lymphoid malignancies with rearrangements of the genes coding for immunoglobulin and T-cell receptor chains [11-13]. Similarly, the role of *in vivo* topoisomerase-II cleavage sites has been extensively studied in specific types of myeloid leukemia with rearrangements of the *MLL* gene [14-17]. However, a convincing causal role of such sites in the generation of translocation breakpoints has been difficult to establish. Similarly, various sequence elements and structural features of chromatin have been analyzed in other translocation breakpoint sequences [18, 19]. Despite all this work, no single feature (or combination of features) has been unequivocally associated with the generation of a translocation breakpoint in its vicinity.

Since these studies rely on the analysis of translocation sequences from different partner genes and different tumor types, the lack of success at associating specific sequence features with translocation breakpoints is most likely due to the heterogeneity of the mechanisms involved in different translocations. Identifying sequence motifs or features overrepresented in translocation sequences from many different fusions and tumor types is a difficult task, but searches focused on specific tumor types or gene fusions might be more productive. Furthermore, if a sequence feature is to be associated to translocation breakpoints in different fusions and tumors, such feature will be fairly common throughout the genome. This has been highlighted by the recent finding that a hot-spot for translocation breakpoints in the *MLL* gene coincides with an active internal promoter [20], suggesting that translocation breakpoints, at least for this gene, are located preferentially in regions in which chromatin adopts an open conformation due to transcription initiation. However, many such regions are present in the human genome, as shown by recent data from the ENCODE Project [21] and by the identification of thousands of intronic transcription units in 74% of all human RefSeq genes [22]. Therefore, since the prior probability that a translocation breakpoint is near an intragenic transcription initiation site is rather high, the significance of such association is difficult to interpret, and establishing a convincing causal link becomes a very difficult task. This also applies to other features and sequence motifs that are expected to be present at high numbers throughout the genome. For example, 2500-3000 copies of a 10-nucleotide motif are expected, by chance alone, in a mammalian-sized genome.

"Non-randomness" due to Functional Selection of Random Events

The widely held view that local sequence factors are responsible for the presence of translocation breakpoints at specific genomic sites assumes that the localization of DSBs throughout the genome is revealed exclusively by the position of known translocation breakpoints. Thus, if translocation breakpoints are non-randomly distributed, the inference is made that DSBs were also created non-randomly across the genome, due to the non-random distribution of putative sequence elements responsible for the generation of those DSBs. However, this is not necessarily the case. In fact, this reasoning is fundamentally flawed because it is reasonable to suppose that most of the DSBs created during the lifetime of a somatic cell have been properly repaired −otherwise the cell will undergo apoptosis due to surveillance mechanisms. This means that translocation breakpoints detected in tumor cells represent only a minority of the total number of DSBs generated in those cells. This scenario, in which DSBs are created more randomly throughout the genome, fits in better with the widespread genomic occurrence of sequence motifs and features that are responsible for the initiation of DSBs. According to this view, on a background of randomly (or near-randomly) generated DSBs, a few of these are misrepaired as translocation events, but only a small subset of these will result in oncogenic translocation fusions and will eventually be found in tumors. This is the subset of non-random translocation breakpoints that drive tumor growth and that we can detect in cancer cells.

A clear implication of this hypothesis is that the factors responsible for "non-randomness" in the genomic distribution of translocations breakpoints are not necessarily related to the initial generation of DSBs; most likely, they are related to the selection process by which only certain DSBs eventually make it to a tumor. Such selection is the result of the spatial and functional properties of the genes involved in a given chromosomal rearrangement. A brief review of these properties will shed some light on the factors that govern the localization of translocation breakpoints in human cancers.

Nuclear Localization

The importance of chromosome localization inside the nucleus has only recently been recognized as an important pre-requisite that dictates which chromosomal rearrangements are possible. Over the last few years, studies on the position of chromosomes in the cell nucleus have established the concept of chromosome territories [23-25]. More recently, it has been shown that chromatin loops can move short distances in response to biological cues; such movements are necessary for coordinate gene regulation, leading to the concept of transcription factories [26-29]. In this context, it must be noted that a pre-requisite for the formation of a translocation is that two DSBs are generated in different genes at the same time. Since the free ends of a DSB are relatively fixed [30], those genes must be in close proximity so that the free ends can make contact within the cell nucleus and be joined together. Thus, the non-random arrangement of chromosomes with respect to each other is one important factor that dictates the probability of finding specific chromosomal translocations in tumors [26, 31, 32]. Since co-regulation is an important factor for co-localization of two genes to the same transcription factory (assuming the both genes are in neighboring territories) [26, 32], it is reasonable to speculate that genes involved in a translocation must be located in neighboring chromosomal territories and are co-expressed in the particular cell type where the tumor is initiated. This spatial requirement implies that only certain gene pairs are capable of engaging in a translocation, depending of their nuclear position and transcriptional status. This could explain why certain translocations are recurrent, and why some genes are preferentially fused with each other in specific tumor types.

Oncogenic Potential

Any selection process implies some form of survival, so it is reasonable to expect that factors responsible for the selection of a specific subset of chromosomal translocations will be related to the functional properties of the translocation products. Surprisingly, very little attention has been given to the role that functional properties can play in creating a non-random distribution of fused gene pairs and translocation breakpoints. In this respect, it must be kept in mind that the analysis of tumor samples is an extreme case of ascertainment bias; by definition, we will only detect translocations that are important for tumor growth, and we will miss all other possible translocations that did not provide a proliferative advantage to the cell. Keeping this in mind, it becomes clear that any DSBs that might participate in a rearrangement, but have been left unrepaired, will never be detected in tumors, because unrepaired DSBs trigger apoptosis in normal cells [7]. Moreover, most random translocations are expected to be deleterious to the cell, since two different gene alleles (one allele of each gene) have been inactivated by the breakage, and the resulting fusion gene will not necessarily have an advantageous biological function. Again, cells carrying those translocations will eventually disappear from the tissue and will not be detected in tumor samples. In the end, the only translocations that can be found in tumor samples are those specific translocations which create fusion genes with the potential to initiate tumor growth.

The relevance of this is best exemplified by chromosomal translocations that create chimeric genes translated as fusion proteins, an important group of reciprocal translocations that accounts for 20% of cancer morbidity in humans [4]. In this type of translocations, two partner genes are broken and fused together in such a way that the fusion product must conserve an intact reading frame if it is to be functionally relevant. Additionally, the oncogenic potential of the resulting fusion protein depends on the presence of specific protein domains encoded by both partner genes. All these requirements work as a selective "filter", so that only rearrangements between specific genes and only breakpoints located at specific positions are compatible with tumor development. This fact could be crucial for the localization of translocation breakpoints in tumor samples, as illustrated in Figure 1. In that example, two genes are theoretically capable of participating in a reciprocal translocation with oncogenic properties, due to the protein domains encoded by some regions of those genes. Even if both genes co-localize to the same transcription factory and sustain unrepaired DSB simultaneously, not all possible breakpoints will lead to the generation of a fusion gene with oncogenic potential. Looking at the position of the regions that code for the necessary protein domains, and considering the reading frames of the various exons involved, it becomes clear that an oncogenic fusion protein will only be generated if breakpoints are located within specific introns. Due to the ascertainment bias mentioned above, when we analyze tumor samples we will only detect translocations containing these breakpoints, because all other possible breakpoints would lead to the loss of an important functional domain in the fusion protein, or to an out-of-frame product, and will never be found in tumor samples.

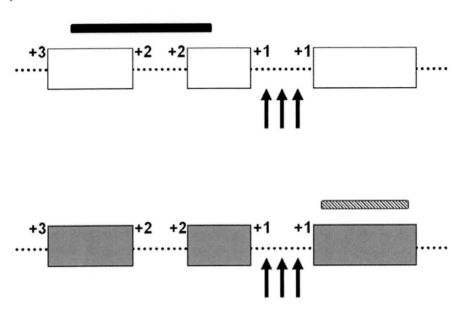

Figure 1. Functional requirements determine the localization of translocation breakpoints in specific genomic regions in tumor samples. The figure shows two hypothetical genes, each of them with three exons (white and gray boxes, respectively), that participate in a reciprocal translocation to generate a fusion gene. The reading frame with which each exon begins and ends is also shown (numbers after the + symbol). Above each gene, regions coding for important protein domains are represented as a solid bar (top gene, a functional domain is encoded by the first two exons) or as a hashed bar (bottom gene, a functional domain is encoded by exon 3). Generation of many DSBs at random in these genes would create an opportunity for many possible translocations. However, only those combinations of breakpoints that keep an intact reading frame and include both functional domains will be found in tumor samples, because they are the only ones that will result in a fusion product with oncogenic potential. Thus, distinct functional requirements will define the region where translocation breakpoints will be found in tumors (vertical arrows).

Final Remarks

The evidence reviewed lends strong support to the notion that two important features of oncogenic chromosomal translocations, namely the recurrence of the genes involved and the non-random localization of breakpoints, are not necessarily due to the non-random genomic distribution of sequence elements responsible for the generation of DSBs. My contention is that both facts, particularly in translocations that result in gene fusions, can be explained by the spatial and functional requirements that must be met in order to generate a translocation product with oncogenic potential. This hypothesis can be computationally tested by an exhaustive analysis of the protein domains, biological functions and reading frames of all fusion proteins known to date in human tumors. Even though technically demanding, this task is now feasible thanks to the wealth of information and databases available in the public domain.

References

[1] Albertson DG, Collins C, McCormick F, Gray JW. Chromosome aberrations in solid tumors. *Nat. Genet.* 2003 Aug;34(4):369-76.

[2] Mitelman F, Johansson B, Mertens F. Fusion genes and rearranged genes as a linear function of chromosome aberrations in cancer. *Nat. Genet.* 2004 Apr;36(4):331-4.

[3] Aplan PD. Causes of oncogenic chromosomal translocation. *Trends Genet.* 2006 Jan;22(1):46-55.

[4] Mitelman F, Johansson B, Mertens F. The impact of translocations and gene fusions on cancer causation. *Nat. Rev. Cancer.* 2007 Apr;7(4):233-45.

[5] Agarwal S, Tafel AA, Kanaar R. DNA double-strand break repair and chromosome translocations. DNA Repair (Amst). 2006 Sep 8;5(9-10):1075-81.

[6] Mills KD, Ferguson DO, Alt FW. The role of DNA breaks in genomic instability and tumorigenesis. *Immunol. Rev.* 2003 Aug;194:77-95.

[7] van Gent DC, Hoeijmakers JH, Kanaar R. Chromosomal stability and the DNA double-stranded break connection. *Nat. Rev. Genet.* 2001 Mar;2(3):196-206.

[8] Wyman C, Kanaar R. DNA double-strand break repair: All's well that ends well. *Annu. Rev. Genet..* 2006;40:363-83.

[9] Vilenchik MM, Knudson AG. Endogenous DNA double-strand breaks: Production, fidelity of repair, and induction of cancer. *Proc. Natl. Acad. Sci.* U S A. 2003 Oct 28;100(22):12871-6.

[10] Mitelman F, Mertens F, Johansson B. Prevalence estimates of recurrent balanced cytogenetic aberrations and gene fusions in unselected patients with neoplastic disorders. *Genes Chromosomes Cancer.* 2005 Aug;43(4):350-66.

[11] Lieber MR, Yu K, Raghavan SC. Roles of nonhomologous DNA end joining, V(D)J recombination, and class switch recombination in chromosomal translocations. DNA Repair (Amst). 2006 Sep 8;5(9-10):1234-45.

[12] Marculescu R, Vanura K, Montpellier B, Roulland S, Le T, Navarro JM, et al. Recombinase, chromosomal translocations and lymphoid neoplasia: Targeting mistakes and repair failures. DNA Repair (Amst). 2006 Sep 8;5(9-10):1246-58.

[13] Raghavan SC, Swanson PC, Ma Y, Lieber MR. Double-strand break formation by the RAG complex at the bcl-2 major breakpoint region and at other non-B DNA structures in vitro. *Mol. Cell Biol.* 2005 Jul;25(14):5904-19.

[14] Aplan PD. Chromosomal translocations involving the MLL gene: Molecular mechanisms. DNA Repair (Amst). 2006 Sep 8;5(9-10):1265-72.

[15] Felix CA, Kolaris CP, Osheroff N. Topoisomerase II and the etiology of chromosomal translocations. DNA Repair (Amst). 2006 Sep 8;5(9-10):1093-108.

[16] Mirault ME, Boucher P, Tremblay A. Nucleotide-resolution mapping of topoisomerase-mediated and apoptotic DNA strand scissions at or near an MLL translocation hotspot. *Am. J. Hum. Genet.* 2006 Nov;79(5):779-91.

[17] Sung PA, Libura J, Richardson C. Etoposide and illegitimate DNA double-strand break repair in the generation of MLL translocations: New insights and new questions. DNA Repair (Amst). 2006 Sep 8;5(9-10):1109-18.

[18] Kolomietz E, Meyn MS, Pandita A, Squire JA. The role of alu repeat clusters as mediators of recurrent chromosomal aberrations in tumors. *Genes. Chromosomes Cancer.* 2002 Oct;35(2):97-112.

[19] Zhang Y, Rowley JD. Chromatin structural elements and chromosomal translocations in leukemia. DNA Repair (Amst). 2006 Sep 8;5(9-10):1282-97.

[20] Scharf S, Zech J, Bursen A, Schraets D, Oliver PL, Kliem S, et al. Transcription linked to recombination: A gene-internal promoter coincides with the recombination hot spot II of the human MLL gene. *Oncogene.* 2007 Mar 1;26(10):1361-71.

[21] ENCODE Project Consortium, Birney E, Stamatoyannopoulos JA, Dutta A, Guigo R, Gingeras TR, et al. Identification and analysis of functional elements in 1% of the human genome by the ENCODE pilot project. *Nature.* 2007 Jun 14;447(7146):799-816.

[22] Nakaya HI, Amaral PP, Louro R, Lopes A, Fachel AA, Moreira YB, et al. Genome mapping and expression analyses of human intronic noncoding RNAs reveal tissue-specific patterns and enrichment in genes related to regulation of transcription. *Genome. Biol.* 2007;8(3):R43.

[23] Bolzer A, Kreth G, Solovei I, Koehler D, Saracoglu K, Fauth C, et al. Three-dimensional maps of all chromosomes in human male fibroblast nuclei and prometaphase rosettes. *PLoS. Biol.* 2005 May;3(5):e157.

[24] Pederson T. The spatial organization of the genome in mammalian cells. *Curr. Opin. Genet. Dev.* 2004 Apr;14(2):203-9.

[25] Meaburn KJ, Misteli T. Cell biology: Chromosome territories. *Nature.* 2007 Jan 25;445(7126):379-781.

[26] Branco MR, Pombo A. Intermingling of chromosome territories in interphase suggests role in translocations and transcription-dependent associations. *PLoS. Biol.* 2006 May;4(5):e138.

[27] Fraser P, Bickmore W. Nuclear organization of the genome and the potential for gene regulation. *Nature.* 2007 May 24;447(7143):413-7.

[28] Kosak ST, Scalzo D, Alworth SV, Li F, Palmer S, Enver T, et al. Coordinate gene regulation during hematopoiesis is related to genomic organization. *PLoS. Biol.* 2007 Nov 20;5(11):e309.

[29] Osborne CS, Chakalova L, Brown KE, Carter D, Horton A, Debrand E, et al. Active genes dynamically colocalize to shared sites of ongoing transcription. *Nat. Genet.* 2004 Oct;36(10):1065-71.

[30] Soutoglou E, Dorn JF, Sengupta K, Jasin M, Nussenzweig A, Ried T, et al. Positional stability of single double-strand breaks in mammalian cells. *Nat. Cell Biol.* 2007 Jun;9(6):675-82.

[31] Meaburn KJ, Misteli T, Soutoglou E. Spatial genome organization in the formation of chromosomal translocations. *Semin. Cancer Biol.* 2007 Feb;17(1):80-90.

[32] Osborne CS, Chakalova L, Mitchell JA, Horton A, Wood AL, Bolland DJ, et al. Myc dynamically and preferentially relocates to a transcription factory occupied by igh. *PLoS. Biol.* 2007 Aug;5(8):e192.

In: New Research on DNA Damage
Editors: Honoka Kimura and Aoi Suzuki

ISBN 978-1-60456-581-2
© 2008 Nova Science Publishers, Inc.

Chapter 13

Current Knowledge on Lead as an Inducer of Human DNA Damage

Joana Roma-Torres[1]
Portuguese National Institute of Health,
Centre of Environmental and Occupational Health, Portugal

Abstract

Since most ancient times lead has been widely used due to its physical and chemical unique properties that make it an excellent metal with innumerable uses. Long ago human kind has also found out about its adverse effects to health. Even so its utilisations kept increasing exponentially alongside with industrialization and technology improvements. Not until the two last decades of the 20th century has the earth begun to be protected against its anthropogenic sources of widespread dissemination through environmental systems. Steps taken in this direction are too important of a measure that allows keeping its environmental concentrations essentially under control. Meanwhile this may lead to the misconception that its total world production and use over the last years has been diminishing, although real numbers point out to a constant increase [1, 2], meaning there is still a huge number of people throughout the world exposed to it and, consequently, to its toxic effects.

Lead is essentially a chronic or cumulative toxin, which can potentially affect every organs and systems. International Agency for Research on Cancer (IARC) has classified lead and inorganic lead compounds, back in 1987, as possibly carcinogenic in humans – IARC group 2B [3], judging evidences to be inadequate in humans. IARC has however undertaken a recent reevaluation of lead's carcinogenicity and changed that classification to probably carcinogenic to humans – IARC group 2A [4] based in several studies that concluded on a relationship between exposure to lead and cytogenetic markers frequencies, such as micronucleus and chromosomal aberrations and on an increase of incidence of overall cancer, and lung and bladder cancer [5, 6] in individuals exposed.

---

[1] Praça Coronel Pacheco, 15, 4050-453 Porto, Portugal.

Genetic effects of lead seem to be mediated by modulation of reactive oxygen species together with interaction with proteins, including those involved in DNA repair in a way that can be considered indirect, by means of decreasing cells capability of protecting and repairing damaged DNA in spite of directly damaging it [7]. Potential genotoxic effects of lead might contribute for development of normal to cancerous cells by inducing or allowing loss of genomic stability and acquisition of genetic alterations [8, 9].

Within this chapter findings of genotoxicity in human populations and proposed mechanisms for lead effects in genetic systems will be reviewed in order to obtain a state of the art of such effects of lead in humans.

Introduction

Metals

Metals have long been known to men and therefore recognised as toxic agents to humans. Living organisms require merely a few metals and even so in very low doses (this demand applies for sodium, potassium, calcium, iron, copper, nickel, magnesium and manganese). When at high concentrations even those metals essential for life become toxic and dangerous for biological systems. On the other hand a few other metals (including lead, mercury, cadmium, chromium and arsenic) have no nutritional or biochemical functions and is therefore harmful in any concentration.

Metal extraction and applications grew considerably alongside with industrial development and this increase reflected itself in generalised contamination of the environment and increasing of exposure of populations. Human exposure to metals can therefore occur trough inhalation, ingestion and/or dermal absorption of contaminated items, as air, water, earth, and foodstuffs.

Extension of human absorption, distribution and excretion as long as extension of toxicity and danger to human health of different metals depend of several physical and chemical characteristics (as solubility, ions stability, particle size, chemical speciation, biochemical interactions, electron stability, etc).

Metals are widely spread and redistributed naturally throughout the environment by both geological and biological cycles and by anthropogenic activities. According to Duffus[2] [11] metals may be chemically defined as elements that conduct electricity, have a metallic lustre, are malleable and ductile, form positive ions and have basic oxides and most elements might be described as metals.

Different classifications and several terms have been used in specifying groups of metals. As such, metals can be considered as 'common' or 'noble' based in its ability to form positive ions. Another classification is as 'heavy' or 'light' metals (lead has widely been defined as a 'heavy metal'). Nonetheless a consensus in defining 'heavy metal' is difficult to achieve and this type of classification is somehow difficult to understand in a scientific basis. Some authors refer to it based in a classification by density while others choose defining it based in

---

[2] Citating Atkins [10].

atomic masses and/or in chemical and toxicological properties. In an International Union of Pure and Applied Chemistry (IUPAC) Technical Report prepared by John Duffus [11], a very complete review of all these terms is made and the author concludes that the term 'heavy metal' is not used with consistency enough to be considered as a single group of metals with similar chemical properties and the author defends that classification as 'heavy metals' should be abandoned. Accordingly to this, term 'heavy metal' will be avoided within this chapter and lead will be referred to simply as a metal.

Lead - General Characteristics

Lead occurs naturally in the earth's crust and is nowadays found in almost every system of the environment. Its chemical symbol is Pb (from *plumbum,* Latin word for "liquid silver"). It is a metal from group 14 of the table of chemical elements with atomic number 82, atomic weight 207.19 and density of 11.34. It has four naturally occurring stable isotopes with different atomic numbers that are, with indication of estimated abundances within commas, ^{208}Pb (51-53%), ^{206}Pb (23,5-27%), ^{207}Pb (20,5-23%) e ^{204}Pb (1,35-1,5%) and three oxidation states, Pb(0), Pb(II) and Pb(IV) [6].

Although metallic lead in its elemental form Pb(0) does exist in nature (it is very soft and ductile, bluish white in colour but changing to grey when in contact with air) it is extremely scarce and exists in the environment primarily as Pb(II) and Pb(IV). It forms extremely hard compounds when together with other metals (examples are antimony, arsenic, copper and zinc) [6].

Most lead in the world crust (~86,6%) is found as lead sulphide PbS (galena) but is also found as anglesite ($PbSO_4$), cerussite ($PbCO_3$) and other lead ores [6]. Nevertheless, as a result of human activity, lead is nowadays also found in the atmosphere, mainly as $PbSO_4$ and $PbCO_3$.

Historical Overview

Special characteristics of lead (as low melting point, ductibillity, resistance to corrosion and easiness in forming metallic alloys) made of it one of the first metals exploited by mankind (alchemists considered it as the "oldest metal") and it has been widely used since ancient times in domestic tools, ammunitions, ornaments and statuettes. Because of the bright colours characteristic of most lead compounds (black, white, yellow and read) it has also been used as additives to paints, pigments, and cosmetics.

Use of lead was particularly important within the Roman Empire. Technology needed for large-scale piped water demanded for a huge use of lead sheets for tanks coating and piping. Romans also used lead compounds for glazed ceramics and for cooking utensils. They also used to boil wine in lead pots as a way of preserving and sweetening it (properties of lead acetate, $Pb(C_2H_3O_2)_2$, "lead sugar" [12]) producing a drink highly consumed within the Empire[3].

Industrial revolution, however, brought a dramatic increase in the use of lead worldwide. Its consequences were the occurrence of epidemic lead poisoning and the generalized environmental lead contamination and were therefore followed by an increase of lead concentrations in general population's blood [16, 17]. Afterwards, finding of antiknock and octane level strengthener properties[4] of addition of lead to gasoline, as the organic compound tetra-ethyl lead, (TEL) made of that metal an important and economic contribution for motor vehicle and performance development since the 1930s. TEL was therefore routinely added to gasoline to prevent knocking[5] or premature detonation in internal combustion [18].

In the early nineties world total lead consumption was up to 3 million tons a year. Addition of lead to gasoline became by far the greatest use of the metal and its most significant source of environmental dissemination, polluting earth, air and water in places as further from pollution sources as the Arctic [19-21].

Although harmful effects of lead have been well described long ago (Hipócrates, 460-377 AC) its use kept increasing [13, 22]. Eventually its huge toxicity for all living organisms became much too evident and its danger could no longer be ignored. Since the 1980s important measures have been taken in developed countries in order to keep lead usage under control. Two significant examples are phase out of lead from gasoline and abolition of incorporation of that metal in tin paints, packages, and ceramics[6]. Legislation concerning lead and lead compounds in products in different countries can be found in a review from the Nordic Council of Ministers from 2003 [23].

Despite measures taken several sources of environmental lead contamination continue to exist. Lead and its compounds are nowadays still used worldwide being lead-acid storage batteries by far the most important consumer (>80%) [2]. Lead oxide is pasted on the battery grids, which are immersed in a tank of dilute sulphuric acid, and is the active material in the electrochemical reaction. These batteries are used in motor vehicles, electric powered vehicles and as stationary output as a means of back up power emergency source in cases of power failure [24].

Other important applications for lead are shields against radiation, glass, glaze, plastic, functional ceramics, building and construction industries, electronic technologies (television and computer screens are made of leaded glass to restrain electromagnetic radiation), smelters and welding. Efforts have been made in finding out alternatives to lead in these areas too but

---

[3] Some authors explain the fall of the Roman Empire as a consequence of both infertility and psychosis rates raising and Intelligent Quotient (IQ) diminishment, which they impute to the vast use of lead [13, 14]. Results of an experiment by German K. B. Hofmann back in 1883, referred to by Lessler [13] demonstrated that wine treated and kept as Romans did could contain up to 30 mg/L of lead. Marqués [15] states that average wine consumption in Ancient Rome would be in between 1 and 5 litres per day and per person. Hernberg [12] reports findings of high concentrations of lead in archaeological Roman bones.

[4] Special property of lead to increase engine performance by preventing self-ignition (engine knock) was discovered by Thomas Midgley, Jr and Thomas A. Boyd at the General Motors Research Laboratory in 1921. Lead additives enabled auto manufactures to produce more powerful engines by increasing the octane of gasoline and also functions as a lubricant of the exhaust valves, particularly the valve seats [18].

[5] When compression rate (degree of compression of fuel and air) is too high, part of the air-fuel mixture detonates and explodes (creating a knock), resulting in loss of power and overheating [18].

[6] European Directive 84/500/CEE, changed by European Directive 2005/31/CE.

hypothesis developed so far showed not to be as efficient in most cases, or to be as much or more toxic than lead itself. While efficient alternatives are not found demand for lead will continue to grow worldwide.

Numbers

Refined lead can be obtained from mined ores in many countries (primary lead) and/or obtained from recycled materials such as battery plates and lead pipes (secondary lead). Its total production (both primary and secondary) kept increasing and came up to values up to 3 million tons per year back in the seventies [1]. Meanwhile an increasing proportion of supply of lead is being met by recycling (over 50%). Nowadays China, United States, and Australia occupy the first three positions in world production. Altogether with Peru, Canada and Mexico these six countries alone account for 82% of the worlds mine production [6].

Before 1970, almost all gasoline contained lead frequently in concentrations up to 0,84 grams per litre. Phasing down of lead content in gasoline began in the 1970s. Since the 1980s the trend has been to phase-out lead content in gasoline and was followed in the 1990s by a global consensus and measures to phase it out in most developed countries, within Organization of Economic Co-operation and Development [7] [25]. By 2001 forty-five nations worldwide had definitely banned its use and tendencies are for poor countries to be next to follow richer nations in abilities and will of solving the problem [26].

In Portugal, the phase-out of lead additives to gasoline did not begin until the early 1990s. However, its complete elimination from gasoline was not reached before 1999. According to World Watch, in 1993 only 21% of the gasoline used in Portugal was unleaded (in that year, 1.3 million metric tons of leaded gasoline contained 0.4 g Pb/l) [27, 28]. In most countries where lead is still added to gasoline its amount reduced significantly.

Table 1. World production and consumption (Adapted from ILZSG [2])

LEAD	World annual values (Thousand tonnes)				Jan-Sep (thousand tonnes)	
	2003	2004	2005	2006	2006	2007
Mined production	3120	3138	3436	3458	2603	2707
Total Lead production	6763	6957	7636	7922	5889	6097
Total consumption	6824	7282	7811	8008	5965	6186

---

[7] OECD Member Countries: Australia, Austria, Belgium, Canada, Czech Republic, Denmark, Finland, France, Germany, Greece, Hungary, Iceland, Ireland, Italy, Japan, Korea, Luxemburg, Mexico, Netherlands, New Zealand, Norway, Poland, Portugal, Slovak Republic, Spain, Sweden, Switzerland, Turkey, United Kingdom, and United States.

According to data from International Lead and Zinc Study Group (ILZSG), exposed next in Table 1, world numbers of lead production and consumption are nearly the same nowadays and will probably continue to rise slowly within years to follow [2]. Predominant key developments that influence world consumption of lead are first, the emergence of China as a major force and as a significant producer and consumer of lead and, second, the enormous growth in industrial battery manufacture [29].

Predominant uses of lead are nowadays in lead–acid batteries and, to a lesser extent, in construction, ammunition as well as glass and plastics industries [24].

Human Exposure to Lead

Lead can enter the environment at any stage from its mining to final uses, including recycling, and as a result of continuous years of its anthropogenic use, lead environment contamination is huge, covering crops, soil, water, food, air and dust. Having once entered the environment lead persists there because it does not undergo degradation [4].

Main sources of human exposure to lead are therefore environmental sources (presumably controllable, as lead based paints used indoors, contaminated water, lead glazed ceramics) as well as contaminated foodstuffs. Professional exposure in lead industries may also end up in transportation of lead particles (in clothes and shoes) outside the working area when hygiene practices are not well established or effective [30].

Toxicokinetics determines the number of molecules that can reach the target between the uptake and release of lead. It raises questions as "how does lead get in the human body?", "how long does it stay within the body?", "where does it stay?" and "how or when is it removed from the body?" and expects to answer and explain them [31]. Inside the body lead will react with different organs and tissues of the organism, binding to cell constituents, causing biochemical and physiological consequences which leads us to toxicodynamics that answers to the question "what lead may do to the body and how" by determining the number of targets that can interact with the metal.

Although these two topics do not constitute the main subjects of this chapter, they will herein be shortly approached as to give some insights on toxicological mechanisms of lead[8].

Absorption into the Body

Human uptake of lead occurs essentially via inhalation and ingestion. People can be exposed to lead and chemicals containing lead whenever working in or living nearby lead working sites, by breathing air and cigarette smoke, drinking water, eating food and swallowing dust containing lead.

Exposure pathways constitute an important aspect that will influence extension of absorption. Other factors, including both chemical and physical properties of the compound

---

[8] For more complete reviews on these subjects consult the excellent articles of Barton [32] or O'Flaherty [33] for toxicokinetics and Apostoli et al. [34] for toxicodynamics.

and individual factors, as gender, age, physiological and dietary conditions will also influence absorption, mainly when lead enters the body throughout ingestion [35]. People who have just eaten absorb minor amounts of lead (~10 times) than people with empty stomach. Furthermore iron deficiency and poor calcium intake are considered risk factors for an increased lead uptake [36]. On the contrary absorption of inhaled lead depends basically on particle size. Inhaled volume and individual characteristics are less significant in this situation. Inorganic lead uptake through intact skin is minimum, although it may occur in higher rate when contact is made with damaged tissues. Even so lead organic compounds (with higher lipid solubility) are readily absorbed [37].

Transport and Deposition within the Body

Once within the body lead travels promptly into bloodstream. Lead distribution to soft tissues and organs is whatsoever highly dependent on its affinities towards them [38]. In the blood lead binds initially to plasma and is thereafter transferred to red cells (erythrocytes). Equilibrium is obtained when almost all the metal is in the erythrocytes; more than 90% of total lead in blood is eventually found in the erythrocytes, associated to its membrane or bound to hemoglobin and other cell components, as δ-aminolevulinic acid dehydratase - ALAD [32, 38]. On the other hand, free plasmatic lead is easily distributed among tissues and organs. Total body burden lead ends up divided within soft tissues and bones besides already referred blood fraction. Blood and soft tissues form a labile kinetic pool for lead (half-life between 35 and 40 days). In soft tissues concentrations of lead reach higher levels in liver and kidneys but can be found in most tissues of the body.

Majority of lead body burden is stored in bones (>90% in adults) where it substitutes for calcium, and therefore skeletal tissue constitutes the largest and slowest kinetic pool of turnover for lead. Half-life of lead in bone has been estimated to be longer than 20 years but a more recent study points out to 9-12 years [39]. Within the bone lead is divided into trabecular and cortical bone, which represent respectively 20 and 80% of bone volume. This simplified division into two types of bone is very useful and effective for modelling kinetic of lead (see O'Flaherty [33]). Trabecular bone is more labile than cortical bone and therefore turnover of lead is shorter in trabecular bone than it is in the cortical one. Skeletal tissue can therefore be an endogenous and unexpected source of exposure to lead in people who have substantial amount of lead stored in bones during decalcification periods of human life, as during pregnancy, lactation, menopause and osteoporosis. According to Gerhardsson et al. [40] skeletal content in a long-term exposed lead worker can exceed 1g and higher bone concentrations may be found in finger bone (mainly cortical bone) in workers with current or past occupational exposure to lead.

Biotransformation and Elimination of Lead from the Body

Inorganic lead is not in anyway transformed by the organism. It does however bind to several proteins with damaging consequences to important physiological reactions. Only organic forms of lead undergo oxidative dealkylation in liver mediated by cytochrome P-450 dependent monoxygenase system [15]. Any inorganic lead produced from these reactions is therefore distributed within the body the same way as administered inorganic lead.

Absorbed lead is essentially excreted through urine by glomerular filtration in the kidneys (approximately 75-80%). When blood lead levels are high excretion may be augmented by transtubular transport. Faecal excretion is limited to lead amounts that have been ingested (including lead from air that has been swallowed instead of inhaled). It is also excreted in a much lesser degree (<8%) with other body fluids, including milk during lactation. Although it is not very effective as a way of human excretion, milk content of lead constitutes as important risk for newborns, as evidences suggest the existence of a direct correlation between blood and milk lead amounts [16].

Health Effects

In humans, lead can result in a wide range of biological effects, depending upon level and duration of exposure [23]. Effects may range from inhibition of enzymes to the production of marked morphological changes and death, depending on dose ranges. Along with the decrease of lead exposure in both occupational and general environment occurrence of adverse effects has been largely reduced. Instead emphasis has been increasing with respect to subtle and sub-clinical effects related to long term consequences of chronic exposure to low levels of lead. Acute toxic effects are next shortly summarized[9].

Biological Exposure Indices

Lead interferes with heme synthesis and therefore a number of endpoints could be used as exposure indices. Anyway, blood lead level (BLL) is the exposure biomarker generally and spontaneously elected to describe effects of lead to human health mainly due to its improved analytical sensitivity and implementation of quality-control programs for collection, handling and analysis [42]. Units generally used are micrograms of lead per decilitre of blood[10] and it is expected that exposure to lead is evidenced by elevated BLLs. Figure 1 summarizes pertinent information on lead effects to human health described by means of BLL.

Acute Toxicity / Single Exposure

Exposure to high levels of lead rarely occurs nowadays and acute toxic effects are also scarce. Most cases of lead poisoning result from occupational exposure and usually occur by ingestion of lead compounds and/or vapours inhalation.

---

[9] For a deeper approach read the excellent summary document on the subject, by Davidson [41].
[10] Blood Lead Level (BLL) units: $1\mu g/dL = 10\mu g/L = 0,048\mu mol/L$ or $1\mu mol/L = 20,719\mu g/dL$.

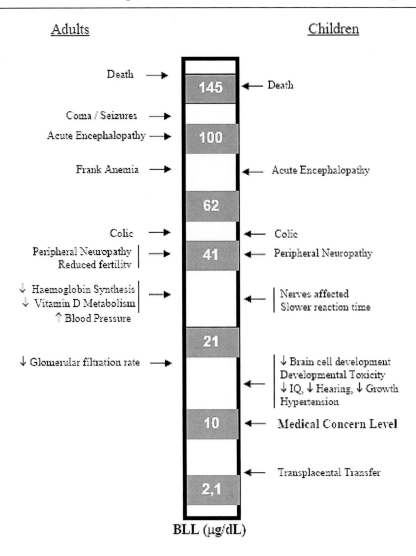

Figure 1. Summary of lead effects in adults and children (adapted from EPA [43], Moreira [17] and ATSDR [5]) described by means of blood lead levels (BLL).

Toxic effects do therefore arise a few hours after exposure has occurred. Acute exposure may also occur as a consequence of a process called as endogenous exposure (as has been referred formerly), when past exposures occurred resulting in lead deposition within skeleton that becomes free in bloodstream in consequence of decalcification processes (during for example pregnancy or bone ruptures).

Acute intoxication by lead is long known as "saturnism"[11]. First symptoms of acute exposure include gastrointestinal disturbances such as anorexia, nausea, vomiting, constipation, and abdominal pain. Other effects, as convulsion, coma, and encephalopathy as well as hepatic and renal damage and hypertension have also been reported [5, 6, 17, 45, 46]. Acute effects may end up with death although recovery is possible and frequent.

---

[11] The word "saturnism" derives from Roman God Saturn. Romans used to believe that lead was "the oldest metal" that had been given to them by Saturn [44].

For a number of neurological, metabolic and behavioural reasons children (and fetuses) are more vulnerable and susceptible to lead exposure and other irreversible symptoms appear as learning difficulties and diminished IQ [23, 30]. Fetuses are also very susceptible to lead effects for the placenta is highly permeable to this metal, and lead toxic effects seem to be related in an accentuated manner with doses [47].

Chronic Toxicity / Repeated Exposure

Although acute important effects may occur when exposure is high, lead is essentially a chronic or cumulative toxin. Most sensitive targets for lead toxicity are haematopoietic, nervous, and gastrointestinal systems and kidneys. However, due to the multimode of action of lead in biological systems lead is potentially able to affect every organs and systems, including cardiovascular, reproductive, and immunologic systems.

Acute health effects are next briefly described. Molecular mechanisms of toxicity and genetic damage will be examined more thoroughly later on.

Haematological effects - Anaemia occurs as consequence of two main effects: shortening of red cells lifespan and reduced haemoglobin synthesis. Lead inhibits two important enzymes within heme biosynthesis pathway (Figure 2): citosolic δ-aminolevulinic acid dehydrogenase (ALAD) and mitochondrial ferrochelatase. As a result δ-aminolevulinic acid synthetase (ALAS) is indirectly stimulated by negative feedback caused by diminished heme synthesis, δ-aminolevulinic acid (ALA) accumulates in cytoplasm and protoporphyrin IX accumulates within erythrocytes [35]. Eventually anaemia appears as the result of reduced haemoglobin synthesis because of the lack of heme substrate for its formation.

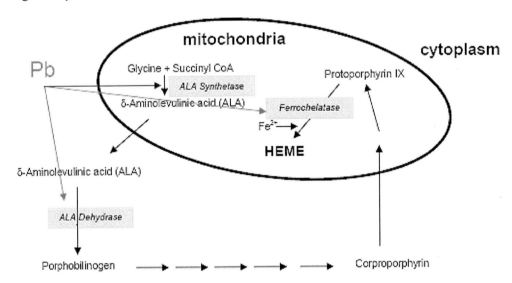

Figure 2. Effects of lead on heme biosynthesis (mitochondria schematic representation adapted from IARC [4]). ALA dehydratase and ferrochelatase are negatively affected by lead (red arrow) whilst ALA synthetase is positively affected (blue arrow) although indirectly through negative feedback by diminished heme synthesis.

Developmental effects – Children have long been recognized as being more susceptible and sensitive to effects of lead exposure due both to developmental and behavioral reasons. For several reasons, children are at higher risks for exposure to lead and absorb more lead than adults due to neurological (developing nervous systems being the most sensitive target), metabolic (higher respiratory, absorption and metabolic rates), and behavioral reasons (hand-to-the mouth activities and swallowing paint chips containing lead, for example) (COWI, 2003). For the time being it is likely that many children are still living in lead-contaminated houses due to the use of lead-based paint which may be a dangerous source of lead exposure for pre-school children; exposure can occur when they ingest chips and flakes of paint as well as when they ingest lead paint-contaminated dusts and soils during normal mouthing activities [27]. Exposure to lead has been also found to be associated with attention dysfunction, aggression and delinquency [4, 44]. Neurological and immunological conditions can arise during adulthood that may be linked to developmental exposure to lead (as will be referred to in specific sections).

Neurotoxic effects – Chronic lead exposure may lead to fatigue, sleep disturbance, headache, irritability and lethargy. It may also result in peripheral neuropathy, affecting nerves responsible for information transmission between brain, spinal marrow and muscles and organs, which may lead to sensibility lost, muscle weakness, pain, tremors, and paralysis. In children effects occur in learning abilities and in IQ performance as well [48]. Some authors do also tend to consider the possibility of developmental exposure to lead (during pregnancy and childhood) as an environmental factor that may contribute for development of neurodegenerative diseases including Alzheimer [49-51].

Renal effects – Classic effect of lead on renal system is chronic nephropathy characterized as a reduction of glomerular filtration rate, intranuclear inclusion bodies containing lead complexed with proteins and irreversible atrophy of proximal and distal tubes [52]. Those changes have as consequence cell atrophy and interstitial fibrosis occurrence. Symptoms include proteinuria, diminished glomerular filtration rate and changes in glucose and anions transport [48]. Chronic exposure to low concentrations of lead is associated with increased urinary excretion of low-molecular-weight proteins and lysosomal enzymes although chronic exposure to high concentrations of lead results in interstitial fibrosis, glomerular sclerosis, tubular dysfunction and, ultimately, in chronic renal failure [4].

Cardiovascular effects – Several studies have found that persistent exposure to high concentrations of lead are associated with hypertension incidence [53, 54]. It seams that exposure to lead even at low doses can cause increase in systolic pressure, remaining unaffected diastolic pressures [3, 55], effects that seem to result secondary from renal toxicity [6].

Reproductive effects – Risk for spontaneous abortion is increased by maternal exposure to high concentrations of lead. In humans, prenatal lead exposure is associated with an increased risk for minor malformations, low birth weight and reduced postnatal growth rate. Effect on postnatal growth rate is apparent only in children with continuing postnatal lead exposure. In children from workers exposed to lead higher rates of congenital epilepsy and cardiovascular conditions are found [48]. Several studies point to reduced sperm counts and mobility as consequence of chronic lead exposure [56, 57].

Immunological effects – Exposure to lead has been associated with changes in immune functions [4] although studies published till now have not shown evidence of marked immunotoxic effects. Nevertheless several studies showed that exposure to lead affects immune response [48], namely affecting B cells, T cells, natural killer cells (NK) and soluble mediators (cytokines, chemokines and nitric oxide) [4]. Immunological problems may as well be a result of developmental (fetuses and children) exposure [58].

Carcinogenicity – Lead and lead compounds have been reviewed four times by International Agency for Research on Cancer (IARC) in the IARC Monographs on the Evaluation of Carcinogenic Risks to Humans (1972, 1980, 1987, and 2006 [4]) having long been considered as 'possibly carcinogenic in humans' - group 2B [3], judging evidences to be inadequate in humans. Currently IARC updated this classification to IARC group 2A [4], 'probably carcinogenic to humans'. This category is used when evidences are considered sufficient of carcinogenicity in experimental animals but considered limited in what respects human population studies. IARC also states that an agent can be classified in this category if there is inadequate evidence of its carcinogenicity in humans together with sufficient evidence of carcinogenicity in experimental animals and strong evidence that the carcinogenesis is mediated by a mechanism that also operates in human. Nevertheless confounding factors such as simultaneous exposure to other carcinogens or smoking habits (as an example) make interpretation of human studies on exposure to lead somehow difficult.

In the other hand, however, organic compounds are considered as 'not classifiable as to their carcinogenicity to humans' (IARC group 3). However organic lead compounds are to some extent metabolized to ionic lead that will be then expected to exert the toxicities associated with inorganic lead [4].

Most frequently found tumors in lead exposed individuals occur in gastrointestinal and respiratory systems [46]. Two important meta-analyses were conducted by reviewing several studies (cohort and case-control) on occupational exposure to inorganic lead and carcinogenic effects [59, 60]. Data suggested the existence of an excess risk of overall cancer as well as lung, bladder, and stomach cancer. Most studies included in both cited reviews have several weaknesses: known co-exposure to carcinogens (as arsenic and chromium) of studied populations within occupational sites, lack of adjustments for confounding factors as smoking habits and diet, and lack of quantitative data on dose-response. This implies that conclusions must be cautiously taken with respect to relating found cancers exclusively to lead.

Genotoxicity – Several studies concluded on a relationship between exposure to lead and cytogenetic markers frequencies, such as micronucleus and chromosomal aberrations in individuals exposed to lead [5, 6]. In what concerns genotoxicity studies in human populations one must however be once again aware of co-exposures to compounds other than lead. It turns out to be difficult to attribute effects to lead alone and conflicting results have been obtained in several studies.

In general, studies carried out in occupational exposed groups resulted into positive changes for several genotoxic endpoints. Studies on DNA damage in lymphocytes of lead-exposed workers by means of Comet assay (single cell gel electrophoresis assay) gave significant increases in tail length or in tail moment in exposed groups. These endpoints are indicative of either direct strand breaks or alkali-labile sites, and therefore of DNA damage occurrence [61-64]. Studies using cytogenetic endpoints as the micronucleus (MN) test [65, 66] also got positive results for exposed versus controls. The same is valid for other studies using genotoxic endpoints (chromosomal aberrations and sister chromatid exchange frequencies, as is summarized in IARC [4]). One study from Wu et al. [67] found increased DNA-protein crosslinks related to high blood lead concentrations. But once again, in several of those studies subjects were exposed to other chemicals known to be genotoxic and a more pronounced effect was found in smoking subjects.

In the other hand there are studies that found no increase in studied endpoints. One of the considered studies measured single strand breaks (using the alkaline elution assay) for which it did not find significant effects related to lead levels in air [68]. Also, studies in measuring non-occupationally exposed groups (children living near lead smelters and subjects from general population volunteering to ingest lead acetate) for sister chromatid exchanges, chromosomal aberrations and oxidative DNA damage gave negative results [4].

Molecular Mechanisms Inducing DNA Damage

Lead has long been known to be toxic by disturbing a number of molecular, biochemical and morphological events. Most important mechanisms at cytotoxic blood lead concentrations are lead's ability to mimic the action of calcium and its strong affinity to bind to sulfhydryl, amine, carboxyl and phosphate groups in enzymes and other proteins, causing damage. Those characteristics result in an important ability of lead to bind to biological membranes, which will by its turn give rise to significant changes in transport processes within cells, in structural and functional integrity of several enzymes, and in several metabolic pathways, as in heme biosynthesis – as shown in Figure 2 [15, 69] - with all the harmful consequences already reviewed within this chapter. These properties of lead may also constitute relevant information to understand its action as a carcinogenic.

Lead doses are important to understand carcinogenic effects of lead. It is well known that at high concentrations lead can bind to DNA and change its conformation as well as cause direct genotoxicity [70].

Whatsoever, most of cohort studies of lead exposure and carcinogenicity or genotoxic effects developed within subjects occupationally exposed to lead failed to identify and control all covariates (as has been seen above). This applies essentially, as has already been said, to co-exposures to carcinogenic and genotoxic compounds in which we can account for cigarette smoke, engine exhausts and other metals found together with lead in industries (as cadmium and arsenic). However, those data can be looked at in a different way. Silbergeld [70] proposed to look at the results under the perspective of finding out evidences of related interactions between lead and those other considered exposures and concludes on the possibility of lead acting by means of facilitating mechanisms that will end up in cancer.

In one hand, data obtained so far failed to come up with evidences that lead does by itself induce cancer, but interactions were noted when simultaneous exposure to lead and to other carcinogenic or genotoxic compounds resulted in increased risks of cancer than when there is no co-exposure to lead [71-73]. Cancers found are mainly associated with target organs for compounds other than lead [70]. There also is little evidence that lead interacts directly with

DNA at non-cytotoxic blood lead concentrations, usually encountered in undertaken genotoxicity studies [70, 74]. In the other hand, studies that measured endpoints for oxidative DNA damage [63, 75] got positive results for oxidative damage in the presence of lead which suggests that oxidative DNA damage may be involved in lead toxicity. These findings all together do then seem to suggest that although lead has indeed an effect on chromosomes, its effect may probably not occur by a direct way, which would mean that even if lead has indeed a role in genotoxicity and carcinogenesis most probably its role is an indirect one, by enhancing carcinogenic effects after its induction has occurred.

Nongenotoxic mechanisms of DNA damage

Lead possible mechanisms for DNA damage appear then to act in part mediated by oxidative DNA damage and in part by interacting with DNA repair processes, resulting in an enhancement of genotoxicity in combination with other DNA damaging agents. DNA repair processes are disturbed at low level and non-cytotoxic concentrations of lead [76].

Oxidative Damage to DNA

Generation of free radicals is a general mechanism for metal toxicity. Lead either induces depletion of endogenous cellular antioxidants such as glutathione, or the production of radical oxygen species (ROS). ROS include oxygen ions, free radicals and peroxides and are highly reactive molecules due to the presence of unpaired valence shell electrons and can therefore cause significant damage to DNA, proteins and enzymes.

ROS can be increased within the cell by a number of mechanisms. Returning to the heme biosynthesis pathway (Figure 2) and to the effects lead has in its enzymes, it has been seen that heme precursor δ-aminolevulinic acid (ALA) accumulates in cytoplasm as a consequence of inhibition of δ-aminolevulinic acid dehydrogenase (ALAD). ALA can generate free radicals in cells and cause DNA oxidative damage. Lead is also believed to undergo Fenton-type reactions in the presence of hydrogen peroxide that will result in oxidative damage and strand breaks in DNA [4].

Lead can also lower cellular concentrations of proteins such glutathione and hematoproteins, which will reduce the inherent capacity of cells to neutralize ROS (generated from several events, some of them normal and frequent within normal cells). In those conditions oxidative damage to DNA will thereby be increased.

Facilitative Mechanisms for DNA Damage

Facilitative mechanisms by which lead may interact with other carcinogenic exposures are considered to be inhibition of DNA repair mechanisms or interference with DNA polymerase and DNA synthesis mechanisms, inducing them to low down efficiency when repairing DNA damages.

Zinc Finger Loop Proteins

One common property of lead toxicity is to compete with essential metal ions. Zinc is one of those metals that is present in several proteins and its presence is essential for several enzyme activities. Lead capacity to bind to zinc binding sites (so-called zinc fingers) can change conformational structure of several DNA-binding proteins, and inhibit them. Protamines, histones and some transcription regulators are examples of that kind of effect from lead. Facilitative mechanisms of lead consist then in binding to those proteins reducing consequently their ability to recognize their own target DNA, bind to DNA sites and therefore exert their functions [77]. This will result in an increased vulnerability of genetic material to damage (as protamines and histones have the important function of binding to DNA and protect it from deleterious attacks). Once they are not able to do so genetic material will be inadequately sheltered from exterior triggered attacks. Changes in nuclear transcription regulators functions have by their turn consequences in genetic expression.

Tumour suppressor protein p53 is a zinc-binding protein as well. Its function is to interfere and stop formation of tumours. If a person only inherits one functional copy of p53 gene they will be more predisposed to cancer and do usually develop several independent tumours in different tissues. Lead's substitution of zinc in such a protein would result in altered defective functional forms of the protein. This might eventually involve posttranslational changes in proteins structure [7].

Conclusion

Carcinogenesis is a multievent process involving multiple and sequential genetic alterations. It is a complex process and involves considerable interactions between various biological variables. Cancer development is usually defined as being a process that involves an initiation stage (genetic errors occurring in normal cells) followed by a promotion stage (first genetic error must be followed by one other) and the progression of cancer occurs if those genetic errors are not corrected. In other words, several genetic errors must occur in one cell for cancer to develop. Another important principle of carcinogenesis is that DNA replication is not completely precise and that every time a cell undergoes division process there is an opportunity for genetic errors to occur [78]. In other words, even under normal cellular circumstances a measurable amount of cellular damage exists [79].

This implies that an agent has the capacity of increasing incidence of cancer by one of several ways: either by specifically damage the DNA of the cell, by increasing the number of cell divisions (which would increase the opportunity for mistakes to occur) or by interfering with cell DNA repair mechanisms. Meaning the efficient repair of DNA lesions is an important step in maintaining DNA integrity. If repair mechanisms are not efficiently functioning cells may accumulate DNA damages. This will increase probabilities of mutations in DNA and thus to tumour formation.

At low concentrations lead is believed not to be directly cytotoxic but mostly to be responsible for increasing oxidative damage to DNA and changing conformational forms of key proteins accounted for protecting the cell from damage in DNA. Whilst first effect will increase genetic instability, second will decrease cell capacity of correcting DNA occurring defects. All these events constitute facilitative or permissive mechanisms of cancer rather than inductive and point out to an epigenic involvement of lead in an altered gene expression [7].

IARC [4] concluded then on considering lead a toxic metal having one expression of this property as being genetic toxicity. Although there is little evidence that it interacts directly with DNA at normally encountered blood concentrations, genetic toxicity of lead appears to be modulated by mechanisms described hereby. Those mechanisms are ROS increases and modulation and interaction with key proteins involved in DNA protection and repair, which may be responsible for enhancing other agents' genotoxicity. They moreover conclude that these properties can result in mutations, changes in gene expression and cell proliferation that can contribute to tumour progression. IARC evaluated then inorganic lead compounds as being 'probably carcinogenic to humans' (group 2A) whilst they evaluated organic lead compounds as 'not classifiable as to their carcinogenicity to humans' (therefore group 3).

Measures taken to control uses of lead and its continuing dissemination constitute big steps in the right direction. However it is not yet completely certain that these steps are sufficiently adequate to protect the environment and human health. There is a continuing need for governments all over the world to regulate uses of lead and to keep surveillance programs on human lead exposure to lead and other toxic metals.

Aknowledgments

The author of this chapter is as PhD student under the program of Occupational Health / Public Health from Nova University of Lisbon (Escola Nacional de Saúde Pública - ENSP). Writing this chapter was made possible by support partly from the Portuguese Foundation for Science and Technology (FCT), within a research project entitled 'Lead exposure. Contribution of the study of genetic and immunologic toxicity. Influence of genetic determinants' (PDCT/SAU-OBS/59821/2004), and partly by a grant from Portuguese National Institute of Health Dr. Ricardo Jorge (BIC 02/2003-I).

References

[1]   USGS. Lead Statistics U.S. Geological Survey (USGS). 2006. Available from: www.usgs.com accessed in December 2007.
[2]   ILZSG. Lead and Zinc Statistics International Lead and Zinc Study Group. 2007. Available from: www.ilzsg.org accessed in December 2007.
[3]   IPCS. Environmental Health Criteria 165: Inorganic Lead. Geneva: International Programme on Chemical Safety (IPCS), World Health Organization; 1995.
[4]   IARC. IARC Monographs on the Evaluation of Carcinogenic Risks to Human, 87: Inorganic and Organic Lead Compounds. Lyon, France: World Health Organization, International Agency for Research on Cancer (IARC); 2006.

[5]   ATSDR. ToxGuide for Lead (CAS# 7439-92-1). Public Health Service U. S. Department of Health and Human Services, Agency for Toxic Substances and Disease Registry (ASTDR).2005.

[6]   ATSDR. Toxicological Profile for Lead (Draft). Public Health Service U. S. Department of Health and Human Services, Agency for Toxic Substances and Disease Registry (ASTDR). 2005.

[7]   Silbergeld, EK; Waalkes, M; Rice, JM. Lead as a carcinogen: experimental evidence and mechanisms of action. *American Journal of Industrial Medicine*, 2000: 38 316-323.

[8]   Gray, JW; Collins, C. Genome changes and gene expression in human solid tumours. *Carcinogenesis*, 2000: 21 (3), 443-452.

[9]   Loeb, KR; Loeb, A. Significance of multiple mutations in cancer. *Carcinogenesis*, 2000: 210 (3), 379-385.

[10] Atkins, P; Jones, L. Chemistry – Molecules, matter and change. 3rd. New York: 1997.

[11] Duffus, JH. Heavy metals - A meaningless term? (IUPAC Technical Report). *Pure Applied Chemistry*, 2002: 74 (5), 793-807.

[12] Hernberg, S. Lead poisoning in a historical perspective. *American Journal of Industrial Medicine*, 2000: 38 244-254.

[13] Lessler, MA. Lead and lead poisoning from Antiquity to Modern Times. *Ohio Journal of Science*, 1988: 88 (3), 78-84.

[14] Needleman, H. Lead poisoning. *Annual Revisions of Medicine*, 2004: 55 209-222.

[15] Marqués, FM. Plomo: criterios toxicologicos actuales para la vigilancia medica de trabajadores expuestos. Barcelona: Instituto Nacional de Seguridad e Higiene en el Trabajo, Centro Nacional de Condiciones de Trabajo; 1993.

[16] Moreira, FR; Moreira, JC. Lead kinetics in human body and its significance to health. *Ciência e Saúde Colectiva*, 2004: 9 (1), 167-181.

[17] Moreira, FR; Moreira, JC. Effects of lead exposure on the human body and health implications (special report). *Pan American Journal of Public Health*, 2004: 15 (2), 119-129.

[18] Lovei, M. Phasing out lead from gasoline: worldwide experience and policy implications. Pollution Management Series, World Bank technical paper N° 397. Washington D.C. World Bank's Environment Department. 1997.

[19] Derome, J; Fairbrother, A; Marcy, S; Wurtz, J; Harding, K. Chapter 6 - Biological effects. In: *AMAP Assessment 2002: Heavy metals in the Artic*. Oslo, Norway: Arctic Monitoring and Assessment Programme; 2004.

[20] Pacyma, J. Chapter 2 - Sources and Emissions. In: *AMAP Assessment 2002: Heavy metals in the Artic*. Oslo, Noruega: Arctic Monitoring and Assessment Programme; 2004.

[21] Marcy, S; Dietz, A; Bignert, A; Borg, H; Braune, B; Brooks, S; Christensen, J; Dam, C; Derome, J; Fairbrother, A; Ford, J; Gordeev, V; Gusev, A; Lindberg, S; Macdonald, R; Outridge, P; Pacyma, J; Puckett, K; Riget, F; Travnikov, O; Wilson, S. Chapter 7 - Conclusions and Recommendations. In: *AMAP Assessment 2002: Heavy metals in the Artic*. Oslo, Norway: Arctic Monitoring and Assessment Programme; 2004.

[22] Cordeiro, R; Lima-Filho, EC. A inadequação dos valores dos limites de tolerância biológica para a prevenção da intoxicação profissional pelo chumbo no Brasil. *Cadernos de Saúde Pública*, 1995: 11 (2), 177-186.

[23] COWI. Lead Review. COWI Consulting Engineers and Planners - Nordic Council of Ministers. 2003.

[24] Thornton, I; Rautiu, R; Brush, S. Lead: The facts. ICON - Imperial College Consultants Ltd. 2001.

[25] OECD. Phasing lead out of gasoline: An examination of Policy Approaches in Different Countries. Organisation for Economic Co-operation and Development (OECD). 1999.

[26] Hilton, FG. Poverty and pollution abatement: Evidence from lead phase-out. *Ecological Economics*, 2006: 56 125-131.

[27] Roma-Torres, J; Silva, S; Costa, C; Coelho, P; Henriques, MA; Teixeira, JP; Mayan, O. Lead exposure of children and newborns in Porto, Portugal. *International Journal of Hygiene and Environmental-Health*, 2007: 210 411-414.

[28] Mayan, O; Henriques, MA; Calheiros, JM. Childhood lead exposure in Oporto, Portugal. *International Journal of Occupational and Environmental Health*, 2001: 7 209-216.

[29] Roberts, H. Changing patterns in global lead supply and demand. *Journal of Power Sources*, 2003: 116 23-31.

[30] Klaassen, CD; Watkins, JB. Toxicologia: a ciência básica dos tóxicos de Casarett e Doull. 5ª edição. Lisboa: McGraw-Hill de Portugal; 2001.

[31] Rabinowitz, MB. Toxicokinetics of bone lead. *Environmental Health Perspectives*, 1991: 91 33-37.

[32] Barton, JC; Conrad, ME. Organ retention and excretion of radiolead administered intravenously in rats: a comparison of erythrocyte- and plasma-associated lead. *The Journal of Trace Elements in Experimental Medicine* 2001: 14 89-98.

[33] O'Flaherty, EJ. A physiologically based kinetic model for lead in children and adults. *Environmental Health Perspectives*, 1998: 106 (Sup6), 1495-1503.

[34] Apostoli, P; Huard, C; Chaumontet, C; Martel, P; Alessio, L; Mazzoleni, G. Effects of four inorganic lead compounds on the proliferation and functional coupling of cultured REL liver cells. *American Journal of Industrial Medicine*, 2000:

[35] ATSDR. Case studies in environmental medicine: Lead toxicity. Atlanta: U. S. Department of Health and Human Services, Public Health Service, Agency for Toxic Substances and Disease Registry (ASTDR); 1992.

[36] Mahaffey, KR. Environmental lead toxicity: nutrition as a component of intervention. *Environmental Health Perspectives*, 1990: 89 75-78.

[37] Staudinger, K; Roth, VS. Occupational lead poisoning. *American Family Physician*, 1998: 57 (4) Available from: http://www.aafp.org/afp/980215ap/stauding.html.

[38] Bergdahl, IA; Vahter, M; Counter, SA; Schütz, A; Buchanan, LH; Ortega, F; Laurell, G; Skerfving, S. Lead in plasma and whole blood from lead-exposed children. *Environmental Research, Section A*, 1999: 80 25-33.

[39] Brito, AA; McNeill, FE; Chettle, DR; Webber, CE; Vaillancourt, C. Study of the relationships between bone lead levels and its variation with time and the cumulative

blood lead index, in a repeated bone lead survey. *Journal of Environmental Monitoring*, 2000: 2 271-276.

[40] Gerhardsson, L; Akantis, A; Lundström, N-G; Nordberg, GF; Schütz, A; Skerfving, S. Lead concentrations in cortical and trabecular bones in deceased smelter workers. *Journal of Trace Elements in Medicine and Biology*, 2005: 19 209-215.

[41] Davidson, KA. Toxicity Summary for lead (inorganic). Oak Ridge National Laboratory Restoration Program. 1994.

[42] Nieboer, E; Fletcher, GG. Toxicological profile and related health issues: Inorganic Lead (for Physicians). Regional Niagara Public Health Department. 2001.

[43] EPA. What lead does to your health. US Environmental Protection Agency (EPA) - Department of Environment and Climate Change NSWI. 2008. Available from: www.environment.nsw.gov.au/leadsafe/leadinf2.htm.

[44] Bechara, JH. Chumbo, intoxicação e violência. *Jornal do Conselho Regional de Química IV Região (SP e MS)*, 2004: 65 8-10.

[45] Andre, C; Velasquez, M. Read my genes: genetic screening in the workplace. *Issues in Ethics*, 1991: 4 (2). Available from: http://scu.edu/ethics/publications/iie/v4n2/genes.html.

[46] Goyer, RA; Clarkson, TW. Toxic effects of metals. In: *Cassarett and Doull's Toxicology. The basic science of poisons*. New York: McGraw-Hill; 2001.

[47] Cheymol, J; Desplanques, L; Deffontaines, D. Foetopathie saturnine. *Archives Pédiatriques*, 2001: 8 (2), 506-507.

[48] Lestón, JG. Evaluation de los efectos tóxicos asociados a la exposición ocupacional a plomo (Graduation thesis). Departamento de Biología Celular y Molecular, Facultad de Ciencias. La Coruña. 2007.

[49] Yokel, RA. Blood-brain barrier flux of aluminum, manganese, iron and other metals suspected to contribute to metal-induced neurodegeneration. *Journal of Alzheimer's Disease*, 2006: 10 223-253.

[50] Basha, MR; Murali, M; Siddiqi, HK; Ghosal, K; Siddiqi, OK; Lashuel, HA; Ge, Y-W; Lahiri, DK; Zawia, NH. Lead (Pb) exposure and its effect on APP proteolysis and Aβ aggregation. *The FASEB Journal*, 2005: 10.1096/fj.05-4375fje.

[51] Basha, MR; Wei, W; Bakheet, SA; Benitez, N; Siddiqi, HK; Ge, Y-W; Lahiri, DK; Zawia, NH. The fetal basis of amyloidogenesis: exposure to lead and latent overexpression of amyloid precussor protein and β-amyloid in the aging brain. *The Journal of Neuroscience*, 2005: 25 (4), 823-829.

[52] Goyer, RA. Lead Toxicity: from overt to subclinical to subtle effects. *Environmental Health Perspectives*, 1990: 86 177-181.

[53] Lee, BK; Lee, G-S; Stewart, WF; Ahn, K-D; Simon, D; Kelsey, KT; Todd, AC; Schwartz, BS. Associations of blood pressure and hypertension with lead dose measures and polymorphisms in the vitamin D receptor and delta-aminolevulinic acid dehydratase genes. *Environmental Health Perspectives*, 2001: 109 (4), 383-389.

[54] Fewtrell, LJ; Prüss-Üstün, A; Landrigan, P; Ayuso-Mateos, JL. Estimating the global burden of disease of mild mental retardation and cardiovascular diseases from environmental lead exposure. *Environmental Research*, 2004: 94 120-133.

[55] Rahman, S; Khalid, N; Zaidi, JH; Ahmad, S; Iqbal, MZ. Non-occupational lead exposure and hypertension in Pakistani adults. *Journal of Zhejiang University Science B*, 2006: 7 (9), 732-737.

[56] Papanikolaou, NC; Hatzidaki, EG; Belivanis, S; Tzanakakis, GN; Tsatsakis, AM. Lead toxicity update. A brief review. *Med Sci Monit*, 2005: 11 (10), 329-336.

[57] Levin, SM; Goldberg, M. Clinical evaluation and management of lead-exposed construction workers. *American Journal of Industrial Medicine*, 2000: 37 23-43.

[58] Bunn, TL; Parsons, PJ; Kao, E; Dietert, RR. Exposure to lead during critical windows of embryonic development: differential immunotoxic outcome based on stage of exposure and gender. *Toxicological Sciences*, 2001: 64 57-66.

[59] Fu, H; Boffetta, P. Cancer and occupational exposure to inorganic lead compounds: a meta-analysis of published data. *Occupational and Environmental Medicine*, 1995: 52 73-81.

[60] Steenland, K; Boffetta, P. Lead and cancer in humans: where are we now? *American Journal of Industrial Medicine*, 2000: 38 295-299.

[61] Danadevi, K; Rozati, R; Banu, BS; Rao, PH; Grover, P. DNA damage in workers exposed to lead using comet assay. *Toxicology*, 2003: 187 183-193.

[62] Ye, X-B; Fu, H; Zhu, J-L; Ni, W-M; Lu, Y-W; Kuang, X-Y; Yang, S-L; Shu, B-X. A study on oxidative stress in lead-exposed workers. *Journal of Toxicology and Environmental Health, Part A*, 1999: 56 161-172.

[63] Fracasso, ME; Perbellini, L; Soldà, S; Talamini, G; Franceschetti, P. Lead induced DNA strand breaks in lymphocytes of exposed workers: role of reactive oxygen species and protein kinase C. *Mutation Research*, 2002: 515 159-169.

[64] Palus, J; Rydzynski, K; Dziubaltowska, E; Wyszynska, K; Natarajan, AT; Nilsson, R. Genotoxic effects of occupational exposure to lead and cadmium. *Mutation Research*, 2003: 540 19-28.

[65] Vaglenov, A; Creus, A; Laltchev, S; Pavlova, S; Marcos, R. Occupational exposure to lead and induction of genetic damage. *Environmental Health Perspectives*, 2001: 109 (3), 295-298.

[66] Zhijian, C; Jianlin, L; Shijie, C; Wei, Z; Wei, W; Lifen, J; Hongping, D; Jiliang, H. Evaluating the genotoxic effects of workers exposed to lead using micronucleus assay, comet assay and TCR gene mutation test. *Toxicology*, 2006: 223 219-226.

[67] Wu, F-Y; Chang, P-W; Wu, C-C; Kuo, H-W. Correlations of blood lead with DNA-protein cross-links and sister chromatid exchanges in lead workers. *Cancer Epidemiology, Biomarkers and Prevention*, 2002: 11 287-290.

[68] Hengstler, JG; Bolm-Audorff, U; Faldum, A; Janssen, K; Reifenrath, M; Götte, W; Jung, D; Mayer-Popken, O; Fuchs, J; Gebhard, S; Bienfait, HG; Schlink, K; Dietrich, C; Faust, D; Epe, B; Oesch, F. Occupational exposure to heavy metals: DNA damage induction and DNA repair inhibition prove co-exposures to cadmium, cobalt and lead as more dangerous than hitherto expected. *Carcinogenesis*, 2003: 24 (1), 63-73.

[69] AGDVA. Final Report of the Expert Panel to Review Special Air Services Health Concerns. Appendix A - Lead. Australian Government Department of Veterans' Affairs (AGDVA). 2003.

[70] Silbergeld, EK. Facilitative mechanisms of lead as a carcinogen. *Mutation Research*, 2003: 533 121-133.

[71] Englyst, V; Lundström, N-G; Gerhardsson, L; Rylander, L; Nordberg, G. Lung cancer risks among lead smelter workers also exposed to arsenic. *Science of the Total Environment*, 2001: 273 (1-3), 77-82.

[72] Lundström, NG; Nordberg, G; Englyst, V; Gerhardsson, L; Hagmar, L; Jin, T; Rylander, L; Wall, S. Cumulative lead exposure in relation to mortality and lung cancer morbidity in a cohort of primary smelter workers. . *Scandinavian Journal of Work, Environment and Health*, 1997: 23 (1), 24-30.

[73] Anttila, A; Heikkilä, P; Pukkala, E; Nykyri, E; Kauppinen, T; Hernberg, S; Hemminki, K. Excess lung cancer among workers exposed to lead. *Scandinavian Journal of Work, Environment and Health*, 1995: 21 (6), 460-469.

[74] IARC. Monographs on the Evaluation of Carcinogenic Risks to Humans. Volume 100: a review of human carcinogens draft planning document (draft). IARC monographs on the evaluation of carcinogenic risks to humans. International Agency for Research on Cancer (IARC) World Health Organization. 2006.

[75] Vaglenov, A; Carbonell, E; Marcos, R. Biomonitoring of workers exposed to lead. Genotoxic effects, its modulation by polyvitamin treatment and evaluation of the induced radioresistence. *Mutation Research*, 1998: 418 79-92.

[76] Hartwig, A. Current aspects in metal genotoxicity. *BioMetals*, 1994: 8 (1), 3-10 (doi: 10.1007/bf00156151).

[77] Landrigan, PJ; Boffetta, P; Apostoli, P. The reproductive toxicity and carcinogenecity of lead: a critical review. *American Journal of Industrial Medicine*, 2000: 38 231-243.

[78] Cohen, SM; Ellwein, LB. Genetic errors, cell proliferation, and carcinogenesis. *Cancer Research*, 1991: 51 6493-6505.

[79] Hartwig, A; Schwerdtle, T. Interactions by carcinogeic metal compounds with DNA repair processes: toxicological implications. *Toxicology Letters*, 2002: 127 47-54.

In: New Research on DNA Damage
Editors: Honoka Kimura and Aoi Suzuki

ISBN 978-1-60456-581-2
© 2008 Nova Science Publishers, Inc.

Chapter 14

DNA Damage Signaling in Human Skin Cells Exposed to Hexavalent Chromium

Emil Rudolf[1]*, Kamil Rudolf[2]†, Věra Králová[1], Ladislava Schrőterová[1], and Miroslav Červinka[1]

1. Department of Medical Biology and Genetics, Charles University in Prague, Czech
2. Department of Rheumatology and Clinical Pharmacology, 2nd Internal Clinic, Czech

Abstract

Hexavalent chromium (Cr (VI)) is known toxin, mutagen and carcinogen in man. In addition, exposure to Cr (VI) has been associated with skin irritation, deep ulceration and cytotoxicity. Intracellular chemistry of Cr (VI) is complex and involves several enzymatic as well as nonenzymatic reductions resulting in the formation of reactive chromate intermediates and reactive oxygen species. These endproducts react with DNA and cause numerous types of lesions which in turn provoke specific signaling pathways in exposed cells. Although these pathways are generally known, their specific details concerning individual steps and involved molecules with their respective roles in biological response of cell populations to this element remain unspecified. The purpose of this study was to investigate the initial stages of Cr (VI)-induced DNA damaging in normal human skin fibroblasts. Primary human skin fibroblasts were exposed to Cr (VI) at a concentration range of 1-50 µM during 24 h. Our results confirm that Cr (VI) dose-dependently stimulates both directly (via its reactive metabolic intermediates) and indirectly (through generated oxidative stress) DNA damaging which results in the activation of DNA damage response pathway during 24 h of treatment. The important members of this pathway include ATM/ATR kinases which stimulate their downstream targets – Chk1, Chk2 and p53 in mediating transient G2/M cell cycle arrest and activating cell death characterized by the specific cleavage of PARP. Inhibition of

---

* Emil Rudolf, Department of Medical Biology and Genetics, Charles University in Prague, Faculty of Medicine in Hradec Králové, Šimkova 870, 500 38 Hradec Králové, Czech Republic, Tel: +420 495816393; Fax: +420 495816495, email: rudolf@lfhk.cuni.cz.
† Faculty Teaching Hospital in Hradec Králové ,Sokolská 581, 500 05 Hradec Králové, Czech Republic.

ATM/ATR pathway and suppresion of oxidative stress in exposed cells significantly suppressed cell damage characterized by specific PARP cleavage.

Keywords: *Hexavalent chromium, Dermal fibroblasts; DNA damage signaling, p53*

1. Introduction

Occupational exposure to hexavalent chromium (Cr (VI)) is often associated with the lower respiratory tract damage, in particular with bronchial asthma and lung cancer. In addition, professional and, above all, repeated contact with this heavy metal may also cause deep ulcerations of skin and nasal mucosa [2] and many epidemiological studies have shown hypersensitivity and allergic contact dermatitis affecting workers in chromium-related industry such as tanning, electroplating or mining [8 ; 10 ; 26].

Despite recent progresses in our understanding of Cr (VI) toxic potential, the specific mechanisms of Cr (VI)-induced cutaneous toxicity are not entirely elucidated, mainly due to three factors. First, there are few thorough toxicological studies dealing with skin damage after exposure to Cr (VI). Moreover, increasing evidence in literature on possible penetration of this metal into deeper dermal regions containing fibroblasts points to multiple possible targets of Cr (VI) toxicity [6]. Second, because of its recognized cytotoxic, genotoxic and procarcinogenic potential along with complex intracellular metabolism, Cr (VI) may induce diverse responses in exposed cells and tissues, involving temporary or terminal growth arrest, cell death (either apoptosis or necrosis) or malignant cell transformation. It has been demonstrated that these different Cr (VI)-induced endpoints might depend on several mutually interfering factors such as employed concentration of this element, varying sensitivity of exposed cells throughout the cell cycle, variety of intracellular targets as well as the nature and extent of inflicted cellular damage [13; 17 ; 20]. Third, there are several mechanisms whereby Cr (VI) might injure the cells, with all of them being dependent on its intracellular reduction. Cr (VI) enters the cell via a non-specific anion transporter and is subsequently reduced by a series of catalyzed reactions as well as by nonenzymatic systems to trivalent chromium (Cr (III) [5 ; 22]. Cr (III) as well as other short-lived intermediates (Cr (IV) and Cr (V)) have been shown to interact directly with DNA and other macromolecules, causing their damage and leading to p53-dependent or -independent apoptosis [19 ; 21].

Despite a plethora of molecular mechanisms and targets whereby Cr (VI) mediates its diverse biological effects in skin as well as lung tissues, the central and most critical target of Cr (VI) toxicity appears to be DNA. DNA damage induced by Cr (VI) metabolism comprises single- and double-strand breaks, Cr-DNA crosslinks, protein-DNA crosslinks, DNA inter- and intra-stand crosslinks, single-gene mutations and chromosome aberrations etc [20]. The types of DNA induced by Cr (VI) have been well researched over the past fifty years and are nowadays well known. In contrast, relatively little is known about particular activation or inactivation of specific DNA-damage signaling pathways in Cr (VI)-exposed cells.

In this study, we examined the early DNA-damage response pathways in primary human skin fibroblasts exposed to Cr (VI) at differing concentration ranges during 24 h. We found that following the exposure to Cr (VI), DNA is damaged in a time- and dose-dependent way which in turn activates ATM/ATR (ataxia teleangiectasia mutated and Rad3-related kinase) pathway. Concomitnat with sensing DNA damage, exposed skin fibroblasts phosphorylate p53 at ser-15 and in a dose-dependent manner cleave PARP at later treatment intervals. The specific inhibition of oxidative stress has only partially decreased the efficiency of DNA-damage signaling but significantly reduced cleavage of PARP. Moreover, the specific inhibition of ATM/ATR pathway using chemical inhibitor as well as siRNA mediated knockdown had low efficiency in preventing PARP cleavage. These results show that DNA of skin fibroblasts exposed to toxic Cr (VI) suistains mutliple changes brought about both by toxic Cr (VI) intermediates as well as by Cr (VI)-mediated oxidative stress. Upon damaging, fibroblasts activate DNA-damage pathway which via ATM/ATR and possibly via DNA-PK (DNA-protein kinase) leads to G_2/M phase arrest characterized by Chk mediated inactivation of cdc2-cyclin B complex and activation and stabilisation of p53. Upon higher employed Cr (VI) concentrations, this arrest is at best only transient and after cleavage of PARP cell undergoes general degradation and death. Our results further show that in Cr (VI)-exposed skin cells, it is oxidative stress rather than Cr (VI) intermediates which are responsible for both DNA damaging as well as final determination of cell fate.

2. Materials and Methods

Cell Line

Human primary skin fibroblasts isolated from a healthy human volunteer as described elsewhere [12] were cultivated in plastic tissue-culture dishes (Nunclon, Roskilde, Denmark). Cultures were maintained in Dulbecco's modified Eagle's medium – DMEM (Gibco, Prague, Czech Republic), supplemented with 10% fetal bovine serum (Gibco, Prague, Czech Republic), 100 U/ml penicillin, and 100 µg/ml streptomycin. Only mycoplasma-free cultures were used.

Treatments

Potassium chromate (Sigma-Aldrich, Prague, Czech Republic) was dissolved in distilled water, sterilized by ultrafiltration and kept at 4 °C as 1.5 mM stock solution. Prior to each experiment, the stock solution was diluted with DMEM to the final concentration of 1 µM, 10 µM and 50 µM. Stock solutions of antioxidant NAC (Sigma-Aldrich, Prague, Czech Republic) was prepared in serum free DMEM. The working concentration of NAC was achieved by diluting its stock solution in treatment medium: NAC (M-acetyl cystein 250 µM – added to cells 24 h prior to Cr (VI) exposure). ATM/ATR inhibitor CGK 733 ($C_{23}H_{18}Cl_3FN_4O_3S$; 200 nM, Calbiochem, EMD Biosciences, Inc., La Jolla, Ca, USA).

Chemiluminescent Quantitation of DNA Synthesis

The rate of DNA synthesis in treated and control cells was estimated by means of measurement of bromodeoxyuridine (BrdU) incorporation into growing DNA strands using Cell proliferation ELISA BrdU kit (Roche s.r.o, Prague, Czech Republic). Cells at a concentration of 30,000 cells/well in 200 μl of DMEM containing 10% fetal bovine serum were seeded in black 96-well microtiter plates, with the first column of wells representing blank. The cells were allowed to settle overnight at 37 °C and in 5 % CO_2. Next, cultures were treated according to protocol supplied by manufacturer and 2-24 h before the end of incubation BrdU was added (10 μM final concentration, Sigma-Aldrich, Prague, Czech Republic). At the end of incubation period, medium was removed and the cells were fixed (30 min, RT) and labeled with anti-BrdU. After incubation (60 min, RT) and three washing cycles, luminol substrate was added and chemiluminescence was measured using a multiplate reader TECAN SpectraFluor Plus (TECAN Austria GmbH, Grödig, Austria). For all measurement, integration time was 1000 ms and gain 130. The results in relative light units (RLU) were expressed as a percentage of control.

Measurement of Oxidative Stress

Generation of hydrogen peroxide and/or hydroxyl radical was monitored by intracellular conversion of 2′-7′- dichlorodihydrofluorescein diacetate (DFCH/DA – Sigma-Aldrich, Prague, Czech Republic) into a fluorescent product dichlorofluorescein (DCF). Dermal fibroblasts were seeded into cultivation flasks and cultivated to 75% confluence at 37 °C and 5 % CO_2. After exposure to Cr (VI), control and treated cells were detached by a cell scraper and collected by centrifugation (50 x g, 5 min, 4 °C – JOUAN M21, Trigon, Prague, Czech Republic). The cells were resuspended in DMEM (pH adjusted to 7.2) and 5 μM DFCH/DA was added (5 min, 37 °C). Changes in the fluorescence intensity (485 nm excitation; 538 nm emission) were measured by Shimadzu UV - Visible Spectrophotometer UV – 1601 (SHIMADZU DEUTSCHLAND GmbH, Duisburg, Germany). The data were expressed as a percentage of fluorescence intensity increase per 10^6 cells.

Measurement of DNA Damage – Comet Assay

DNA damage in treated cells were determined by alkali single-cell gel electrophoresis (comet assay). This assay is based on analysis of labile DNA damage sites where DNA forms characteristic tails – comets. Control and treated dermal fibroblasts were at particular time intervals harvested by 0.25% trypsin, centrifuged for 5 min at 1,500 rpm at 4 °C, suspended in 0.6% agarose and mounted to microscopic slides. Next, cells were lysed in cooled lysis buffer (2.5 M NaCl, 100 mM EDTA, 10 mM Trizma, 1 % Triton X-100 and 10 % DMSO) for 1.5 h at 4 °C. After rinsing in TRIS, cells were allowed to unwind DNA in alkali buffer for 30 min. Electrophoresis was performed at 25 V and 300 mA for 30 min. After neutralizing slides and draining them, cells were stained by 100 μl ethidium bromide (Sigma-

Aldrich, Prague, Czech Republic). One hundred cells from three independent samples were scored for tail migration intensity.

Cell Cycle Analysis

Human primary dermal fibroblasts were seeded into cultivation flasks, cultivated upon standard laboratory conditions (see above) and at the end of each treatment interval were harvested using 0.25% trypsin. After rinsing with cold PBS (5 minutes), cells were fixed in 5 ml of 70% cold ethanol (2 h, 4 °C), rinsed with PBS and resuspended in 0.5 ml propidium iodide (PI – Sigma-Aldrich, Prague, Czech Republic). Following the inclubation with PI (15 minutes, dark, room temperature – RT), the fluorescence emission of examined cells was measured with a flow cytometer (Cell Lab Quanta™ SC, Beckman Coulter Inc. Brea, Ca, USA) with subsequent cell cycle analysis. For each experiment, at least 100,000 cells were analyzed.

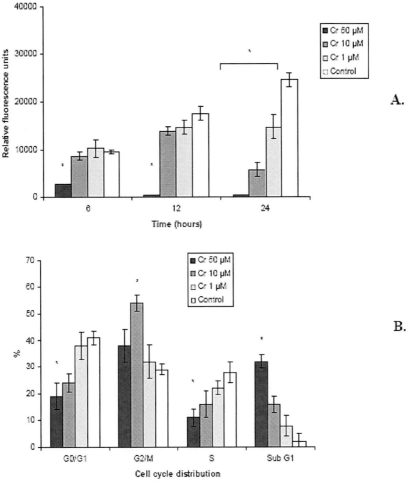

Figure 1. (Continued on next page.)

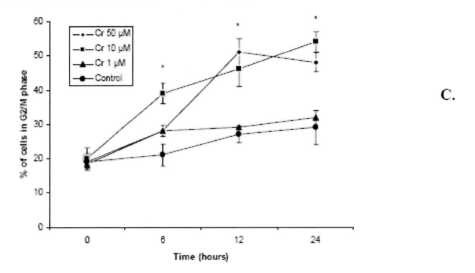

C.

Figure 1. Chemiluminescent quantitation of DNA synthesis as measured by ELISA BrdU kit assay and cell cycle distribution (flow cytometry) in human dermal fibroblasts exposed to hexavalent chromium at a concentration range of 1-50 µM during 24 h. (A) DNA synthesis (B) general distribution of the cell cycle phases at 24 h of the treatment (B) time course of G_2/M arrest in Cr (VI) cells during 24 h. Values represent means ± SD of at least three experiments *P<0.05 with one way-Anova test and Dunnett's post test for multiple comparisons.

Immunocytochemistry

Treated and control skin fibroblasts were seeded into cytospin chambers and cultivated overnight in an incubator at 5 % CO_2 at 37 °C. After exposure to Cr (VI) at 1 µM, 10 µM and 50 µM they were centrifuged (50 x g, 5 min, 4 °C), fixed with 1 ml of 2% paraformaldehyde (20 min, 25 °C), rinsed with PBS with 1 % Triton X (PBS-T) and then treated to skimmed milk for 30 min at 25 °C. The cells were then incubated with mouse anti-phospho Ser-15 p53 (1:200, Sigma-Aldrich, Prague, Czech Republic), rabbit anti-phospho Ser-139 histone H2A.X (1:100, Cell Signaling Technology, Inc., Danvers, MA, USA), mouse anti-phospho Ser-1981 ATM (1:100, Calbiochem, EMD Biosciences, Inc., La Jolla, Ca, USA) and rabbit anti-cleaved Asp-214 PARP (1:200, Cell Signaling Technology, Inc., Danvers, MA, USA) at 4 °C for 1 h. After washing with cold PBS (5 minutes, 25 °C), Alexa Fluor 488 or 546-labeled goat anti-mouse or rabbit IgG (Genetica, Prague, Czech Republic) were added for additional 1 h (25 °C). Next, the specimens were rinsed three times with cold PBS, optionally post-labeled with DAPI (Sigma-Aldrich, Prague, Czech Republic - 10 µg/ml) and mounted into SlowFade® medium (Molecular Probes, Inc., Eugene, U.S.A.). The localization and status of the folowed markers were examined under a fluorescence microscope Nikon Eclipse E 400 (Nikon Corporation, Kanagawa, Japan) equipped with the digital color matrix camera COOL 1300 (VDS, Vosskühler, Germany), using TRITC, FITC and DAPI specific filters. Photographs were taken using the software LUCIA DI Image Analysis System LIM (Laboratory Imaging Ltd., Prague, Czech Republic) and analyzed. For the purpose of analysis, at least 2,000 cells were scored at 200 and 600x magnifications.

Immunoblotting

Treated and control cells were harvested at different time intervals with trypsin, washed with PBS and centrifuged (1000 rpm, 5 min, 4 °C). The resulting pellet was resuspended in 5 ml of ice-cold lysis buffer (137 mM NaCl, 10 % glycerol, 1 % n-octyl-β-D-glucopyranoside, 50 mM NaF, 20 mM Tris, 1 mM sodium orthovanadate, Complete TMMini). The whole cell lysates were boiled for 5 min/95 °C in SDS sample buffer (Tris-HCl pH 6.81, 2-mercaptoethanol, 10 % glycerol, SDS, 0.1 % bromphenol blue) and thereafter they were loaded onto a 12% SDS/polyacrylamide gel. Each lysate contained equal amount of protein (30 μg) as determined by BCA assay. After electrophoresis, proteins were transferred to a PVDF membrane (100 V, 60 min) and incubated at 25 °C for 1.5 h with a solution containing 5% nonfat dry milk, 10 mM Tris-HCl (pH 8.0), 150 mM sodium chloride, and 0.1 % Tween 20 (TBST). Membranes were incubated with primary antibodies (mouse anti-phospho Ser-428 ATR, 1:500, mouse anti-phospho Ser-296 Chk1, 1: 750, mouse anti-Chk1, 1:500, mouse anti-phospho Thr 68 Chk2, 1: 750, mouse anti- Chk2, 1:600 and monoclonal mouse anti-β-actin, 1:100, all Cell Signaling Technology, Inc., Danvers, MA, USA) at 4 °C overnight followed by five 6 min washes in TBST. Next, the blots were incubated with secondary peroxidase-conjugated antibodies (1:1000, 1 h, 25 °C), washed with TBST and the signal was developed with a chemiluminescence (ECL) detection kit (Boehringer Mannheim-Roche, Basel, Switzerland).

Small Interfering RNA (siRNA) Transfections—All siRNA transfections were performed using Lipofectamine 2000 (Invitrogen, Prague, Czech Republic) following the manufacturer's recommendations. Approximately $0.5–0.8 \times 10^5$ cells/well were seeded in 24-well plates with 1 ml of antibiotic-free DMEM with 10% fetal bovine serum. The next day, the cells were treated with Lipofectamine 2000 and 20 pmol of control, ATR, or ATM siRNA - sense strand for ATM and ATR were UAUAUCACCUGUUUGUUAGUU and GCAACUCGCCUAACAGAUAUU (Qiagen Hamburg GmbH, Hamburg, Germany). After 24 h, this procedure was repeated. The cells were analyzed 48 h after the last siRNA transfection.

Statistics

Statistical analysis was carried out with a statistical program GraphPad Prism, using one-way Anova test with Dunnet's post test for multiple comparisons. Results were compared with control samples, and means were considered significant if $P < 0.05$.

3. Results

DNA Synthesis and Cell Cycle

The effects of Cr (VI) at a concentration range of 1-50 μM on DNA synthesis and cell cycle progression in primary human dermal fibroblasts were examined by measurement of

BrdU incorporation into newly synthesized DNA strands and by flow cytometric cell cycle analysis. As shown in Figure 1A, Cr (VI) induced time-dependent inhibition of DNA synthesis; however, there were significant differences upon treatment with different Cr (VI) concentrations. Unlike the highest employed Cr (VI) concentration (50 μM) which significantly suppressed DNA synthesis at all the followed time intervals, lower Cr (VI) concentrations (1 μM and 10 μM) showed this effect only at late phases of exposure (i.e. at 24 h).

The distribution of dermal fibrobalsts with respect to phases of the cell cycle after 24 h of treatment is shown in Figure 1B. It is apparent that in comparison with control cultures, Cr (VI) at higher concentrations induced accumulation of cells in G2/M phase and also increased frequency of cell death as determined by sub G1 peak. The dynamics of G2/M phase accumulation of Cr (VI)-treated fibroblasts shows strong dependency on Cr (VI) concentration and time of treatment too (Figure 1C).

DNA Damage and Oxidative Stress

Generation of oxidative stress in treated and control dermal fibroblasts was followed spectrophometrically. Figure 2 shows elevated levels of hydrogen peroxide/hydroxyl radical in fibroblasts exposed to various concentrations of Cr (VI) during 24 h.

DNA damage in human skin fibroblasts after treatment with Cr (VI) during 24 hours was estimated by means of single cell electrophoresis – comet assay. As shown in Figure 2, Cr (VI) induced dose-dependent DNA damage which was at all the employed concentrations significantly higher than in control cultures.

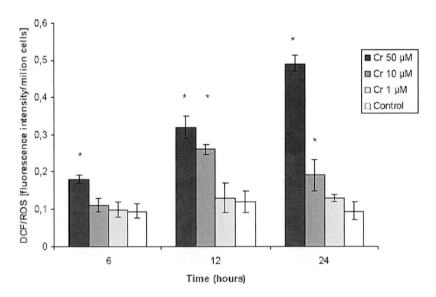

Figure 2. Determination of oxidative stress by spectrophotometric detection of conversion of 2′-7′-dichlorodihydrofluorescein diacetate into a fluorescent product dichlorofluorescein in human dermal fibroblasts exposed to hexavalent chromium at a concentration range of 1-50 μM during 24 h. Values represent means ± SD of at least three experiments *P<0.05 with one way-Anova test and Dunnett's post test for multiple comparisons.

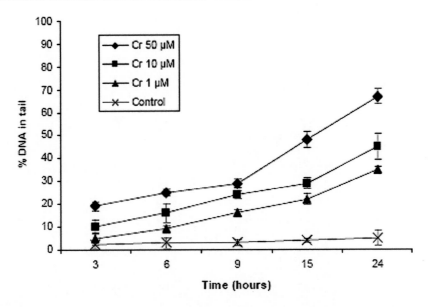

Figure 3. DNA damage in normal human diploid dermal fibroblasts treated with hexavalent chromium (1-50 µM) during 24 h as measured by comet assay. Values represent means ± SD of at least three experiments. All the concentrations of hexavalent chromium at all the treatment intervals with exception of the lowest chromium concentration at 3 h of treatment produced statistically significant response in comparison with controls.

Immunodetection of DNA-Damage Signaling

The activation of specific DNA-damage signaling pathways in dermal fibroblasts exposed to Cr (VI) was followed both by immunocytochemical as well as by western blotting analysis. Cr (VI) stimulated first phosphorylation of DNA-damage sensors ATM and histone H2A.X, which was followed by the specific activation of p53 and delayed cleavage of PARP (Figure 4 A). Time course analyses of these targets revealed their dose-dependent nature (Figure 4 B, C, D, E). In addition, when analyzed further, it was revealed that upon Cr (VI) treatment, ATR, Chk1 and Chk2 kinases are activated too (Figure 5).

Effects of ATM/ATR Inhibition on Activation of PARP

To explore the direct influence of ATM/ATR signaling on cleavage and activation of PARP in Cr (VI)-exposed skin fibroblasts, we next downregulated cellular ATM/ATR expression by means of siRNA mediated knockdown of target genes or chemically blocked the activity of these kinases by means of a specific inhibitor. Figure 6A reveals that the siRNA mediated knockdown of individual kinases was significant in dermal fibroblasts; however, Cr (VI)-associated PARP cleavage did not significantly decrease in ATR manipulated cells unlike ATM downregulated cells where PARP cleavage was suppressed although not entirely abrogated. Conversely, chemical inhibition of both kinases resulted in nearly 70 % inhibition (Figure 6B).

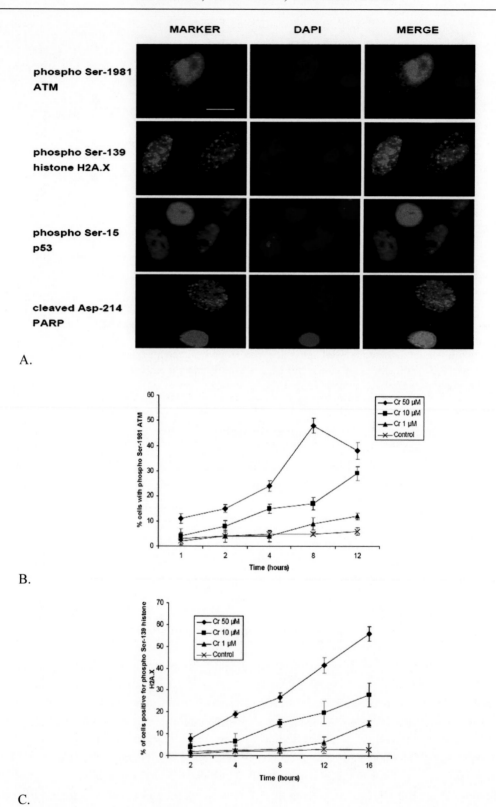

A.

B.

C.

Figure 4. (Continued on next page.)

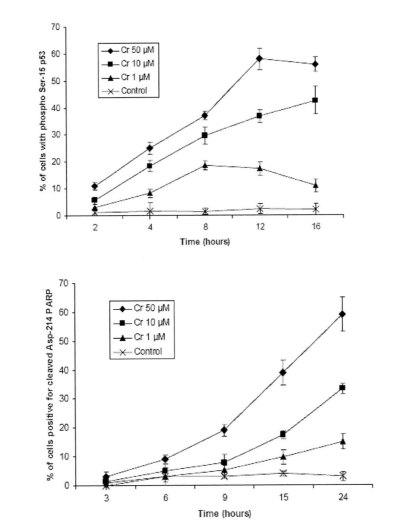

D.

E.

Figure 4. Activation of ATM, H2A.X, p53 and PARP in human dermal fibroblasts treated with hexavalent chromium (1-50 μM) during 24 h as determined by immunohistochemistry with following image analysis as described in Materials and methods section. (A) presence of the activated markers in fibroblasts exposed to hexavalent chromium for 12 h. Fluorescence microscopy 400x. Bar 5 μm. (B) quantitation of cell positive for phospho Ser-1981 ATM during 12 h of exposure (C) quantitation of cell positive for phospho Ser-139 histone H2A.X during 16 h of exposure (D) quantitation of cell positive for phospho Ser-15 p53 during 16 h of exposure (E) quantitation of cell positive for cleaved Asp-214 PARP during 24 h of exposure. Values represent means ± SD of at least three experiments. *P<0.05 with one way-Anova test and Dunnett's post test for multiple comparisons. Ad (B) all treatment intervals and chromium concentrations are significant with exception of the lowest chromium concentration (1 μM). Ad (C) all treatment intervals and chromium concentrations are significant with exception of the lowest chromium concentration (1 μM) at intervals 2-12 h of treatment. Ad (D) all treatment intervals and chromium concentrations are significant with exception of the lowest chromium concentration (1 μM) at treatment interval of 2 h. Ad (E) all treatment intervals and chromium concentrations are significant with exception of the lowest chromium concentration (1 μM) – intervals 3-15 h and 10 μM chromium – intervals 3-9 h of treatment.

Effects of antioxidant on ATM and PARP activation

Since Cr (VI) induces generation of significant levels of free radicals in dermal fibroblasts, we wanted to examine the specific contribution of oxidative stress to DNA damage signaling as well as to the final cell death. Compared to cells with normal levels of antioxidants, antioxidant-pretreated cells, detected levels of free radicals were significantly lower after Cr (VI) treatment (data not shown). Administration of antioxidant NAC reduced the activation of ATM albeit not significantly but markedly suppressed cleavage of PARP in Cr (VI)-treated fibroblasts (Figure 7A and B).

4. Discussion

Following chemically-induced DNA damage in the cell, the specific cellular signaling pathways are activated which determine the final outcome of such an insult. Depending on the nature and extent of induced DNA lesions, cells attempt to restore the integrity of damaged DNA by means of specific repair mechanims while transiently arresting cell cycle at G2/M checkpoint. Alternatively, if the sustained damage is too extensive, irreparable or specific or if the cellular correction machinery does not function, the cell is permanently arrested or activates destruction programs [9].

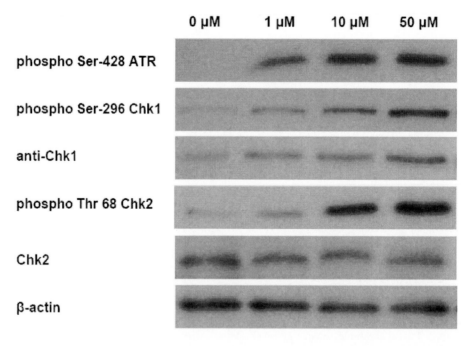

Figure 5. Changes in the expression of selected proteins – ATR, Chk1, Chk2 and β-actin in human dermal fibroblasts treated with hexavalent chromium (1-50 μM) during 24 h as determined by immunoblotting. Cells were harvested and cell lysates were subjected to SDS-PAGE, blotted and probed with antibodies against the above-mentioned proteins. Expression of β-actin was used as control. Data represent results from one of at least three experiments.

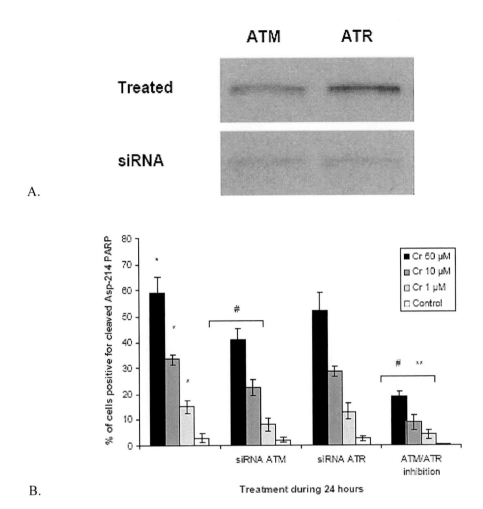

A.

B.   Treatment during 24 hours

Figure 6. Effect of ATM/ATR inhibition on hexavalent chromium-induced cleavage of PARP in human dermal fibroblasts during 24 h of treatment. Prior to exposure to chromium, ATM/ATR expression or activity were inhibited using either siRNA-mediated knockdown or chemical inhibition as described in Materials and methods section. (A) siRNA downregulation of ATM/ATR in dermal fibrobalsts (B) quantitation of the effect of ATM/ATR inhibition on PARP cleavage in treated fibroblasts. Values represent means ± SD of at least three experiments. *P<0.05 with one way-Anova test and Dunnett's post test for multiple comparisons.

Environmental Cr (VI) is known to interact with DNA both directly via Cr (VI) reactive intermediates as well as through stimulated oxidative stress. Both mechanisms are responsible for DNA strand breaks and numerous replication blocking lesions which disturb cellular genomic integrity required for continuous cell cycle progression [13].

We have previously determined that exposure of normal diploid skin fibroblasts to Cr (VI) leads to DNA damaging and activation of p53-dependent cell demise (18).

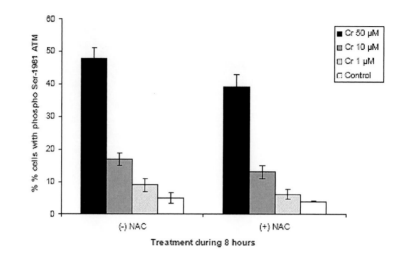

Figure 7. Effect of administered antioxidant N-acetylcystein (NAC) on hexavalent chromium-induced activation of ATM and cleavage of PARP in human dermal fibroblasts during 24 h of treatment. Prior to exposure to chromium, NAC was administered and PARP cleavage as well as ATM activation was determined as described in Materials and methods section. (A) effect of NAC on cleavage of PARP (B) effect of NAC on ATM activation. Values represent means ± SD of at least three experiments. *P<0.05 with one way-Anova test and Dunnett's post test for multiple comparisons.

In this work we wanted to explore in more detail the mechanisms by which Cr (VI) mediated DNA damaging leads to activation of p53 signaling. In addition, we wanted to integrate our knowledge about Cr (VI)-induced cell cycle arrest and cell death.

Our data show that exposure of skin fibroblasts to Cr (VI) leads to time- and dose-dependent generation of oxidative stress, suppression of DNA synthesis and DNA alterations. The nature and biological impacts of these events are obviously very complex as shown for instance in the dynamic nature of induced oxidative stress and its differing profile after various Cr (VI) concentrations. Concomitant with these changes, cells activate the DNA damage response pathways, in particular ATM/ATR kinases. ATM/ATR kinases respond to different types of damage. ATM plays a critical role in sensing DNA double strand breaks while ATR responds to DNA single strand breaks, crosslinks and adducts [4 ; 25]. It has been postulated that with increasing Cr (VI) concentrations, the involvement of ATM becomes less important while there is an increasing participation of ATR [25]. In our model we found that both ATM and ATR kinases were activated in Cr (VI)-exposed fibroblasts and both were likely contributing to our observed phosphorylation of Chk1 and Chk2 kinases and appearance of H2.AX foci (Figure 4), which are indicative of the presence of double-strand breaks. Since the number of skin fibroblasts positive for these foci increased in time upon all the employed Cr (VI) concentrations, it is reasonable to believe that this type of DNA damage was precipitated by several mechanisms which were, nevertheless, concentration-depedent. Thus upon treatment with the higest Cr (VI) concentration of 50 μM, the major contributing factor seems to be an increased level of generated oxidative stress. On the other hand, upon lower Cr (VI) concentrations (10 and 1 μM) where oxidative stress levels peaked at 12 h of treatment and at later intervals decreased, other mechanisms including mismatch repair process or sustained activity of ATM/ATR kinases may play a major role as was reported by others [16].

The p53 protein is a transcription factor that regulates the expression of a large number of target genes mediating a number of different responses including cell cycle arrest, apoptosis or DNA repair [24]. Its role in induction of Cr (VI)-associated cell cycle arrest and cell death in various experimental models including dermal fibroblasts is well established [1 ; 10; 14 ; 18 ; 27]. Phosphorylation and induction of p53 after genotoxic stress is accomplished by several mechanisms. ATM/ATR kinases have been implicated in the activation of p53 both by direct phosphorylation of Ser-15 of p53 and via activation of Chk2 or through decreasing the ability of murine double minute clone 2 protein (MDM2) to transport p53 from the nucleus to the cytoplasm [7]. Consistent with these facts, we found that phosphorylation of Ser-15 of p53 coincides with increased activity of ATM and ATR kinases as well as with activation of their downstream targets Chk1 and Chk2 in Cr (VI)-treated dermal fibroblasts. On the other hand, administration of the chemical inhibitor of ATM/ATR activity had a significant suppressing effect on p53 Ser-15 phosphorylation but not on the overall accumulation of p53 protein (data not shown). These findings clearly indicate that there are two different lines of mechanisms whereby Cr (VI) targets p53 gene in skin fibroblasts. Firstly, by activating ATM/ATR kinases it directly or indirectly phosphorylates protein p53 at Ser-15. This seems to be a predominant mechanism of lower Cr (VI) doses. Secondly, by direct activation of other p53-targeting substrates such as DNA-PK or via generated oxidative stress Cr (VI) stimulates p53 production and activation ATM/ATR-independently; for example via stress kinases. This line of signaling may underlie the exposure to higher Cr (VI) concentrations. Still, concerning the complex role of p53 in Cr (VI)-dependent signaling in dermal fibroblasts but also in other cell populations, it will be very interesting and important to characterize the entire spectrum of Cr (VI)-mediated p53 modifications along with elucidation of other effects contributing to stability, activity and turnover of this important protein.

Poly(ADP-ribose)polymerase (PARP) is a multifunctional zinc-containing enzyme which catalyzes a wide range of reactions. The catalytic activity of PARP is stimulated by diverse phenomena, with DNA damage being among most potent [15 ; 23]. PARP is required for single-strand breaks and base excision repair but upon massive genotoxic insult it undergoes cleavage into four fragments (two large – 89 kDa and 50 kDa and two small – 35 kDa and 40 kDa) with following necrosis. Aletrnatively, PARP may produce two fragments (89 kDa and 24 kDa) which are characteristic of apoptosis [3]. The presence of latter fragment(s) in the studied cell populations is considered as a standard proof of activated cell death – apoptosis [11]. Consistent with these observations we found cleaved PARP in dermal fibroblasts exposed to Cr (VI) at later treatment intervals thus confirming apoptosis. Next we wanted to know whether this specific fragmentation of PARP is linked to Cr (VI)-stimulated ATM/ATR signaling or it is due to other general factors such as the extent of generated oxidative stress. We thus firstly measured the specific PARP cleavage in fibroblasts with downregulated or chemically inhibited ATM or ATR kinases. Our data reveal that both ATM and ATR kinases contribute to signaling leading to PARP cleavage and that their effects are mutually additive as individually downregulated kinases had a lower final effect that combined inhibition of both of them. In addition, pretreatment of skin fibroblasts with antioxidant NAC achieved very significant suppression of PARP cleavage thus suggesting a major role of free radicals in Cr (VI)-induced apoptosis in dermal fibroblasts.

5. Conclusion

Taken together our results confirm that Cr (VI) stimulates both directly (via its reactive metabolic intermediates) and indirectly (through generated oxidative stress) DNA damaging which results in the activation of DNA damage response pathway. The important members of this pathway include ATM/ATR kinases which stimulate their downstream targets – Chk1, Chk2 and p53 in mediating transient G2/M cell cycle arrest and activating cell death characterized by the specific cleavage of PARP. The p53 protein as a key molecule in integration and execution of signals generated by dermal fibroblasts exposed to Cr (VI) here seems to be influenced not only by the aforementioned mechanisms but may also respond to other oxidative stress-mediated pathways such as those under control of MAPK stress kinases. The unravelling of interactions between individual pathway members is thus an exciting perspective of future experimental work.

6. Acknowledgment

This work was supported by Ministry of Education Research Project MSM 0021620820.

7. References

[1]   Bagchi, D, Bagchi, M, Stohs, SJ. Chromium (VI)-induced oxidative stress, apoptotic cell death and modulation of p53 tumor suppressor gene. *Mol. Cell Biochem.* 2001; 222:149-58.

[2]   Barceloux, DG. Chromium. *J. Toxicol. Clin. Toxicol.* 1999; 37:173-94.

[3]   Burkle, A. Poly(ADP-ribose). The most elaborate metabolite of NAD+. FEBS J 2005; 272:4576-89.

[4]   Canman, CE, Lim, DS. The role of ATM in DNA damage responses and cancer. *Oncogene* 1998; 17:3301-8.

[5]   De-Flora, S. Threshold mechanisms and site specificity in chromium(VI) carcinogenesis. *Carcinogenesis* 2000; 21:533-41.

[6]   Ermolli, M, Menne, C, Pozzi, G, Serra, MA, Clerici, LA. Nickel, cobalt and chromium-induced cytotoxicity and intracellular accumulation in human hacat keratinocytes. *Toxicology* 2001; 159:23-31.

[7]   Ha, L, Ceryak, S, Patierno, SR. Chromium (VI) activates ataxia telangiectasia mutated (ATM) protein. Requirement of ATM for both apoptosis and recovery from terminal growth arrest. *J. Biol. Chem.* 2003; 278:17885-94.

[8]   Hansen, MB, Johansen, JD, Menne, T. Chromium allergy: significance of both Cr(III) and Cr(VI). *Contact Dermat.* 2003; 49:206-12.

[9]   Hartwell, LH, Kastan, MB. Cell cycle control and cancer. *Science* N.Y 1994; 266:1821-8.

[10]   Hayashi, Y, Kondo, T, Zhao, QL, Ogawa, R, Cui, ZG, Feril, LB, Jr., Teranishi, H, Kasuya, M. Signal transduction of p53-independent apoptotic pathway induced by hexavalent chromium in U937 cells. *Toxicol. Appl. Pharmacol.* 2004; 197:96-106.

[11]   Heeres, JT, Hergenrother, PJ. Poly(ADP-ribose) makes a date with death. *Curr. Opin. Chem. Biol.* 2007; 11:644-53.

[12]   Jirsova, K, Mandys, V. Induction of micronuclei and granular chromatin condensation in human skin fibroblasts influenced by cisplatin (cis-DDP) in vitro. *Mutat. Res.* 1994; 310:37-44.

[13]   Liu, K, Husler, J, Ye, J, Leonard, SS, Cutler, D, Chen, F, Wang, S, Zhang, Z, Ding, M, Wang, L, Shi, X. On the mechanism of Cr (VI)-induced carcinogenesis: dose dependence of uptake and cellular responses. *Mol. Cell Biochem.* 2001; 222:221-9.

[14]   Meplan, C, Richard, MJ, Hainaut, P. Redox signalling and transition metals in the control of the p53 pathway. *Biochem. Pharmacol.* 2000; 59:25-33.

[15]   Parsons, JL, Dianova, II, Allinson, SL, Dianov, GL. Poly(ADP-ribose) polymerase-1 protects excessive DNA strand breaks from deterioration during repair in human cell extracts. *FEBS J.* 2005; 272:2012-21.

[16]   Peterson-Roth, E, Reynolds, M, Quievryn, G, Zhitkovich, A. Mismatch repair proteins are activators of toxic responses to chromium-DNA damage. *Mol. Cell Biol.* 2005; 25:3596-607.

[17]   Pritchard, DE, Ceryak, S, Ha, L, Fornsaglio, JL, Hartman, SK, O_Brien, TJ, Patierno, SR. Mechanism of apoptosis and determination of cellular fate in chromium(VI)-exposed populations of telomerase-immortalized human fibroblasts. *Cell Growth and Differ*; 2001; 12:487-96.

[18]   Rudolf, E, Cervinka, M. The role of intracellular zinc in chromium(VI)-induced oxidative stress, DNA damage and apoptosis. *Chemico-Biol Interact* 2006; 162:212-27.

[19]   Shi, XL, Dalal, NS. Chromium (V) and hydroxyl radical formation during the glutathione reductase-catalyzed reduction of chromium (VI). *Biochem. Biophys. Res. Commun.* 1989; 163:627-34.

[20] Singh, J, Carlisle, DL, Pritchard, DE, Patierno, SR. Chromium-induced genotoxicity and apoptosis: relationship to chromium carcinogenesis (review). *Oncol. Reports* 1998; 5:1307-18.

[21] Stohs, SJ, Bagchi, D, Hassoun, E, Bagchi, M. Oxidative mechanisms in the toxicity of chromium and cadmium ions. *J. Environ. Pathol. Toxicol. Oncol.* 2000; 19:201-13.

[22] Sugiyama, M. Role of physiological antioxidants in chromium(VI)-induced cellular injury. *Free Radic. Biol. Med.* 1992; 12:397-407.

[23] Tong, WM, Hande, MP, Lansdorp, PM, Wang, ZQ. DNA strand break-sensing molecule poly(ADP-Ribose) polymerase cooperates with p53 in telomere function, chromosome stability, and tumor suppression. *Mol. Cell Biol.* 2001; 21:4046-54.

[24] Vogelstein, B, Lane, D, Levine, AJ. Surfing the p53 network. *Nature* 2000; 408:307-10.

[25] Wakeman, TP, Xu, B. ATR regulates hexavalent chromium-induced S-phase checkpoint through phosphorylation of SMC1. *Mutat. Res.* 2006; 610:14-20.

[26] Winder, C, Carmody, M. The dermal toxicity of cement. Toxicol Ind Health 2002; 18:321-31.

[27] Ye, J, Wang, S, Leonard, SS, Sun, Y, Butterworth, L, Antonini, J, Ding, M, Rojanasakul, Y, Vallyathan, V, Castranova, V, Shi, X. Role of reactive oxygen species and p53 in chromium(VI)-induced apoptosis. *J. Biol. Chem.* 1999; 274:34974-80.

In: New Research on DNA Damage
Editors: Honoka Kimura and Aoi Suzuki

ISBN 978-1-60456-581-2
© 2008 Nova Science Publishers, Inc.

Chapter 15

Comparison of DNA Damage and the Expression of Repair Related Molecules, Including DNA Polymerase β, APE/ref-1, PCNA, and GADD45, in Human T and B Lymphocytes Exposed to Hydrogen Peroxide and Methyl Methanesulfonate

Eunkyung Cho[1], So-Young Park[2] and Donggeun Sul[1,2]

[1]Graduate School of Medicine, Korea Universty, Korea,
[2]Environmental Toxico-Genomic and Proteomic Center, College of Medicine, Korea University, Korea

Abstract

In this study, we evaluated the DNA damage and the expression of repair related molecules, including DNA polymerase β, apurinic/apyrimidinic endonuclease /redox factor-1 (APE/ref-1), proliferating cell nuclear antigen (PCNA), and growth arrest and DNA damage (GADD45) in T and B human lymphocytes that were exposed to hydrogen peroxide (H_2O_2) and methyl methane sulfonate (MMS). DNA damage was evaluated by conducting a Comet assay of T and B cells that were exposed to H_2O_2 (25 and 50 μM) and MMS (25 and 50 μM) for 5 min. The mean value of the Olive Tailmoment of the control lymphocytes was 1.34 ± 0.02 and 1.41 ± 0.01 ($p=0.084$) in the T- and B-lymphocytes, respectively, which indicates that there was no significant difference in the level of DNA damage that occurred. However, after being exposed to 25 μM and 50 μM of H_2O_2, the mean values of the Olive Tailmoments of the T-lymphocytes were 1.92 ± 0.11 ($p=0.001$) and 2.16 ± 0.32 ($p=0.001$) whereas those of the B-lymphocytes were 1.98 ± 0.11 ($p=0.001$) and 2.24 ± 0.30 ($p=0.001$), which indicates that a significant level of DNA damage occurred. In addition, after cells were exposed to 25 μM and 50 μM of MMS, the mean values of the Olive Tailmoments of the T-lymphocytes were 1.80 ± 0.09 ($p=0.001$) and 2.02 ± 0.31 ($p=0.001$) whereas those of the B-lymphocytes were 1.88 ±

0.14 (p=0.001) and 2.12 ± 0.33 (p=0.001), which also indicates that a significant level of DNA damage occurred. Furthermore, the level of DNA damage was found to be significantly greater in B-lymphocytes than in T-lymphocytes. Taken together, these results indicate that human B-lymphocyte may be a more sensitive target than T-lymphocytes for the evaluation of DNA damage when conducting human biomonitoring.

When the expression of DNA polymerase β, APE/ref-1, GADD45 and PCNA was evaluated, their relative intensities were found to increase significantly with increasing concentrations of H_2O_2 and MMS in both T- and B-lymphocytes (p<0.05). In addition, the relative intensity of GADD45 was significantly greater in the B-lymphocytes than in T-lymphocytes.

In summary, a Comet assay showed that DNA damage occurred in response to H_2O_2 and MMS level in human T- and B-lymphocytes, and that this occurred in a dose dependent fashion. In addition, the amount of DNA damage that occurred was greater in B-lymphocytes than in T-lymphocytes, which indicates that human B-lymphocyte are more sensitive target than T-lymphocytes for the evaluation of DNA damage when conducting human biomonitoring. Futhermore, when the DNA repair enzyme and protein expressions were compaired, GADD45 was found to be more sensitive to DNA damage than DNA polymerase β, APE/ref-1, and PCNA in human T- and B-lymphocytes, which could be useful in the evaluation of DNA damage as a result of genetic toxicants.

Keywords: *B-lymphocytes, Comet assay, DNA damage, MACS, Repair enzyme, T-lymphocytes*

Introduction

DNA repair genes can be sub-grouped into genes that are associated with signaling and regulation of DNA repair and those that are associated with distinct repair mechanisms, such as mismatch repair (MMR), base excision repair (BER), nucleotide excision repair (NER), direct damage reversal and DNA double-strand break (DSB) repair [1]. Among these types of repair mechanisms, BER is a ubiquitous mechanism that removes damage induced by spontaneous chemical reaction and reactive oxygen species (ROS), as well as DNA damage induced by a variety of environmental genotoxicants [2]

BER functions by removing abnormal or damaged bases using DNA glycosylase, which plays a role in the enzymatic hydrolysis of the N-glycosyl bond. This hydrolysis then leads to the formation of an apurinic/apyrimidinic (AP) site or a single strand break (SSB) with 3'-α,β-unsaturated aldehyde and 5'-phosphate ends, depending on the type of DNA glycosylase [1, 2, 3], which are subgrouped to Type I and Type II by their functions, such as 8-oxoG DNA glycosylase (OGG1), endonuclease III homolog 1 (NTH1), MutM homolog (MYH), and nei-like (NEIL) [1, 2].

AP sites serve as a substrate for apurinic/apyrimidinic endonuclease/redox factor-1 (APE/ref-1), which incises the DNA backbone immediately 5' to the AP site via its 5'endonuclease activity, producing a single strand break with a normal 3'-hydroxyl group and an abnormal 5'-deoxyribose 5-phosphate residues [3, 4, 5]. APE/ref-1 then cleaves the AP sites in the area of DNA that has been damaged, thereby allowing them to be repaired by other enzymes involved in the dual pathways of BER, including DNA polymerases, ligases, and various repair related proteins [1, 2, 3, 4, 6].

DNA polymerases mediate the insertion of either a new single nucleotide or several nucleotides via the short- and long-patch mode of BER [1, 2, 3, 6] Although a short-patch BER pathway is limited to the excision of only the terminal abasic residue most by DNA polymerase β in mammalian cells, the long-patch BER pathway removes the 5'-terminal AP sites in short segments of DNA, which results in longer repair patches of up to 10 nucleotides by DNA polymerase δ and ε together with PCNA, flap endonuclease (FEN1) and replication factor C (RF-C) [1, 2, 6, 7].

In the PCNA dependent BER pathway, PCNA forms a complex with polymerase δ and ε which initiates long-patch BER and it also interacts with other repair proteins, such as FEN 1 or DNA ligase, which continue the DNA repair process [1, 2, 8, 9, 10].

A transcriptional target of p53, GADD45, was recently found to bind to PCNA [11]. GADD45 induction competes with p21, which has been shown to bind to and inhibit PCNA-dependent DNA polymerase δ replication *in vitro* [12, 13], thereby leading to the binding of PCNA and promoting excision repair [11].

In concerning with DNA repair, the method by DNA damage detected involves evaluation of DNA damage that occurs after low level exposure to toxicants *in vitro* and *in vivo*. Recently, single cell gel electrophoresis (SCGE), otherwise known as the Comet assay, has been used to evaluate DNA damage including strand breaks, alkali-labile sites, DNA crosslinking, and incomplete excision repair sites in cells, animals, and human [14, 15].

The SCGE technique is a rapid, simple and sensitive method for measuring DNA breakage with a small number of cells and detects intercellular differences in DNA damage [14, 15].

In this study, we determined the DNA damage and the expression of repair related molecules, including DNA polymerase β, APE/ref-1, PCNA, and GADD45 in T and B human primary lymphocytes that were exposed to hydrogen peroxide (H_2O_2) and methyl methanesulfonate (MMS) to evaluate the association of DNA damage and the repair system in human T- and B-lymphocytes. However, the cells were treated with only a low concentration of H_2O_2 and MMS for a short time in an attempt to mimic the level of environmental toxicants that humans are actually be exposed to.

The results of this study shows that different level of DNA damage and repair occur between T- and B-lymphocyte that are exposed to genotoxic compounds.

Materials and Methods

Subjects

This study was conducted on 10 healthy males that were selected between June 5 and Oct 10, 2007. All subjects completed a questionnaire that included questions regarding smoking, drinking, age, medication, etc. The mean of age of subjects included in this study was 25 year (ranges 24 to 28), and all subjects were non-smokers with no history of medication. This study was approved by the IRB at the Hospital of Korea University.

Cell Preparation

Blood cell samples were prepared as previously described [16]. Briefly, blood samples were collected by heparinized venipuncture from human subject and delivered immediately to the laboratory. Comet assay was carried out within 3 h. T-lymphocytes and B-lymphocytes were positively selected with magnetic beads [Magnetic cell sorting (MACS) CD3 or CD19 isolation kit; Miltenyi Biotech] according to the manufacturer's instruction. The unfractionated leukocytes were then prepared by removing the red blood cells from whole blood by treatment with Dextran (Sigma Co.). The leukocytes were incubated with each kind of monoclonal antibody (20 µl of MACS microbeads per 10^7 total cells) for 15 min at 6-12°C. After washing cells by adding 10-20X the labeling volume of PBS buffer, the cells were centrifuged at 300 x g for 10 min and the supernatant was completely removed. Cells were resuspended in an appropriate amount of buffer (500 µl of buffer per 10^8 total cells) and applied to a prepared MS column (Miltenyi Biotech), placed in the magnetic field of a MACS separator and washed with 500 µl of buffer. After elimination of the negative cells, the column was removed from the MACS separator and placed on a suitable collection tube where each type of cells was collected and washed with PBS buffer for further studies.

Chemical Treatments

Chemical treatment was performed according to Andreoli, with minor modification [17]. Briefly, the harvested lymphocytes were washed with PBS buffer to remove the excess media and were then counted prior to exposure of chemical treatment. T- and B-lymphocytes were resuspended in PBS buffer at a concentration of 1 x 10^6/ml and were then exposed to H_2O_2 (25 and 50 µM) and MMS (25 and 50 µM) for 5 min on ice. Following the exposure period, cells were washed with PBS buffer and then used for the Comet assay and western blot assay.

Comet Assay

The Comet assay was performed according to Singh with minor modification [18]. Briefly, normal melting point agarose (Ameresco, NMA) and low melting point agarose (Ameresco, LMA) were dissolved in PBS (Gibco BRL) using microwave. 100 µl of 1 % NMA was added onto a fully frosted slides that were precoated with 50 µl of 1 % NMA for a firm attachment and the slides were then allowed to solidify with cover slips in the refrigerator for 5 min. After solidification of the gel, the cover slips were removed and lymphocytes in 50 µl mixed with 50 µl of 1 % LMA was added. The cover slips were added on the layer and the slides were allowed to solidify in the refrigerator for 5 min. After removing cover slips, 100 µl of 0.5 % LMA was added on the third layer and the slides were placed with cover slips again in the refrigerator for 5 min. The slides were submersed in the lysing solution (2.5 M NaCl, 100 mM EDTA-2Na, 10 mM Tris-HCl, pH 10; 1% Triton X-100 and 10 % DMSO, pH 10 were added fresh) for 1 h. The slides were then placed in unwinding buffer (1 mM EDTA and 300 mM NaOH, pH 13) for 20 min and electrophoresis was carried out using the same solution for 20 min at 25 V and 300 mA (0.8 v/cm). After electrophoresis, the slides were neutralized by washing three times with neutralization buffer (400 mM Tris-HCl, pH 7.4) 5 min each and were stained with 50 μl of 10 μg/ml ethidium bromide.

The slides were examined using a Komet 4.0 image analysis system (Kinetic Imaging, Liverpool, UK) fitted with an Olympus BX50 fluorescence microscope equipped with an excitation filter of 515-560 nm and a barrier filter 590 nm. For each treatment group, two slides were prepared and each 50 randomly chosen cells (total 100 cells) were scored manually. The parameter, Olive Tailmoment [=(Tail.mean-Head.mean)*Tail%DNA /100], was calculated automatically using the Komet 4.0 image analysis system, which was used for global comet description.

Western Blot Assay

Lymphocytes were solubilized in lysis buffer (pH 7.4) containing a protease inhibitor cocktail (Roche, Germany) on ice using a homogenizer. The lysates were then clarified by centrifugation at 12,000 rpm for 15 min at 4°C and the protein concentration of the total lysate was determined using a Bradford protein assay (Bio-Rad Laboratory, Richmond, CA, USA). Next, an equal amount of protein per lane was separated by electrophoresis on 8 and 12 % SDS-polyacrylamide gels, and then transferred to polyvinylidene difluoride membranes (Millopore Corporation, MA, USA) at 350 mA for 1 h using a transfer buffer (pH 8.3). The membranes were blocked with blocking buffer [PBS containing 5% skim milk] for 1 h at room temperature, followed by incubation with primary antibodies overnight at 4°C. After washing the membranes with 3 times for 10 min with PBS, they were further incubated with horseradish peroxidase-conjugated secondary antibodies [anti-rabbit IgG and anti-mouse IgG (Santicruz, 1:1000 dilution)] for 1 h at room temperature and washed 3 times for 10 min with PBS. After washing extensively, the immune complexes were then detected using an ECL and ECL Plus systems (Amersham Pharmacia Biotech, Pisctaway, NJ). Primary antibodies against DNA polymerase β (Abcam, 1:1000 dilution), APE/ref-1 (Santa Cruz, 1:100 dilution), PCNA (Santa Cruz, 1:100 dilution), and GADD45 (Santa Cruz, 1:500 dilution) were applied at the optimized concentrations. Bands were visualized by chemiluminescence and scanned using a flat-bed scanner. The digitalized images were then analyzed using Scion image analysis software (Scion Co, Frederick, MD).

Statistical Analysis

Statistical analyses were performed using SAS version 8.2. The Student's t-test was used to determine the significances of differences between the exposed and control groups. The level of statistical significance employed in all cases was $p<0.05$.

Results

DNA Damages in T-lymphocytes

DNA damage in T and B cells that were exposed H_2O_2 (25 and 50 µM) and MMS (25 and 50 µM) for 5 min was evaluated using a Comet assay. The mean value of the Olive Tailmoment of the control lymphocytes was 1.34 ± 0.02 in the T lymphocytes (Figure 1A). After being exposed to 25 µM and 50 µM of H_2O_2, the mean values of the Olive Tailmoments of the T-lymphocytes were 1.92 ± 0.11 (p=0.001) and 2.16 ± 0.32 (p=0.001), respectively, which indicates that significant level of DNA damage occurred. After the cells were exposed to 25 µM and 50 µM of MMS, the Olive Tailmoments were 1.80 ± 0.09 (p=0.001) and 2.02 ± 0.31 (p=0.001), respectively, which also indicates that a significant level of DNA damage occurred.

In addition, the level of DNA damage was found to be greater in T-lymphocytes that were exposed to H_2O_2 than in T-lymphocytes that were exposed to MMS, however, this difference was not statistically significant.

DNA Damages in B-lymphocytes

DNA damage in T and B cells that were exposed H_2O_2 (25 and 50 µM) and MMS (25 and 50 µM) for 5 min was evaluated using a Comet assay. The mean value of the Olive Tailmoment of the control lymphocytes was 1.41 ± 0.01 in the B lymphocytes (Figure 1B). After being exposed to 25 µM and 50 µM of H_2O_2, the mean values of the Olive Tailmoments of the B-lymphocytes were 1.98 ± 0.11 (p=0.001) and 2.24 ± 0.30 (p=0.001), respectively, which indicates that a significant level of DNA damage occurred. After cells were exposed to 25 µM and 50 µM of MMS, the Olive Tailmoments were 1.88 ± 0.14 (p=0.001) and 2.12 ± 0.33 (p=0.001), respectively, which also indicates that a significant level of DNA damage occurred.

In addition, the level of DNA damage was found to be greater in B-lymphocytes exposed to H_2O_2 than in B-lymphocytes exposed to MMS, however, this difference was not statistically significant.

Comparison of DNA Damage between T- and B-lymphocytes

The level of DNA damage was compared between T- and B-lymphocytes exposed to H_2O_2 (25 and 50 µM) and MMS (25 and 50 µM) for 5 min (Figure 1). The mean value of the Olive Tailmoment of the control lymphocytes was 1.34 ± 0.02 and 1.41 ± 0.01 (p=0.084) in the T- and B-lymphocytes, respectively, which indicates that there was no significant difference in the level of DNA damage. However, the level of DNA damage was found to be greater in B-lymphocytes than in T-lymphocytes and there was a significant difference in the level of DNA damage that occurred between T-and B-lymphocytes exposed to H_2O_2 and MMS (p<0.05).

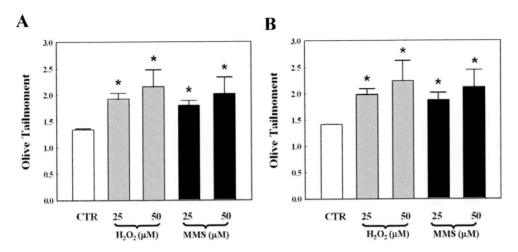

Figure 1. Distribution of the Olive Tailmoments of T- and B-lymphocytes exposed to H_2O_2 and MMS. **A**: DNA damage in T-lymphocytes. **B**: DNA damage in B-lymphocytes. Data represent the means ± SD (n=7). * : Significantly different with control by Duncan test and ANOVA ($p<0.05$) (n=7).

Expression of DNA Repair Enzymes Including DNA Polymeras β and APE/ref-1 by Western Blot Assay

A western blot assay to evaluate the expression of DNA polymerase β and APE/ref-1, which are major key repair enzymes in the BER pathway, was performed using human T- and B-lymphocytes. Human T- and B-lymphocytes were isolated using the MACS system and then exposed to H_2O_2 (25 and 50 μM) and MMS (25 and 50 μM) for 5 min. T- and B-human lymphocytes were then solubilized in homogenization buffer on ice using a homogenizer. The lysates were then subjected to 12 % SDS-polyacrylamide gel electrophoresis after determination of protein concentration using a Bradford protein assay.

The relative intensity showed that DNA polymerase β expression was significantly greater in human T-lymphocytes exposed to H_2O_2 and MMS than in control lymphocytes (Figure 2). In addition, although DNA polymerase β expression was found to be greater in human B-lymphocytes than T-lymphocytes, there was no significant difference in the level of DNA polymerase β expression that occurred between T-and B-lymphocytes exposed to H_2O_2 and MMS ($p<0.05$).

APE/ref-1 expression showed similar pattern of DNA polymerase β expression in human T- and B-lymphocytes (Figure 3). The relative intensity showed that APE/ref-1 expression was significantly greater in human T-and B-lymphocytes exposed to H_2O_2 and MMS than in control lymphocytes. Additionally, the difference in APE/ref-1 expression between T- and B-lymphocytes was evaluated, and no significant difference was observed ($p>0.05$).

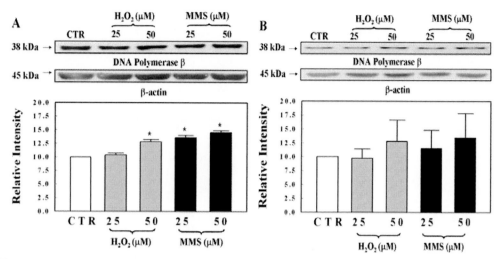

Figure 2. Western blot analysis and relative intensity of expression of DNA polymerase β in human T- and B-lymphocytes exposed to H₂O₂ and MMS. **A**: Western blots of DNA polymerase β and β-actin in T-lymphocytes. Relative intensity of expression of DNA polymerase β was normalized by β-actin expression. **B**: Western blots of DNA polymerase β and β-actin in B-lymphocytes. Relative intensity of expression of DNA polymerase β was normalized by β-actin expression. Total extracts of human T- and B-lymphocytes (30 μg) were loaded in each lane. * : Significantly different with control by Duncan test and ANOVA ($p<0.05$) (n=7).

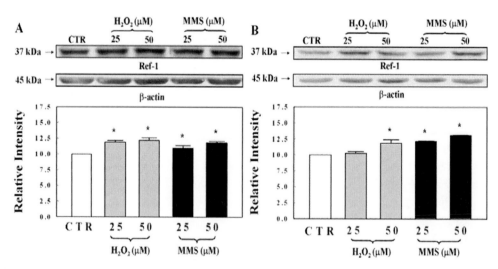

Figure 3. Western blot analysis and relative intensity of expression of APE/ref-1 in human T- and B-lymphocytes exposed to H₂O₂ and MMS. **A**: Western blots of APE/ref-1 and β-actin in T-lymphocytes. Relative intensity of expression of APE/ref-1 was normalized by β-actin expression. **B**: Western blots of APE/ref-1 and β-actin in B-lymphocytes. Relative intensity of expression of APE/ref-1 was normalized by β-actin expression. Total extracts of human T- and B-lymphocytes (30 μg) were loaded in each lane. * : Significantly different with control by Duncan test and ANOVA ($p<0.05$) (n=7).

Expression of DNA Repair Related Molecules Including PCNA and GADD45 by Western Blot Assay

Western blot assays for the PCNA and GADD45 repair proteins in the BER pathway, were performed using human T- and B-lymphocytes. Human T- and B-lymphocytes were isolated using the MACS system and then exposed to H_2O_2 (25 and 50 μM) and MMS (25 and 50 μM) for 5 min. T- and B-human lymphocytes were solubilized in homogenization buffer on ice using a homogenizer. The lysates were then subjected to 12 % SDS-polyacrylamide gel electrophoresis after determination of the protein concentration using a Bradford protein assay.

Relative intensity showed that the PCNA expression increased significantly in human T- and B-lymphocytes exposed to H_2O_2 and MMS when compared with that of control lymphocytes, however no significant difference was not found in PCNA expression in cells treated with H_2O_2 and MMS (Figure 4). Furthermore, when the difference in PCNA expression between T- and B-lymphocytes was evaluated, no difference in the level of PCNA expression between T-lymphocyte and B-lymphocytes was observed.

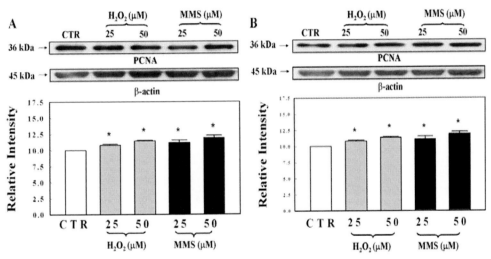

Figure 4. Western blot analysis and relative intensity of expression of PCNA in human T- and B-lymphocytes exposed to H_2O_2 and MMS. **A**: Western blots of PCNA and β-actin in T-lymphocytes. Relative intensity of expression of PCNA was normalized by β-actin expression. **B**: Western blots of PCNA and β-actin in B-lymphocytes. Relative intensity of expression of PCNA was normalized by β-actin expression. Total extracts of human T- and B-lymphocytes (30 μg) were loaded in each lane. * : Significantly different with control by Duncan test and ANOVA ($p<0.05$) (n=7).

The relative intensity revealed that GADD45 expression was increased in human T- and B-lymphocytes exposed to H2O2 and MMS when compared with that of control lymphocytes (Figure 5). In addition, the induction of GADD45 by MMS was stronger than that of H2O2 in human T- and B-lymphocytes. Furthermore, when the difference in GADD45 expression between T- and B-lymphocytes was evaluated, the level of GADD45 expression was found to be greater in B-lymphocytes, and the expression level of T- and B-lymphocytes exposed to

H2O2 and MMS was also significantly different (p<0.01). Additionally, the increase in GADD45 expression was shown to be dependent on the increase of DNA damage in T- and B-lymphocytes.

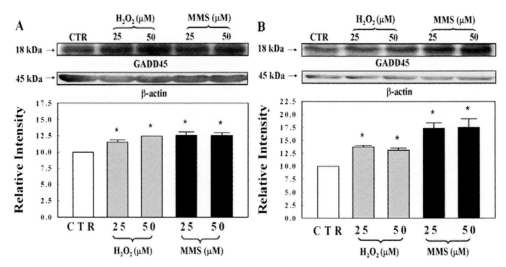

Figure 5. Western blot analysis and relative intensity of expression of GADD45 in human T- and B-lymphocytes exposed to H_2O_2 and MMS. **A**: Western blots of GADD45 and β-actin in T-lymphocytes. Relative intensity of expression of GADD45 was normalized by β-actin expression. **B**: Western blots of GADD45 and β-actin in B-lymphocytes. Relative intensity of expression of GADD45 was normalized by β-actin expression. Total extracts of human T- and B-lymphocytes (30 μg) were loaded in each lane. * : Significantly different with control by Duncan test and ANOVA ($p<0.05$) (n=7).

Discussion

Human beings are continuously exposed to a variety of environmental toxicants, which induce DNA damage, however, these toxins are generally present in low levels [19]. Human biomonitoring using the SCGE or Comet assay is a novel approach for the assessment of genetic damage in the exposed population [14], because it is a very sensitive technique for measuring DNA damage and requires a small number of human lymphocytes or granulocytes [16, 20, 21, 22].

Based on the generally low levels of toxicants encountered by humans, genotoxic experiments should be conducted using low concentrations of toxicants to provide data that is applicable to humans.

In this study, T- and B-lymphocytes were treated with low levels of genotoxic compounds, such as H_2O_2 and MMS, for a short time, and the level of DNA damage that occurred was then determined using a Comet assay. In previous studies, the general toxicity and the genetic damage caused by H_2O_2 was investigated in human lymphocytes [17, 23, 24], and a significant DNA damage was observed in human lymphocytes exposed to various concentration of H_2O_2. In addition, the effects of an alkylating agent, MMS, on human lymphocytes were also evaluated to determine if damage to DNA occurred [17, 25], and MMS was found to induce DNA lesions that led to strand breaks in the alkaline Comet assay [25].

In this study, H_2O_2 and MMS induced a significant amount of DNA damage in human T- and B-lymphocytes, and the amount of DNA damage that occurred was found to be significantly greater in B-lymphocytes than in T-lymphocytes. In a previous environmental human study, DNA damage in T- and B-lymphocytes, and granulocytes obtained from workers exposed to benzene showed similar results, with B-lymphocytes being more sensitive to low levels of benzene than T-lymphocytes and granulocytes [16]. In addition, it has also been reported that B-lymphocytes are more susceptible to DNA damage than T-lymphocytes in emission inspection and incineration workers exposed to polycyclic aromatic hydrocarbons [20]. Based on these results, B-lymphocytes are a useful target for biomonitoring of human exposure to low levels of genotoxic compounds.

Conversely, the DNA repair system acts as a defense mechanism against DNA damage in the biological systems. In this study, the expression of DNA repair enzymes and proteins, including DNA polymerase β, APE/ref-1, PCNA, and GADD45 were determined using western blot assays. In biological systems, abasic sites (AP sites) are the most common DNA lesions generated by both spontaneous and induced base loss [26]. These DNA lesions are processed by one of the central components of BER, the AP endonuclease that specially hydrolyzes the phosphodiester on the 5'-side of the basic residue to produce 3'end, thereby facilitating subsequent repair synthesis by DNA polymerase [6, 8].

A significant number of 5'-cleaved abasic sites were detected in human HeLa cells exposed to H_2O_2 [30], and H_2O_2 and hypochloric acid are known to cause induction of APE/ref-1 through activation of the APE/ref-1 promoter [27, 28]. Furthermore, in Raji B-lymphocytes, APE/ref-1 rapidly re-localizes into mitochondria following H_2O_2 activation [29]. A similar pattern of APE/ref-1 expression was observed in the current study, with APE/ref-1 expression being found to increase significantly in human T- and B-lymphocytes exposed to H_2O_2 and MMS. However, their expression in T- and B-lymphocytes was not found to be significantly different, which indicates that a similar repair response exists in both T- and B-lymphocytes.

Another major repair enzyme, DNA polymerase has been found to at least fourteen types (α, β, γ, δ, ε, ζ, η, θ, ι, κ, λ, μ, σ, φ, and Rev1) [30, 31, 32]. Of these enzymes, DNA polymerase α is the major enzyme involved in DNA replication, however, DNA polymerase β, γ, δ and ε play a role in the repair of DNA in the BER pathway [30, 32]. In the present study, DNA polymerase β expression showed similar pattern of APE/ref-1 expression in human T- and B-lymphocytes. A significant increase of DNA polymerase β expression was observed in human T-lymphocytes exposed to H_2O_2 and MMS.

In the BER pathway, PCNA is an intracellular communicator involved in DNA replication and other important cellular events, including DNA repair [7]. In the present study, although PCNA expression showed similar pattern of APE/ref-1 and DNA polymerase β expression in human T- and B- lymphocytes, no significant difference of PCNA expression was found in human T-lymphocytes, indicating that a different repair response occurred between T- and B-lymphocytes.

GADD45, one of the base excision repair proteins, was evaluated in human T- and B-lymphocytes in this study. Although the pattern of GADD45 expression was similar to those of APE/ref-1 and DNA polymerase β, their expressions in T- and B-lymphocytes was significantly different. Their expression in both lymphocytes was found to be dependent on the amount of DNA damage that occurred, as was shown by the higher GADD45 in B-lymphocytes than in T-lymphocytes.

In summary, a Comet assay showed that DNA damage occurred in response to H2O2 and MMS level in human T- and B-lymphocytes, and that this occurred in a dose dependent fashion. In addition, the amount of DNA damage that occurred was greater in B-lymphocytes than in T-lymphocytes, which indicates that human B-lymphocytes are more sensitive target than T-lymphocytes for the evaluation of DNA damage when conducting human biomonitoring. Futhermore, when the DNA repair enzyme and protein expressions were compared, GADD45 was found to be more sensitive to DNA damage than DNA polymerase β, APE/ref-1, and PCNA in human T- and B-lymphocytes, which could be useful in the evaluation of DNA damage as a result of genetic toxicants.

Acknowledgements

This research was supported by the Grant of Medical Research Center for Environmental Toxico-Genomics & Proteomics, funded by Korea Science and Engineering Foundations and Ministry of Science & Technology.

References

[1]   Christmann, M; Tomicic, MT; Roos, WP; Kaina, B. Mechanisms of human DNA repair: an update. *Toxicology,* 2003 199, 3-34.

[2]   Izumi, T; Wiederhold, LR; Roy, G; Roy, R; Jaiswal, A; Bhakat, KK; Mitra, S; Hazra, TK. Mammalian DNA base excision repair proteins: their interactions and role in repair of oxidative DNA damage. *Toxicology,* 2003 193, 43-65.

[3]   Raffoul, JJ; Cabelof, DC; Nakamura, J; Meira, LB; Friedberg, EC; Heydari, AR. Apurinic/apyrimidinic endonuclease (APE/Ref-1) haploinsufficient mice display tissue-specific differences in DNA polymerase beta-dependent base excision repair. *J. Biol. Chem,* 2004 279, 18425-18433.

[4]   Friedberg, EC; Walker, GC; Sieede, W. *DNA repair and mutagenesis.* 2nd Ed, pp. 208-270. Washington, D.C: American Society for Microbiology; 1995.

[5]   Fritz, G; Grösch, S; Tomicic, M; Kaina, B. APE/Ref-1 and the mammalian response to genotoxic stress. *Toxicology,* 2003 193, 67-78.

[6]   Demple, B; DeMott, MS. Dynamics and diversions in base excision DNA repair of oxidized abasic lesions. *Oncogene,* 2002 21, 8926-8934.

[7]   Stucki, M; Pascucci, B; Parlanti, E; Fortini, P; Wilson, SH; Hübscher, U Dogliotti, E. Mammalian base excision repair by DNA polymerases δ and ε. *Oncogene,* 1998 17, 835-843.

[8] Dianov, G. L; Sleeth, KM; Dianova, II; Allinson, SL. Repair of abasic sites in DNA. *Mutat. Res,* 2003 531, 157-163.

[9] Wu, X; Li, J; Li, X; Hsieh, CL; Burgers, PM; Lieber, MR. Processing of branched DNA intermediates by a complex of human FEN-1 and PCNA. *Nucl. Acids Res,* 1996 24, 2036-2043.

[10] Montecucco, A; Rossi, R; Levin, DS; Gary, R; Park, MS; Motycka, TA; Giarrocchi, G; Villa, A; Biamonti, G; Tomkinson, A. DNA ligase I is recruited to sites of DNA replication by an interaction with proliferating cell nuclear antigen: identification of a common targeting mechanism for the assembly of replication factories. *EMBO J,* 1998 17, 3786-3795.

[11] Sanchez, Y; Elledge, SJ. Stopped for repairs. *BioEssay,* 1995 17, 545-548.

[12] Waga, S; Bauer, G; Stillman, B. Reconstitution of complete SV40 DNA replication with purified replication factors. *J. Biol. Chem,* 1994 269, 10923-10934.

[13] Flores-Rozas, Hp; Kelman, Z; Dean, FB; Pan, ZQ; Haper, JW; Elledge, SJ; O'Donnell, M; Hurwitz, J. Cdk-interacting protein 1 directly binds with proliferating cell nuclear antigen and inhibits DNA replication catalyzed by the DNA polymerase delta holoenzyme. *Proc. Natl. Acad. Sci. USA,* 1994 91, 8655-8659.

[14] Kassie, F; Pazefall, W; Knasmüler, S. Single cell gel electrophoresis assay : a new technique for human biomonitoring studies. *Mutat. Res,* 2000 463, 13-31.

[15] Meller, P; Knudsen, LE; Wallin, H. The comet assay as a rapid test in biomonitoring occupational exposure to DNA-damaging agents and effect of confounding factors. *Cancer Epidemiology, Biomarker and Preventions,* 2000 9, 1005-1015.

[16] Sul, D; Lee, D; Im, H; Oh, E; Kim, J; Lee, E. Single strand DNA breaks in T- and B-lymphocytes and granulocytes in workers exposed to benzene. *Toxicol. Letters,* 2002 134, 87-95.

[17] 17 Andreoli, C; Leopardi, P; Rossi, S; Crebelli, R. Processing of DNA damage induced by hydrogen peroxide and methyl methanesulfonate in human lymphocytes: analysis by alkaline single cell gel electrophoresis and cytogenetic methods. *Mutagenesis,* 1999 14, 497-503.

[18] Singh, NP; McCoy, MT; Tice, RR; Schnider, EL. A simple technique for quantitation of low levels of DNA damage in individual cells. *Exp. Cell Res,* 1988 175, 1840-191.

[19] Møller, P. The alkaline comet assay: towards validation in biomonitoring of DNA damaging exposures. *Basic and Clin. Pharmacol. Toxicol,* 2006 98, 336-345.

[20] Sul, D; Oh, E; Im, H; Yang, M; Kim, CH; Lee, E. DNA damage in T- and B-lymphocytes and granulocytes in emission inspection and incineration workers exposed to polycyclic aromatic hydrocarbons. *Mutat. Res,* 2003 538, 109-119.

[21] Lee, E; Oh, E; Lee, J; Sul, D; Lee, J. Use of the tail moment of the lymphocytes to evaluate DNA damage in human biomonitoring studies. *Toxicol. Sci,* 2004 81, 121-132.

[22] Oh, E; Lee, E; Im, H; Kang, HS; Jung, WW; Won, NH; Kim, EM; Sul, D. Evaluation of immuno- and reproductive toxicities and association between immunotoxicological and genotoxicological parameters in waste incineration workers. *Toxicology,* 2005 210, 65-80.

[23] Chang, JL; Chen, G; Lampe, JW; Ulrich, CM. DNA damage and repair measurements from cryopreserved lymphocytes without cell culture-a reproducible assay for intervention studies. *Environ. Molecul. Mutagen*, 2006 47, 503-508.

[24] Anderson, MA; Hellman, B. Evaluation of catechol-induced DNA damage in human lymphocytes: a comparison between freshly isolated lymphocytes and T-lymphocytes from extended-term culture. *Toxicol. in Vitro*, 2007 21, 716-722.

[25] Pfuhler, S; Wolf, HU. Detection of DNA-crosslinking agents with the alkaline comet assay. *Environ. Molecul. Mutagen*, 1996 27, 196-201.

[26] Nakamura, J; La, DK; Swenberg, JA. 5'-nicked apurinic/apyrimidinic sites are resistant to beta-elimination by beta-polymerase and are persistent in human cultured cells after oxidative stress. *J. Biol. Chem*, 2000 25, 5323-5328.

[27] Grösch, S; Fritz, G; Kaina, B. Apurinic endoclease (Ref-1) is induced in mammalian cells by oxidative stress and involved in clastogenic adaptation. *Cancer Res*, 1998 58, 4410-4416.

[28] Grösch, S; Kaina, B. Transcriptional activation of apurinic/apyrimidinic endonuclease (Ape, ref-1) by oxidative stress requires CREB. *Biochem. Biophys. Res. Commun*, 1999 261, 859-863.

[29] Frossi, B; Tell, G; Speddotto, P; Colombatti, A; Vitale, G; Pucillo, A. H2O2 induces translocation of APE/ref-1 to mitochondria in the Raji B-cell line. *J. Cellula Physiol*, 2002 193, 180-186.

[30] Hübscher, U; Nasheuer, HP; Syväoja, JE. Eukaryotic DNA polymerases, a growing family. *TIBS*, 2000 25, 143-147.

[31] Friedberg, EC; Wagner, R; Radman, M. Specialized DNA polymerases, cellular survival, and the genesis of mutations. *Science*, 2002 296, 1627-1630.

[32] Hübscher, U; Maga, G; Spadari, S. Eukaryotic DNA polymerases. *Ann. Rev. Biochem*, 2003 71, 133-163.

In: New Research on DNA Damage
Editors: Honoka Kimura and Aoi Suzuki

ISBN 978-1-60456-581-2
© 2008 Nova Science Publishers, Inc.

Chapter 16

Mutational Hotspots of *TP53* Gene Associated to DNA Damage

Angélica Rangel-López and José Ramón Paniagua-Sierra
Unidad de Investigación Médica en Enfermedades Nefrológicas, Hospital de
Especialidades. Centro Médico Nacional Siglo XXI. IMSS. México, D.F. México

Abstract

TP53 is the most commonly mutated gene in human cancers, and the p53 protein is a potent inhibitor of cell growth, arresting cell cycle progression at several points and inducing apoptosis of cells undergoing uncontrolled growth. The loss of p53 function by mutation is too common in cancer. However, most natural p53 mutations occur at a late stage in tumor development, and many clinically detectable cancers have reduced p53 expression but no p53 mutations.

Approximately 90% of the *TP53* gene mutations are localized between domains encoding exons 5 to 8. Much research suggests that *TP53* mutations have prognostic importance and sometimes are a significant factor in clinical Oncology. The presence of specific p53 mutational hotspots in different types of cancer implicates environmental carcinogens and endogenous processes in the etiology of human cancer. Oxidative stress and the generation of reactive species may cause mutations in cancer-related genes, and affect key regulator proteins of DNA repair, cell cycle, and apoptosis.

This review gives a brief perspective of some of the landmark discoveries in mutation research. The molecular and biochemical characteristics of *TP53* and p53 are then covered, followed by an overview of how it can be studied in the laboratory. Finally, the implications of mutational hotspots of *TP53* gene at the level of DNA damage are discussed.

Glossary

The following terms are used in the text of this chapter.

Allele — an alternative form of a gene.

Alternative splicing — A regulatory mechanism by which variations in the incorporation of a gene's exons, or coding regions, into messenger RNA lead to the production of more than one related protein, or isoform.

Conservative mutation — a change in a DNA or RNA sequence that leads to the replacement of one amino acid with a biochemically similar one.

Epigenetic — A term describing nonmutational phenomena, such as methylation and histone modification, that modify the expression of a gene.

Exon — A region of a gene that codes for a protein.

Frame-shift mutation — addition or deletion of a number of DNA bases that is not a multiple of three, thus causing a shift in the reading frame of the gene. This shift leads to a change in the reading frame of all parts of the gene that are downstream from the mutation, often leading to a premature stop codon and ultimately, to a truncated protein.

Gain-of-function mutation — A mutation that produces a protein that takes on a new or enhanced function.

Genomics — study of the functions and interactions of all the genes in the genome, including their interactions with environmental factors.

Genotype — A person's genetic makeup, as reflected by his or her DNA sequence.

Heterozygous — Having two different alleles at a specific autosomal (or X chromosome in a female) gene locus.

Homozygous — Having two identical alleles at a specific autosomal (or X chromosome in a female) gene locus.

Intron — A region of a gene that does not code for a protein.

Loss-of-function mutation — A mutation that decreases the production or function of a protein (or does both).

Missense mutation — a substitution of a single DNA base leads to an alternative amino acid, because of the way in which it changes the three-base sequence, or codon, that codes for an amino acid.

Motif — a DNA-sequence pattern within a gene that, because of its similarity to sequences in other known genes, suggests a possible function of the gene, its protein product, or both.

Nonconservative mutation — a change in the DNA or RNA sequence that leads to the replacement of one amino acid with a very dissimilar one.

Nonsense mutation — is a more dramatically deleterious type of point mutation that change the codon to a "stop" codon, thus leading to the truncation of a protein.

Penetrance — The likelihood that a person carrying a particular mutant gene will have an altered phenotype.

Phenotype — The clinical presentation or expression of a specific gene or genes, environmental factors, or both.

Point mutation — The substitution of a single DNA base in the normal DNA sequence.

Regulatory mutation — A mutation in a region of the genome that does not encode a protein but affects the expression of a gene.

Repeat sequence — A stretch of DNA bases that occurs in the genome in multiple identical or closely related copies.

Silent mutation — Substitution of a single DNA base that produces no change in the amino acid sequence of the encoded protein.

Single-nucleotide polymorphism (SNP) — A common variant in the genome sequence; the human genome contains about 10 million SNPs.

Stop codon — A codon that causes the termination of the protein instead of producing an amino acid. The three stop codons are TGA, TAA, and TAG.

Tautomeric shifts — Chemical fluctuations of Hydrogen atoms that can move from one position in a purine or pyrimidine to another position, for example, from an amino group to a ring nitrogen.

Transitions — Mutations resulting from tautomeric shifts in the bases of DNA involve the replacement of a purine in one strand of DNA with the other purine and the replacement of a pyrimidine in the complementary strand with the other pyrimidine.

Transvertions — Base-pair substitutions involving the replacement of a purine with a pyrimidine and vice versa.

Introduction

During their life, normal cells are constantly exposed to various endogenous and exogenous stresses that alter their normal behavior. Alterations in the chemical structure of the DNA occur frequently, interfere with transcription and replication, and kill the organism if allowed to accumulate. This accumulation activates the transcription of a wide range of genes involved in various activities, including cell cycle inhibition and apoptosis depending on the cellular context, the extent of damage or other unknown parameters. For all that "wearandtear" of DNA can take two forms: mutation and DNA damage. Genetic insults that can lead to mutations are particularly harmful, as their transmission to daughter cells can lead to different alterations, including complex diseases such as cancer [1].

Cancer is a disease resulting from the breakdown of several checkpoints and tumor-suppressing mechanisms. Carcinogenesis typically involves multiple somatic mutations or, less commonly, germline mutations in caretaker and gatekeeper genes [2, 3]. The caretakers are broadly defined DNA repair genes that are responsible for maintenance of genome stability. Mutations in the caretaker genes, which are considered to be typical tumor suppressors, compromise genome stability and, more specifically, increase the probability of mutation in the gatekeepers which include both tumor suppressor genes and oncogenes [4, 5].

Tumor suppressors are genes that control cell proliferation, in particular, by causing cell death in response to DNA damage; accordingly, mutational inactivation of tumor suppressors may cause transformation. In contrast, oncogenes are genes that, when mutated, acquire new functions promoting cell proliferation and, eventually, transformation [2].

Of more than 200 human cancer genes reported in the current databases, ~90% have somatic mutations, 20% have germline mutations and 10% have both, and inactivation of tumor suppressors is considered to be the main driving force of tumorigenesis [6].

In the post-genomic era, interest is beginning to focus on the differences between the genomes of individuals and on the effects of mutations. Today, the term *mutation* often is used in a narrow sense to refer only to changes occurring within genes. The immediate effects of the mutation and its ability to produce a phenotypic change are determined by its dominance, the type of cell in which it occurs, and the time at which it takes place during the life cycle of the organism. However, changes in the genotype, and thus in the phenotype, of an organism that result from recombination events that produce new combinations of preexistings genetic variation must be carefully distinguished from changes caused by new mutations. Both events sometimes give rise to new phenotypes at very low frequencies. Mutational changes in the genotype of an organism include changes in chromosome number and structure, as well as changes in the structures of individual genes [7].

Mutation data fall largely into two classes: single nucleotide polymorphisms (SNPs) and disease-related mutations. Further sub-divisions are possible including the split between non-coding, silent, mis-sense and nonsense mutations. Mutations occur naturally in DNA, but are generally corrected through DNA repair systems. Mutations are rarely maintained and inherited by daughter cells or future generations [8]. When Watson and Crick in 1953 described the double-helix structure of DNA and proposed its semiconservative replication based on specific base-pairing to account for the accurate transmission of genetic information from generation to generation, they also proposed a mechanism to explain spontaneous mutation, by *tautomeric shifts*. Although tautomeric shifts are rare, they may be of considerable importance in DNA metabolism because some alter the pairing potential of the bases. The more stable keto forms of thymine and guanine and the amino forms of adenine and cytosine may infrequently undergo tautomeric shifts to less stable enol and imino forms, respectively. The bases would be expected to exist in their less stable tautomeric forms for only short periods of time. However, if a base existed in the rare form at the moment that it was being replicated or being incorporated into a nascent DNA chain, a mutation would result. When the bases are present in their rare imino or enol states, they can form adenine-cytosine and guanine-thymine base pair. The net effect of such an event, and the subsequent replication required to segregate the mismatched base pair, is an A: T to G: C or a G: C to A: T base-pair substitution. Mutations resulting from tautomeric shifts in the bases of DNA involve the formation of *transitions* and *transversions*. Four different transitions and eight different transversions are possible [9].

Clearly, mutations may affect organisms in very different ways; they may exhibit the complete range of phenotypes from drastic detrimental effects, through mild and completely phenotypically silent effects to minor improvements or the introduction of new function [10]. The larger the change brought about by the mutation, the more likely it is to have a drastically affected phenotype. For example, frameshifts, deletions, insertions, repetitions or nonsense codons leading to early termination of a protein are almost guaranteed to have a drastic effect, whereas single amino acid mutations may have a much more limited effect on phenotype. Because around 90% of sequence variants in humans are single DNA base changes [11], there is an increasing interest in this family of mutations [12, 13]. Formally,

SNPs can be defined as alleles which exist in normal individuals in a population with the least frequent allele having an abundance of at least 1% [14]. In principle, SNPs could be bi-, tri- or tetra-allelic variations, but tri- and tetra-allelic SNPs are very rare in humans. In practice, the term SNP is often applied in a more generic context and may encompass disease-causing mutations which are recessive, or low-penetration dominant alleles, the latter generally being present at much lower frequencies [15].

The discovery of chemical mutagens with known effects on DNA led to a better understanding of mutation at the molecular level. DNA is damaged by both environmental and cellular (endogenous) sources. Many of the environmental agents that damage DNA have been demostrated to be mutagens. Epidemiologic data indicate that many of these agents are also human carcinogens. DNA damage by chemicals can be divided into two categories: (i) those that produce large bulky adducts and are repaired by the nucleotide excision pathway; and (ii) those that cause small alterations, such as alkylating agents that add methyl and ethyl groups onto nucleotides in DNA, and are repaired by the base excision repair pathway. Also, chemical mutagens can be divided into two groups: (1) those that are mutagenic to both replicating and nonreplicating DNA, such as the alkylating agents and nitrous acid; and (2) those that are mutagenic only to replicating DNA, such as base analogs—purines, and pyrimidines with structures similar to the normal bases in DNA. The base analogs must be incorporated into DNA chains in the place of normal bases during replication in order to exert their mutagenic effects. Mutations can also result from radiation, in which the portion of the electromagnetic spectrum with wavelengths shorter and of higher energy than visible light is subdivided into ionizing radiation (X rays, gamma rays, and cosmic rays) and nonionizing (ultraviolet light). Ionizing radiations are of high energy they penetrate living tissues for substantial distances. These high-energy rays collide with atoms and cause the release of electrons, leaving positively charged free radicals or ions. Ultraviolet rays, having lower energy that ionizing radiations and dissipate their energy to atoms that they encounter, raising the electrons in the outer orbitals to higher energy levels, a state referred to as excitation. The increased reactivity of atoms present in DNA molecules is responsible for the mutagenicity of ionizing radiation and ultraviolet light [16, 17].

When we consider mutations in terms of the inactivation of the gene, most genes within a species show more or less similar rates of mutation relative to their size. This suggests that the gene can be regarded as a target for mutation, and that damage to any part of it can abolish its function. As a result, susceptibility to mutation is roughly proportional to the size of the gene. But consider the sites of mutation within the sequence of DNA some base pairs in a gene more than susceptible to be mutated than others. So some sites will gain one, two, or three mutations, while others will not gain any. But some sites gain far more than the number of mutations expected from a random distribution; they may have 10x or even 100x more mutations than predicted by random hits. These sites are called *hotspots*. Defining such hotspot regions and natural mutants is of invaluable help in defining critical regions in an unknown protein. Spontaneous mutations may occur at hotspots; and different mutagens may have different hotspots.

Sites containing 5-methylcytosine, generated by a methylase enzyme that adds a methyl group to a small proportion of the cytosine residues—at specific sites in the DNA, provide hotspots for spontaneous point mutations. The reason for the existence of the hotspots is that

5-methylcytosine suffers spontaneous deamination at an appreciable frequency; replacement of the amino group by a keto group converts 5-methylcytosine to thymine (causing C•G to T•A transitions) [18, 19].

To understand the role of individual mutants in carcinogenesis and to assess the possibility of rescuing their function, it is important to know the effect of the mutation not only on the overall stability but also on the local structure. Qualitative NMR studies indicate that hotspot mutants evince characteristic local structural changes [20].

The Role of the *TP53* Gene

The *TP53* gene is the most prominent and best studied tumor suppressor. Its a single copy gene located on the short arm of chromosome 17 (17p13.1), and is composed of 11 exons, 10 intervening introns and 393 amino acids (MIM # 191117). *TP53* was the first gene to be identified as a mutant in tumours, in 1979 [21], and it has been figuratively called the "genome guard" [22]. Thus, this gene coordinates all the essential processes of maintaining genome stability, and its one of the most important tumour suppressor genes controlling DNA transcription and cell cycle regulation. Therefore, this gene is both a caretaker (by inducing DNA repair) and a gatekeeper (by inducing apoptosis in the case of irreparable damage) [23]. And it has an unusually large number of functions in the cell, binds to many other proteins and ligands, and has a complex architecture [24, 25]. *TP53* gene encodes a transcription factor with multiple, anti-proliferative functions activated in response to several forms of cellular stress.

The *TP53* gene is mutated in nearly 60% of human tumors. The spectrum of somatic mutations in the *TP53* gene, of which ~85% are missense mutations, implicates environmental carcinogens and endogenous processes in the etiology of human cancer, and occur at over 200 codons within the central portion of the gene [26]. This somatic *TP53* gene alterations are frequent in most human cancers [27-34], and inherited *TP53* mutations predispose to a wide spectrum of early onset cancers (e.g., Li-Fraumeni Syndrome, LFS; MIM# 151623). Most *TP53* mutations result in gain of oncogenic functions including attenuating the function of the *p73* gene [35]. The types of mutations observed in the germline and sporadic cancer cases are similar, with a high prevalence of missense mutations (>75%). Thus, *TP53* differs from other large tumor suppressor genes such as *RB1* (27 exons, 928 amino acids), *APC* (15 exons, 2843 amino acids), or *BRCA1* (24 exons, 1863 amino acids), which are frequently inactivated by deletions, frameshift mutations, or nonsense mutations. *TP53* missense mutations are scattered throughout the coding sequence but 97% of them cluster in exons encoding the DNA-binding domain (DBD). In this domain, six mutation hotspots (defined by a mutation frequency superior to 2% of all mutations) have been identified at codons 175, 245, 248, 249, 273, and 282. The position and nature of the mutations vary from one cancer type to the other, and in some instances from one cohort to another —suggesting that mutation patterns may reveal clues on the mutagenic mechanism involved in causing cancer [36].

There is a database of all published mutations which is maintained at the International Agency for Research on Cancer (IARC). The IARC *TP53* Mutation Database compiles all

TP53 gene mutations identified in human cancers and cell lines that have been reported in the peer-reviewed literature since 1989. The database has been updated with data reported in publications edited in PubMed in 2005. This R11, version release in October 2006 is the lates, contains 23544 somatic mutations, 376 germline mutations, functional data on 2314 mutant proteins and TP53 gene status of 1569 cell-lines. (http://www-p53.iarc.fr/p53database.html [37].

The p53 Protein

The protein p53 is probably the most popular molecule in the field of cellular biology [38-40]. p53 is a polyfunctional protein which functions in the nucleus. The *TP53* gene is continuously transcribed and translated, but the protein is rapidly subjected to ubiquitin-dependent degradation in proteosomes [41, 42]. Therefore, the concentrations of p53 in cells of most tissues are quite low and may be at the limit of detection. The activation of p53 as a response to various stresses and damages proceeds mainly post-translationally via a decrease in its degradation rate and a change of its conformation to generate increased functional activity. Several functions and activities are attributed to p53. This ubiquitous factor is kept in a repressed state in normal cells, but is activated by post-translational modifications in response to multiple forms of stress, both genotoxic (such as irradiation, chemical carcinogens, or cytotoxic agents used in cancer therapy) or non-genotoxic (such as hypoxia, depletion of ribonucleotides, and oncogenic activation of growth signaling cascades) [43]. When active, the p53 protein accumulates to high levels in the nucleus and acts as a multi-functional transcription factor to enhance or repress the expression of several sets of genes involved in cell cycle progression, apoptosis, adaptive response to stress, differentiation, and DNA repair [24].

Thus, p53 controls and coordinates anti-proliferative responses to prevent DNA replication from occurring when cells are exposed to adverse conditions. The mechanism of the p53 mediated suppression of cell cycle progression involves arrest within the G1 phase [23, 44], as a consequence of the p53 induced synthesis of p21, an inhibitor of cyclin E/cdk2 and cyclin A/cdk2 kinases. In this way, p53 gives DNA repair mechanisms time to correct damage before the genome is replicated. If damage to the cell is too severe, p53 initiates apoptosis by inducing transcription of genes encoding proapoptotic factors [45, 46] p53 also enhances or represses the expression of genes involved in the adaptive response to stress, differentiation, and the DNA repair process. These properties have led to the concept that p53 plays a central role in carcinogenesis.

As a transcription factor, p53 mediates many cellular responses to genotoxic insults and hypoxia [24, 25, 47]. Through coordination of over 50 genes, activated p53 is central to a variety of biological functions including cell cycling, apoptosis, differentiation, cellular senescence [23, 44, 48], angiogenesis [49, 50], and the removal of DNA damage [51-55]. Analysis of p53-regulated global gene expression reveals differences in strength, kinetics, and specificity that depend on the levels of p53, its posttranslational modifications, its degradation, nature of stress, cell type, and other as yet unidentified parameters [56-59]. It is likely that subsets of genes can be chosen from the complex spectrum of potentially inducible genes to mediate a specific p53 response in a given physiological situation [60].

Within the open reading frame of human p53 codes for 393 amino acids, the p53 molecule forms a tetrameric complex that recognizes a specific DNA sequence and stimulates transcription of several genes having an appropriate DNA element adjacent to the promoter. The DNA element with which p53 couples consists of two "semi-sites" of general structure PuPuPuC(A/T)(A/T)GPyPyPy positioned one after another at 0-13 nucleotides distance consisting of three major structural domains: an N-terminal domain which contains a strong transcription activation signal [61], a DNA-binding core domain, and C-terminal domain which mediates oligomerization. Comparisons of p53 sequences from different species indicate five blocks – boxes I-V —of highly conserved residues which coincide with mutation clusters found in p53 in human cancers. The majority (approximately 80%) are missense mutations comprising GC to AT transitions at cytosine phosphate guanine dinucleotides and occur principally in five hotspot codons (175, 245, 248, 249, 273, and 282) in exons 5 to 8, in highly conserved areas, and in three principal structural domains of the *TP53* protein (L2, L3, and loop-sheet-helix [LSH]). The most frequent changes are missense mutations in the DNA-binding domain (DBD) of the protein. These can lead to nuclear accumulation of mutant p53 protein and loss of its normal functions, such as transcriptional activation of target genes [37, 62].

The DNA-binding core domain of the protein has been structurally characterized in complex with its cognate DNA by x-ray crystallography [63-65] and in its free formin solution by NMR [66]. It consists of a central ß-sandwich that serves as a basic scaffold for the DNA-binding surface. The DNA-binding surface is composed of two large loops (L2 and L3) that are stabilized by a zinc ion and a loop–sheet–helix motif. Together, these structural elements form an extended surface that makes specific contacts with the various p53 response elements. The six amino acid residues that are most frequently mutated in human cancer are located in or close to the DNA-binding surface (compare release R10 of the *TP53* mutation database at www-p53.iarc.fr) [37]. These residues have been classified as "contact" (Arg-248 and Arg-273) or "structural" (Arg-175, Gly-245, Arg-249, and Arg-282) residues, depending on whether they directly contact DNA or play a role in maintaining the structural integrity of the DNA-binding surface [63].

Urea denaturation studies have shown that the contact mutation R273H has no effect on the thermodynamic stability of the core domain, whereas structural mutations substantially destabilize the protein to varying degrees, ranging from 1 kcal/mol for G245S and 2 kcal/mol for R249S up to >3 kcal/mol for R282W [67]. The destabilization has severe implications for the folding state of these mutants in the cell. Because the wild-type core domain is only marginally stable and has a melting temperature only slightly above body temperature, highly destabilized mutants such as R282W are largely unfolded under physiological conditions and, hence, are no longer functional [68].

A flexible proline-rich domain is located between amino acids 63 and 97 in which the PxxP elements are found. This domain is needed for the full suppressor activity of p53. Although the mechanism of action of the proline-rich domain is not completely clear, it is supposed to take part in both transcription-dependent and transcription-independent apoptosis [69]. A locus between amino acids 323 and 356 is responsible for tetramerization of p53 molecules. This locus has a clear *alpha*-helical structure. Loss of the ability of p53 to oligomerize occurs if the *alpha*-helical domain is damaged, and this causes functional inactivation [70].An alkaline domain essential for the regulation of p53 activity is located immediately at the C-terminus of the molecule (amino acids 363-393).This domain is a target for a series of modifying enzymes. The unmodified alkaline domain prevents formation of the complex of DNA and the central DNA-binding domain of the p53. Removal of the alkaline domain stimulates the DNA-binding activity of p53 *in vitro* [71]. The C-terminal domain is essential for regulation of p53 activity *in vivo*. Modification of this element by kinases, acetylases, glycosylases, and binding with other proteins causes a delicate transformation of the DNA-binding and transactivation ability of p53. Also, the C-terminal p53 fragment is able to bind nonspecifically with single-stranded DNA elements, unpaired bases, and DNA ends indicating its possible involvement in the process of recognition of damaged DNA [72]. The structure supports the hypothesis that DNA binding is critical for the biological activity of p53, and provides a framework for understanding how mutations inactivate it [63].

TP53 Screening Techniques

Although the publication of the human genome sequence and the immense technological advancements have facilitated the analysis of cancer genomes, detection of mutations in tumor specimens may still be challenging and fraught with technical problems. Today it is generally accepted that molecular analyses in tumor samples should be performed in precisely defined homogeneous tumor cells with low or even no contamination by nontumor cells. Therefore, the success of nucleic acid diagnostic in the clinical setting depends heavily on the method used for purification of the nucleic acid target from biological samples.

Actually, exists a variety of methods for the detection of point mutations as well as small deletions or insertions, the number of methods that may be used for detection of genetic variability is growing steadily. Most methods are applicable only in situations where the location and type of variability have been defined. These include the allele-specific oligonucleotide assay [73], the oligo-ligation assay [74], minisequencing [75, 76], TaqMan assay [77], Invader assay [78], pyrosequencing [79] Real-time PCR [80], and PCR-restriction fragment length polymorphism analysis [81]. Other methods that can detect genetic variability irrespective of the location and type of aberration are less common and, in general, less reliable. These methods include heteroduplex analysis [82], single strand conformation polymorphism (SSCP) [83], desnaturing gradient gel electrophoresis [84], chemical cleavage [85], dideoxy fingerpriting [86], denaturing HPLC (dHPLC) [87], primer extension [88], and Microarray technology [89-91]. that facilitates large-scale mutation/polymorphism detection. Finally, dideoxy-sequencing has difficulty in detecting heterozygous mutations, and is of limited utility in the analysis of solid tumors where mutant DNA may represent as little as 15% of the total. Other methods include *in vitro* transcription/translation-based approaches, chemical and enzymatic mismatch cleavage detection (e.g. Cleavase, RNase, T4 endonuclease VII, MutS enzymes and CEL I) [92, 93]. *In vitro* mismatch cleavage methods encounter variability in signal intensity compared with background bands. But, for the appropriate choice of any one of these methods, several criteria must be considered, some of them are:

1. What type of nucleic acid is analyzed (DNA or RNA)?
2. What kind of specimen is analyzed (e.g., peripheral blood, bone marrow, tissues, secretions, excretions)?
3. Are the mutations to be detected known before analysis?
4. How large is the number of potential mutations to be detected?
5. Need each of the potential mutations be detected?
6. What is the ratio between wild-type and mutant alleles?
7. How reliable is the method to be used, and how far can it be standardized?
8. How does the test perform?
9. Is the test suited for routine diagnosis?
10. What kind of quality assessment can be achieved?

In general, PCR is either used for the generation of DNA fragments, or is part of the detection method. Screening methods for unknown mutations as well as methods for the detection of known mutations must be are included. DNA sequencing is considered the gold standard and remains the definitive procedure for the detection of mutations so far. For this reason, mutations assumed from the results of screening methods must be confirmed by DNA sequencing. Any one of the above methods is suited for the analysis of allelic differences in hereditary disease. Non-gel-based detection systems have been developed for most of the assays described, making these methods favorable for application in routine laboratories. For each technique, reaction conditions must be standardized and appropriate internal controls must be included. In cases in which a large number of different mutations or polymorphisms are to be detected, the DNA chip technology most probably will be the method of choice in the near future. At present, one technique addresses by combining the ability of termostable Endonuclease V (Endo V) enzyme to recognize and nick mismatched DNA, with the high fidelity of thermostable DNA ligase to suppress nicks at matched DNA [94]. Endo V can nick either or both strands of the mismatch. Unlike other enzymes, Endo V nicks DNA close to the mismatched base. This allows the thermostable ligase to effectively discriminate between perfectly matched and mismatched regions of the DNA [95] and to ligate only perfectly matched nicks. This results in greatly reduced background noise. This method has very high sensitivity, and can distinguish one mutant sequence in a 20 fold excess of unaltered DNA [96].

At level for detect the protein status the adequate method its immunohistochemistry techniques, Western-blot and Flow cytometry that using different monoclonal antibodies [97, 98].

Despite the accumulation of studies on *TP53* mutations, their significance for cancer detection and prognosis remains elusive. One of the reasons for this is the functional heterogeneity of mutations. It's important therefore to develop studies aimed at better understanding the lessons that can be learned from *TP53* mutation detection. For example: in liver cancer, mutations can be found ahead of diagnosis, in free DNA fragments retrieved in the plasma, thus providing a possible mean for early cancer detection. In Western Africa, a region where chronic infection by HBV and dietary contamination by aflatoxin is widespread, the so-called « *aflatoxin-signature* » mutation at codon 249 is found in the plasma DNA of chronic HBV carriers, with seasonal variations reflecting variations of exposure to aflatoxin [99]. Thus, in this case, plasma *TP53* mutation appears to be a biomarker of exposure to a mutagen, rather than of early cancer development. Another factor of complexity is the possible impact of *deltaN isoforms of p53* family members. In keratinocytes infected by skin-type HPVs such as HPV38, expression of deltaNp73 contributes to inhibit p53 activity and to protect cells against p53-dependent apoptosis during virus-induced immortalization. Thus, expression of isoforms may, in specific contexts, provide alternative mechanisms to down-regulate p53 function during progression towards cancer [100]. Another example to be consider its that p53 is a short-lived transcription factor that has evolved to respond to a variety of stimuli to initiate cell cycle arrest or apoptotic programs, or to induce genes that participate in some forms of DNA repair. As p53 participates in life and death decisions, it is critical that its output be stringently regulated. The importance of the p53 pathway for tumor suppression is demonstrated by mutation of the p53 gene or alterations in its negative regulators in almost all cancers [101]. Besides abrogating the tumor suppressor activity of the wt p53 protein, some of the frequently encountered tumor-associated mutant p53 isoforms often also elicit a pro-oncogenic gain of function. One of the manifestations of this gain of function is increased resistance to killing by anti-cancer agents.

There is evidence that at least some of the anti-apoptotic gain of function of mutant p53 is due to its ability to modulate the transcription of apoptosis-related genes. One such example is CD95/Fas, a death receptor whose gene is subject to transcriptional repression by mutant p53 [102]. Another mutant p53-respressed gene is MSP (macrophage stimulating protein). While the literature suggests that MSP has anti-apoptotic effects, some study shows that, in cultured tumor cells, it actually contributes to apoptosis. Analysis of MSP gene expression in tumors supports the notion that its downregulation may benefit at least some human tumors [103]. Most notably, mutant p53 contributes to activation of NF-kB in cancer cells, resulting in enhanced induction of anti-apoptotic genes and increased resistance to apoptosis. The underlying mechanism may involve recruitment of mutant p53 protein to genomic NF-kB binding sites, which may be facilitated by a physical interaction between mutant p53 and NF-kB. NF-kB is a well-documented contributor to cancer development and therapy resistance. Its hyperactivation by mutant p53 may thus provide substantial benefits to tumors. Thus, mutant p53 may constitute an important target for future anti-cancer therapies [104].

There are five regions – boxes I-V - in p53 protein which reveal strikingly high conservation between species, suggesting they are functionally important. Box I comprises the binding site of mdm2, which supports the importance of negative regulation of p53 by mdm2. Boxes II-V, residing in DNA binding domain of p53 are the most frequent sites of mutations found in human tumours. p53 mutants with deletions of conserved boxes II-V behave like tumor derived point mutants in this region in that they fail to bind DNA and are therefore not transcriptionally active. In addition, these mutants adopt a conformation associated with tumor derived p53 mutants [70].

p53 point mutants are stable in human tumors and expressed at higher levels in tumor cells compared to wild-type p53. However, recent studies of mutant p53 knock-in mice suggest that these p53 proteins are not stable in normal tissue, indicating that a failure to activate expression of Mdm2 is not the underlying cause of mutant p53 stability in tumors. Another possibility is that the stability of mutant p53 is related to the over-expression of ARF. However, exist some studies have suggested that inhibiting ARF expression does not reduce the stability of mutant p53 in tumor cell lines [105]. Although mutant p53 has been reported to be sensitive to Mdm2-mediated degradation, previous studies be showed that mutations in the DNA binding region could render p53 resistant to degradation by HPV E6. *In vitro* assays the p53 deletion mutants are less efficiently ubiquitinated by Mdm2 compared to wild type p53. These results suggest that the degradation of mutant p53s by Mdm2 may not be dependent on efficient ubiquitination [106]. Interestingly, significantly higher levels of ubiquitination of each of the mutant p53s were found in Mdm2 null cells compared to wild type p53, suggesting that the mutants may acquire an increased sensitivity to other E3 ligases such as Cop1 or Pirh2 [107].

Implications of Mutational Hotspots of *TP53* Gene at Level of DNA Damage

In general terms "Damage" to DNA consists of any change introducing a desviation from the usual double-helical structure. We can divide such changes into two general classes: *single base changes* and *structural distortions*.

Single base changes affect the sequence but not the overal structure of DNA. They do not affect transcription or replication, when the strands of the DNA duplex are separated. So these changes exert their damaging effects on future generations through the consequences of the change in DNA sequence. Such an effect is caused by the conversion of one base into another that is not properly paired with the partner base. For example deamination of cytosine (spontaneously or by chemical mutagen) creates a mismatched T·G pair; while a replication error that inserts adenine instead of cytosine creates an A·G pair. Similar consequences could result from covalent addition of a small group to a base that modifies its ability to base pair. These changes may result in very minor structural distortion (as in the case of T·G pair) or quite significant change (as in the case of A·G pair), but the common feature is that the mismatch persists only until the next replication.

Structural distortions may provide a physical impediment to replication or transcription, e.g., introduction of covalent links between bases on one strand of DNA or between bases on opposite strands inhibits replication and transcription. A well studied example of a structural distortion is caused by ultraviolet irradiation, which introduces covalent bonds between two adjacent thymine bases, giving the intrastrand pyrimidine dimer. Similar consequences could result from addition of a bulky adduct to a base that distorts the structure of the double helix. A single-strand nick or the removal of a base prevents a strand from serving as a proper template for synthesis of RNA or DNA. The common feature in all these changes is that the damaged adduct remains in the DNA, continuing to cause structural problems and/or induce mutations, until it is removed. Repair systems can often recognize a range of distortions in

DNA as signals for action, and a cell may have several systems able to deal with DNA damage. We may divide them into several general types:

1. *Direct repair* is rare and involves the reversal or simple removal of the damage. Photoreactivation of pyrimidine dimers, in which the offending covalent bonds are reversed by a light-dependent enzyme, is the best example.

2. *Excision repair* is initiated by a recognition enzyme that sees an actual damaged base or a change in the spatial path of DNA. Recognition is followed by excision of a sequence that includes the damaged bases; then a new stretch of DNA is synthesized to replace the excised material. Such systems are common; some recognize general damage to DNA, while others act upon specific types of base damage (glycosylases remove specific altered bases; AP endonucleases remove residues from sites at which purine bases have been lost). There are often multiple excision repair systems in a single cell type, and they probably handle most of the damage that occurs.

3. Mismatch repair is accomplished by scrutinizing DNA for apposed bases that do not pair properly. Mismatches that arise during replication are corrected by distinguishing between the "new" and "old" strands and preferentially correcting the sequence of the newly synthesized strand. Mismatches also occur when hybrid DNA is created during recombination, and their correction upsets the ratio of parental alleles. Other systems deal with mismatches generated by base conversions, such as the result of deamination. The importance of these systems is emphasized by the fact that cancer is caused in human populations by mutation of genes related to those involved in mismatch repair in yeast.

4. *Tolerance systems* cope with the difficulties that arise when normal replication is blocked at a damage site. They provide a means for a damaged template sequence to be copied, probably with a relatively high frequence of errors. They are especially important in higher eukaryotic cells.

5. *Retrieval systems* comprise another type of tolerance system. When damage remains in a daughter molecule, and replication has been forced to bypass the site, a retrieval system uses recombination to obtain another copy of the sequence from an undamaged source. These "recombination-repair" systems are well characterized in bacteria; it is not clear how important they are elsewhere.

Most of the mutations in the *TP53* gene occur in the part encoding the DNA-binding domain (DBD). In this domain, every residue has been found to be targeted for substitutions in human cancers (with one exception, residue 123) [37]. These mutations in DBD that inactivate p53 evidently impair or abolish the ability of p53 to bind to specific DNA sequences that are embedded in its target genes, thereby preventing the transcriptional activation of these genes. Thus, mutations in the DBD are typically recessive, loss-of-function mutations. Other types of mutations are found in the C-terminal homo-oligomerization domain (OD) portion of the polypeptide. Molecules of p53 with these type of mutations dimerize with wild-type p53 polypeptides and prevent the wild-type polypeptides from functioning as transcriptional activators. Thus, mutations in the OD have a *dominant negative* effect on p53 function [108-110]. However, some codons are more frequently mutated than others. Mutations at five major hotspots account for about 30% of all known mutations. These codons are R175, G245, R248, R249, R273 and R282. The apparent hypermutability of these sites is due to two factors. First, these codons encompass CpG sites where cytosines are often methylated, and their spontaneous deamination induces a transition mutation from C to T [111]. This type of mutation is frequent in all cancers. Second, these residues play important roles at the surface of contact between the protein and target DNA. Thus, substitution of these residues results in a protein with decreased affinity for DNA, which has lost the capacity to suppress proliferation [112]. Hotspot mutations can thus be explained by an interplay between mutagenesis, which occurs at specific sites, and selection, which gives to cells with deficient *TP53* function a selective, proliferative advantage during tumour progression. There are many mutagens that can damage DNA in specific ways, leaving fingerprints in the genome of cancer cells. However, many of the mutations found in cancers probably arise spontaneously, through endogenous mechanisms. The most common of these mechanisms are polymerase errors during DNA replication or repair and deamination of methylated cytosine in CpG motifs to form thymine. The latter is enhanced by nitric oxide (NO) — an important bioregulatory agent and signaling molecule that mediates a variety of physiological functions such as vasodilation, neurotransmission, host defense, and iron metabolism— and this type of mutations developed by accumulation nitrotyrosine in the inflamed mucosa of patients and the formation of peroxynitrite are common in tumours occurring within a chronic inflammatory context, such as colorectal or stomach cancer [113].

So far, the identification of precise fingerprints left by mutagens in *TP53* has been possible in a number of cancers where there is good, experimental and molecular demonstration that specific carcinogens play an important role. The most significant examples are liver cancer arising in a context of chronic infection by hepatitis viruses and dietary intoxication by aflatoxins, skin cancers (other than melanoma) resulting from exposure to solar radiations, and lung cancers linked with tobacco smoke. A well-documented mutagen fingerprint is found in non-melanoma skin cancers (NMSC) in relation to sunlight exposure [114]. The *TP53* mutation spectrum in NMSC shows a high frequency of C to T transitions (56% of all mutations), including tandem CC to TT transitions (6%) that are not found in other tumours. They are due to inefficient repair of a common photoproduct, cyclobutane pyrimidine dimers. In individuals with the inherited syndrome xeroderma pigmentosum, a multi-trait disease associated with hypersensitivity to UV, CC to TT transitions represent about half of all observed mutations, though with important differences depending upon the complementation group of the patient [115]. Thus, the CC to TT transitions can be taken as good evidence of the direct DNA-damage generated by exposure to UV. In lung cancers of smokers, the *TP53* mutation pattern is consistent with mutagenesis by at least some classes of tobacco carcinogens [116]. Overall, lung cancer differs from cancers unrelated to smoking by a high prevalence of G to T transversions (30% in lung cancer, compared to an average of 9% in non-tobacco related cancers such as brain, breast or colorectal cancers). These transversions are preferentially located on the non-transcribed strand of *TP53* DNA, and often occur at codons 157, 158, 245, 248 and 273. Although data on non-smokers are still limited, it is known that this type of transversion is not frequent in lung cancers of non-smokers (12%) [117]. Tobacco smoke contains many agents that can potentially induce G to T transversions, particularly oxidative stress agents, nitrosamines, aromatic amines and polycyclic aromatic hydrocarbons. However, the bases at which the G to T transversions occur in lung cancers of smokers are the same as those where benzo(*a*)pyrene preferentially forms DNA adducts *in vitro* [118]. It seems that the presence of a methylated cytosine adjacent to a guanine is an important factor for preferential adduct formation and a direct mutagenic effect of some major tobacco components in lung cancers of smokers [119].

Hepatocellular carcinoma (HCC), the major manifestation of primary liver cancer, is one of the most frequent and malignant disease worldwide and offers one of the most striking example of a mutation "fingerprint" left by a carcinogen in the human genome. The major HCC risk factors include various chemicals and viruses. Among those, chronic HBV and HCV infections attribute to the HCC development in many areas of the world. Other known risk factors, including Aflatoxin B1, cigarette smoking, or heavy alcohol consumption are capable of inducing HCC alone, but they also have synergetic effects. Aflatoxins are mycotoxins produced by species of *Aspergillus* that frequently contaminate staple foods. AFB1 is one of the most potent hepatocarcinogens known, is the predominant form of exposure in humans, *TP53* is mutated in about 30% of HCCs in low-incidence areas, e.g. Western Europe and the U.S.A., and these mutations are scattered along the DNA-binding domain of the gene, with no particular hotspot. However, in areas of high incidence resulting from aflatoxin B1 exposure and HBV infections, *TP53* is mutated in over 50% of cases, with a high proportion of a single missense mutation at codon 249, AGG to AGT, leading to the substitution of an arginine by a serine (Ser-249) [120]. This mutation represents 26% of all *TP53* mutations described to date in HCC and is rather uncommon in other cancers, with no tumour type having more than 2% of Ser-249 mutations. Ser-249 is by far the predominant mutation in areas of high HCC incidence and high aflatoxin exposure, like Mozambique, Senegal, Qidong country in China, [121], and The Gambia [122]. In contrast, the prevalence of Ser-249 is lower in other areas of China as well as in those African and Asian countries (such as Thailand) where average levels of aflatoxin exposure are lower, and it is virtually absent in HCCs from Europe and the U.S.A., where alcohol but not aflatoxin is an important contributor to liver carcinogenesis. There is good evidence that metabolites of aflatoxin can induce this mutation *in vitro* as well as in cultured cells [123, 124]. However, this is not the only type of mutations that aflatoxin can generate in *TP53* DNA and the reasons for its almost exclusive presence in tumours of high-incidence areas are not yet elucidated. It is possible that Ser-249 has specific, functional properties conferring a capacity to enhance liver carcinogenesis. Indeed, it is quite remarkable that this mutant is rare in tumours other than HCC [125].

An increased cancer risk occurs in tissues of the body undergoing chronic inflammation [126]. Reactive oxygen and nitrogen species —hydrogen peroxide (H_2O_2), nitric oxide ($NO^\bullet$), and reactive intermediates such as hydroxyl radicals ($OH^\bullet$), superoxide ($O_2^{-\bullet}$), and peroxynitrite ($ONOO^-$)— produced by inflammatory cells can interact with key genes involved in carcinogenic pathways such as *TP53*, DNA mismatch repair genes, and even DNA base excision-repair genes [127]. Free radicals, as well as hydroxyurea, can also lead to DNA replication stress involving the ATR kinase network [128, 129]. Although it appears that the onset of carcinogenesis associated with inflammation is mediated by free radical species, identification of specific free radicals and their targets remains vague.

In most researches be has hypothesized that the inflammatory microenvironment activates the p53 network and inactivates the tumor suppressor activity by mutation of the *TP53* gene by NO pathway — NO is a candidate free radical, and the p53 tumor suppressor is a candidate molecular target— and *TP53* mutations contribute to clonal cellular expansion and genomic instability through deregulation of cell cycle checkpoints, DNA repair, and apoptosis [130, 131]. However, before somatic mutations, *TP53* mediates these anticarcinogenic cellular functions through a DNA damage-response [24, 127].

To place the molecular pathogenesis of some tumors, it is first helpful to appreciate the molecular events involved in the development of neoplasia. Neoplasia arises as a result of genomic instability, and the two main types of genomic instability that contribute to carcinogenesis are chromosomal instability (CIN) and microsatellite instability (MSI). Chromosomal instability results in abnormal segregation of chromosomes and abnormal DNA content (aneuploidy). As a result, loss of chromosomal material [loss of heterozygosity (LOH)] often occurs, contributing to the loss of function of key tumor suppressor genes such as *APC* and *TP53*. These genes can also be rendered nonfunctional by mutation. In either event, it is the accumulation of molecular disturbances mainly in tumor suppressor genes that drives the sporadic adenomacarcinoma progression, and therefore this pathway has sometimes been referred to as the "suppressor pathway" [132].

Epigenetic alterations also contribute to altered gene expression in carcinogenesis. A recently recognized molecular alteration is the CpG island methylator phenotype (CIMP) [133]. CpG islands are dense aggregates of cytosine-guanine dinucleotide sequences that may occur in the promoter region of genes. Extensive methylation of the cytosine bases is associated with promoter silencing and loss of gene expression. Many genes involved in cell cycle control, cell adhesion, and DNA repair can be methylated in colon cancer [134].

To reduce the level of reactive oxidants and limit their damaging effects (particularly to DNA, RNA, proteins, and lipids), several defense mechanisms have evolved. In addition to reactive oxidants, the microenvironmental changes within inflamed tissues are typically associated with hypoxic conditions, in which oxygen tensions <10 mm Hg (i.e., <1% oxygen) have been reported [135]. Thus, hypoxia is an additional cell stress mediator concurrently found during chronic inflammation [136].

Conclusions

Over the course of evolution, mammalian cells have acquired an intrincate network of protective mechanisms to safeguard the genomic integrity. A serious consequence from a failure in the safety networks is cancer. The fact that p53 pathway is defective in the majority of human cancers, underscores its importance in protecting the cells from genetic, biochemical, and physiological dysregulation that can contribute to tumor development. Moreover, with the development of new, sensitive and high-throughput methods for mutation detection, analysis of *TP53* hotspots mutations may become an essential aid to the identification of specific cancer risk factors in human populations. Currently, the number of types of *TP53* mutations described in the world literature increases by two to three thousand every year. It is very likely that this trend will continue in the coming years, confirming the status of *TP53* as a central piece of the puzzle in the molecular biology of human cancer.

References

[1]   Vogelstein B, Kinzler KW: Cancer genes and the pathways they control. *Nat. Med.* 2004, 10(8): 789-799.

[2]   Knudson AG: Cancer genetics. *Am. J. Med. Genet.* 2002,111(1): 96-102.

[3]   Blagosklonny MV: Molecular theory of cancer. *Cancer Biol. Ther.* 2005, 4(6):621-627.

[4]   Kinzler KW, Vogelstein B: Cancer-susceptibility genes. Gatekeepers and caretakers. *Nature* 1997; 386(6627): 761, 763.

[5]   Levitt NC, Hickson ID: Caretaker tumour suppressor genes that defend genome integrity. *Trends Mol. Med.* 2002, 8(4):179-186.

[6]   Futreal PA, Coin L, Marshall M, Down T, Hubbard T, Wooster R, Rahman N, Stratton MR: A census of human cancer genes. *Nat. Rev. Cancer* 2004, 4(3):177-183.

[7]   Guttmacher AE, and Collins F. Genomic Medicine— A primer. *N. Engl. J. Med.* 2002; 347(19): 1512-1520.

[8]   Li W, Ellsworth D, Krushkal J, Chang B and Hewett-Emmett D. Rates of nucleotide substitution in primates and rodents and the generation-time effect hypothesis. *Mol. Phylogenet. Evol.* 1996; 5, 182–187.

[9]   Drake, JW, Charlesworth B, Charlesworth D, and Crow JF. Rates of spontaneous mutation. *Genetics* 1998; 148: 1667-1686.

[10]   Ohno S. Birth of a unique enzyme from an alternative reading frame of the preexisted, internally repetitious coding sequence. *Proc. Natl. Acad. Sci. USA* 1984; 81: 2421–2425.

[11]   Collins F, Brooks L and Chakravarti A. A DNA polymorphism discovery resource for research on human genetic variation. *Genome Res.* 1998; 8: 1229–1231.

[12]   Casillas S and Barbadilla A. PDA: a pipeline to explore and estimate polymorphism in large DNA databases, *Nucleic Acids Res.* 2004; 32: W166-W169.

[13]   Capriotti E, Fariselli P and Casadio R. A neural-network-based method for predicting protein stability changes upon single point mutations. *Bioinformatics* 2004; 20,Suppl. 1: I63–I68.

[14]   Brookes A. The essence of SNPs. *Gene* 1999; 234: 177–186.

[15]   Kirk Brian, Feinsod M, Favis R, Kliman R, Barany F. Single nucleotide polymorphism seeking long term association with complex disease. *Nucleic Acids Res.* 2002; 30: 3295-3311.

[16]   Snustad DP, Simmons MJ. Principles of Genetics. 2nd Edition. New York: John Wiley and Sons Inc. 2000.

[17]   Lewin B. Genes VII. New York. Oxford University Press. 2000.

[18]   Modrich P. Mismatch repair, genetic stability, and cancer. *Science* 1994; 266: 1959-1960.

[19]   Loeb KR, and Loeb LA. Significance of multiple mutations in cancer. *Carcinogenesis* 2000; 21(3): 379-395.

[20] Wong KB, DeDecker BS, Freund SM, Proctor MR, Bycroft M, Fersht AR. *Proc. Natl. Acad. Sci. USA* 1999; 96:8438–8442.

[21] Linzer DI, Levine AJ. Characterization of a 54 K dalton cellular SV40 tumor antigen present in SV 40-transformed cells uninfected embryonal carcinoma cells. *Cell* 1979; 17: 43-52.

[22] Lane DP. Cancer. p53, guardian of the genome. *Nature* 1992; 358: 15-16.

[23] Levine AJ: p53, the cellular gatekeeper for growth and division. *Cell* 1997, 88(3):323-331.

[24] Vogelstein B, Lane D and Levine AJ. Surfing the p53 network. *Nature* 2000; 408: 307–310.

[25] Vousden KH, and Lu X. Live or let die: the cell's response to p53. *Nat. Rev. Cancer* 2002; 2: 594–604.

[26] Hollstein M, Sidransky D, Vogelstein B, Harris CC: p53 mutations in human cancers. *Science* 1991, 253(5015):49-53.

[27] Beroud C and Soussi T. p53 gene mutation: software and database. *Nucleic Acids Res.* 1998; 26:200–204.

[28] Greenblatt MS, Bennett WP, Hollstein M, Harris CC. (1994) Mutations in the p53 tumor suppressor gene: clues to cancer etiology and molecular pathogenesis. *Cancer Res.*; 54: 4855–78.

[29] Hainaut P, Hernandez T, Robinson A, Rodriguez-Tome P, Flores T, Hollstein M, Harris CC, and Montesano R. IARC database of p53 gene mutations in human tumors and cell lines: updated compilation, revised formats and new visualisation tools. *Nucleic Acids Res* 1998; 26:205–213.

[30] Hollstein M, Marion MJ, Lehman T, Welsh J, Harris CC, Martel-Planche G, Kusters I, and Montesano R. p53 mutations at A:T base pairs in angiosarcomas of vinyl chloride-exposed factory workers. *Carcinogenesis* 1994; 15: 1–3.

[31] Hollstein M, Rice K, Greenblatt MS, Soussi T, Fuchs R, Sorlie T, Hovig E, Smith-Sorensen B, Montesano R, and Harris CC. Database of p53 gene somatic mutations in human tumors and cell lines. *Nucleic Acids Res.* 1994; 22: 3551–3555.

[32] Ozbun MA and Butel JS. Tumor suppressor p53 mutations and breast cancer: a critical analysis. *Adv. Cancer Res.* 1995; 66: 71–141.

[33] Sigal A and Rotter V. Oncogenic mutations of the p53 tumor suppressor: the demons of the guardian of the genome. *Cancer Res.* 2000; 60: 6788–6793.

[34] Soussi T, Dehouche K, and Beroud C. p53 website and analysis of p53 gene mutations in human cancer: forging a link between epidemiology and carcinogenesis. *Hum. Mutat.* 2000; 15: 105–113.

[35] Hainaut P, Hollstein M. p53 and human cancer: the first ten thousand mutations. *Adv. Cancer Res* 2000; 77: 81-137.

[36] Hollstein M, Hergenhahn M, Yang Q, Bartsch H, Wang ZQ, Hainaut P. New approaches to understanding p53 gene tumor mutation spectra. *Mutat. Res.* 1999; 431: 199-209.

[37] Olivier M, Eeles R, Hollstein M, Khan MA, Harris CC, Hainaut P. The IARC TP53 database: new online mutation analysis and recommendations to users. *Hum. Mutat.* 2002; 19: 607–614.

[38] Bargonetti J, Manfredi JJ. Multiple roles of the tumor suppressor p53. *Curr. Opin. Oncol.* 2002; 14: 86–91.

[39] Hofseth LJ, Hussain SP, Harris CC. p53: 25 years after its discovery. *Trends Pharmacol. Sci.* 2004; 25: 177–181.

[40] Levine AJ, Finlay CA, Hinds PW. *TP53* is a tumor suppressor gene. *Cell* 2004; Suppl. 116: S67-S69.

[41] Blagosklonny MV. P53: an ubiquitous target of anticancer drugs. *Int. J. Cancer* 2002; 98: 161-166.

[42] Urist M, Prives C. p53 leans on its siblings. *Cancer Cell* 2002; 1: 311-3.

[43] North S, Hainaut P. P53 and cell-cycle: a finger in every pie. *Pathol. Biol.* 2000; 48:255-270.

[44] Ko L, Prives C. p53: puzzle and paradigm. *Genes. Dev.* 1996; 10: 1054-1072.

[45] Lakin N, Jackson S. Regulation of p53 in response to DNA damage. *Oncogene* 1999; 18: 7644-7655.

[46] Chao C, Saito S, Kang J, Anderson C, Appella E, Xu Y. p53 transcriptional activity is essential for p53-dependent apoptosis following DNA damage. *EMBO J.* 2000;19: 4967-4975.

[47] Prives C and Hall PA. The p53 pathway. *J. Pathol.* 1999; 187: 112–126.

[48] Oren M. Decision making by p53: life, death and cancer. Cell Death Differ 2003;10: 431–442.

[49] Bouvet M, Bold RJ, Lee J, Evans DB, Abbruzzese JL, Chiao PJ, McConkey DJ, Chandra J, Chada S, Fang B, and Roth J A. Adenovirus-mediated wild-type p53 tumor suppressor gene therapy induces apoptosis and suppresses growth of human pancreatic cancer. *Ann. Surg. Oncol.* 1998; 5: 681–688.

[50] Dameron KM, Volpert OV, Tainsky MA, and Bouck N. Control of angiogenesis in fibroblasts by p53 regulation of thrombospondin-1. *Science* 1994; 265: 1582–1584.

[51] Ford JM, and Hanawalt PC. Li-Fraumeni syndrome fibroblasts homozygous for p53 mutations are deficient in global DNA repair but exhibit normal transcription- coupled repair and enhanced UV resistance. *Proc. Natl. Acad. Sci. USA* 1995; 92: 8876–8880.

[52] Offer H, Zurer I, Banfalvi G, Reha'k M, Falcovitz A, Milyavsky M, Goldfinger N, and Rotter V. p53 modulates base excision repair activity in a cell cycle-specific manner after genotoxic stress. *Cancer Res.* 2001; 61: 88–96.

[53] Sengupta S and Harris CC. p53: traffic cop at the crossroads of DNA repair and recombination. *Nat. Rev. Mol. Cell Biol.* 2005; 6: 44–55.

[54] Wani MA, Zhu QZ, El-Mahdy M, and Wani AA. Influence of p53 tumor suppressor protein on bias of DNA repair and apoptotic response in human cells. *Carcinogenesis* 1999; 20: 765–772.

[55] Zhou J, Ahn J, Wilson SH, and Prives C. A role for p53 in base excision repair. *EMBO J.* 2001; 20: 914–923.

[56] Appella E and Anderson CW. Post-translational modifications and activation of p53 by genotoxic stresses. *Eur. J. Biochem.* 200; 268: 2764–2772.

[57] Samuels-Lev Y, O'Connor DJ, Bergamaschi D, Trigiante G, Hsieh JK, Zhong S, Campargue I, Naumovski L, Crook T, and Lu X. ASPP proteins specifically stimulate the apoptotic function of p53. *Mol. Cell* 2001; 8: 781–794.

[58] Yu J, Zhang L, Hwang PM, Rago C, Kinzler KW, and Vogelstein B. Identification and classification of p53-regulated genes. *Proc. Natl. Acad. Sci. USA* 1999; 96: 4517–14522.

[59] Zhao R, Gish K, Murphy M, Yin Y, Notterman D, Hoffman WH, Tom E, Mack DH, and Levine AJ. Analysis of p53-regulated gene expression patterns using oligonucleotide arrays. *Genes. Dev.* 2000; 14: 981–993.

[60] Wahl GM and Carr AM. The evolution of diverse biological responses to DNA damage: insights from yeast and p53. *Nat. Cell Biol.* 2001; 3: E277–E286.

[61] Vogelstein B and Kinzler KW, X-rays strike p53 again. *Nature* 1994; 370: 174-175.

[62] Bode AM and Dong Z. Post- translational modification of p53 in tumorigenesis. *Nat. Rev. Cancer* 2004; 4: 793–805.

[63] Cho Y, Gorina S, Jeffrey PD, Pavletich NP. Crystal structure of a p53 tumor suppressor-DNA complex: understanding tumorigenic mutations. *Science* 1994; 265:346–355.

[64] Kitayner M, Rozenberg H, Kessler N, Rabinovich D, Shaulov L, Haran TE, Shakked Z. Structural basis of DNA recognition by p53 tetramers. *Mol. Cell* 2006; 22:741–753.

[65] Ho WC, Fitzgerald MX, Marmorstein R. Structure of the p53 core domain dimer bound to DNA. *J. Biol. Chem.* 2006; 281:20494–20502.

[66] Canadillas JM, Tidow H, Freund SM, Rutherford TJ, Ang HC, Fersht AR. Solution structure of p53 core domain: structural basis for its instability. *Proc. Natl. Acad. Sci. USA* 2006; 103:2109–2114.

[67] Bullock AN, Fersht AR. Rescuing the function of mutant p53. *Nat. Rev. Cancer* 2001; 1:68–76.

[68] Bullock AN, Henckel J, Fersht AR. Quantitative analysis of residual folding and DNA binding in mutant p53 core domain: definition of mutant states for rescue in cancer therapy. *Oncogene* 2000; 19:1245–1256.

[69] Venot CM, Maratrat C, Dureuil E, Conseiller L, Debussche L. The requierement for the p53 proline-rich functional domain for mediation of apoptosis is correlated with specific PIG3 gene transactivation and with transcriptional represión. *EMBO J.* 1998; 17: 4668-4679.

[70] Martin ACR, Fachiano AM, Cuff AL, Hernandez-Boussard T, Olivier M, Hainaut P, Thornton JM. Integrating mutation data and structural analysis of the TP53 tumor-suppressor protein. *Hum. Mutat.* 2002; 19: 149-164.

[71] Schmitt CA, fridman JS, Yang M, Baranov E, Hoffman RM, Lowe SW. Dissecting p53 tumor suppressor functions in vivo. *Cancer Cell* 2002; 1: 289-298.

[72] Brooks CI, Gu W. Ubiquitination, phosphorylation and acetylation: the molecular basis for p53 regulation. *Curr. Opin. Cell Biol* 2003; 15: 164-171.

[73] Shuber AP, Skoletsky J, Stern R, Handelin BL. Efficient 12-mutation testing in the CFTR gene: a general model for complex mutation analysis. *Hum. Mol. Genet.* 1993; 2: 153-158.

[74] Delahunty C, Ankener W, Deng Q, Eng J, Nickerson DA. Testing the feasibility of DNA typing for human identification by PCR and an oligonucleotide ligation assay. *Am. J. Hum. Genet.* 1996; 58: 1239-46.

[75] Syvänen AC, Ikonen E, Manninen T, Bengtström M, Söderlund H, Aula P, Peltoner L. Convenient and quantitative determination of the frequency of a mutant allele using solid-phase minisequencing: application to aspartylglucosaminuria in Finland. *Genomics* 1992; 12: 590-595.

[76] Nyrén P, Pettersson B, Uhlen M. Solid phase DNA minisequencing by an enzymatic luminometric inorganic pyrophosphate detection assay. *Anal. Biochem.* 1993; 208: 171-175.

[77] Holland PM, Abramson RD, Watson R, Gefland DH. Detection of specific polymerase chain reaction products by utilizing the 5′to 3′exonuclease activity of *Thermus aquaticus* DNA polymerase. *Proc. Natl. Acad. Sci. USA* 1991; 88: 7276-80.

[78] Wilkins Stevens P, Hall JG, Lyamichev V, Neri BP, Lu M, Wang L, Smith LM, and Kelso DM. Analysis of single nucleotide polymorphisms with solid phase invasive cleavage reactions *Nucleic Acids Res.* 2001; 29: e77.

[79] Ronaghi M, Karamohamed S, Pettersson B, Uhlén M, Nyrén P. Real-time DNA sequencing using detection of pyrophosphate releases. *Anal. Biochem.* 1996; 242: 84-89.

[80] Heid CA, Stevens J, Livak KL, and Williams PM. Real time quantitative PCR. *Genome Res.* 1996; 6: 986-994.

[81] Pushnova E, Akhmedova SN, Shevtsov SP, Schwarts EI. A rapid and simple DNA fingerprinting method using RFLP and SSCP analysis of the hypervariable noncoding region of human mitochondrial DNA. *Hum. Mutat.* 1994; 3: 292-6.

[82] White MB, Carvalho M, Derse D, O′Brien SJ, Dean M. Detecting single base substitutions as heteroduplex polymorphisms. *Genomics* 1992; 12: 301-6.

[83] Orita M, Iwahana H, Kanazawa H, Hayashi K, Sekiya T. Detection of polymorphisms of human DNA by gel electrophoresis as single-strand conformation polymorphisms. *Proc. Natl. Acad. Sci. USA* 1989; 86: 2766-70.

[84] Fisher SG, Lerman LS. DNA fragments differing by single base-pair substitutions are separated in denaturing gradient gels: correspondence with melting theory. *Proc. Natl. Acad. Sci. USA* 1983; 80: 1579-83.

[85] Cotton RGG, Rodriguez NR, Campbell RD. Reactivity of cytosine and thymine in single-base-pair mismatches with hydroxylamine and osmium tetroxide and its application to the study of mutations. *Proc. Natl. Acad. Sci. USA* 1988; 85: 4397-401.

[86] Sarkar G, Yoon H, Sommer S. Dideoxy fingerprinting (ddE): a rapid and efficient screen for the presence of mutations. *Genomics* 1992; 13: 441-3.

[87] Oefner PJ, Underhill PA. Comparative DNA sequencing by denaturing high-performance liquid chromatography (DHPLC). *Am. J. Hum. Genet.* 1995; 57, suppl: A266.

[88] Syvanen AC, Aalto-Setala K, Harju L, Kontula K, and Soderlund H. A primer-guided nucleotide incorporation assay in the genotyping of apolipoprotein E. *Genomics* 1990; 8: 684-692.

[89] Hacia JG, Brody LC, Chee MS, Fodor SP, and Collins FS. Detection of heterozygous mutations in BRCA1 using high density oligonucleotide arrays and two-colour fluorescence analysis. *Nature Genet.* 1996; 14: 441-447.

[90] Lipshutz RJ, Morris D, Chee M, Hubbell E, Kozal MJ, Shah N, Shen N, Yang R, and Fodor SP. Using oligonucleotide probe arrays to access genetic diversity. *Biotechniques* 1995; 19: 442-447.

[91] Guo Z, Guilfoyle RA, Thiel AJ, Wang R, and Smith LM. Direct fluorescence analysis of genetic polymorphisms by hybridization with oligonucleotide arrays on glass supports *Nucleic Acids Res.* 1994; 22: 5456-5465.

[92] Del Tito BJ Jr, Poff HE II, Novotny MA, Cartiedge DM, Walker RI II, Earl CD, Bailey AL. Automated fluorescent analysis procedure for enzymatic mutation detection. *Clin. Chem.* 1998; 44: 731-9.

[93] White MB, Giraud-Panis M-JE, Pöhler JRG, Lilley DM. Recognition and manipulation of branched DNA structure by junction-resolving enzymes *J. Mol. Biol.* 1997; 269: 647-64.

[94] Tong J, Cao W, and Barany F. Biochemical properties of a high fidelity DNA ligase from *Thermus species AK16D. Nucleic Acids Res* 1999; 27: 788-794.

[95] Smith J, and Modrich P. Mutation detection with MutH, MutL and MutS mismatch repair proteins *Proc. Natl. Acad. Sci.* USA 1996; 93: 4374-4379.

[96] Huang J, Kirk B, Favis R, Soussi T, Paty P, Cao W, and Barany F. An endonuclease/ligase based mutations scanning method especially suited for analysis of neoplastic tissue. *Oncogene* 2002; 21: 1909-1921.

[97] Schiffer D, Cavalla P, Di Sapio A, Giordana MT, Mauro A. Mutation and immunohistochemistry of p53 and proliferation markers in astrocytic tumors of childhood. *Child's Nerv. Syst.* 1995; 11: 517-522.

[98] Meck DW. Multisite phosphorylation and the integration of stress signals at p53. *Cell Signal* 1998; 10: 159-166.

[99] Aguilar F, Harris CC, Sun T, Hollstein M, Cerrutti P. Geographic variation of p53 mutational profile in nonmalignant human liver. *Science* 1994; 264: 1317-1319.

[100] Accardi R, Dong W, Smet A, Cui R, Hautefeuille A, Gabet AS, Sylla BS, Gissmann L, Hainaut P, Tommasino M. Skin human papillomavirus type 38 alters p53 functions by accumulation of deltaNp73. *EMBO Rep.* 2006; 7(3): 334-40.

[101] Schumacher B, Gartner A. Translational regulation of p53 as a potential tumor therapy target. *Future Oncol.* 2006; 2(1): 145-53.

[102] Amanullah A, Libermann DA, Hoffman B. Deregulated c-Myc prematurely recruits both Type I and II CD95/Fas apoptotic pathways associated with terminal myeloid differentiation. *Oncogene* 2002; 21(10): 1600-10.

[103] Chen YQ, Zhou YQ, Wang MH. Activation of the RON receptor tyrosine kinase protects murine macrophages from apoptotic death induced by bacterial lipopolysaccharide. *J. Leukoc. Biol.* 2002 ;71(2): 359-66.

[104] Scian MJ, Stagliano KE, Anderson MA, Hassan S, Bowman M, Miles MF, Deb SP. Tumor-derived p53 mutants induce NF-kappaB2 gene expression. *Mol. Cell Biol.* 2005; 25(22): 10097-110.

[105] Rodriguez-Viciana P, Collins CH, Moule MG, Fried M. Chromosomal instability at a mutational hotspot in polyoma middle T-antigen affects its ability to activate the ARF-p53 tumor suppressor pathway. *Oncogene* 2006; 25(10): 1454-62.

[106] Camus S, Higgins M, Lane DP, Lían S. Differences in the ubiquitination of p53 by Mdm2 and the HPV protein E6. *FEBS Lett.* 2003; 536(1-3): 220-4.

[107] Duan W, Gao L, Wu X, Zhang Y, Otterson GA, Villalona-Calero MA. Differential response between the p53 ubiquitin-protein ligases Pirh2 and MdM2 following DNA damage in human cancer cells. *Exp. Cell Res.* 2006; 312(17):3370-8.

[108] De Vries A, Flores ER, Miranda B, Hsich HM, van Oostrom CTM, Sage J, Jacks T. Targeted point mutations of p53 lead to dominant-negative inhibition ofwild-type p53 function. *Proc. Natl. Acad. Sci.* 2002; 99: 2948-53.

[109] Schmitt CA, Fridman JS, Yang M, Baranov E, Hoffman RM, Lowe SW. Dissecting p53 tumor suppressor functions in vivo. *Cancer Cell* 2002; 1: 289-98.

[110] Brooks CI, Gu W. Ubiquitination, phosphorylation and acetylation. The molecular basis for p53 regulation. *Curr. Opin. Cell Biol.* 2003; 15: 164-71.

[111] Pfeifer GP, p53 mutational spectra and the role of methylated CpG sequences *Mutat. Res.* 2000; 450: 155-166.

[112] Harris SL, Levine AJ: The p53 pathway: positive and negative feedback loops. *Oncogene* 2005, 24(17):2899-2908.

[113] Goodman JE, Hofseth LJ, Hussain SP, Harris CC. Nitric oxide and p53 in cancer-prone chronic inflammation and oxyradical overload disease. *Environ. Mol. Mutagen.* 2004; 44(1): 3-9.

[114] Daya-Grosjean L, Dumaz N, Sarasin A. The specificity of p53 mutation spectra in sunlight induced human cancers. *J. Photochem. Photobiol. B.* 1995; 28: 115–24.

[115] Giglia G, Dumaz N, Drougard C, Avril MF, Daya-Grosjean L, Sarasin A. p53 mutations in skin and internal tumors of xeroderma pigmentosum patients belonging to the complementation group C. *Cancer Res* 1998; 58: 4402–9.

[116] Pfeifer GP, Denissenko MF, Olivier M, Tretyakova N, Hecht SS, Hainaut P. Tobacco smoke carcinogens, DNA damage and p53 mutations in smoking-associated cancers. *Oncogene* 2002; 21: 7435–51.

[117] Liu Z, Muehlbauer KR, Schmeiser, Hergenhahn M, Belharazem, and Hollstein M. p53 mutations in benzo(a)pyrene-exposed human knock-in murine fibroblasts correlate with p53 mutations in human lung tumors. *Cancer Res*2005; 65(7): 2583-87.

[118] Smith LE, Denissenko MF, Bennett WP, Li H, Amin S, Tang M, Pfeifer GP. Targeting of lung cancer mutational hotspots by polycyclic aromatic hydrocarbons. *J. Natl. Cancer Inst.* 2000; 92: 803–11.

[119] Cetin-Atalay R, Ozturk M. p53 mutations as fingerprints of environmental carcinogens. *Pure Appl. Chem.* 2000; 72: 995-9.

[120] Montesano R, Hainaut P, Wild CP. Hepatocellular carcinoma: from gene to public health. *J. Natl. Cancer Inst.* 1997; 89: 1844–51.

[121] Kirk GD, Lesi OA, Mendy M, Szymañska K, Whittle H, Goedert JJ, Hainaut P, Montesano R. 249 [ser] TP53 mutation in plasma DNA, hepatitis B viral infection, and risk of hepatocellular carcinoma. *Oncogene* 2005; 24: 5858-67.

[122] Denissenko MF, Koudriakova TB, Smith L, O'Connor TR, Riggs AD, Pfeifer GP. The p53 codon 249 mutational hotspot in hepatocellular carcinoma is not related to selective formation or persistence of aflatoxin B1 adducts. *Oncogene* 1998; 17: 3007–14.

[123] Jackson PE, Qian GS, Friesen MD, Zhu YR, Lu P, Wang JB, Wu Y, Kensler TW, Vogelstein B, and Groopman JD. Specific p53 mutations detected in plasma and tumors of hepatocellular carcinoma patients by electrospray ionization mass spectrometry *Cancer Res.* 2001; 61: 33-35.

[124] Qian GS, Kuang SY, He X, Groopman JD and Jackson PE. Sensitivity of electrospray ionization mass spectrometry detection of codon 249 mutations in the p53 gene compared with RFLP. *Cancer Epidemiol. Biomarkers Prev.* 2002; 11: 1126-1129.

[125] Jackson PE, Kuang SY, Wang JB, Strickland PT, Muñoz A, Kensler TW, Qian GS, and Groopman JD. Prospective detection of codon 249 mutations in p53 in plasma of hepatocellular carcinoma patients. *Carcinogenesis* 2003; 24, 1657-1663.

[126] Hussain SP, Harris CC. P53 biological Network: At the crossroads of the cellular-stress response pathway and molecular carcinogenesis. *J. Nippon. Med. Sch.* 2006; 73(2): 54-64.

[127] O´reilly MA. DNA damage and cell cycle checkpoints in hyperoxic lung injury: braking to facilitate repair. *Am J Physiol Lung Cell Mol Physiol* 2001; 281: L291-L305.

[128] Hussain SP, Hofseth LJ, Harris CC. Radical causes of cancer. *Nat. Rev. Cancer* 2003; 3: 276-285.

[129] Hofseth LJ, Hussain SP, Wogan GN, Harris CC. Nitric oxide in cancer and chemoprevention. *Free Radic. Biol. Med.* 2003; 34: 955-68.

[130] Thomsen LL, Miles DW, Happerfield L, Bobrow LG, Knowles RG, Moncada S. Nitric oxide synthase activity in human breast cancer. *Br. J. Cancer* 1995; 72: 41-44.

[131] Hofseth LJ. Saito S, Hussain SP, Espey MG, Miranda KM, Araki Y. Nitric oxide induced cellular stress and p53 activation in chronic inflammation. *Proc. Natl. Acad. Sci. USA* 2003; 100: 143-148.

[132] Oren M. Decision making by p53: life, death and cancer. Cell Death Differ 2003;10: 431–442.

[133] Santini V, Kantarjian HM, and Issa JP. Changes in DNA methylation in neoplasia: pathophysiology and therapeutic implications. *Ann. Intern. Med.* 2001; 134: 573–586.

[134] Toyota M, Ahuja N, Ohe-Toyota M, Herman JG, Baylin SB, and Issa JP. CpG island methylator phenotype in colorectal cancer. *Proc. Natl. Acad. Sci. USA* 1999; 96: 8681–8686.

[135] Appella E, and Anderson CW. Post-translational modifications and activation of p53 by genotoxic stresses. *Eur. J. Biochem.* 2001; 268: 2764–2772.

[136] Hofseth LJ. The adaptive imbalance to genotoxic stress: genome guardians rear their ugly heads. *Carcinogenesis* 2004; 25: 1787-1793.

In: New Research on DNA Damage   ISBN 978-1-60456-581-2
Editors: Honoka Kimura and Aoi Suzuki   © 2008 Nova Science Publishers, Inc.

Chapter 17

Mutation Detection in *TP53* Gene: Alternatives in Point Mutation Technologies

Angélica Rangel-López, [1-3] *Alfonso Méndez-Tenorio,* [3] *Mauricio Salcedo,* [1] *Rogelio Maldonado,* [3] *and Kenneth L. Beattie* [4]

1. Unidad de Investigación Médica en Enfermedades Oncológicas. Hospital de Oncología. Centro Médico Nacional S XXI. IMSS, México, D. F., México.
2. Unidad de Investigación Médica en Enfermedades Nefrológicas. Hospital de Especialidades. Centro Médico Nacional S XXI. IMSS, México, D. F, México.
3. Laboratorio de Tecnología del DNA, Departamento de Bioquímica, Escuela Nacional de Ciencias Biológicas IPN, México, 11340, D. F., México;
4. Amerigenics, Inc., 1326 Open Range Rd., Crossville, TN 38555 USA.

One of the major challenges involved mainly in searching of point mutations for clinical relevance is the technology used; in particular for cancer research we will focus on the gains or loss-of-suppression function, v.gr. in cancer genes as *RET*, *TP53*, *RAS*, etc. *TP53* has been used as an excellent model for point mutation detection, because of its more than 20,000 different mutations this gene is the most frequently found in many human cancers.

Furthermore, there are uncommon somatic and germline mutations that might be related to specific cancers or predispositions. In particular case, the precise nature of the *TP53* mutation presents both challenges and opportunities for alternate treatment strategies in specific cancers. These highlight the clinical need to accurately identify often unknown inherited aberrations or infrequently represented mutations in mixed populations of DNA molecules.

Different polymorphisms or mutation detection technologies have been developed to identify known changes: these include DNA microarrays, the polymerase chain reaction/ligase detection reaction (PCR/LDR), now used in combination with the universal DNA microarray and primer extension assays. On the other hand, the technologies used for unknown mutations: hybridization analysis using high-density oligonucleotide arrays, denaturing high-performance liquid chromatography (DHPLC), capillary electrophoresis-based single strand conformation polymorphism (CE-SSCP), denaturing gradient gel electrophoresis (DGGE) and heteroduplex analysis (HA). Finally, dideoxy-sequencing has difficulty in detecting heterozygous mutations, and is of limited utility in the analysis of solid tumors where mutant DNA may represent as little as 15% of the total. Some other methods include *in vitro* transcription/translation-based approaches, chemical and enzymatic mismatch cleavage detection (e.g. Cleavase, RNase, T4 endonuclease VII, MutS enzymes and CEL I). *In vitro* mismatch cleavage methods encounter variability in signal intensity compared with background bands.

Hybridization analysis using low-density oligonucleotide arrays for unknown mutations, certainly might have the potential for custom fabrication and the detection of all desired features and could conveniently provide reliable results and decrease production cost considerably. A variant of this kind of technique is based on tandem hybridization. Tandem hybridization attempts to compare the annealing of matched versus mismatched probes to targets ("probe" typically refers to the DNA immobilized on the surface, whereas "target" generally refers to DNA in solution) over a range of hybridization conditions. Moreover, tandem hybridization method offers several advantages over traditional oligonucleotide array configuration, mainly because a unique feature of tandem hybridization is that unlabeled target DNA is annealed with relatively long-labeled stacking oligonucleotides which bind at a unique site together with short capture probes positioned immediately adjacent to stacking oligonucleotides. As a consequence, this system is a highly specific and sensitive one because capture and stacking probes must be contiguous, in order to obtain a specific hybridization signal. This system has been successfully applied to *RET* oncogene and *TP53* gene. In this particular context, we have designed a small microarray directed against the hotspot mutations that are more commonly observed in exons 5, 7 and 8 of *TP53* because in this region are clustered the most frequent mutations found in clinical samples. The minimum amount of target detected, as estimated by the proportion of equimolar amount of labeled stacking oligonucleotide annealed with the sample. It is important to comment that the intensity of signals seen with the same sample, using 7-mer probes, under traditional, single tandem and double tandem hybridizations increases from 3 to 6 times in Single Tandem Hybridization (which uses only a single stacking oligonucleotide) and 6 to 12 times in the Double Tamdem Hybridization (which uses both stacking oligonucleotides) when compared to traditional hybridization. Some mutations, such as those causing G's mismatched, are very stable, and for this reason are difficult to discriminate with the traditional hybridization techniques due especially to the length of the probes that are normally used (20-25 nt or even longer). Short duplexes are considerably more destabilized by even relatively stable mismatches than longer duplexes, and for this reason short probes (7-mer) have higher discrimination power. However, short probes when used individually (without tandem hybridization) are not quite adequate because theses sequences can occur by random chance multiple times within relatively long targets, which would limit their specificity in the single-probe approach. However, this is not the case in the tandem hybridization approach because the specificity arises from the short probes plus the contiguous stacking oligonucleotides (the fact that they must be contiguous in order to see a hybridization signal is an important requirement for this technique). In other words, only 7-mer sites located adjacent to the stacking oligonucleotides are interrogated, since the stacking hybridization allows only their detection since isolated 7-mer duplexes (not stabilized by the base stacking) are unstable under the hybridization conditions used. Finally, in order to decide whether one another method is adequate to detect point mutations it is important first to know the mutation frequency expected for any non-selected gene in normal human and in tumor tissue which makes the analysis less difficult.

References

[1]   Maldonado-Rodríguez R, Espinosa-Lara M, Barrera-León O, Colin-Tovar C, González-Yebra B, Salcedo-Vargas M, Santiago-Hernández JC, Méndez-Tenorio A, Beattie KL: Detection of RET proto-oncogene codon 634 mutations using double tandem hybridization. *Mol. Biotechnol.* 2003; 25:113-129.

[2]   Maldonado-Rodríguez R, Beattie KL: Analysis of nucleic acids by tandem hybridization on oligonucleotide microarrays. *Methods Mol. Biol.* 2001; 170:157-171. 3.

[3]   Beattie KL, Beattie WG, Meng L, Turner S, Varma S, Bishop C, Dao DD: Hybridization of DNA targets to glass-tethered oligonucleotide probes. *Mol. Biotechnol.* 1995, 4:213-225.

[4]   Angélica Rangel-López, Rogelio Maldonado-Rodríguez, Mauricio Salcedo-Vargas, Juana Mercedes Espinosa-Lara, Alfonso Méndez-Tenorio and Kenneth L Beattie. Low density DNA microarray for detection of most frequent *TP53* missense point mutations. *BMC Biotechnology* 2005; 5:8.

In: New Research on DNA Damage
Editors: Honoka Kimura and Aoi Suzuki

ISBN 978-1-60456-581-2
© 2008 Nova Science Publishers, Inc.

Chapter 18

The Induction and Repair of DNA-Protein Crosslinks in Mammalian Cells

Sharon Barker, * *Michael Weinfeld and David Murray*
Department of Oncology, Division of Experimental Oncology,
University of Alberta, Edmonton, Alberta, Canada

Abstract

DNA-protein crosslinks (DPCs), which are generated by covalent linkage of proteins to the DNA duplex, comprise an under-studied class of DNA lesions. They can be induced by commonly encountered agents including environmental chemicals, cancer-chemotherapeutic drugs and ionizing radiation. DPCs could pose a serious threat to cellular function because they may disrupt the progression of the replication and transcription machineries. A number of problems have plagued researchers examining this type of DNA damage. Many agents can induce DPCs by more than one chemical mechanism. Furthermore, these agents invariably induce other types of DNA damage. Measurements of DPC damage have also been hampered by the lack of stringent and sensitive methodologies for their isolation. However, recent advances in DPC-isolation methodology have allowed for more in-depth analyses of these lesions. Additionally, advances in the study of chromatin structure have provided further understanding of the influence of chromatin dynamics on the induction and repair of DPCs. At the same time, our improving knowledge of many DNA-repair pathways has afforded opportunities for assessing the involvement of these pathways in the removal of DPCs from the genome. This chapter will discuss the impact of these advances on our understanding of DPCs and their biological consequences.

* Correspondence: Dr. S. Barker, Division of Experimental Oncology, Cross Cancer Institute, 11560 University Ave., Edmonton, Alberta T6G 1Z2, Canada. Phone: (780)-432-8427, FAX: (780)-432-8428, E-mail: barkersh@cancerboard.ab.ca.

1. Introduction

DPCs have not received as much of the research spotlight as have other types of DNA damage despite their induction by numerous endogenous and exogenous agents and their potentially serious cellular and biological consequences. The induction of DPCs has been shown for numerous synthetically-produced and naturally-occurring agents such as aldehydes, metals and ionizing radiation (IR), as well as a number of cancer-chemotherapeutic drugs. The covalent crosslinking of proteins to DNA has numerous ramifications for genome stability. This type of lesion interferes with DNA metabolic processes, disrupting DNA replication, repair, recombination, and transcription, as well as chromatin remodeling processes. However, the impact of DPCs has been difficult to clarify in part because these lesions can be induced by a number of different chemical routes, even for a single agent. The different types of DPCs have been reviewed recently [1] and can be broadly classified as crosslinks formed directly between protein and DNA by oxidative free radical mechanisms, proteins crosslinked to DNA through the physical intermediacy of the agent itself, or proteins crosslinked to DNA through coordination with a metal atom.

Understanding the biological effects of DPCs is further complicated by the fact that these lesions are typically induced in a background of other types of damage, both to DNA and protein. Over the past two decades a small body of work has accumulated that has attempted to determine the contribution of DPCs to genome alterations, mutagenesis, cytotoxicity, and carcinogenesis (reviewed in [1]) and has succeeded in highlighting the relevance of this type of damage and its cellular consequences.

DPCs represent challenging lesions for the cellular repair machinery because of their multiple chemistries and size/conformation. Various attempts have been made to determine the repair pathway(s) involved in removing these lesions from the genome. The most important of these pathways appear to be nucleotide excision repair (NER) and homologous recombination (HR), although the results have been somewhat conflicting to date. As our knowledge and understanding of DPCs has evolved, so have our approaches to defining the repair routes of DPCs.

The goal of this chapter is to highlight the current advances in the study of DPCs and to clarify their emerging role in the cytotoxic, mutagenic and carcinogenic effects of various agents. The cellular impact of DPCs must be assessed in order to begin to understand the role of this type of damage *in vivo* and to devise approaches to best exploit such effects for chemotherapeutic advantage and for improving the assessment of environmental exposure risk. Elements to consider include gaining a detailed characterization of the different chemical types of DPCs induced by various agents as well as the cellular conditions that impact on their induction, the biological consequences of these lesions, and the routes available for repairing or coping with these lesions.

2. DPC Induction and Chemistry

The ability of a number of both man-made and naturally-occurring compounds to induce DPCs is well established and the list continues to grow. Recent studies have focused on the ability of various compounds to induce DPCs *in vivo* and to correlate the induction of this type of damage with toxic or mutagenic consequences. For example, a recent study examined the ability of sulfur dioxide (SO_2) (an ubiquitous environmental pollutant produced by combustion of fossil fuels) to induce both DPCs and protein oxidative damage *in vivo* in mice [2]. This study addressed an important question in DPC chemistry as the contribution of protein damage in DPC formation has been under-investigated. The levels of both protein oxidative damage and DPCs in the hearts, lungs, and livers of mice exposed to SO_2 showed concentration-dependent increases, suggesting that protein oxidative damage is involved in the generation of these DPCs.

The understanding of the induction of DPCs by platinating agents has also benefited from recent advances [3]. The predominant (~90%) type of damage induced by the anti-cancer agent, cisplatin, is intrastrand crosslinks, while monoadducts, interstrand crosslinks (ICLs) and DPCs comprise smaller percentages of the total damage [3]. Because cisplatin can induce DPCs, and because DPCs play an important role in cytotoxicity within the clinically-relevant cisplatin dose range, Chvalova *et al.* [3] investigated the ability of various cisplatin adducts to be converted to DPCs. Synthetic oligonucleotides (20-40mers) were treated with either cisplatin or its clinically ineffective isomer, transplatin, and then characterized for extent of platination and type of damage. Labeled oligonucleotides containing intrastrand crosslinks, monoadducts, or ICLs were incubated with Klenow fragment of DNA polymerase I or histone H1 protein and covalent complex formation was assessed by gel shift using denaturing SDS/PAGE. The intrastrand-crosslinked and mono-adducted substrates were capable of crosslinking proteins whereas the interstrand crosslinked or transplatin-treated substrates were not. The extent of crosslinking of protein increased with time of incubation, but still only represented a small percentage of the total damage. The conversion of these substrates to DPCs more than doubled when the length of the substrate oligonucleotide was increased by 5-10-fold, indicating that these results may have relevance *in vivo* where longer stretches of DNA are available. Further supporting the possible *in vivo* consequences of such lesions, these DPCs were shown to inhibit the progression of DNA polymerase *in vitro* and to resist excision by NER nucleases [3].

The abovementioned results provide an important detail in the mechanism of action of these types of compounds, since they infer the possibility of additional crosslinking reactions over time as cellular conditions change. Delayed DPC induction has implications for understanding the kinetics of the repair of these lesions. The monoadducts and intrastrand crosslinks were readily repaired by NER, yet the DPC substrates were found to inhibit the NER incision reaction; thus, the monoadducts and intrastrand crosslinks were converted in time to less-readily-repairable lesions [3]. This knowledge may provide a route for modulating the crosslinking activity of these compounds and optimizing their clinical effectiveness. The additional reaction steps that convert monoadducts or intrastrand crosslinks to the more persistent DPCs may depend on cell type, exposure level, or other, as yet unknown, cellular parameters. Moreover, this mechanism may have wider implication to understanding the crosslinking action of related compounds, both platinum-based as well as, potentially, other families of alkylating agents (see Section 6) and in the development of additional more potent and clinically-effective compounds.

The reaction mechanism of another family of DPC inducers has also been under investigation recently. The furocoumarin family of alkylating agents includes 8-methoxypsoralen (8MOP), 4,6,8,9-tetramethyl-2H-furo[2,3-h]quinolin-2-one (HFQ), and 1,4,6,8-tetramethyl-2H-furo[2,3-h]quinolin-2-one (FQ). 8MOP in combination with ultraviolet light has been widely used and studied for its ability to induce ICLs; however, HFQ and FQ are incapable of inducing ICLs. While 8MOP can induce DPCs in addition to ICLs, both HFQ and FQ induce more DPCs than 8MOP (2-fold and 7-fold, respectively) [4]. DPC induction was examined in this study using both *in vivo* and *in vitro* approaches. Interestingly, it was determined that HFQ and FQ induce DPCs by different mechanisms [4]. FQ induces DPCs by a bi-photonic process involving the sequential absorption of 2 photons; it first forms a monoadduct with DNA and, upon absorption of the second photon, it reacts further to form a covalent bridge between the DNA and protein molecules. On the other hand, HFQ absorbs one photon and does not appear to be physically involved in the DNA-protein crosslink, thereby creating a DPC of differing size and stereochemistry than the FQ-mediated DPC.

The mechanism of formation of DPCs under oxidative stress has also been further investigated. To date, few details have emerged regarding the chemical structures and reactions involved in the generation of DPCs by oxidative damage. Studies by Dizdaroglu's group [5-12] have elucidated several key aspects of the nature of these linkages induced by IR (reviewed in [1]). More recently, *in vitro* studies demonstrated the formation of DPCs through reaction of a guanine radical in a short oligonucleotide with a tri-peptide [13]. Guanine radical cations are readily formed through oxidation of DNA. The mechanism of crosslinking was found to involve the nucleophilic addition of the ε-amino group on the lysine residue to the C-8 atom of the guanine radical cation. These "model DPCs" were formed readily and in significant yield, which suggests that they might be relevant *in vivo*, especially because lysine is a common amino acid in histones, which are in close contact with DNA. The induction of this DPC was not linear with IR dose and plateaued rapidly, a response which this group attributed to secondary reactions of the initially formed crosslink. Additional reactions are possible as other lysine-guanine DPCs were formed, albeit to a lesser extent. The induction of these additional crosslink forms was favored at acidic pH, providing support for the idea that cellular conditions can alter response to DPC-inducers.

Guanine radical cations formed through reaction of DNA with oxidants (such as the hydroxyl radical) can charge "migrate" through DNA; this process, termed DNA charge transport (DNA-CT), has been shown to continue up to 20 nm away from the site of initiation [14, 15]. Since DNA is normally present in the cell in a compact, protein-rich form, and because DPCs can be formed in chromatin, a recent study examined the ability of the guanine radical to induce DPCs in nucleosome core particles (NCPs) rather than naked DNA [16]. The NCPs were reconstituted *in vitro* with DNA containing a commonly used 601 NCP positioning sequence with linker DNA and a tethered DNA photooxidant (anthraquinone) to initiate the charge. DNA-CT reactions were not inhibited by the packing of DNA into NCPs; thus, the guanine radical cation can be formed and migrate through regions of contact of DNA and protein (histones). DNA-CT can continue until the radical cation undergoes reactions with protein residues or with competing species like water or oxygen. DPCs were shown to be readily formed between the DNA and the histone H3 protein in the NCPs through guanine radical reaction in this *in vitro* system [16]. The linkage was shown to be a guanine-tyrosine crosslink. Thus, the induction of DPCs in chromatin is likely to be dependent on the sequence, conformation and length of the DNA-protein interface and, due to the dynamic nature of chromatin, this may cause variation in the DPC-induction profiles in response to a given agent.

Assessing the involvement of DNA-CT in DPC induction in cellular systems became more complicated with the revelation that DNA-CT may have a role in modulating p53, an important regulator of the DNA damage-response pathway [17]. The migration of charge through DNA can promote reactions at sites distant from the initial oxidation site. DNA-CT has been shown to be influenced by distance, base-pairing, base damage, and the presence of DNA-binding proteins (reviewed in [17]). Because only some sequences are amenable to long-range oxidation reactions, this suggests a possible mechanism for sequence-discrimination of protein-binding reactions. Through the use of mass spectrometric methods, Augustyn *et al.* [17] demonstrated the oxidation of p53 in the above photooxidation-driven model. The long-range oxidation of p53 caused its dissociation from specific promoters (sequence-specific control), and this dissociation likely functioned to regulate p53 activity because it correlated with appropriate cellular responses to oxidative stress.

The oxidation of DNA in this system (and thus the generation and migration of charge in the DNA) resulted in the dissociation of p53 from the Gadd45 promoter, which has a role in activation of some DNA-repair processes. Upon oxidative damage, p53 was also shown to dissociate from the Mdm2 promoter; failure to transcribe this negative regulator of p53 ensures that adequate cellular levels of p53 are maintained.

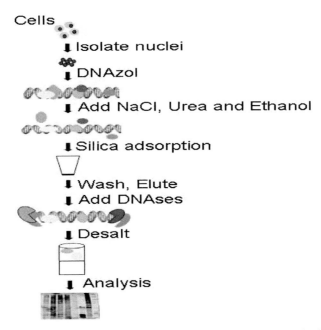

A schematic representation of the steps involved in the "DNAzol-Silica" DPC isolation method, which involves the use of chaotropes and salts to stringently strip non-covalently bound proteins from DNA adhering to silica fines (adapted from [19]).

Figure 1. DPC isolation method.

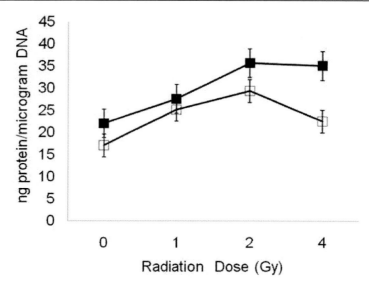

Chinese hamster ovary (CHO) cells were exposed to 0-4 Gy of γ-rays under either aerated [□] or hypoxic [■] conditions (adapted from [20]). DPCs were isolated and quantified using the method of Barker *et al.* [19] (schematically represented in Figure 1).

Figure 2. Dose-responsiveness of total DPC induction by γ-radiation (n = 5).

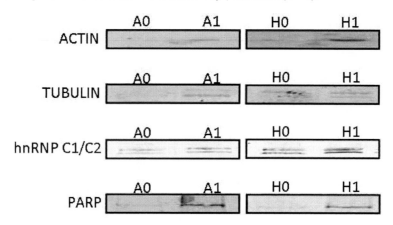

DPCs isolated from CHO cells exposed to 1 Gy of γ-rays were separated by SDS-PAGE, transferred to a nitrocellulose membrane, and Western-blotted with antibodies to a number of proteins to assess their involvement in γ-ray-induced DPCs and the oxygen-dependence thereof (adapted from [20]). A: aerated; H: hypoxic. Data are shown for four representative proteins.

Figure 3. Induction of some specific DPCs by γ-radiation.

However, p53 was not seen to dissociate from the p21 promoter, which would permit transcription of this protein, which is important for cell-cycle arrest. This work suggests a novel mechanism for the regulation of p53 function in the cellular DNA-damage response. Upon oxidative damage, DNA-CT appears to be involved in the sequence-specific (and therefore gene-specific) control of p53 activation of cell-cycle arrest and inhibition of DNA repair and p53 down-regulation. The above results are particularly interesting when considered with the findings that a novel anti-tumour agent, NSC 652287 (discussed in

Section 6), is a potent DPC inducer and appears to alter the ability of p53 to interact with its protein partners [18].

The measurement of DPCs in mammalian cells has been hampered by the lack of suitably stringent and sensitive assays for these lesions (reviewed in [1] and [19]). For our own investigations of cellular DPC induction by IR, we developed a novel method using chaotropic agents to stringently strip tightly-bound, but non-covalently crosslinked, proteins from DNA, which greatly reduces the level of "background" DPCs ([19]; Figure 1). This method allowed the quantification of DPCs at biologically-relevant doses of IR (0.5-2 Gy) [20]. We found that DPC-induction in mammalian cells was a linear function of dose in the 0-2 Gy range, but then appeared to plateau at higher doses (Figure 2). We also used this assay to examine the influence of cellular oxygenation on the yield of DPCs. Earlier studies [21-25] had reported an increase in DPC yields under hypoxic conditions, which may be attributable to the increased lifetime of radical precursors in the absence of molecular oxygen. In our study [20], however, we did not see a significant influence of oxygen on overall DPC induction (Figure 2). What we *did* see was that individual proteins exhibited different induction kinetics and were differentially influenced by the presence of oxygen – indicating that there is likely more than one reaction mechanism for DPC induction by IR (Figure 3).

3. Chromatin Constraints

The studies discussed in Section 2 highlight the fact that the dynamic DNA-protein environment present in cells has a significant impact on the nature of DPC-induction kinetics. Recent investigations of chromatin dynamics have revealed the mechanism for coordination of nucleosome disruption and reassembly to accommodate replication fork progression [26, 27]. This mechanism involves the Asf1 histone chaperone protein, histones H3 and H4, and the putative replicative helicases MCM2-7. Disruptions in the mobility of any of these proteins (e.g., through covalent crosslinking to DNA) would have serious implications for chromatin remodeling. Previous studies have already shown that histones are targets for crosslinking to DNA by various agents ([20] and reviewed in [1]). Not only must nucleosome disruption and reassembly be coordinated during DNA-replication, but it must also be tightly regulated for DNA repair, recombination and transcription. DNA has to become accessible for these processes to occur and then accurately restored after such events are completed. DNA damage can lead to long-range disturbances in chromatin organization which could have negative consequences for genome stability (reviewed in [27]).

It is known that chromatin undergoes decondensation in response to DNA damage (reviewed in [28]), presumably to allow access of proteins for lesion recognition and DNA-repair activities. Murga and colleagues [29] examined the correlation between the strength of the DNA-damage response (activation of cell-cycle checkpoints) and the degree of chromatin compaction. They found that the DNA-damage response is limited by the degree of compaction of chromatin, being stronger in open chromatin. Furthermore, the data suggested that even small differences in chromatin compaction can account for variations in the strength of the response to DNA damage.

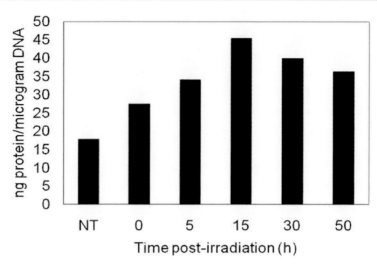

Human GM00637 cells were exposed to 0.5 Gy of γ-rays. DPCs were either isolated immediately, or cells were incubated at 37°C for 5-50 h to allow metabolic processing. DPCs were isolated, analyzed, and quantified according to the method of Barker *et al.* [19].

Figure 4. Time-course of γ-ray-induced total DPCs (n = 3).

DPCs might inhibit re-assembly, enhance compaction, or prevent necessary decompaction, and thereby influence the cell's ability to respond to and repair damage (including the DPCs themselves).

Additionally, the degree of compaction of chromatin (which will be altered in response to treatment with DNA-damaging agents) may influence DPC-induction processes because compaction results in tight associations of proteins with DNA. Furthermore, compaction of chromatin might confound DPC isolation attempts because very tight, but non-covalent, DNA-protein associations may not be stringently disrupted by all methods. Indeed, a very high level of "background" DPCs has been reported in some studies, suggesting insufficiently stringent isolation of "true" DPCs (reviewed in [1, 19]). The very fact that proteins are so tightly (even covalently, in some cases) associated with DNA as part of normal cellular processes raises the question of how cells are able to recognize DPCs as "damage". How inappropriately covalently-linked proteins (i.e., DPCs) are distinguished from appropriate covalent or very tight DNA-protein associations is clearly a critical question, and will be discussed in Section 5.

The impact of DNA-protein associations is particularly relevant when IR is the DNA-damaging agent because of the unique nature of damage induction with this agent. The occurrence of micro-heterogeneous "tracks" of ionization associated with the passage of charged particles through an aqueous medium results in regions of clustered/localized damage to DNA [30, 31] as well as the production of mobile damage (migration of radicals). Clustered lesions are considered to occur when 2 or more individual lesions are present within 1-2 helical turns of DNA. Understanding the role of DPCs in IR-induced damage is therefore complicated by the presence of other nearby lesions. For example, the presence of proximal lesions can influence the repair of both lesions ([32, 33] and references therein).

4. Biological Relevance

As noted above, the biological relevance of DPCs has been difficult to interpret due to the induction of these lesions in a background of many other types of DNA damage. This challenge will be partially overcome with the identification of DPC-inducers that have less complex damage profiles and induce more significant proportions of DPCs.

Since many DPC inducers also generate ICLs, studies using the novel furocoumarin analogs FQ and HQP (see Section 2), which induce DPCs but are not capable of generating ICLs, have provided some insight into the cellular consequences of DPCs. Both of these compounds have much stronger antiproliferative activity than the parent compound, 8MOP, in mammalian cells [34]. A direct correlation was observed between the induction of DPCs by these agents and the level of chromosomal aberrations [34, 35]. Chromatid aberrations (including sister chromatid exchanges, breaks and rings) were 2-3-fold higher for FQ versus HFQ, 8MOP and 4,5',8-trimethylpsoralen, suggesting that these types of aberrations are a result of DPCs and not ICLs [34, 35]. These data also suggest that DPCs induced by FQ are more damaging than those induced by HFQ, which occur by a chemically distinct mechanism; this observation indicates that DPC chemistry is a determinant of biological outcome. By 24 h post-treatment, FQ was also found to induce a much higher level of DNA double-strand breaks (DSBs) compared to the other two drugs, and it was inferred that DSBs are generated during DPC processing [35]. Interestingly, 4,5',8-trimethylpsoralen induces a greater level of DPCs than FQ and yet displays a lower amount of DSB induction and chromatid aberrations [35]. These authors proposed that the induction of ICLs by 4,5',8-trimethylpsoralen somehow traps proteins necessary for the repair of DPCs, thereby preventing their conversion to DSBs.

A protein covalently crosslinked to DNA would be expected to block progression of DNA replication and transcription complexes, and this outcome has been verified by a number of studies [3, 34-42]. The analysis of additional endpoints has not received as much attention. Although many DPC-inducing agents are known mutagens, the actual contribution of DPCs to this mutagenesis could not usually be ascertained, largely because of the above-mentioned concomitant induction of other types of damage. Several studies have shown increased cumulative DNA/chromosomal damage *in vivo* (gaps, breaks, sister chromatid exchanges, etc.) after exposure to known DPC-inducers (typically chromium, nickel, arsenic); however, these observations are again difficult to interpret due to the ability of these agents to induce multiple forms of DNA damage. Interestingly, an increased level of sister chromatid exchange was observed in Chinese hamster ovary (CHO) cells when they were exposed to X rays under hypoxic (versus aerated) conditions [43], an observation that the authors interpreted to suggest that IR-induced DPCs are responsible for these exchanges.

Recently, the Lloyd group assessed the mutagenic potential of DPCs in mammalian cells [44]. Synthetic DPC substrates were constructed by inducing a crosslink between a peptide amino group and the N6 position of deoxyadenosine or the N2 position of deoxyguanosine using acrolein-derived adducts. These crosslinks are Schiff-base-mediated and are therefore typical of aldehyde-induced crosslinks. The oligonucleotide (12 or 30-mer) with crosslinked peptide was inserted into a single-stranded shuttle vector. The outcome of replication of this vector in mammalian cells was then evaluated.

Table 1. Proteins previously found to be crosslinked to DNA *in vivo*

Protein	Nuclear Role(s)	Crosslinking Agent(s)
ARCHITECTURAL/STRUCTURAL		
Ninein	microtubule anchoring; localizes to nuclei in interphase [103]	IR [20]
Tubulin	component of microtubule organizing centre in nucleus [104]	IR [20]
Actin	nuclear scaffold, chromatin remodeling [105], regulation of DNA replication and/or transcription [106, 107], senescence marker [108]	IR [20] Chromium [48, 109] Cisplatin [110] Pyrrolizidine Alkaloids [111] Mitomycin C [112]
Cofilin	actin-regulatory protein; nuclear accumulation in senescence [108]	IR [20]
Tropomyosin	actin-regulatory protein	IR [20]
Radixin	actin organizing protein, localizes to nucleus [113]	IR [20]
HET/SAF-B	Nuclear scaffold [114]	Cisplatin [115]
Cytokeratins	Structural proteins	Arsenic [116]
CHROMATIN MODIFICATION		
Vimentin	chromatin remodeling, recombination [117]	IR [20] Formaldehyde[118] Metabolic byproducts[118]
Histone H1	Chromatin structure	IR [20] Formaldehyde [49]
Histone H2A	Chromatin structure, modified forms involved in DNA repair [119]	IR [20] Formaldehyde [49]
Histone H2B	Chromatin structure	IR [20] Formaldehyde [49]
Histone H3	Chromatin structure, telomere binding [120]	IR [20] Formaldehyde [49] Gilvocarcin V[50]
Histone H4	Chromatin structure, modified forms involved in DNA repair [119]	IR [20] Formaldehyde [49]
CGI-55 Protein	chromatin remodeling factor [121]	IR [20]
Histone deacetylase I	Histone modification	Cisplatin [115]
hnRNP K	mRNA processes, chromatin remodeling [122]	Cisplatin [115]
DNA METABOLIC TRANSACTIONS		
Polynucleotide Kinase, PNK	DNA repair	IR [20]
Poly(ADP) Ribose Polymease (PARP)	DNA repair	IR [20]
Splicing Factor - PTB Protein Associated	homologous pairing promoter [123]	IR [20]
Nuclease Sensitive Element Binding Protein 1	recognizes unusual DNA structures [124]	IR [20]

Protein	Nuclear Role(s)	Crosslinking Agent(s)
Glyceraldehyde 3-Phosphate Dehydrogenase	repair of thioguanylated DNA [125], transcription [107]	IR [20]
hnRNP A2/B1	mRNA splicing factor, telomere formation and/or stabilization [126], control of apoptosis [127]	IR [20]
hnRNP A1	mRNA splicing factor, FEN-1 stimulator [128], telomere formation and/or stabilization [126], control of apoptosis [127]	IR [20]
hnRNP C1/C2	mRNA processing, telomere maintenance [126]	Cisplatin [115]
Aminoglycoside nucleotidyl transferase	Nucleotidyl transfer	Chromium [48]
Lectin	Pre-mRNA splicing, cell cycle progression and apoptosis, unwinding and annealing activities, enhancers of DNA polymerase [129]	Chromium [48]
CELLULAR HOMEOSTASIS		
Calumenin/Crocalbin	Ca++ regulatory protein, localizes to ER and Golgi [130]	IR [20]
Alpha-2-Macroglobulin Receptor-Associated Protein	protein folding, localizes to ER [131]	IR [20]
Thioredoxin Peroxidase II	Oxidative stress response [132, 133], apoptosis inhibitor [134], maintenance of genome stability [135]	IR [20]
Serotransferrin Precursor	iron transport, transferrin localizes to endosomes [136]	IR [20]
Protein disulfide isomerase	Molecular chaperone	Cisplatin [137]
GDP/GTP BINDING		
Rho GDP-Dissociation Inhibitor 1 (GDI 1)	modulator of Rho GTPases; nuclear localization? [138, 139]	IR [20]
STRESS RESPONSE		
10kDa Heat Shock Protein, mitochondrial (chaperonin10)	Stress response, protein folding, localizes to mitochondria and secretory compartments [140]	IR [20]
78kDa Glucose Regulated Protein (GRP78)	stress response, protein folding; localizes to ER [141]	IR [20] Gilvocarcin V[50]
TRANSCRIPTION/RNA PROCESSING		
40S Ribosomal Protein S24	part of hnRNP complex involved in mRNA processing	IR [20]
TLS-Associated SR Protein, TASR-2	mRNA splicing factor; TLS is nuclear [142, 143]	IR [20]
hnRNP A3	mRNA splicing factor, nuclear localization [144]	IR [20]
Elongation Factor 1 alpha 1	actin organization, transcription; nuclear localization in apoptotic cells [145]	IR [20]
Estrogen receptor	Transcription factor	

Translesion synthesis allowed replication past the adducted peptide; however, differences were detected in the ability of each of these two types of DPCs to induce mutations. The most common types of mutation induced were base substitutions. Bypass of the peptide crosslinked through the N2 position of guanine (which would be expected to be in the minor groove of DNA – access to which is important for the binding/action of many enzymes, including DNA polymerases) generated an ~10-fold higher mutation frequency than bypass of the peptide crosslinked through the N6 position of adenine (which would be expected to be in the major groove) [44]. These results indicate that differences in DPC chemistry and orientation greatly affect the biological impact of these lesions. Previous work by the Lloyd group has indicated that the size of the crosslinked protein also influences the biological impact of these lesions [45, 46] (discussed in Section 5). The extent to which these crosslinks represent DPCs that would be encountered *in vivo* is not clear at this point as debate continues regarding whether or not DPCs are proteolytically processed *in vivo* (see Section 5).

Of major biological relevance is the identity of the specific proteins that become crosslinked to DNA. To date, the *in vivo* DNA-crosslinking of proteins with roles in various processes (including DNA repair, chromatin modification, cell cycle regulation, structural maintenance, stress response, and transcriptional regulation) has been reported (see Table 1). This list includes several familiar proteins with novel emerging roles in DNA-metabolic processes. As discussed in Section 3, the crosslinking of histones would be expected to cause serious consequences in all DNA transactions because essential chromatin modifications would be prevented. Several studies have demonstrated the crosslinking of histones to DNA by various agents [20, 47-50], and further work is needed to clarify the effect of these specific crosslinks on DNA-metabolic processes. Anchoring of proteins to DNA can impact on transcription by invoking conformational changes in the DNA-protein interface, thereby blocking access to promoters or trapping regulators on promoters. Indeed, in a large-scale study of cellular proteins crosslinked to DNA by IR, we identified several proteins with roles in transcription, including hnRNPs [20]. The relevance of this type of action may be difficult to assess given that it has now been proposed [17] that p53, a key genome regulator, has its binding activity modified through the very same processes that have been suggested to result in DPC formation [13, 16] (see Section 3).

DPCs may also exert detrimental effects by trapping/sequestering proteins needed for DNA repair (see Section 5). Crosslinking of repair proteins to DNA during attempted repair events has been previously noted for a number of prokaryotic and eukaryotic enzymes including *E. coli* endonuclease III and endonuclease VIII and mammalian NEIL1, DNA polymerase β and XRCC1 ([51], and reviewed in [1] and [52]). These findings have led to the suggestion that the level of *in vivo* oxidative stress (i.e., damage load) can overwhelm DNA polymerase β-dependent long-patch base excision repair (BER) and result in the use of the short-patch BER pathway, which is more prone to DPC formation between the repair intermediate 2-deoxyribonolactone (a modified deoxyribose moiety) and polymerase β [52, 53]. Investigations have been carried out to clarify the relevance of the crosslinking of DNA polymerase β to *in vivo* DNA transactions [54]. In one study, mouse embryonic fibroblast cells deficient in DNA polymerase β were shown to be markedly sensitive to IR relative to wild-type cells, but only when confluent [55]. This group has suggested that polymerase β is involved in the cellular response to IR, but that there is likely an additional short-patch repair mechanism for abasic sites that involves an alternative polymerase. The Demple group has suggested the possibility that long-patch BER can be overwhelmed under conditions of extensive oxidative stress and thus some damage will be repaired by short-patch BER [52], which could result in the induction of additional DPCs. Taken together, these studies suggest that the interplay between a number of DNA-repair pathways modulated by the level of oxidative stress in the cell will play a part in determining the fate of 2-deoxyribonolactone residues. Perhaps it is the impact of DPCs on DNA polymerase progression that signals the use of the long-patch repair mechanism – possibly to avoid reaction with these modified deoxyribose substrates?

Crosslinking of DNA-repair proteins to DNA in mammalian cells exposed to IR has also been demonstrated by us using a proteomics approach (see [20] and Table 1). The proteomics approach was complemented and extended by immunodetection using antibodies to additional known DNA-repair proteins; repair enzymes such as poly(ADP-ribose) polymerase (PARP) and polynucleotide kinase/phosphatase (PNKP) were indeed involved in such lesions.

Other close, functionally-critical, associations of DNA with proteins could also be affected by DNA-crosslinking. It has recently been demonstrated that genetic loci are physically transported to Cajal bodies for transcription *in vivo* in mammalian cells through an actin-dependent mechanism [56]. This study also demonstrated that disrupting actin prevented this movement and would therefore alter transcription [56]. Similarly, a role for nuclear actin in chromatin remodeling at sites of DSBs has been suggested (Dr. Michael Hendzel, personal communication). Our analysis of IR-induced crosslinks demonstrated that actin and a number of actin regulatory proteins all become crosslinked to DNA after γ-ray exposure [20]. The anchoring of transcription machinery would have serious consequences for the expression of numerous proteins and warrants further investigation.

The persistence of DPCs will be another important consideration for their biological relevance. As with many other aspects of the DPC literature, there are conflicting reports regarding the time-course of these lesions. Such differences are likely due to the diversity of chemically-distinct DPCs induced by the various DPC-inducing agents used. For example, formaldehyde and acetaldehyde-induced DPCs have been shown to be hydrolytically unstable [57-59], whereas DPCs induced by malondialdehyde are stable for weeks [60]. The DPCs induced by guanine radical cation reactions in nucleosome core particles (NCPs) *in vitro* are also chemically stable, persisting for at least 2 days at 37°C [16].

Several lines of evidence suggest that some cellular DPCs are also longer lived than most other forms of DNA damage, such that these lesions have the potential for greater/continued impact on cellular processes. For example, DPCs induced by sodium dichromate persisted after 36 h in rat kidney and lung cells, but not in liver cells [61]. Our measurements of IR-induced DPCs in mammalian cells demonstrated that these lesions are present at levels significantly above background even as late as 50 h post-exposure [62] (Figure 4). The induction of DPCs by IR was observed to increase in the initial hours following IR exposure, an interesting phenomenon indicating that there are secondary crosslinking reactions mediated by longer-lived species than the initial, rapid, radical-mediated reactions. Clearly, then, a variety of parameters can affect the time course of DNA-protein crosslinking. Our data further reveal that different proteins become crosslinked to and are removed from DNA with different kinetics, as illustrated in Figure 5 for DPCs involving vimentin and actin.

These particular blots are in fact representative of the two main types of crosslinking profiles that we observed.

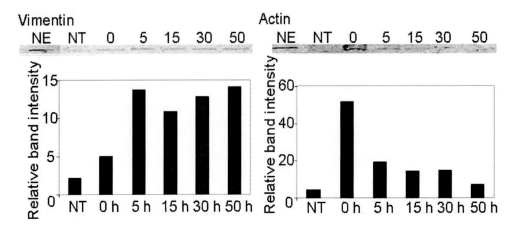

CHO cells were exposed to 1.5 Gy of γ-rays. DPCs were isolated, separated, and analyzed by Western blotting using antibodies to vimentin and actin. Fluorescently-labelled secondary antibodies were used and blots were analyzed and quantified as described [20].

Figure 5. Time-course of γ-ray-induced specific DPCs.

The delayed induction/persistent DPCs include those involving vimentin and PARP; the rapidly formed/removed DPCs include those involving actin and histone H2B. Interestingly, vimentin and PARP have roles in DNA repair, while actin and histone H2B have structural roles. Thus, "total" DPC time-course profiles are comprised of many different individual protein-crosslinking profiles and therefore may not be especially informative with respect to mechanism.

Consideration of the DPC time-course literature as a whole indicates that crosslinks can be induced by a number of separate mechanisms occurring simultaneously, but proceeding with very different kinetics. Crosslinks formed through reactions of free radicals would occur rapidly as the lifetimes of these very reactive species are short. Some oxidative intermediates, such as the charge initiated at the guanine radical cation (Section 2), can migrate through DNA, but this migration and the subsequent trapping reaction will also occur on a rapid timescale. The distance over which this charge migrates will depend on guanine-richness of sequence and on bound proteins and possibly other interactions [13]. Other species, such as protein carbonyls produced by oxidative damage of proteins, are chemically stable and capable of inducing DPCs on a longer time scale [2]. Other longer-lived DPC-inducers include reactive aldehydes and protein hydroperoxides. Determining the biological relevance of DNA-protein crosslinking events will require a thorough dissection and analysis of the individual crosslinking identities and kinetics. It should also be noted that some disagreement in DPC lifetime data is also likely attributable to the differences in the stringency and detection limits of methods for DPC isolation and analysis (reviewed in [1] and [19]).

5. DPC Repair

The involvement of various DNA-repair pathways in DPC removal has been scantly investigated. As mentioned earlier, the interpretation of much of the data gathered will be hindered by the presence of multiple types of DNA damage in cells treated with DPC-inducers, by the fact that many different forms of DPCs exist within that classification, because of the abovementioned complexity of the time-course of DPC formation and resolution, and because some types of DPCs may be released hydrolytically rather than by active repair (reviewed in [1]). To date, the data have suggested that both NER and HR might contribute to the enzymatic repair of DPCs (reviewed in [1]); however, many questions linger. Much of the data supporting the involvement of NER in DPC removal is predicated on the proteolytic processing of crosslinked proteins into small crosslinked peptides which are then excised by the NER machinery. It will be useful to clarify which pathways do in fact repair DPCs *in vivo*, how proteolysis is involved in DPC repair, and how DPCs are distinguished from appropriate (albeit tight) DNA-protein interactions.

It has previously been shown that both the bacterial and mammalian NER excision nucleases are capable of incising small peptides (8-12 amino acids) crosslinked to DNA, although excision efficiency does not appear to be strictly linearly correlated with size of peptide [40, 45, 46, 63], suggesting that conformation may also play a role in DPC recognition and repair. Furthermore, the bacterial NER system is capable of excising a larger crosslinked moiety, the 16 kDa T4 pyrimidine DNA glycosylase protein, whereas the mammalian NER system is not [40, 45, 46, 63]. As is frequently the case in studies of DNA-repair mechanisms, there can be significant differences in repair activities in eukaryotes versus prokaryotes. Differences in the processing of DPCs in bacterial versus mammalian systems have indeed been noted [4, 42]. These data also indicate that the nature of the crosslink will influence the individual cellular impact of these lesions. In agreement with this premise, more recent studies using bulky DPCs induced by platinating agents demonstrated that mammalian NER was incapable of excising "larger" crosslinked proteins, in this case, histone H1, which is only 22 kDa [3, 41].

The involvement of proteolysis in the NER of DPCs in mammalian cells continues to be investigated. Baker *et al.* [42] constructed synthetic DPCs using the HhaI DNA methyltransferase enzyme crosslinked to DNA (oligonucleotide or plasmid). Products of *in vitro* excision reactions by wild type, XPG-deficient, and XPG-complemented mammalian cell extracts were monitored. There was little excision of crosslinked proteins unless they were first proteolytically processed. *In vivo* assays involved monitoring repair of crosslink-containing plasmids in mammalian cells [42]. The plasmid was non-replicating and contained a radiolabel which was lost if the DPC was repaired. A second plasmid-based assay used in the same study looked for the reactivation of green fluorescent protein (GFP) subsequent to the repair of a site-specific DPC. Using both assays, significant repair was apparent. Additionally, treating the cells with a proteasome inhibitor reduced (to less than 50%) the restoration of GFP signal, indicating that the DPC repair observed *in vivo* is dependent on an active 26S proteasome. Significant (albeit ~30% reduced compared to wild type) restoration of GFP signal occurred in XPG-deficient cells, suggesting that XPG either does not have an essential role in the NER of DPCs or that (more likely) there are alternative DPC-repair pathways available *in vivo*.

The role of the direct proteolytic processing of DPCs in their removal is complicated by the fact that the proteasome has additional roles in NER and other repair responses. There is evidence to suggest that the ubiquitin-proteasome pathway interacts with the NER pathway (reviewed in [64]). In yeast, RNAPII transcription stalls when it encounters DNA damage, which results in both the recruitment of the NER machinery and the Def-1-dependent ubiquitination of RNAPII to target it for degradation by the 26S proteasome. Because there is evidence of coordination between DNA damage recognition and repair and proteasome activity, it is possible that the proteasome is also involved in degrading other proteins at the stall site. This review [64] also discussed earlier data indicating that the NER protein, Rad23, has two functions in NER. One function involves a Rad23-proteasome interaction that does not necessarily involve proteolytic activity. The second function is a putative E3 ubiquitin ligase activity involved in regulating Rad4 through its proteolytic degradation. Support for these functions comes from separate studies indicating that non-proteolytic functions of the proteasome pathway are involved in regulating NER [65-67]. Additionally, these studies [65-67] suggest a role for the novel E3 ubiquitin ligase of Rad23 in the proteolytic-dependent function of the proteasome in regulating NER through degradation of Rad4. A novel ubiquitin ligase activity has also been reported for the TFIIH transcription regulator, and it is thought to function in correlating transcription with the DNA-damage response [68]. These two novel ubiquitin ligases may function in controlling the transcriptional response to DNA damage [64]. This in turn may involve the ubiquitination and subsequent degradation of proteins crosslinked to DNA if the transcription complex collides with a DPC.

The role of proteolysis in DPC removal is further complicated when IR is the DPC-inducer because the proteasome is itself a target for IR-induced damage (and indeed for other forms of oxidative damage) [69]. Proteasome function was shown to be inhibited by even very low doses of IR and the activity recovered over a 24-h period [69]. This is particularly relevant when considering potential repair routes of IR-induced DPCs (see Section 5).

In contrast to these data with eukaryotic cells, the repair of DPCs by NER in bacteria may not be so dependent on proteolytic processing of the protein moiety. Mutants defective in any of the four *E. coli* cytosolic ATP-dependent proteases did not display either increased sensitivity to formaldehyde or azacytidine or a reduced rate of removal of crosslinked proteins, indicating that proteolysis is not involved in DPC removal [70]. To examine the influence of the size of crosslinked protein on DPC repair, a series of synthetic substrates with specific, oxanine-induced DPCs was constructed [70]. Oxanine is an endogenously induced form of base damage that readily reacts to form DPCs [71, 72]. Proteins used varied in size from 1.8 kDa to 44 kDa and included histones and DNA-repair proteins. Proteins were crosslinked to a 60-mer oligonucleotide and these substrates were assayed for excision by the bacterial NER proteins. Excision efficiency increased with size of crosslinked protein up to 2.1 kDa (which exhibited an excision efficiency of only 19%) and then decreased with crosslinked protein size. The mechanism by which NER incision is inhibited was investigated using gel-shift assays to measure the ability of each of these substrates to bind UvrA and load UvrB onto the DNA [70]. Larger crosslinked proteins inhibited the efficiency of UvrB-DNA complex formation such that UvrB was not efficiently bound to the DPC. These data indicate that larger DPCs are too bulky to accommodate binding of the NER proteins and therefore excision by NER is not possible.

Using *E. coli* mutants of various components of either NER or HR, the involvement of each of these repair pathways in DPC removal was assessed [70]. This study examined the removal of two chemically-different types of DPCs: those induced by formaldehyde and those induced by azacytidine. Azacytidine covalently crosslinks DNA methyltransferases to DNA; formaldehyde is capable of inducing multiple forms of damage, with DPCs involving various proteins being the most prominent. NER-deficient cells (uvrA) were hypersensitive to formaldehyde but not to azacytidine, whereas HR-deficient cells (recA) were hypersensitive to both of these DPC inducers.

Combining mutations in both NER and HR (uvrArecA) resulted in increased sensitivity to formaldehyde but not azacytidine, suggesting that NER and HR cooperate to remove formaldehyde-induced DPCs, whereas HR (but not NER) is involved in removing azacytidine-induced DPCs.

Removal of formaldehyde-induced DPCs was examined in wild type and NER-deficient uvrA cells by SDS/PAGE analysis [70]. Although the initial yield of protein crosslinking to DNA was similar in wild-type and uvrA cells, the wild-type cells lost smaller crosslinked proteins (≤11 kDa) at a faster rate than the mutant cells; however, both cell lines lost large DPCs at similar rates. Considered with the oxanine data discussed above, Nakano *et al.* [70] proposed that NER preferentially participates in the removal of DPCs involving smaller proteins.

To further dissect the role of HR in DPC repair, additional HR mutants were examined for sensitivity to DPC inducers [70]. *E. coli* mutants in the RecBCD pathway (which repairs DSBs) and the RecFOR pathway (which repairs daughter strand gaps) were tested for sensitivity to formaldehyde and azacytidine. The recB mutant was hypersensitive to both agents, while the recF mutant was sensitive to neither agent. This result implies that the RecFOR pathway is not involved in bacterial DPC repair, but the RecBCD pathway is, which further suggests that DPCs might be processed to DSBs during repair. Several cell lines (wild type, recF, recB, and recA) were used to examine the ability of DPCs to induce recombinogenic intermediates (that would necessitate repair by HR). The HR-deficient *E. coli* cell lines were transformed with a plasmid containing a formaldehyde-induced histone H1 crosslink. Recombination was stimulated by the presence of DPCs and appeared to require both recA and recB, although the induction of recombinants was not entirely abolished by recA mutation, indicating the potential involvement of a non-recA-dependent recombination pathway. Mutants in ruvA, ruvC, ruvABC, and recG were sensitive to both formaldehyde and azacytidine, indicating that the RuvABC Holliday junction resolvase and the RecG Holliday junction translocase/helicase activities are involved in the HR of DPCs. Nakano *et al.* [70] therefore proposed that if NER is involved in processing the smaller DPCs, then HR might be required to process DPCs that are too large for the NER machinery. It was further suggested [70] that DPCs are converted to DSBs before being processed by the recBCD pathway, although the mechanism of DSB creation is not yet clear (components of their model are included in Figure 6). DPCs do not appear to be converted to DSBs by a replication-dependent mechanism because the use of a polymerase III temperature-sensitive mutant did not result in accumulation of DPCs [70].

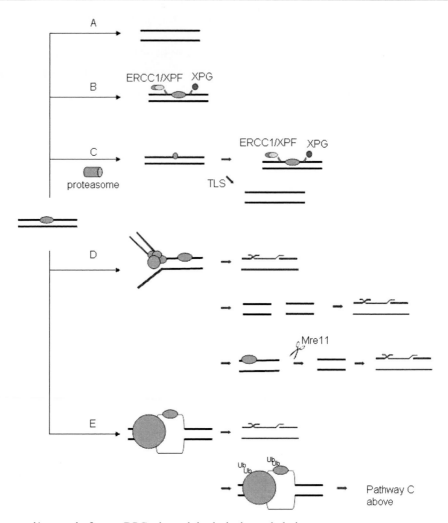

Passive removal/reversal of some DPCs through hydrolysis or chelation.

Removal of crosslinked proteins of < 12 kDa by nucleotide excision repair (NER).

Proteolysis of crosslinked protein to small DNA-bound peptide followed by NER. Saturation of NER results in persistence of the peptide crosslinks and translesion synthesis (TLS) results in mutagenesis.

A DPC leads to replication fork stalling which is restarted via homologous recombination (HR). A DPC could alternatively lead to the induction of a DSB at stalled forks; such DSBs would also be repaired by HR. There are also enzymes capable of digesting some specific protein-bound DNA ends (e.g., Tdp1, Mre11).

A DPC leads to transcription complex stalling which stimulates HR. Alternatively, this stalling might lead to the ubiquitination and consequent proteolytic degradation of stalled components (e.g., as occurs for RNAPII). This second process might work in cooperation with NER, which would then remove the proteolytically-digested DPC.

Figure 6. Key pathways participating in the removal of DPCs (adapted from [1, 70, 73]).

Studies using repair-deficient mutants have also shed some light on the role of HR in DPC repair in eukaryotic cells [73]. One such study used an extensive panel of DT40 chicken cell mutants defective in components of BER, NER, trans-lesion synthesis (TLS), HR, nonhomologous end joining (NHEJ), or cell cycle checkpoint regulation and assessed the sensitivity of these cells to formaldehyde, which is a by-product of normal cellular metabolism. Cells were therefore exposed to levels of formaldehyde that fall within the normal range for human plasma (13-97 μmol/L). Cells with defects in the BRCA/FANC pathway (HR) exhibited the greatest sensitivity. DT40 cells deficient in FANCD2 were the most sensitive, and cells deficient in FANCD1 (BRCA2) were also highly sensitive. Cells deficient in BRCA1, XRCC2, XRCC3, RAD51C, RAD51D, and RAD54 also all displayed increased sensitivity.The FANCD2/BRCA2 mutant cells displayed marked sensitivity at doses (10-15 μmol/L) well below average plasma levels (~80 μmol/L). This sensitivity and aberrant processing of DPCs might be relevant to cancer development in highly proliferating (e.g., bone marrow) cells in individuals with Fanconi's Anemia. Human FANCC and FANCG cells were also hypersensitive to plasma-like levels of formaldehyde, further supporting a role for this pathway in responding to DPCs [73]. The extremely sensitive FANCD2 cells were also tested for hypersensitivity to other DPC inducers: acetaldehyde, acrolein, crotonaldehyde, glyoxal, and methylglyoxal; but were only found to be sensitive to formaldehyde and acetaldehyde. This finding supports the prevailing idea that chemically-distinct DPCs induce different biological responses and are likely repaired by different mechanisms. The FANC/BRCA pathway involves the activation of FANCD2 via its mono-ubiquitination in response to stalling of replication forks. FANCD2 then interacts with BRCA1 at repair foci active in HR. The observation that mutants in this pathway are sensitive to DPC-inducers supports the hypothesis, as mentioned previously, that DPCs may cause stalling of replication forks and that this might be the mode of recognition of this type of DNA damage.

Additionally, some formaldehyde hypersensitivity was apparent in chicken cells defective in other pathways – including polβ (BER), PARP1 (BER and other pathways), XPA (NER), REV1, REV3 and RAD18 (TLS) mutants – indicating that HR is probably not the only pathway to function in the processing of formaldehyde-induced DPCs [73]. From these observations, Ridpath et al. [73] formulated a model for the possible interactions of the multiple repair pathways in eukaryotic cells that act to process DPCs (components of which are included in Figure 6).

Given the numerous studies indicating that DPCs are sufficiently bulky lesions to block the progression of DNA polymerases [3, 34-42, 63], it is reasonable to assume that the stalling of replication forks might underlie the biological consequences of these lesions. An additional study [63] demonstrated that DNA polymerase (phage T4 DNA polymerase) is blocked before reaching the site of protein crosslinking. It was therefore implied [63] that DPC repair is stimulated by replication fork stalling because this event could provide a simple mechanism for discrimination between tightly, but appropriately, bound proteins and covalent crosslink damage.

In preliminary investigations we have examined the removal of IR-induced DPCs from repair-proficient and NER- and/or HR-deficient mammalian cells. DPCs were induced by 1.5 Gy of IR and the cells were incubated for 0-50 h before DPCs were isolated and quantified (Figure 7). The CHO cell lines used were the parental AA8 strain, the NER-deficient strain UV24 (XPB⁻), the NER/HR-deficient strains UV20 (ERCC1⁻) and UV41 (XPF⁻), and the HR-deficient strain irs1SF (XRCC3⁻). DPCs in both the parental and mutant strains were found to be very persistent; the levels were still markedly above background at 50 h post-irradiation. It was apparent that DPC levels continued to increase following irradiation, suggesting the operation of delayed DPC-induction mechanisms in addition to the rapid free radical-mediated reactions.

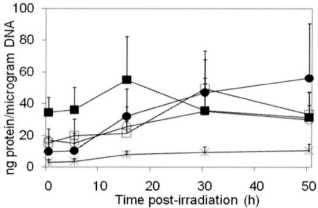

CHO AA8 (■), UV20 (●), UV24 (✱), UV41 (□) and irs1SF (○) cells were exposed to 1.5 Gy of γ-rays. DPCs were either isolated immediately, or cells were incubated at 37°C for 5-50 h to allow metabolic processing. DPCs were isolated, analyzed, and quantified according to the method of Barker *et al.* [19].

Figure 7. Total DPC formation and removal in wild-type and repair-deficient CHO cells.

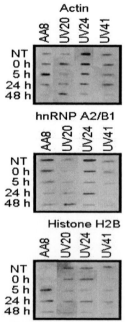

DPCs were induced, isolated and analyzed as above. Protein isolates were slot-blotted on nitrocellulose membranes and probed with antibodies to specific proteins previously shown to be crosslinked to DNA. Signals from labelled secondary antibodies were captured on Kodak X-OMAT film.

Figure 8. Comparison of time course of specific DPCs in wild-type and repair-deficient CHO cells.

The DPC time-course profiles revealed subtle differences among the cell types: whereas DPCs induced in parental AA8 cells peaked at ~15 h and then decreased slightly, the DPCs induced in the NER- and/or HR-deficient mutants continued to increase throughout the time period analyzed. Thus, NER and HR do appear to be involved in removing a sub-group of DPCs in the rodent background.

We do not understand why the repair-deficient mutant cells, and particularly the UV24 (XPB⁻) strain, showed unexpectedly low levels of IR-induced DPCs, especially at the early time points. However, it should be noted that these mutants were derived from severely mutagenized AA8 cultures and as yet we have no DPC data for complemented cell lines derived from these mutants, which should clarify any putative role of the repair protein defect *per se* in these events.

Analysis of the DPC-induction profiles of specific proteins using Western blotting analysis (Figure 8) revealed that different proteins (illustrated here by actin, hnRNP A2/B1 and histone H2B) become crosslinked to DNA with different kinetics and are therefore likely crosslinked by different reactions. Again, this complexity adds to the challenge of determining the biological relevance of the crosslinking of specific proteins.

There are other possible mechanisms for the removal/repair of cellular DPCs. One possibility that has been under investigation is the ability of the tyrosyl-DNA phosphodiesterase (Tdp1) to excise different DPCs. This enzyme was first characterized for its ability to cleave DNA topoisomerase I (TopI) bound to a 3'-DNA end [74]. Yeast Tdp1 is also capable of excising peptides covalently bound to DNA by a 5'-phosphotyrosyl linkage [75], and Tdp1-deficient yeast cells are sensitive to topoisomerase II-induced damage [75]. Human Tdp1 can cleave a number of different substrates, including the DNA-protein linkage created between Tdp1 molecules and the 3'-end of DNA as part of its own reaction mechanism [76]. Combining Tdp1 deficiency with other mutations has demonstrated additional pathways for removing TopI-mediated damage which rely on nucleases and other proteins involved in NER and HR (Rad1-10, Rad52, Mus81) [77, 78]. Thus, it is possible that multiple pathways are available for the removal of protein-bound DNA. One such pathway might involve the digestion of the protein-bound DNA by the Mre11 nuclease which has been shown to digest the Spo11 DPC created during meiosis [79] and may yet be found to have wider substrate specificity. Mre11 may be involved in processing several structures encountered during DNA transactions [80]. Thus, the existence of additional enzymatic activities capable of digesting DNA with covalently-bound protein cannot be ruled out.

6. Advances in Cancer Therapeutics

DPCs are induced by some antitumor agents including IR and several chemotherapeutic drugs (alkylating/platinating agents) (reviewed in [1]). The contribution of DPCs to the cytotoxic effects of these drugs is beginning to emerge and such knowledge will advance the understanding of clinical effectiveness and drug tolerance. Production of DPCs targeted to tumor cells has the potential for therapeutic benefit [81-85]. Advances in understanding DPC chemistry and consequences will allow the development of more clinically-effective therapeutic approaches. Several groups are already developing and investigating additional DPC-inducing agents for potential clinical use.

Whereas transplatin has proven clinically ineffective, novel trans-platinated compounds have been identified that are potent DPC-inducers and display increased cytotoxicity relative to cisplatin. These compounds are capable of inducing DPCs to a much greater extent and therefore must have a different mode of cytotoxicity than cisplatin. One of these novel platinated drugs is a platinum-iminoether complex, which is not only more cytotoxic than cisplatin, but also demonstrated significant anti-tumor activity in both cisplatin-sensitive and -resistant cells [86-88]. Additionally, the DPC adducts of this compound inhibited both progression of DNA polymerase and excision activity of the NER nuclease [3, 41].

Another well-studied anticancer agent that induced both ICLs and DPCs is mitomycin C (MMC). The clinical utility of MMC is limited by its toxicity, although a number of new MMC-related compounds are being developed. The FR family of anti-tumor antibiotics is a novel class of anti-tumor drugs typified by FR900482, a naturally-occurring compound discovered in a screen for anti-tumor agents [89]. Unlike MMC, FR900482 induces specific DPCs. This compound was capable of crosslinking proteins that bind in the minor groove of DNA (HMG I/Y, HMG-1, HMG-2), but not proteins that bind in the major groove [90]. The DPC-inducing ability of the FR family of compounds has been suggested to be a novel anti-tumor mechanism of these drugs [90]. While FR900482 was initially thought to be a more clinically promising drug than MMC because of its reduced toxicity and distinct mechanism of action, it is no longer undergoing clinical trials. However, the knowledge gained from these studies has allowed the development of a number of derivatives of this compound which are being investigated for anti-tumor activity and clinical utility. In addition to FR900482, FK317 and FR66979 have both been shown to induce DPCs [91]. FK317 has advanced from phase I to phase II clinical trials [91] and studies continue on this and related compounds. Another recently developed FR derivative has been reported to induce DPCs and to significantly inhibit both transcription and nucleosome assembly on DNA *in vitro* [91].

Another novel compound, 2, 5-bis(5-hydroxymethyl-2-thienyl)furan (NSC 652287), was identified in the NCI Anticancer Drug Screen and has demonstrated potent and selective anti-tumour activity [92]. NSC 652287 was shown to induce persistent DPCs that correlated with cytotoxicity [93]. NSC 652287 has been termed "RITA" in more recent studies due to the discovery that it is able to Reactivate p53 and Induce Tumour cell Apoptosis [18]. RITA was shown to bind wild-type p53 and induce its accumulation in tumour cells [18]. Furthermore, binding of p53 by RITA induces a conformational change in wild-type p53 that reduces the ability of p53 to bind to negative regulators, including HDM-2, an interaction that is critical for targeting p53 for proteolytic degradation. Previous work on this compound suggested that DPCs were important in the cytotoxic mechanism [93], and the results of Issaeva *et al.* [18] indicate that complex formation between RITA and p53 is important, but there was no assessment made of whether or not p53 or its negative regulators are in fact crosslinked to DNA in this mechanism [18]. Alternatively, the binding of p53 by RITA may alter the DNA-CT p53 regulatory mechanism, which is thought to control the interaction of p53 with some of its binding partners (discussed in Section 2). A mechanism involving covalent crosslinking has not been ruled out. Augustyn *et al.* [17] suggested that the presence of RITA does not interfere with p53 regulation by charge transport; however the exact mechanism by which RITA influences p53 protein-partner binding is still unclear.

Yet another compound identified in the NCI Anticancer Drug Screen is 5-amino-2,3-fluorophenyl-6,8-difluoro-7-*methyl*-4*H*-1-benzopyran-4-one (NSC 686288) [94]. This compound is an aminoflavone and exhibits potent anti-tumor activity, but its mechanism of action has not yet been fully elucidated. DPCs are suspected to contribute to the cytotoxic effects of NSC 686288 as it induces high levels of DPCs, ~10-fold more DPCs than single strand breaks [94]. The induction of DPCs and histone H2AX phosphorylation/focus formation by this agent was concentration-dependent, suggesting that DPCs interfere with DNA replication, possibly inducing DSBs, although further details regarding the interplay of DPCs with replication progression are needed.

DPCs induced by these two novel anti-tumor candidates have also been shown to be persistent. DPCs induced by NSC 652287 were still present 12 h after removal of drug and their levels correlated with cytotoxicity [93]. Similarly, NSC 686288-induced DPCs were also found to persist; these DPCs showed no decrease in their levels by 3 h after drug removal [95].

These studies allow us some insight into the mechanisms of action of DPC inducers as well as on the role of DPCs in cytotoxicity. As additional screens are performed, more clinically-effective drugs will be discovered. This expanded knowledge will allow further refinements in the design of novel drugs. Advances in understanding DPC induction and its biological relevance will not only allow the development of novel chemotherapeutic approaches, but will also identify additional approaches for protection and prevention of carcinogenesis. Measurements of total or protein-specific DPCs can be developed as tools in biomonitoring for exposure to DPC-inducing agents (e.g., as has been attempted with formaldehyde exposure [96-98] and industrial or environmental exposure to particular metal compounds [99-101]) as well as for baseline DPC levels which would be a reflection of total environmental exposure (cigarette smoke, combustion products, IR, etc.) [102].

7. Conclusion

The role of DPCs in the biological effects of numerous genotoxic agents is beginning to be appreciated. These lesions can be extremely persistent and can clearly result in the accumulation of various types of chromosomal damage. DPCs are induced by multiple different chemistries operating with distinct kinetics, and these lesions are repaired by more than one route. It is likely that at least some DPCs result in stalling of the replication or transcription machinery and that such events serve to activate their recognition and repair, which would provide a cell with a reasonable means for distinguishing inappropriate DNA-protein associations (i.e., DPCs) from the many appropriate DNA-protein associations occurring in the very dynamic chromatin environment. Because proteins with a wide variety of functions can become crosslinked to DNA on exposure to DPC-inducing agents, it would be beneficial to more thoroughly dissect the "total" DPC-induction profiles to determine which crosslinks are of greatest biological consequence. In order to target the impact of these lesions for maximum therapeutic benefit, there are many additional questions to be answered.

References

[1] Barker, S.L., M. Weinfeld, and D. Murray, DNA-protein crosslinks: their induction, repair and biological consequences. *Mutat. Res.*, 2005. 589(2): p. 111-135.

[2] Xie, J., R. Fan, and Z. Meng, Protein oxidation and DNA-protein crosslink induced by sulfur dioxide in lungs, livers, and hearts from mice. *Inhal Toxicol*, 2007. 19(9): p. 759-65.

[3] Chvalova, K., V. Brabec, and J. Kasparkova, Mechanism of the formation of DNA-protein cross-links by antitumor cisplatin. *Nucleic Acids Res*, 2007. 35(6): p. 1812-21.

[4] Bordin, F., et al., DNA damage induced by 4,6,8,9-tetramethyl-2H-furo[2,3-h]quinolin-2-one, a new furocoumarin analog: photochemical mechanisms. *Photochem. Photobiol*, 2000. 71(3): p. 254-62.

[5] Dizdaroglu, M. and E. Gajewski, Structure and mechanism of hydroxyl radical-induced formation of a DNA-protein cross-link involving thymine and lysine in nucleohistone. *Cancer Res.*, 1989. 49(13): p. 3463-7.

[6] Dizdaroglu, M., et al., Structure of a hydroxyl radical induced DNA-protein cross-link involving thymine and tyrosine in nucleohistone. *Biochemistry*, 1989. 28(8): p. 3625-8.

[7] Dizdaroglu, M. and M.G. Simic, Radiation-induced crosslinking of cytosine. *Radiat. Res.*, 1984. 100(1): p. 41-6.

[8] Dizdaroglu, M. and M.G. Simic, Radiation-induced crosslinks between thymine and phenylalanine. Int. J. Radiat. Biol. Relat. Stud. Phys. *Chem. Med.*, 1985. 47(1): p. 63-9.

[9] Gajewski, E., A.F. Fuciarelli, and M. Dizdaroglu, Structure of hydroxyl radical-induced DNA-protein crosslinks in calf thymus nucleohistone in vitro. *Int. J. Radiat. Biol.*, 1988. 54(3): p. 445-59.

[10] Karam, L.R., M. Dizdaroglu, and M.G. Simic, Intramolecular H atom abstraction from the sugar moiety by thymine radicals in oligo- and polydeoxynucleotides. *Radiat. Res.*, 1988. 116(2): p. 210-6.

[11] Margolis, S.A., et al., Structure of a hydroxyl radical induced cross-link of thymine and tyrosine. *Biochemistry*, 1988. 27(17): p. 6353-9.

[12] Gajewski, E. and M. Dizdaroglu, Hydroxyl radical induced cross-linking of cytosine and tyrosine in nucleohistone. *Biochemistry*, 1990. 29(4): p. 977-80.

[13] Perrier, S., et al., Characterization of lysine-guanine cross-links upon one-electron oxidation of a guanine-containing oligonucleotide in the presence of a trilysine peptide. *J. Am. Chem. Soc*, 2006. 128(17): p. 5703-10.

[14] Henderson, P.T., et al., Long-distance charge transport in duplex DNA: the phonon-assisted polaron-like hopping mechanism. *Proc. Natl. Acad. Sci. U S A*, 1999. 96(15): p. 8353-8.

[15] Nunez, M.E., D.B. Hall, and J.K. Barton, Long-range oxidative damage to DNA: effects of distance and sequence. *Chem. Biol*, 1999. 6(2): p. 85-97.

[16] Bjorklund, C.C. and W.B. Davis, Stable DNA-protein cross-links are products of DNA charge transport in a nucleosome core particle. *Biochemistry*, 2007. 46(38): p. 10745-55.

[17] Augustyn, K.E., E.J. Merino, and J.K. Barton, A role for DNA-mediated charge transport in regulating p53: Oxidation of the DNA-bound protein from a distance. *Proc. Natl. Acad. Sci.* U S A, 2007. 104(48): p. 18907-12.

[18] Issaeva, N., et al., Small molecule RITA binds to p53, blocks p53-HDM-2 interaction and activates p53 function in tumors. *Nat. Med*, 2004. 10(12): p. 1321-8.

[19] Barker, S., et al., A method for the isolation of covalent DNA-protein crosslinks suitable for proteomics analysis. *Anal. Biochem.*, 2005. 344(2): p. 204-215.

[20] Barker, S., et al., Identification of mammalian proteins cross-linked to DNA by ionizing radiation. *J. Biol. Chem*, 2005. 280(4): p. 33826-33838.

[21] Fornace, A.J., Jr., Detection of DNA single-strand breaks produced during the repair of damage by DNA-protein cross-linking agents. *Cancer Res.*, 1982. 42(1): p. 145-9.

[22] Fornace, A.J., Jr. and J.B. Little, DNA crosslinking induced by x-rays and chemical agents. *Biochim. Biophys. Acta*, 1977. 477(4): p. 343-55.

[23] Meyn, R.E., W.T. Jenkins, and D. Murray, Radiation damage to DNA in various animal tissues: Comparison of yields and repair in vivo and in vitro, in Mechanisms of DNA Damage and Repair: Implications to Carcinogenesis and Risk Assessment, M.G. Simic, L. Grossman, and A.C. Upton, Editors. 1986, Plenum Press: New York. p. 151-158.

[24] Meyn, R.E., S.C. vanAnkeren, and W.T. Jenkins, The induction of DNA-protein crosslinks in hypoxic cells and their possible contribution to cell lethality. *Radiat. Res.*, 1987. 109(3): p. 419-29.

[25] Xue, L.Y., L.R. Friedman, and N.L. Oleinick, Repair of chromatin damage in glutathione-depleted V-79 cells: comparison of oxic and hypoxic conditions. *Radiat. Res.*, 1988. 116(1): p. 89-99.

[26] Groth, A., et al., Regulation of replication fork progression through histone supply and demand. *Science,* 2007. 318(5858): p. 1928-31.

[27] Groth, A., et al., Chromatin challenges during DNA replication and repair. *Cell*, 2007. 128(4): p. 721-33.

[28] Monks, T.J., et al., Ros-induced histone modifications and their role in cell survival and cell death. *Drug Metab. Rev*, 2006. 38(4): p. 755-67.

[29] Murga, M., et al., Global chromatin compaction limits the strength of the DNA damage response. *J. Cell Biol.*, 2007. 178(7): p. 1101-8.

[30] Ward, J.F., The complexity of DNA damage: relevance to biological consequences. *Int. J. Radiat. Biol*, 1994. 66(5): p. 427-32.

[31] Goodhead, D.T., Initial events in the cellular effects of ionizing radiations: clustered damage in DNA. *Int. J. Radiat. Biol*, 1994. 65(1): p. 7-17.

[32] Lomax, M.E., S. Cunniffe, and P. O'Neill, Efficiency of repair of an abasic site within DNA clustered damage sites by mammalian cell nuclear extracts. *Biochemistry*, 2004. 43(34): p. 11017-26.

[33] Weinfeld, M., et al., Response of base excision repair enzymes to complex DNA lesions. *Radiat. Res*, 2001. 156(5 Pt 2): p. 584-9.

[34] Marzano, C., et al., DNA damage induced by 4,6,8,9-tetramethyl-2H-furo[2,3-h]quinolin-2-one, a new furocoumarin analog: biological consequences. *Photochem. Photobiol,* 2000. 71(3): p. 263-72.

[35] Marzano, C., E. Severin, and F. Bordin, Can a mixed damage interfere with DNA-protein cross-links repair? *J. Cell Mol.Med*, 2001. 5(2): p. 171-7.

[36] Bedinger, P., et al., Properties of the T4 bacteriophage DNA replication apparatus: the T4 dda DNA helicase is required to pass a bound RNA polymerase molecule. *Cell*, 1983. 34(1): p. 115-23.

[37] Pinto, A.L. and S.J. Lippard, Sequence-dependent termination of in vitro DNA synthesis by cis- and trans-diamminedichloroplatinum (II). *Proc. Natl. Acad. Sci.* USA, 1985. 82(14): p. 4616-9.

[38] Briggs, J.A. and R.C. Briggs, Characterization of chromium effects on a rat liver epithelial cell line and their relevance to in vitro transformation. *Cancer Res.*, 1988. 48(22): p. 6484-90.

[39] Heck, H. and M. Casanova, Pharmacodynamics of formaldehyde: applications of a model for the arrest of DNA replication by DNA-protein cross-links. *Toxicol. Appl. Pharmacol*, 1999. 160(1): p. 86-100.

[40] Reardon, J.T. and A. Sancar, Repair of DNA-polypeptide crosslinks by human excision nuclease. *Proc. Natl. Acad. Sci.* U S A, 2006. 103(11): p. 4056-61.

[41] Novakova, O., et al., DNA-protein cross-linking by trans-[PtCl(2)(E-iminoether)(2)]. A concept for activation of the trans geometry in platinum antitumor complexes. *Nucleic Acids Res.*, 2003. 31(22): p. 6450-60.

[42] Baker, D.J., et al., Nucleotide excision repair eliminates unique DNA-protein cross-links from mammalian cells. *J. Biol. Chem.*, 2007. 282(31): p. 22592-604.

[43] Tofilon, P.J. and R.E. Meyn, Enhancement of X-ray-induced sister chromatid exchanges in hypoxic cells. *Radiat Res*, 1987. 109(3): p. 449-55.

[44] Minko, I.G., et al., Mutagenic potential of DNA-peptide crosslinks mediated by acrolein-derived DNA adducts. *Mutat. Res*, 2008. 637(1-2): p. 161-72.

[45] Minko, I.G., Y. Zou, and R.S. Lloyd, Incision of DNA-protein crosslinks by UvrABC nuclease suggests a potential repair pathway involving nucleotide excision repair. *Proc. Natl. Acad. Sci.* USA, 2002. 99(4): p. 1905-1909.

[46] Minko, I.G., et al., Initiation of repair of DNA-polypeptide cross-links by the UvrABC nuclease. *Biochemistry*, 2005. 44(8): p. 3000-9.

[47] Mee, L.K. and S.J. Adelstein, Predominance of core histones in formation of DNA-protein crosslinks in gamma-irradiated chromatin. *Proc. Natl. Acad. Sci.* USA, 1981. 78(4): p. 2194-8.

[48] Mattagajasingh, S.N. and H.P. Misra, Analysis of EDTA-chelatable proteins from DNA-protein crosslinks induced by a carcinogenic chromium (VI) in cultured intact human cells. *Mol. Cell. Biochem.*, 1999. 199: p. 149-162.

[49] O'Connor, P.M. and B.W. Fox, Isolation and characterization of proteins cross-linked to DNA by the antitumor agent methylene dimethanesulfonate and its hydrolytic product formaldehyde. *J. Biol. Chem.*, 1989. 264(11): p. 6391-7.

[50] Matsumoto, A. and P.C. Hanawalt, Histone H3 and heat shock protein GRP78 are selectively cross-linked to DNA by photoactivated Gilvocarcin V in human fibroblasts. *Cancer Res.*, 2000. 60: p. 3921-3926.

[51] Nazarkina, Z.K., et al., XRCC1 interactions with base excision repair DNA intermediates. DNA Repair (Amst), 2007. 6(2): p. 254-64.

[52] Sung, J.S. and B. Demple, Roles of base excision repair subpathways in correcting oxidized abasic sites in DNA. *Febs J*, 2006. 273(8): p. 1620-9.

[53] DeMott, M.S., et al., Covalent trapping of human DNA polymerase beta by the oxidative DNA lesion 2-deoxyribonolactone. *J. Biol. Chem.*, 2002. 277(10): p. 7637-40.

[54] Sung, J.S., M.S. Demott, and B. Demple, Long-patch Base Excision DNA Repair of 2-Deoxyribonolactone Prevents the Formation of DNA-Protein Cross-links with DNA Polymerase {beta}. *J. Biol. Chem*, 2005. 280(47): p. 39095-103.

[55] Vermeulen, C., et al., Role for DNA polymerase beta in response to ionizing radiation. DNA Repair (Amst), 2007. 6(2): p. 202-12.

[56] Dundr, M., et al., Actin-dependent intranuclear repositioning of an active gene locus in vivo. *J. Cell Biol*, 2007. 179(6): p. 1095-103.

[57] Quievryn, G. and A. Zhitkovich, Loss of DNA-protein crosslinks from formaldehyde-exposed cells occurs through spontaneous hydrolysis and an active repair process linked to proteosome function. *Carcinogenesis*, 2000. 21(8): p. 1573-1580.

[58] Kuykendall, J.R. and M.S. Bogdanffy, Formation and stability of acetaldehyde-induced crosslinks between poly-lysine and poly-deoxyguanosine. *Mutat. Res.*, 1994. 311(1): p. 49-56.

[59] Costa, M., et al., DNA-protein cross-links produced by various chemicals in cultured human lymphoma cells. *J. Toxicol. Environ. Health*, 1997. 50(5): p. 433-449.

[60] Voitkun, V. and A. Zhitkovich, Analysis of DNA-protein crosslinking activity of malondialdehyde in vitro. *Mutat. Res.*, 1999. 424: p. 97-106.

[61] Tsapakos, M.J., T.H. Hampton, and K.E. Wetterhahn, Chromium(VI)-induced DNA lesions and chromium distribution in rat kidney, liver, and lung. *Cancer Res.*, 1983. 43(12 Pt 1): p. 5662-7.

[62] Barker, S., M. Weinfeld, and D. Murray, Low-dose ionizing radiation-induced DNA-protein crosslinks are persistent lesions in mammalian cells. in preparation, 2008.

[63] Reardon, J.T., Y. Cheng, and A. Sancar, Repair of DNA-protein cross-links in mammalian cells. *Cell Cycle*, 2006. 5(13): p. 1366-70.

[64] Reed, S.H. and T.G. Gillette, Nucleotide excision repair and the ubiquitin proteasome pathway--do all roads lead to Rome? DNA Repair (Amst), 2007. 6(2): p. 149-56.

[65] Gillette, T.G., et al., Distinct functions of the ubiquitin-proteasome pathway influence nucleotide excision repair. *Embo J*, 2006. 25(11): p. 2529-38.

[66] Gillette, T.G., et al., Physical and functional association of RNA polymerase II and the proteasome. *Proc. Natl. Acad. Sci.* U S A, 2004. 101(16): p. 5904-9.

[67] Gillette, T.G., et al., The 19S complex of the proteasome regulates nucleotide excision repair in yeast. *Genes. Dev*, 2001. 15(12): p. 1528-39.

[68] Takagi, Y., et al., Ubiquitin ligase activity of TFIIH and the transcriptional response to DNA damage. *Mol. Cell*, 2005. 18(2): p. 237-43.

[69] McBride, W.H., et al., The role of the ubiquitin/proteasome system in cellular responses to radiation. *Oncogene*, 2003. 22(37): p. 5755-73.

[70] Nakano, T., et al., Nucleotide excision repair and homologous recombination systems commit differentially to the repair of DNA-protein crosslinks. *Mol. Cell*, 2007. 28(1): p. 147-58.

[71] Nakano, T., et al., DNA-protein cross-link formation mediated by oxanine. A novel genotoxic mechanism of nitric oxide-induced DNA damage. *J. Biol. Chem.*, 2003. 278(27): p. 25264-72.

[72] Nakano, T., et al., Activity of nucleotide excision repair enzymes for oxanine cross-link lesions. Nucleic Acids Symp Ser (Oxf), 2005(49): p. 293-4.

[73] Ridpath, J.R., et al., Cells deficient in the FANC/BRCA pathway are hypersensitive to plasma levels of formaldehyde. *Cancer Res*, 2007. 67(23): p. 11117-22.

[74] Pouliot, J.J., et al., Yeast gene for a Tyr-DNA phosphodiesterase that repairs topoisomerase I complexes. *Science*, 1999. 286(5439): p. 552-5.

[75] Nitiss, K.C., et al., Tyrosyl-DNA phosphodiesterase (Tdp1) participates in the repair of Top2-mediated DNA damage. *Proc. Natl. Acad. Sci.* U S A, 2006. 103(24): p. 8953-8.

[76] Interthal, H., H.J. Chen, and J.J. Champoux, Human Tdp1 cleaves a broad spectrum of substrates, including phosphoamide linkages. *J. Biol. Chem*, 2005. 280(43): p. 36518-28.

[77] Vance, J.R. and T.E. Wilson, Yeast Tdp1 and Rad1-Rad10 function as redundant pathways for repairing Top1 replicative damage. *Proc. Natl. Acad. Sci.* U S A, 2002. 99(21): p. 13669-74.

[78] Liu, C., J.J. Pouliot, and H.A. Nash, Repair of topoisomerase I covalent complexes in the absence of the tyrosyl-DNA phosphodiesterase Tdp1. *Proc. Natl. Acad. Sci.* U S A, 2002. 99(23): p. 14970-5.

[79] Neale, M.J., J. Pan, and S. Keeney, Endonucleolytic processing of covalent protein-linked DNA double-strand breaks. *Nature*, 2005. 436(7053): p. 1053-7.

[80] Hopfner, The Mre11/Rad50/Nbs1 Complex, in DNA Damage Recognition, W. Siede, Y.W. Kow, and P.W. Doetsch, Editors. 2005, Taylor and Francis: New York. p. 711-719.

[81] Larsen, A.K., et al., Unusual potency of BN 80915, a novel fluorinated E-ring modified camptothecin, toward human colon carcinoma cells. *Cancer Res*, 2001. 61(7): p. 2961-7.

[82] Poddevin, B., et al., Dual topoisomerase I and II inhibition by intoplicine (RP-60475), a new antitumor agent in early clinical trials. *Mol. Pharmacol*, 1993. 44(4): p. 767-74.

[83] Vladu, B., et al., 7- and 10-substituted camptothecins: dependence of topoisomerase I-DNA cleavable complex formation and stability on the 7- and 10-substituents. *Mol. Pharmacol*, 2000. 57(2): p. 243-51.

[84] Topcu, Z., DNA topoisomerases as targets for anticancer drugs. *J. Clin. Pharm. Ther*, 2001. 26(6): p. 405-16.

[85] Gowher, H. and A. Jeltsch, Mechanism of inhibition of DNA methyltransferases by cytidine analogs in cancer therapy. *Cancer Biol. Ther*, 2004. 3(11): p. 1062-8.

[86] Coluccia, M., et al., A trans-platinum complex showing higher antitumor activity than the cis congeners. *J. Med. Chem.*, 1993. 36(4): p. 510-2.

[87] Coluccia, M., et al., Platinum(II) complexes containing iminoethers: a trans platinum antitumour agent. *Chem. Biol. Interact.*, 1995. 98(3): p. 251-66.

[88] Coluccia, M., et al., In vitro antitumour activity and cellular pharmacological properties of the platinum-iminoether complex trans-[PtCl2[E-HN=C(OMe)Me]2]. *Int. J. Oncol.*, 1999. 15(5): p. 1039-44.

[89] Iwami, M., et al., A new antitumor antibiotic, FR-900482. I. Taxonomic studies on the producing strain: a new species of the genus Streptomyces. *J. Antibiotic* (Tokyo), 1987. 40(5): p. 589-593.

[90] Beckerbauer, L., et al., FR900482 class of anti-tumor drugs cross-links oncoprotein HMG I/Y to DNA in vivo. *Chem. Biol.*, 2000. 7(10): p. 805-12.

[91] Subramanian, V., et al., Effects of photochemically activated alkylating agents of the FR900482 family on chromatin. *Chem. Biol*, 2007. 14(5): p. 553-63.

[92] Rivera, M.I., et al., Selective toxicity of the tricyclic thiophene NSC 652287 in renal carcinoma cell lines: differential accumulation and metabolism. *Biochem. Pharmacol*, 1999. 57(11): p. 1283-95.

[93] Nieves-Neira, W., et al., DNA protein cross-links produced by NSC 652287, a novel thiophene derivative active against human renal cancer cells. *Mol. Pharmacol*, 1999. 56(3): p. 478-84.

[94] Phillips, L.R., et al., Identification of the principal circulating metabolite of a synthetic 5,4'-diaminoflavone (NSC 686288), an antitumor agent, in the rat. *J. Chromatogr. B. Biomed. Sci. Appl.*, 2000. 741(2): p. 205-11.

[95] Meng, L.H., et al., DNA-protein cross-links and replication-dependent histone H2AX phosphorylation induced by aminoflavone (NSC 686288), a novel anticancer agent active against human breast cancer cells. *Cancer Res*, 2005. 65(12): p. 5337-43.

[96] USEPA, Formaldehyde Risk Assessment Update. 1991, Washington, D.C.: Office of Toxic Substances.

[97] Casanova, M., et al., Covalent binding of inhaled formaldehyde to DNA in the respiratory tract of rhesus monkeys: pharmacokinetics, rat-to-monkey interspecies scaling, and extrapolation to man. *Fundam. Appl. Toxicol.*, 1991. 17(2): p. 409-28.

[98] Casanova, M., et al., DNA-protein cross-links and cell replication at specific sites in the nose of F344 rats exposed subchronically to formaldehyde. *Fundam. Appl. Toxicol.*, 1994. 23(4): p. 525-36.

[99] Shuker, D.E., The enemy at the gates? DNA adducts as biomarkers of exposure to exogenous and endogenous genotoxic agents. *Toxicol. Lett.*, 2002. 134(1-3): p. 51-6.

[100] Zhitkovich, A., et al., Utilization of DNA-protein cross-links as a biomarker of chromium exposure. Environ. *Health Perspect.*, 1998. 106 Suppl 4: p. 969-74.

[101] Whiteman, M., et al., Hypochlorous acid-induced DNA base modification: potentiation by nitrite: biomarkers of DNA damage by reactive oxygen species. *Biochem. Biophys Res. Commun.*, 1999. 257(2): p. 572-6.

[102] Wu, F.Y., et al., Association of DNA-protein crosslinks and breast cancer. *Mutat. Res.*, 2002. 501(1-2): p. 69-78.

[103] Bouckson-Castaing, V., et al., Molecular characterisation of ninein, a new coiled-coil protein of the centrosome. *J. Cell Sci*, 1996. 109 (Pt 1): p. 179-90.

[104] You, Y., et al., Role of f-box factor foxj1 in differentiation of ciliated airway epithelial cells. *Am. J. Physiol. Lung Cell Mol. Physiol*, 2004. 286(4): p. L650-7.

[105] Zhao, K., et al., Rapid and phosphoinositol-dependent binding of the SWI/SNF-like BAF complex to chromatin after T lymphocyte receptor signaling. *Cell,* 1998. 95(5): p. 625-36.

[106] Fidlerova, H., et al., Replication-coupled modulation of early replicating chromatin domains detected by anti-actin antibody. *J. Cell Biochem*, 2005.

[107] Mitsuzawa, H., et al., Glyceraldehyde-3-phosphate dehydrogenase and actin associate with RNA polymerase II and interact with its Rpb7 subunit. *FEBS Lett*, 2005. 579(1): p. 48-52.

[108] Kwak, I.H., et al., Nuclear accumulation of globular actin as a cellular senescence marker. *Cancer Res*, 2004. 64(2): p. 572-80.

[109] Miller, C.A., 3rd and M. Costa, Analysis of proteins cross-linked to DNA after treatment of cells with formaldehyde, chromate, and cis-diamminedichloroplatinum(II). *Mol. Toxicol.*, 1989. 2(1): p. 11-26.

[110] Miller, C.A.I., M.D. Cohen, and M. Costa, Complexing of actin and other nuclear proteins to DNA by cis-diamminedichloroplatinum(II) and chromium compounds. *Carcinogenesis*, 1991. 12: p. 269-276.

[111] Coulombe, R.A.J., G.L. Drew, and F.R. Stermitz, Pyrrolizidine alkaloids crosslink DNA with actin. *Toxicol. Appl. Pharmacol.*, 1999. 15: p. 198-202.

[112] Kim, H.Y., F.R. Stermitz, and R.A. Coulombe, Jr., Pyrrolizidine alkaloid-induced DNA-protein cross-links. *Carcinogenesis,* 1995. 16(11): p. 2691-7.

[113] Batchelor, C.L., A.M. Woodward, and D.H. Crouch, Nuclear ERM (ezrin, radixin, moesin) proteins: regulation by cell density and nuclear import. *Exp. Cell Res*, 2004. 296(2): p. 208-22.

[114] Townson, S.M., et al., HET/SAF-B overexpression causes growth arrest and multinuclearity and is associated with aneuploidy in human breast cancer. *Clin. Cancer Res,* 2000. 6(9): p. 3788-96.

[115] Samuel, S.K., et al., In situ cross-linking by cisplatin of nuclear matrix-bound transcription factors to nuclear DNA of human breast cancer cells. *Cancer Res.*, 1998. 58(14): p. 3004-8.

[116] Ramirez, P., et al., Arsenite induces DNA-protein crosslinks and cytokeratin expression in the WRL-68 human hepatic cell line. *Carcinogenesis*, 2000. 21(4): p. 701-6.

[117] Tolstonog, G.V., M. Sabasch, and P. Traub, Cytoplasmic intermediate filaments are stably associated with nuclear matrices and potentially modulate their DNA-binding function. *DNA Cell Biol.,* 2002. 21(3): p. 213-39.

[118] Tolstonog, G.V., et al., Isolation of SDS-stable complexes of the intermediate filament protein vimentin with repetitive, mobile, nuclear matrix attachment region, and mitochondrial DNA sequence elements from cultured mouse and human fibroblasts. *DNA Cell Biol.*, 2001. 20(9): p. 531-54.

[119] Harvey, A.C. and J.A. Downs, What functions do linker histones provide? *Mol. Microbiol*, 2004. 53(3): p. 771-5.

[120] Lowell, J.E. and G.A. Cross, A variant histone H3 is enriched at telomeres in Trypanosoma brucei. *J.Cell Sci.*, 2004. 117(Pt 24): p. 5937-47.

[121] Lemos, T.A. and J. Kobarg, CGI-55 interacts with nuclear proteins and co-localizes to p80-coilin positive-coiled bodies in the nucleus. *Cell Biochem. Biophys*, 2006. 44(3): p. 463-74.

[122] Bomsztyk, K., O. Denisenko, and J. Ostrowski, hnRNP K: one protein multiple processes. *Bioessays*, 2004. 26(6): p. 629-38.

[123] Akhmedov, A.T. and B.S. Lopez, Human 100-kDa homologous DNA-pairing protein is the splicing factor PSF and promotes DNA strand invasion. *Nucleic Acids Res.*, 2000. 28(16): p. 3022-30.

[124] Kolluri, R., T.A. Torrey, and A.J. Kinniburgh, A CT promoter element binding protein: definition of a double-strand and a novel single-strand DNA binding motif. *Nucleic Acids Res.*, 1992. 20(1): p. 111-6.

[125] Krynetski, E.Y., et al., A nuclear protein complex containing high mobility group proteins B1 and B2, heat shock cognate protein 70, ERp60, and glyceraldehyde-3-phosphate dehydrogenase is involved in the cytotoxic response to DNA modified by incorporation of anticancer nucleoside analogues. *Cancer Res.*, 2003. 63(1): p. 100-6.

[126] Ford, L.P., W.E. Wright, and J.W. Shay, A model for heterogeneous nuclear ribonucleoproteins in telomere and telomerase regulation. *Oncogene*, 2002. 21(4): p. 580-3.

[127] Gerner, C., et al., The Fas-induced apoptosis analyzed by high throughput proteome analysis. *J. Biol. Chem*, 2000. 275(50): p. 39018-26.

[128] Chai, Q., et al., Interaction and stimulation of human FEN-1 nuclease activities by heterogeneous nuclear ribonucleoprotein A1 in alpha-segment processing during Okazaki fragment maturation. *Biochemistry*, 2003. 42(51): p. 15045-52.

[129] Wang, J.L., et al., Nucleocytoplasmic lectins. *Biochim. Biophys. Acta*, 2004. 1673(1-2): p. 75-93.

[130] Vorum, H., et al., Human calumenin localizes to the secretory pathway and is secreted to the medium. *Exp. Cell Res*, 1999. 248(2): p. 473-81.

[131] Abbate, M., et al., Location of gp330/alpha 2-m receptor-associated protein (alpha 2-MRAP) and its binding sites in kidney: distribution of endogenous alpha 2-MRAP is modified by tissue processing. *Eur. J. Cell Biol.*, 1993. 61(1): p. 139-49.

[132] Radyuk, S.N., R.S. Sohal, and W.C. Orr, Thioredoxin peroxidases can foster cytoprotection or cell death in response to different stressors: over- and under-expression of thioredoxin peroxidase in Drosophila cells. *Biochem. J.*, 2003. 371(Pt 3): p. 743-52.

[133] Ross, S.J., et al., Thioredoxin peroxidase is required for the transcriptional response to oxidative stress in budding yeast. *Mol. Biol. Cell*, 2000. 11(8): p. 2631-42.

[134] Berggren, M.I., et al., Thioredoxin peroxidase-1 (peroxiredoxin-1) is increased in thioredoxin-1 transfected cells and results in enhanced protection against apoptosis caused by hydrogen peroxide but not by other agents including dexamethasone, etoposide, and doxorubicin. *Arch Biochem. Biophys*, 2001. 392(1): p. 103-9.

[135] Huang, M.E., et al., A genomewide screen in Saccharomyces cerevisiae for genes that suppress the accumulation of mutations. *Proc. Natl. Acad. Sci.* U S A, 2003. 100(20): p. 11529-34.

[136] Gruenheid, S., et al., The iron transport protein NRAMP2 is an integral membrane glycoprotein that colocalizes with transferrin in recycling endosomes. *J. Exp. Med*, 1999. 189(5): p. 831-41.

[137] VanderWaal, R.P., et al., Evidence that protein disulfide isomerase (PDI) is involved in DNA-nuclear matrix anchoring. *J. Cell Biochem.*, 2002. 85(4): p. 689-702.

[138] Murphy, G.A., et al., Signaling mediated by the closely related mammalian Rho family GTPases TC10 and Cdc42 suggests distinct functional pathways. *Cell Growth Differ*, 2001. 12(3): p. 157-67.

[139] Tsuda, M., et al., Crk associates with ERM proteins and promotes cell motility toward hyaluronic acid. *J. Biol. Chem*, 2004. 279(45): p. 46843-50.

[140] Sadacharan, S.K., A.C. Cavanagh, and R.S. Gupta, Immunoelectron microscopy provides evidence for the presence of mitochondrial heat shock 10-kDa protein (chaperonin 10) in red blood cells and a variety of secretory granules. *Histochem Cell Biol*, 2001. 116(6): p. 507-17.

[141] Bole, D.G., et al., Immunocytochemical localization of BiP to the rough endoplasmic reticulum: evidence for protein sorting by selective retention. *J. Histochem Cytochem*, 1989. 37(12): p. 1817-23.

[142] Zinszner, H., et al., A topogenic role for the oncogenic N-terminus of TLS: nucleolar localization when transcription is inhibited. *Oncogene*, 1997. 14(4): p. 451-61.

[143] Zinszner, H., et al., TLS (FUS) binds RNA in vivo and engages in nucleo-cytoplasmic shuttling. *J. Cell Sci*, 1997. 110 (Pt 15): p. 1741-50.

[144] Laz, E.V., C.A. Wiwi, and D.J. Waxman, Sexual dimorphism of rat liver nuclear proteins: regulatory role of growth hormone. *Mol. Cell Proteomics*, 2004. 3(12): p. 1170-80.

[145] Billaut-Mulot, O., et al., Trypanosoma cruzi elongation factor 1-alpha: nuclear localization in parasites undergoing apoptosis. *Gene*, 1996. 174(1): p. 19-26.

Index

B

D

E

H

J

K

L

M

N

O

Q

R

T

W

X

Y

Z